A Structural Approach to Arithmetic

CHARLES R. PARISH
ROY L. McCORMICK
Ball State University

VAN NOSTRAND REINHOLD COMPANY
New York / Cincinatti / Toronto / London / Melbourne

*To our families for their constant
understanding and encouragement.*

Acknowledgements

This book came into being as a result of the need for reading materials for prospective elementary teachers taking courses in content mathematics at Ball State University. We wish to thank those individuals of the Mathematics Department who in any way assisted us with the project. Throughout the period of writing preliminary drafts, Professor George B. Grunwald read sizable portions of the material. His suggestions and constructive criticisms resulted in a number of improvements. For his constant interest and valuable assistance we are most grateful. A special vote of thanks goes to Miss Sue A. Satterfield who, with great care and accuracy, typed the final manuscript.

Muncie, Indiana C.R.P. and R.L.M.

Van Nostrand Reinhold Company Regional Offices:
Cincinnati, New York, Chicago, Millbrae, Dallas

Van Nostrand Reinhold Company International Offices:
London Toronto Melbourne

Copyright © 1970 by Litton Educational Publishing Inc.
Library of Congress Catalog Card Number 72-110341

Published by Van Nostrand Reinhold Company
450 West 33rd Street, New York, N.Y. 10001

Published simultaneously in Canada by
Van Nostrand Reinhold Ltd.

10 9 8 7 6 5 4 3 2 1

Preface

During recent years the high school mathematics background of students who are preparing to become elementary school teachers seems significantly to have improved. This text has been written to provide what we consider a respectable treatment of number systems and their associated arithmetics. A constructive development of these number systems is of prime importance because it requires that the student be actively involved rather than be merely a spectator.

The development used may be described as *bimodal* from the point of view of intuition versus rigor. The presentation is intended to make the student feel comfortable before commencing with the rigorous establishment of the arithmetic properties. In conjunction with this bimodal structuring, we use a spiral approach, via the concept of isomorphism, so that the similarities of finite cardinals, integers, rational numbers, and real numbers can be stressed. The basic development is essentially that summarized in the following paragraph.

The first two chapters consist of an essentially intuitive discussion of the concepts of sets, finite cardinals and their numerals along with the introduction of some rigor. Chapters 3 through 7 offer a rather formal development of properties of finite cardinals. In Chapter 8, where arithmetic using other base numeration systems and modular arithmetic are discussed, the presentation again becomes more intuitive, continues in this fashion into Chapter 9 where the need for a "larger" system is discussed, and ends with the formulation of the concept of *integer*. Many of the properties of integers are then developed at a fairly rigorous level in Chapters 10 through 12. Here, of course, the concept of isomorphism results in a furthering of the spiral effect by recycling student thought to a comparison of the systems of finite cardinals and integers. In Chapter 13 the need for a more "satisfactory" system of numbers is discussed and this leads to the development of the concept of *rational numbers* which are then studied fairly rigorously in Chapters 14 through 16. Here again the spiraling effect due to the isomorphisms allows the student to compare the structure of the systems of rational numbers, integers, and, in turn, finite cardinals. In Chapter 17, decimal numeration for the rationals is discussed at a rather intuitive level and this type of presentation is carried over into Chapter 18 where the concepts of function and real numbers are considered.

The structure may be schematically depicted as follows.

PART I

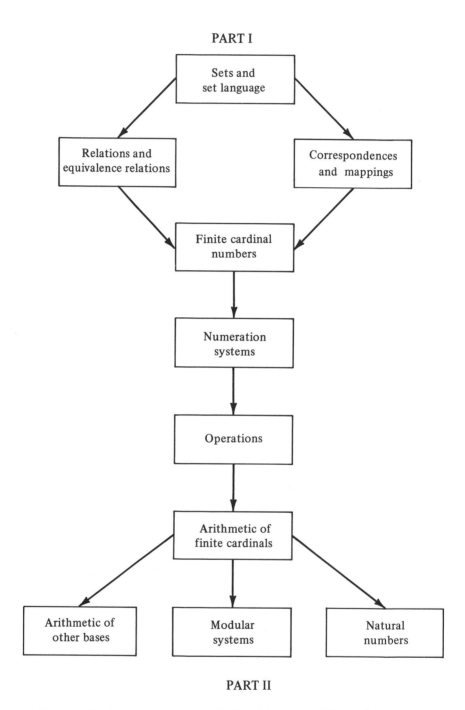

PART II

Here we return to the concepts of cardinal number, ordered pairs, and equivalence relations in order to develop the integer concept. Later, rationals are introduced by using ordered pairs of integers and another equivalence relation.

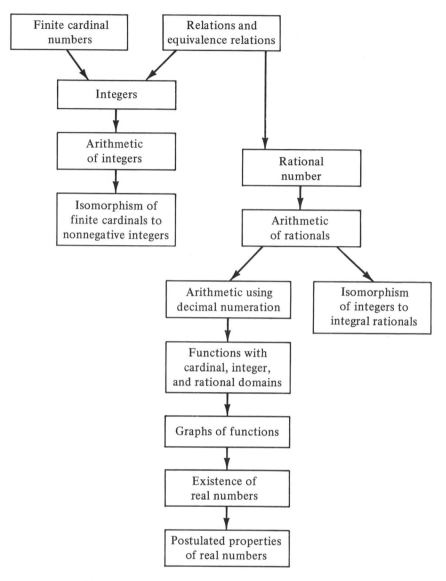

There is sufficient material for a one-semester course of from 3 to 5 credit hours or for two 4-credit-hour courses for schools on a quarter system.

To cover the material in one semester, one may want to omit Sections 8-2 and 8-3 on modular systems and Peano Postulates respectively as well as Sections 16-3 on absolute value, 17-4 on intuitive limits, and 17-5 on percents. One could also combine Section 8-1 on arithmetic in bases other than ten with consideration of the arithmetic operations as they are developed. In addition to these one could give only a cursory treatment of integers and then proceed to the development of rational numbers thus using integers as a vehicle to get from the finite cardinals to the rationals.

For classes on the quarter system, Sections 8-3, 16-3 and 17-4 may still be omitted and one can combine treatment of arithmetic using other bases with the regular development with practically no loss of continuity. We have found a natural break-point for our two-quarter sequence on number systems to be at the end of Chapter 8. In the second quarter we spend approximately two and one half weeks on integers and devote the remaining time to a discussion of rational numbers.

In general, we have found a time lag in student comprehension during the early part of the discussion of sets in Chapter 1. This we attribute to newness of concepts and language, and it appears to be overcome as the concepts are used in the development of finite cardinal arithmetic. From that point onward things move rather smoothly due in part to the spiral development.

A few remarks are in order regarding the enumeration of definitions and theorems. These are numbered consecutively in each chapter. For example, Definition 5-2 refers to Definition Two in Chapter 5 and Theorem 10-19 refers to Theorem Nineteen of Chapter 10. Occasionally we refer to, say, Section 15-5 which means Section Five of Chapter 15. In addition to these, we also use the symbol ▌ to denote the completion of proofs of theorems.

We are assuming that you who study this material are much like the students we have worked with throughout the five years during which the book has been under development. That is, many of you will study this material in conjunction with the meeting of state requirements. Some of you have a fear of mathematics and others of you genuinely enjoy it.

If you consider your mathematics background inadequate, there is no need to despair provided that you keep the following points in mind. We have found that generally some time is required, perhaps five weeks or so, before "modern" mathematics begins to make sense. For this reason you should be patient and above all work diligently on the exercise sets to try to see how prior discussions apply. You will find that, as time passes, you will meet certain ideas repeatedly, and as this happens these ideas should begin to fall into place. It is absolutely essential that you participate in the development given, for, if you do not, your experience with mathematics cannot be very meaningful. In conjunction with this, you should keep pencil and paper handy while reading as well as for working on the exercises. Remember that mathematics is *not* a "spectator sport."

For those of you who already have a good mathematics background, there are included in the exercise sets several problems which are rather challenging. Some of these may give you ideas for extending some of the results in the reading or for formulating interesting problems of your own. In addition to this, there are numerous instances where theorems are stated but not proved. This has been done especially with you in mind. We invite you — in fact, challenge you — to try them.

We hope that you will enjoy this book as much as we have enjoyed working with students like yourself during its preparation. If these materials are of any benefit to you, we charge you to share this as much as possible with your future students.

Contents

PART II
INTEGERS, RATIONAL NUMBERS,
AND REAL NUMBERS

PART I Sets and cardinal numbers

CHAPTER 1 Sets and their properties

1. The Language of Sets

We shall begin our discussion by returning to some of our previous work in mathematics at the high school level. There, in our study of geometry, we learned that it is not possible to give a satisfactory mathematical definition of what a point is even though we have a good intuitive notion of what some of its properties are. Once this intuitive notion was accepted by the student, he was then led to consider certain collections of points. Some of these collections were called *lines,* some were called *triangles,* some were called *circles,* and so on. Once this was done, the student then tried to determine some of the mathematical properties of those collections and in so doing he also found several instances where his results could be applied in the physical world.

Just as the term "point" was used in geometry, so shall we use the term "set." That is, we shall use the concept of set as the basic building block for the discussion which follows. Like the term "point," the term "set," cannot be defined in a way which is mathematically precise, for if we try, we find that we use other words which carry the same meaning. Some of these synonyms are *collection, aggregate, class,* and *family.* The term *group* is used occasionally, but since this term has a precise mathematical meaning all its own, we shall agree *not* to use it as a synonym for set in our discussions.

Since a set may also be called a collection, we see that the collections of points referred to above are sets. Hence sets may be abstractions such as conjured up in the mind. However, we are all familiar with sets of physical objects as well. For example,

    (1) the collection of clothes in a wardrobe,

    (2) the collection of coins in a purse, and

    (3) the collection of students at a college

are also sets.

The objects which belong to a given set are called *elements* or *members* of that set. A set may be denoted by a pair of braces with its members listed inside the braces, separated by commas. For example, the set whose elements are the words blue, red, yellow, and green can be denoted by

$$\{\text{blue, red, yellow, green}\}$$

Likewise, if a set has as elements the first three lower case letters of the English alphabet, it may be denoted by

$$\{a, b, c\}$$

If we wish to write that a is an element of the set $\{a, b, c\}$, we write

$$a \in \{a, b, c\}$$

where the symbol $\in$ is read "is an element of" or "is a member of." This method of denoting a set is called the *roster method* since the elements are all listed by name.

Now it may be that a set has many elements which all possess some common property. If this is the case, we may use the common property to define our set. That is, if we wish to consider the set of all United States citizens who are six feet tall, we may designate this set by

$$\{x | x \text{ is a U.S. citizen who is six feet tall}\}$$

In this method of designating a set the symbol x is a *generic* element (that is, one which represents any element of the set) and the symbol | is to be read "such that." Hence the set just listed is read "the set of all x such that x is a U.S. citizen who is six feet tall." This is often referred to as using *set-builder* notation, and $\{ \ | \ \}$ is often called the set-building symbol. Some sets may be conveniently listed by both the roster method and set-builder notation. For example, $\{a, e, i, o, u\}$ may be listed as $\{x | x \text{ is a common vowel}\}$ since all of the letters a, e, i, o, u have that identifying characteristic. As another example consider the set of counting numbers which are smaller than ten. This set may be listed as

$$\{1,2,3,4,5,6,7,8,9\}$$

or as

$$\{x | x \text{ is a counting number smaller than ten}\}$$

In either of the methods just described for designating a set, there may be a considerable amount of writing involved, and so it seems reasonable to employ a device which will save us some effort. In order to effect this savings in time and effort, we often denote a set simply by a capital letter. For example, we could write

$$A = \{a,b,c\}$$
$$S = \{\text{red, blue, yellow, green}\}$$
$$X = \{x | x \text{ is a U.S. citizen who is six feet tall}\}$$

In the discussion which follows, we will often use capital letters to designate sets and lower case letters to designate the elements of sets. Then we can write a $\in$ A instead of a $\in$ {a, b, c}. This practice will not only be a saving of effort, but will often clarify and simplify our discussion.

Oftentimes, during a discussion in which a set is involved, we shall want to focus our attention on just a part of the set. That is, we may or may not be interested in all of the elements of the set. If this is the case, we shall call the collection of elements in which we are interested a subset of the given set. We shall now define this concept more precisely.

Definition 1-1: If A and B are sets, then A is called a **subset** of B if every element of A is an element of B. Symbolically we write $A \subseteq B$ where $\subseteq$ is read "is a subset of."

We might note that the symbol $\subseteq$ is often read as "is contained in" but we shall refrain from using this descriptive phrase. If we wish to speak about some elements of a set, but not the entire set, we shall use a special symbol so that no misunderstandings result when we wish to differentiate between the two.

To illustrate Definition 1-1, let B = {a, e, i, o, u} and A = {i, o, u}. Then $A \subseteq B$ because i $\in$ B and o $\in$ B and u $\in$ B. Some other subsets of B are {a}, {a, e}, {e, i, o, u}, and {a, e, i, o, u}. Notice that we have listed {a, e, i, o, u} $\subseteq B$. As a matter of fact, it is true that *every* set is a subset of itself. This can be shown simply by using Definition 1-1.

There is another type of subset which is of some interest as we shall see in the discussion which follows. Let us define it now so that when we need the concept, we shall have it.

Definition 1-2: If A and B are sets, then A is called a **proper subset** of B if A is a subset of B and if B contains at least one element which A does not contain. Symbolically, we write $A \subset B$ where $\subset$ is read as "is a proper subset of."

For example, if B = {a, b, c, d, e} and A = {a, b, c}, then $A \subset B$, since $A \subseteq B$ and B has at least one element which A does not. The element d is such an element that B contains but A does not. So also is the element e.

Note however, that B is *not* a proper subset of itself. That is, B has no element which is not in B. If we wish to state that B is not a proper subset of itself we write $B \not\subset B$. Likewise,

(1) $a \notin A$ means a is not an element of A,

(2) $A \not\subseteq B$ means A is not a subset of B, and

(3) $A \not\subset B$ means A is not a proper subset of B.

In most discussions, whether mathematical or not, the parties involved assume frames of reference for statements made during those discussions. Each of these frames of reference is called a universe of discourse. Likewise we shall, in each of our discussions which follow, restrict ourselves to a certain set of elements. This set is called a *universal set* and is generally denoted by the letter $\mathscr{U}$ to remind us of *universal*. Note that if a discussion changes it is very likely that our universal set or *universe* will also change. We now state a formal definition of a universal set.

Definition 1-3: A **universal set** (or **universe**) is a specified set of elements to which a given discussion is limited. Any objects which are mentioned during that discussion are to be elements of this particular universal set.

We note that there will be cases in the following pages in which the universe is not explicitly stated, but it should be clear from the context of the discussion what universe is being considered.

The reader will note that of the sets listed so far, all have actually contained elements. This leads us to consider a very special set, namely the set which has no elements. An example of such a set is the set $\{x \mid x$ is a human being having six heads$\}$. Let us now list names for these two types of sets considered thus far.

Definition 1-4: If a set has at least one element, then it is called a **non-empty** set.

Definition 1-5: If a set has no elements, it is called the **empty** set. The empty set is usually denoted by $\{\ \}$ or $\emptyset$.

The empty set is also often called the *void* set or the *null* set.

The reader should note that in Definition 1-5, we have said *the* empty set. There is just one empty set, for regardless of how we denote sets which have no elements, the fact remains that there is just one set for which this is true. That is, either a set is empty or it is not empty.

If we return for a moment to the notion of subsets and proper subsets, it is easy to see that

(1) $\emptyset$ is a subset of every set, and

(2) $\emptyset$ is a proper subset of every non-empty set.

Also in connection with subsets and proper subsets, it may be of interest to try to determine how many subsets and proper subsets a given set has. We shall list three sets, their subsets, and proper subsets and leave it as an exercise for the reader to extend the results listed below.

Set	Subsets	Proper subsets
$\{\ \}$	$\{\ \}$	none
$\{a\}$	$\{\ \}, \{a\}$	$\{\ \}$
$\{a,b\}$	$\{\ \}, \{a\}, \{b\}, \{a,b\}$	$\{\ \}, \{a\}, \{b\}$

As the reader will have noticed, we have used the symbol of equality, =, with reference to sets. Let us now sharpen the usage of this symbol by actually defining equality for sets.

Definition 1-6: Two sets A and B are said to be **equal** if they contain precisely the same elements. Symbolically we write $A = B$ to indicate this.

Thus if $A = \{a, b, c, d, e\}$ and $B = \{b, a, d, c, e\}$, then $A = B$, since Definition 1-6 is satisfied. Also from this definition and example, we see that equality does not depend on what order the elements appear, but rather, depends solely on *whether* they appear. Since we are only interested in whether certain elements are in a set or not, this means that one should list an element just once to show that it belongs to a given set. That is, $\{a, a\} = \{a\}$ and we shall prefer the listing on the right except in special situations. The only exception will arise later when place-value numerals are discussed. Other than that, we shall agree to list each element of a given set just once.

As a third example consider the sets

$$A = \{u,v,w,x,y,z\} \text{ and}$$
$$B = \{a,b,c,d,e,f\}$$

Here we see that Definition 1-6 is not satisfied and so we conclude that A and B are not equal. We denote this fact by writing $A \neq B$.

It is interesting to notice that by using Definition 1-6 it is possible to determine another test for equality of sets. We shall state this in the form of a theorem and prove it.

Theorem 1-1: If A and B are sets, then $A = B$ if and only if $A \subseteq B$ and $B \subseteq A$.

Proof: In order to have a valid proof for the theorem, we must prove two things, namely,
  1) if $A = B$ then $A \subseteq B$ and $B \subseteq A$, and
  2) if $A \subseteq B$ and $B \subseteq A$, then $A = B$.
1) If $A = B$, then A and B contain precisely the same elements. Hence every element of A is an element of B and every element of B is an element of A. That is, $A \subseteq B$ and $B \subseteq A$.
2) If $A \subseteq B$ then every element of A is an element of B and if $B \subseteq A$ then every element of B is an element of A. Consequently, A and B contain precisely the same elements and so by Definition 1-6, $A = B$. Hence if we wish to establish the equality of two sets we may now use Theorem 1-1 as a firm and reliable test. As a matter of fact, we shall show you the power of this theorem shortly.

There is one other useful and important concept which we have not yet mentioned. As you have seen in previous examples, there were cases where the sets involved had no common elements. This is going to be very important later when we develop the arithmetic of cardinal numbers. Let us now give a definition for this situation.

Definition 1-7: If A and B are sets which have no common elements, then they are called **disjoint** sets.

An example of such a pair of sets is

$$A = \{a,b,c,d\}$$
$$B = \{u,v,y\}$$

Here there are no elements which belong to both sets, and so according to the definition of disjointness, these two sets are disjoint. On the other hand, if we choose

$$A = \{a,b,c,d\}$$
$$\text{and } B = \{a,c,e,f\}$$

we see that in this case A and B are not disjoint because $a \in A$ and $a \in B$. Of course it is also true that $c \in A$ and $c \in B$, but it is sufficient to show sets are not disjoint if we can find just one element which is in both sets. This would be enough to insure that the sets are not disjoint.

EXERCISE SET 1-1

1. Given that $A = \{1,2,5,7,8\}$, $B = \{a,b,c,j,z\}$, and $C = \{p,q,r,s,t,v\}$ write $\in$ or $\notin$ in the blank in order to make a true statement.

3 ___ A	u ___ C	i ___ B	T ___ C
b ___ B	t ___ C	q ___ A	J ___ B
9 ___ A	z ___ B	8 ___ C	a ___ A

2. Let $A = \{1,2,3,4,5,6,7,8,9\}$, $B = \{3,6,9,\ldots,99\}$, and $C = \{5,10,15,\ldots\}$ where the three dots indicate that the respective number patterns continue in the same manner.

   (a) Insert in the following blanks the correct symbol $\in$ or $\notin$.

3 ___ A	3 ___ B	3 ___ C
15 ___ A	15 ___ B	15 ___ C
8 ___ A	8 ___ B	8 ___ C
300 ___ A	300 ___ B	300 ___ C

   (b) Is it true that $1\frac{1}{2} \in A$? That $1 \in B$? That $1001 \in C$?
   (c) If $x \in A$ and also $x \in C$, then x must be in what set?
   (d) How many elements are there in A? In B? In C?

3. Change each of the following to the roster form.
   (a) $\{x|x$ is less than five and greater than zero$\}$
   (b) $\{x|x$ was a U.S. President who served two non-consecutive terms$\}$
   (c) $\{x|x$ is a month of the year having less than 30 days$\}$
   (d) $\{x|x$ is a month of the year having more than thirty-one days$\}$

4. Write in roster form each of the following sets:
   (a) $D = \{x|x$ is the teacher of this course and section$\}$
   (b) $E = \{x|x$ was a major party presidential nominee in 1932$\}$
   (c) $F = \{x|x$ is a counting number larger than 2 but smaller than 3$\}$
      (Note: Counting numbers are those you counted with as a child, viz., 1,2,3,4, etc.)

5. A teacher gives as an assignment a set of problems whose numbers are described by the set $P = \{x|x$ is an even number less than 36$\}$. Write out the list of assigned problems in roster form.

6. Write in rule form each of the following sets:
   (a) $A = \{a,b,c,d,e,f,g,h,i,j,k,l,m,n,o,p,q,r,s,t,w,x,y,z\}$
   (b) $B = \{1,2,3,4,5,6,7,8,9,10,11,12\}$
   (c) $C = \{$George Washington$\}$

7. Change each of the following to the form $\{x|x\ldots\}$.
   (a) $\{$Volkswagon, Saab, Renault, Austin, Mercedes Benz, $\ldots$, Jaguar$\}$
   (b) $\{$oak, maple, locust, paw-paw, cherry, birch, $\ldots$, cottonwood$\}$
   (b) $\{$Sudan, Kentucky blue, rye, $\ldots$, crab$\}$

8. In each of the following sets, the elements listed exhibit some common characteristic. Find a characteristic for each of the sets listed.
   (a) { plastic screw, razor blade, chisel, monkey-wrench}
   (b) { cow, cat, alligator, chair}
   (c) { human, ape, clock}
   (d) { mouse, human, bat, whale}
   (e) { Los Angeles, Salt Lake City (Utah), New York City, Baku, Odessa}
   (f) { Australia, Bechuanaland, Mali, Saudi Arabia}
   (g) { one, two, for, six, ten, the, cow, pen, pin, tin, din, den, net}
   (h) { frog, told, toad, cold, feet}
   (i) { Ja, Da, Si, yes, oui}
   (j) { mope, rope, dope, lope, cope, hope, nope}
   (k) { glad, bad, cad, fad, lad, had, mad, sad, pad}
   (l) { cane, lane, mane, pane, sane, vane}
   (m) { feed, feet, heed, reed, reel, feel, heel, eel}
   (n) { pneumonia, pneumatic, gnu, know, knife, ptarmigan, psoriasis}

9. Given that $\mathcal{U} = \{x | x$ is a lower case letter of the English alphabet$\}$, $A = \{a,b,c,d,f\}$, $B = \{a,b,e,g,h,j\}$, $C = \{z\}$, $D = \{p,q,r,s,t,u,v,w\}$, and $E = \{a,b,e,g,h,f,j,k,m,c,n,p,d\}$, which of the following are true?
   (a) $c \not\subset \mathcal{U}$ (e) $D \subset E$
   (b) $E \not\subseteq D$ (f) $B \subseteq E$
   (c) $A \subset B$ (g) $C \subseteq D$
   (d) $B \subseteq D$

10. Let the universe in this problem be $\mathcal{U} = \{x | x$ is a letter of the English alphabet$\}$. Let $A = \{a,b,c,d,e,f,g,h,i,j\}$, $P = \{a,c,e,g,i\}$, $S = \{b,d,f,h,j\}$, $T = \{b,c,d,f,h\}$, $I = \{e,j\}$, $V = \{b,f,j\}$, $W = \{a,e,i\}$, $Y = \{d\}$, $Z = \{a\}$.
    (a) Which of the following statements are true (T) and which are false (F)?
       $P \subset A$ $T \subset A$ $I \subset P$
       $W \subset P$ $S \subset T$ $Y \subset T$
    (b) According to our definitions, is it correct to say $P \subset P$? $\emptyset \subset T$?
    (c) Consider an unknown set X about which you have the following information: $X \subseteq P$ and $X \subseteq W$.
       Which of the sets $\mathcal{U}, A, P, S, T, I, V, W, Y, Z$, can be equal to X, if any?

11. (a) Does $\{\{a\}, \{b\}\} = \{a,b\}$?
    (b) Does $\{a,b,c\} = \{c,b,a\}$?
    (c) Which of the following are true and which are false?
       $a \in \{a,b,c\}$ $a \subset \{a,b,c\}$
       $\{a\} \in \{a,b,c\}$ $\{a\} \subset \{a,b,c\}$

12. Is x a subset of $\{x,y\}$? Explain.

13. (a) List all subsets of $\{a,b,c\}$. How many are there?
    (b) List all of the subsets of the set $\{a,b,c,d\}$. How many are there?
    (c) Generalize the results of parts (a) and (b).

14. In problem 13, replace "subsets" by "proper subsets" and work the problem.

15. List all the subsets of
    (a) { }   (e) Which of the subsets in each of the
    (b) $\{a\}$ foregoing parts is a proper subset?
    (c) $\{ \{a\} \}$
    (d) $\{ \{a\}, \{b\} \}$

16. Which of the following pairs are examples of disjoint sets?
    (a) $\{a,b,c,d\}$ and $\{b,a,d,c\}$
    (b) $\{a,b,d\}$ and $\{c,d,q\}$
    (c) $\{p,q,r\}$ and $\{x\}$
    (d) $\{a,b,c,d\}$ and $\{b,d,e,f\}$
    (e) $\{a\}$ and $\emptyset$

2. Correspondences and Mappings

We are well aware of the fact that even a young child who knows nothing of numbers often matches objects of one set with those of a second set. For example, if a family has guests to dinner, a young child may match (associate) in some way people with chairs at the table and conclude either that there are enough chairs or that there are not enough chairs for everyone. This seemingly simple process is basic to mathematics and in particular to our development of arithmetic. Matchings such as that just mentioned illustrate the fact that we often set up what is called a *correspondence* between elements of sets. This process of matching the elements can be referred to as *setting up* (establishing) *a correspondence* between the sets involved. There are many other examples of such correspondences in our everyday life. Some of them are
    (1) the correspondence of the months of the year to their names,
    (2) the correspondence of cards in a library card file to the books owned by that library,
    (3) the correspondence of each employed person in the U.S.A. to his social security number,
    (4) the correspondence of each person in the U.S.A. to a postal ZIP code number,
    (5) the correspondence of each college student to his student identification number

and so on.

This setting up of correspondences between sets is a very important concept and as can be seen from the above examples, there is more than one type of matching possible. In fact there are four types of correspondences between sets. These are
    (1) many-to-many,
    (2) many-to-one,
    (3) one-to-many, and
    (4) one-to-one.

Examples of each of these exist in the every day world and we shall list some of each.

Examples of many-to-many correspondences:

    (1) The correspondence from the set of enacted laws in the U.S. to the set of citizens of the U.S.A. is a many-to-many correspondence since many people are subject to the same laws and many laws apply to many people.

(2) The correspondence from the set of college professors to the set of all college students is a many-to-many correspondence, since professors have many students and the students have many professors.

Examples of many-to-one correspondences:

(1) The correspondence from the set of all refrigerators to the set of all companies which manufacture refrigerators is a many-to-one correspondence, since makers of refrigerators make more than one such appliance.
(2) The correspondence from the set of all citizens of the U.S.A. to the set of postal ZIP code numbers is a many-to-one correspondence since many people have the same ZIP code number.
(3) The correspondence from the set of U.S. congressmen to the set of houses of congress is a many-to-one correspondence since there are several congressmen in each of the two houses of congress.

Examples of one-to-many correspondences:

(1) The correspondence from the set of public libraries to the set of all books is a one-to-many correspondence, since public libraries contain more than one book each.
(2) The correspondence from the set of grades received by college students to the set of all college students is a one-to-many correspondence since the same grade is often earned by more than one student.
(3) The correspondence from the set of U.S. citizens to the set of names for people is a one-to-many correspondence since each of these individuals generally has at least a first and a last name.

Examples of one-to-one correspondences:

(1) The correspondence from the set of social security numbers in use to the set of people who hold social security numbers is a one-to-one correspondence, since each person who has a social security number has just one such number assigned to him.
(2) The correspondence from the set of college students in a given college to the set of student identification numbers at that college is a one-to-one correspondence since each assigned number belongs to just one student.
(3) The correspondence from the set of digits on one normal person's hand to the set of digits on that person's other hand is a one-to-one correspondence since normally people have the same number of digits on either hand.

Schematically, these types of correspondences might appear as in Figure 1-1 where in each example arrows are used to represent the desired correspondence used.

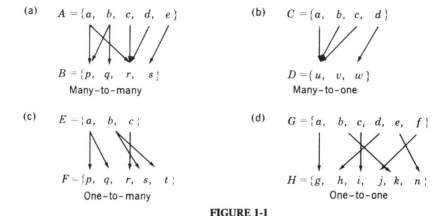

FIGURE 1-1

Of the correspondences we have just considered, there are two types which have the special property that each element of the first set has associated with it one and only one element of the second set. This will be of particular value to us in developing our arithmetic, as we shall soon see. Since this is the case, we shall give a precise definition of this type of correspondence.

Definition 1-8: If A and B are sets, a correspondence which associates with each element of A exactly one element of B is called a **mapping** of A **into** B.

This means that each element of A has an element of B associated with it, but no more than one. Hence, as you will see by referring to the diagrams above, many-to-one and one-to-one correspondences are into mappings, while many-to-many and one-to-many are not.

One can observe from the examples listed in Figure 1-1 that each member of the first set has a member of the second set associated with it. This member of the second set is called the *image* of the element of the first set. Thus in Figure 1-1 (b)

u is the image of $a, b,$ and c
and w is the image of $d.$

In Figure 1-1 (d)

g is the image of $a,$
h is the image of $d,$
i is the image of $c,$ and so on.

In general, the set of elements which are images is called the *image set*. We also see from Figure 1-1 (b) and (d) that the image set is always a subset of the second set involved in the mapping. That is, if A is mapped into B, then the image set is a subset of B.

Now if the image set happens to be all of set B, as in Figure 1-1 (d), then we say that the mapping is a mapping of A *onto* B. To be more precise, we define an onto mapping as follows.

Definition 1-9: If A is mapped into B and the image of A is equal to B, then we say that A is mapped **onto** B.

If we consider Figure 1-1 (d) again, we note that each image element in set H is associated with precisely one element in set G. This property illustrates one of the most important concepts we will encounter and so we define it now.

Definition 1-10: If A is mapped onto B and no element of B is the image of more than one element of A, then the mapping is called a **one-to-one** mapping of A **onto** B.

In order to illustrate how Definition 1-10 can be used, we shall consider two examples. The first illustrates a mapping which is one-to-one and onto while the second is not one-to-one, but is onto.

Example: Consider the mapping

$$A = \{a,\ b,\quad c,\quad d,\ e,\quad f,\quad g,\quad h\}$$

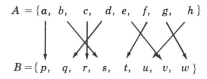

$$B = \{p,\quad q,\quad r,\quad s,\quad t,\quad u,\quad v,\quad w\}$$

Note first of all that since each element of B is the image of an element of A, the mapping is an *onto* mapping. This is true because the set of images *is* the set B. Secondly, we see that no element of B is the image of more than one element of A. Hence by Definition 1-10, this onto mapping is one-to-one.

It is a fact that an onto mapping is not necessarily one-to-one, as the next example will illustrate.

Example: Consider the mapping

$$A = \{a,\quad b,\quad c,\quad d,\ e,\quad f,\ g\}$$

$$B = \{u,\quad v,\quad w,\quad x,\ y\}$$

This mapping does map A *onto* B, since the set of image elements is the set B. However, it is *not* one-to-one, since v is the image of more than one element of A. That is, v is the image of b and c. Just one such case is enough to insure that the mapping is not one-to-one. In this example, however, there is another case which also insures that we do not have a one-to-one mapping, namely the case provided by the mapping of e and f in A to the element x in B.

EXERCISE SET 1-2

1. Let

$$A = \{a, \quad b, \quad c, \quad d, \quad e\}$$
$$\downarrow \quad \downarrow \quad \downarrow$$
$$B = \{f, \quad g, \quad h\}$$

Does this represent a mapping of A into B? Why or why not?

2. Why does the following not represent a mapping?

$$A = \{a, \quad b, \quad c\}$$
$$B = \{a, \quad b, \quad c, \quad d, \quad e\}$$

3. Suppose that

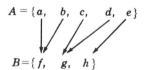

$$A = \{a, \quad b, \quad c, \quad d, \quad e\}$$
$$B = \{f, \quad g, \quad h\}$$

(a) Does this represent a mapping of A onto B?
(b) Does this represent a mapping of A into B?
(c) Is the mapping one-to-one?

4. Let $a = \{x | x$ is a lower case letter of the English alphabet$\}$
$\beta = \{x | x$ is a capital letter of the English alphabet$\}$
To each lower case letter, associate the corresponding capital letter.
(a) What is the image of a? c? x? z?
(b) Is this an onto mapping?
(c) Is this a one-to-one mapping?

5. To each element in column A associate that element of column B that you would encounter by a horizontal motion to the right from the given element of column A. Then consider the correspondences from columns A to B, A to C, A to D, A to E, A to F, A to G, A to H, and A to I.

A	B	C	D	E	F	G	H	I
1	1		30	2	5	3	4	1
2	7	4	40	4	1	5	4	3
	4							
3	5	3	50		3	4	4	5
4	6		10	1	4	5	4	3
	2							
5	3	2	20	5	2	3	4	1

(a) Which correspondences represent mappings?
(b) Which of the mappings are many-to-one?
(c) Which of the mappings are one-to-one?

6. For each of the following sets, elements are listed in the form (x,y) where y is to be interpreted as the image of x. Decide which are *into*, which are *onto*, which are one-to-one, and determine the sets involved.

(a) $\{(a,1), (b,2), (c,4), (d,4), (e,1), (f,3)\}$

(b) $\{(0,0), (2,1), (4,2), (6,3), (8,4), (10,5)\}$

(c) $\{(1,0), (2,1), (3,2), (4,3), (5,4), (6,5), (7,6)\}$

(d) $\{(1,0), (2,1), (3,0), (4,1), (5,0), (6,1), (7,0), (8,1)\}$

(e) How was the set in part (c) formed?

(f) How was the set in part (d) formed?

3. Equivalent Sets and Infinite Sets

We have already mentioned the fact that children who know nothing of the concept of number can and do work with sets. They often compare sets and are even able to tell when two sets are the same "size." That is, just by manipulating sets, children form a general notion of size.

If we refer back to Definition 1-10 of a *one-to-one onto* mapping, we see that in the comparison of two sets just mentioned, the child is really setting up a one-to-one onto mapping from one set to the other. It is here that the child obtains one of his first notions of the concept of size.

An important aspect to note in the mapping situation above is that the child may get the concept of sameness of size while using different sets of objects and mapping one of the sets *one-to-one onto* another. This concept is to play a very important role in our development and because of its importance, we shall give it precise meaning in the following definition.

Definition 1-11: If A and B are sets and if A can be mapped one-to-one onto B, then A is said to be **equivalent** to B. This is denoted by $A \sim B$, read "A is equivalent to B."

Example:

Since A is mapped one-to-one onto B, we have $A \sim B$.

Example: If, on the other hand, we have

then B is mapped one-to-one onto A and so we have that $B \sim A$.

Another example of two equivalent sets is the set of ladies and the set of men who form a "square" at a square dance. Later, we shall see other examples of equivalent sets, but for the time being, let us consider another way in which sets may be compared.

In many of the examples cited thus far, we have chosen specific sets to illustrate the concepts which were discussed. The sets, for the most part, have been listed in roster form, with all of the elements named. There have been instances, however, where the elements were not individually named. This leads us to try to classify sets according to some intuitive notion of size. There are various ways in which this might be done. For example we might classify them simply as being large or small. The obvious problem with such a method of classification is that the terms *large* and *small* are relative. That is, the terms have a different meaning for different people. Since in our study, we want to gain rather precise notions from discussions with each other, we shall have to find a way to classify sets which will have the same meaning for all involved.

Another possibility for a classification of sets would be to talk either of infinite sets or finite sets. Each of us has an intuitive notion of what types of sets should be assigned to each of these categories. For example, one might describe an infinite set as a set which, if its elements are listed, goes on without end. Likewise, another individual might say that it is so large that it cannot be comprehended. The trouble with such descriptions is that they do not give us any really precise insight to such sets. That is, there is a vagueness which really adds nothing to such discussions beyond the intuitive level. What we need, then, is a means (specific in nature) which will be both meaningful and precise for determining whether or not a given set is infinite. The means which we adopt is as follows.

Definition 1-12: A set A is said to be **infinite** if it is equivalent to a proper subset of itself. Otherwise A is called a **finite** set.

This means that in order to show that a set is infinite, we must be able to do two things:

(1) Select a proper subset A' of A in such a way that

(2) $A \sim A'$.

In order to give some illustrations which are meaningful to you, we shall assume *for the moment* that you are familiar with whole numbers and some of the operations on them such as addition.

Example: Show that the set $A = \{1,2,3,4, \ldots\}$ is an infinite set.

Solution: Choose $A' = \{2,3,4,5, \ldots\}$. Then we set up the one-to-one onto mapping as follows.

$$A = \{1, \quad 2, \quad 3, \quad 4, \quad \ldots \quad k, \quad \ldots\}$$

$$A' = \{2, \quad 3, \quad 4, \quad 5, \quad \ldots \quad k+1, \quad \ldots\}$$

Here we have $A' \subset A$ and $A \sim A'$. Hence by Definition 1-12, A is an infinite set.

There are several things which should be noted regarding this example.
(1) The three dots, . . . , following an indicated pattern mean that the pattern continues in the same manner.
(2) When setting up the one-to-one onto mapping, either every pairing of elements must be given in detail or else a rule must be given which clearly indicates how elements are to be paired.

The way we have indicated in the example is sufficient for the present. Here we have indicated that to determine the second member of a given pair, we choose the first member of the pair from A and then add one to it to get the second member. This second member is an element of A'.

As a second example we consider the following.

Example: Determine whether or not $B = \{a,b,c\}$ is infinite.

Solution: Select a proper subset B' of B, say $B' = \{a,b\}$.
Next we try to set up the one-to-one onto mapping from B to B'.

$$B = \{a, \quad b, \quad c\} \qquad \text{or} \qquad B = \{a, \quad b, \quad c\}$$

$$B' = \{a, \quad b\} \qquad\qquad\qquad\qquad B' = \{a, \quad b\}$$

It is clear that there is no one-to-one onto mapping possible. Hence we must conclude that B is not infinite and consequently B must be finite. Of course there are other possibilities for choosing the proper subsets, but each choice leads to the conclusion that B is not infinite.

We shall see in the latter part of Chapter 1 that finite sets, infinite sets, and equivalent sets play a very important role. For this reason, you should make sure that you have a rather clear understanding of these concepts. Exercises are provided for this purpose, but we also encourage you to make up examples of your own.

EXERCISE SET 1-3
1. Is (a) $\{a,b,c\} \sim \{d,e,f\}$?
   (b) $\{a,b,c\} \sim \{1,2,3\}$?
   (c) $\{a,b,c\} \sim \{\square,\bigcirc,\triangle\}$?
   (d) $\{a,b,c\} \sim \{c,a,b\}$?
   (e) $\{a,b,c\} \sim \{p,q,r,s\}$?

(f) $\{a,b,c\} \sim \{b,c,a\}$?

(g) $\{a,b,c\} \sim \{\{a\}, \{b\}, \{c\}\}$?

2. List a set which is equivalent to the set

$$\{x|x \text{ is a lower case letter of the English alphabet}\}.$$

3. Which of the following pairs of sets are equivalent?

$A = \{\text{Priscilla Pringle}\}$

$B = \{x|x \text{ was a major party presidential nominee in 1964}\}$

$C = \{1,2,3\}$

$D = \{x|x \text{ is the teacher of this particular math class}\}$

$E = \{x|x \text{ is a counting number which is larger than 2 but smaller than 3}\}$

$F = \{a,e,f\}$

$G = \{\text{true, false}\}$

4. (a) List two sets which are *not equal* but which *are* equivalent.

(b) List two sets which are *not equivalent* but which *are* equal.

5. Decide which of the sets listed below are finite.

(a) $\{a,b,c \ldots, y,z\}$ (b) $\{1,2,3, \ldots\}$

(c) $\{2,4,6, \ldots, 1002\}$ (d) $\{2,4,6, \ldots\}$

(e) $\{10000001, \ldots, 5,3,1\}$ (f) $\{\ldots, 5,3,1\}$

(g) $\{x|x \text{ is a grain of sand on some beach on this earth}\}$

6. Show that each of the following sets is infinite. In doing so, actually draw arrows to indicate the correspondence you set up.

(a) $\{0,1,2,3,4, \ldots\}$ (e) $\{4,8,12,16, \ldots\}$

(b) $\{0,2,4,6,8, \ldots\}$ (f) $\{3,4,5,6, \ldots\}$

(c) $\{1,3,5,7,9, \ldots\}$ (g) $\{1,4,9,16,25, \ldots\}$

(d) $\{3,6,9,12,15, \ldots\}$ (h) $\{1,5,9,13,17, \ldots\}$

4. Building New Sets from Existing Ones

At this point, the reader has been introduced to the concept of set and many related ideas including mappings from one set to another. It is possible to develop a theory of sets for its own sake; however we shall only pursue those ideas of set theory which will be of value in the development of arithmetic. What we shall do is to manipulate existing sets in a specified manner in order to build new sets which will be of particular interest to us in developing our arithmetic.

Before doing this, we shall make an agreement which will be very helpful in visualizing the new sets to be formed. The agreement is as follows.

Agreement: Rather than listing the elements of sets in which we are interested, we agree to draw closed curves in the plane so that the regions enclosed by the curves represent the sets under consideration. The resulting pictures are known as *Venn diagrams.*

For example, if $\mathcal{U} = \{a,b,c,d,e,f\}$ and $A = \{a,b,c\}$, we could draw the following picture to represent these sets.

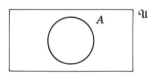

In the picture, the region inside the closed curve labelled A represents $\{a,b,c\}$ and the region inside the curve labelled $\mathscr{U}$ represents $\{a,b,c,d,e,f\}$. Thus since $A \subset \mathscr{U}$, the region representing A should be "smaller than" the region representing $\mathscr{U}$, and this is indeed true.

The manipulation of sets in order to form new sets has much of its foundation in the physical world. We have all performed most of these manipulations at one time or another. Most of us, for example, have watched children playing with various sets of toys. On some occasions a child has two sets of toys when he starts to play, but during his play he puts all of his toys together. That is, he *joins* them into just one set — a new set. Such a physical example gives us a way of making a new set from two existing sets.

If we begin with sets

$$A = \{a,b,c\} \text{ and}$$
$$B = \{e,f,g\}$$

and then join them together we have now a third set

$$C = \{a,b,c,e,f,g\}$$

This is exactly analogous to the child and his toys. We shall make this concept more precise by means of the following definition.

Definition 1-13: The **union** (or join) of two sets A and B is the set of elements which are in A or B. We denote this new set by $A \cup B$, often read "A union B."

We note that in Definition 1-13 the word "or" is used in the inclusive sense. That is, when we say "A or B" in Definition 1-13, we mean A or B (possibly both). Thus if A and B are disjoint, $A \cup B$ contains each element of A and each element of B. If A and B are *not* disjoint, then $A \cup B$ contains all distinct elements of A and B. That is, the elements which are common are listed just once in $A \cup B$.

For example, if

$$A = \{a,b,c\}$$

and

$$B = \{d,e\}$$

then

$$A \cup B = \{a,b,c,d,e\}$$

but if

$$A = \{a,b,c\}$$

and

$$B = \{b,c,d\}$$

then

$$A \cup B = \{a,b,c,d\}$$

The pictures which illustrate the union of two sets would look like one of those in Figure 1-2 in which $A \cup B$ is shaded.

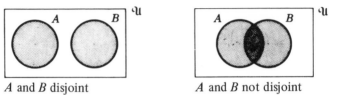

A and B disjoint   A and B not disjoint

FIGURE 1-2

As a preview of what is to come, we note that (assuming for the moment that we understand numbers and counting) if

$$A = \{a,b,c\} \text{ and } B = \{e,f\},$$

then

$$A \cup B = \{a,b,c,e,f\}.$$

That is, we took a set with three elements, joined it with a set having two elements and obtained a set having five elements. This is very suggestive of addition, and indeed, it is related to it, but there is more to be said regarding the subject. In fact, there is quite a lot more to be said, and so let us defer further discussion of this until we can discuss it in considerable detail. It is interesting to note, however, that even now we can see where we are headed.

Next, let us consider a child who has a set of blocks of different colors each bearing a letter of the alphabet. If asked which blocks are red and bear the letter A, the child may select the red blocks and then, after observing these, select those with letter A. The mathematical concept involved here is that of *set intersection* which we now formalize.

Definition 1-14: The **intersection** (or meet) of two sets A and B is the set whose elements are in A and B. We denote this set by $A \cap B$, often read "A intersect B."

For example, if $A = \{a,b,c,d,e\}$ and $B = \{a,b,g,h,i\}$ then

$$A \cap B = \{a,b\}$$

since a and b are the only elements which are in both of the original sets.

Venn diagrams which illustrate set intersection could look like one of the illustrations in Figure 1-3 in which $A \cap B$ is the shaded region.

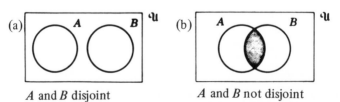

A and B disjoint   A and B not disjoint

FIGURE 1-3

Note that in Figure 1-3 (a) there is no shaded region. This is because of the fact that disjoint sets have no common elements. That is, if A and B are disjoint sets, then $A \cap B = \emptyset$. This is often taken as a definition for disjointness of sets, and from the figure it is easy to see why this is done.

The next concept we deal with will eventually be used to define subtraction, and we believe the connection will be clear from the following illustration. Suppose a child has a set of blocks whose elements are labelled a, b, c, d, e, f, and g. Suppose now that we ask him what set he has left if we remove the blocks labelled c, d, and e. He would then put these latter blocks in a pile by themselves and point to the set which remains. The set which he points to would be the set of all blocks of the original set which are not in the set of blocks which were removed. In this process, we are finding what we call the *complement* of a set. We shall now state this more formally as a definition and then list some examples.

Definition 1-15: If $\mathcal{U}$ is a universal set and A is a subset of $\mathcal{U}$, then the **complement** of A relative to $\mathcal{U}$ is the set of elements of $\mathcal{U}$ which are not elements of A. We denote this set by $c(A)$, read "the complement of A."

For example, if $\mathcal{U} = \{p,q,r,s,t,u\}$ and $A = \{r,s,t\}$ then

$$c(A) = \{p,q,u\}.$$

Also, if $\mathcal{U}$ = {Carpella, Grunella, Garble}
and A = {Carpella, Garble},
then $c(A)$ = {Grunella}.

The Venn diagram which illustrates the concept of the set complement of A relative to $\mathcal{U}$ is the shaded region pictured in Figure 1-4.

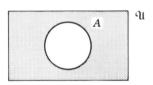

FIGURE 1-4

It is interesting to look ahead to see how this concept might apply to subtraction. If we want to subtract three from six, we might select $\mathcal{U} = \{a,b,c,d,e,f\}$ and $A = \{a,c,e\}$ and find that $c(A) = \{b,d,f\}$. That is, we started with two sets, one with six elements and one with three elements, and ended up with a set having three elements. It is a fact that something like this is done to define subtraction, but again, since there is more than this involved, we shall defer further discussion until we can do it in considerable detail.

The next situation has been faced by most people at least by the time they have entered college. That is, from a given set of clothes how many outfits can be obtained? To be more specific, suppose a young lady has a blue skirt, a grey skirt, a plaid skirt, a blue blouse, a white blouse, and a pink blouse. How many outfits can she obtain from these clothes. If we list the possible combinations, the results are as follows.

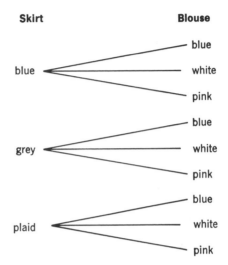

Skirt   **Blouse**

If the young lady has chosen shades carefully, she has nine possible outfits which she can use. The important thing to note in this example is that in choosing these combinations the young lady has been forced into choosing *pairs*. Now this can be done in two ways, either by choosing skirts first and then choosing blouses or vice-versa. However, the fact of the matter is that the manner of choosing is important, as the next example illustrates.

Suppose one decides to put on shoes and socks. Here there are two sets, shoes and socks. It is easy to agree that we have choices available as to whether we put on socks first or shoes first. The important thing to notice is that different results occur in our appearance depending on whether we put on the socks first or shoes first.

By making the choices described in the two examples above, we are forced to admit that the members of the pairs are ordered. That is, there is a *first* member of the pair and a *second* member of the pair. From the second example, we see that ordered pairs are the same if and only if the corresponding members of the pairs are the same. Hence we shall define the abstract concept of ordered pair in a similar fashion.

Definition 1-16: (a) An **ordered pair** consists of two objects, a and b, one of which is chosen first, the other chosen second. This is denoted by (a,b) and read "the ordered pair a comma b."
(b) Two ordered pairs (a,b) and (c,d) are **equal** if and only if $a = c$ and $b = d$.

This definition says in a more precise way the same things as referred to in the two examples.

The selecting of possible pairs in a given order can be accomplished in a precise manner by forming what is called the *Cartesian product* of two sets. Let us now define this and show that our claim is valid.

Definition 1-17: The **Cartesian product** of two sets A and B is the set of all ordered pairs such that the first member of the pair is an element of A and the second member is an element of B. This set is denoted by $A \times B$, often read "*A* cross *B*."

Returning to our first example, we have

$$A = \{\text{blue skirt, grey skirt, plaid skirt}\}$$
$$B = \{\text{blue blouse, white blouse, pink blouse}\}$$

and

$$A \times B = \left\{ \begin{array}{l} \text{(blue skirt, blue blouse), (blue skirt, white blouse),} \\ \text{(blue skirt, pink blouse), (grey skirt, blue blouse),} \\ \text{(grey skirt, white blouse), (grey skirt, pink blouse),} \\ \text{(plaid skirt, blue blouse), (plaid skirt, white blouse),} \\ \text{(plaid skirt, pink blouse)} \end{array} \right\}$$

By comparing these pairs with previous results, one finds that these are precisely the same combinations which were obtained in the first example. Do the examples used here give the reader an idea as to how we might define multiplication? We shall most assuredly return to consider this later in the book.

In order to draw a picture to illustrate the Cartesian product, we shall need to resort to a different scheme from the Venn diagrams which we used previously. The reason for this is that not only do we build a new set by forming the Cartesian product, but we also form new *elements*. That is, we form sets of ordered pairs. What we can do is to draw two perpendicular line segments and pick points on these segments which are to represent the elements of the two sets as illustrated in Figure 1-5. We shall take $A = \{a, b, c\}$, $B = \{\triangle, \nabla\}$ and calculate $A \times B$.

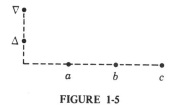

FIGURE 1-5

Next we draw lines through the points labelled *a*, *b*, *c*, $\triangle$, and ∇ and label the intersection points as in Figure 1-6.

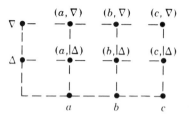

FIGURE 1-6

The "lattice" points named by the ordered pairs in Figure 1-6 represent $A \times B$. Similarly, $B \times A$ would appear as in Figure 1-7 below.

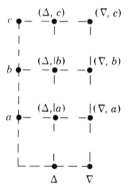

FIGURE 1-7

EXERCISE SET 1-4

1. Let $\mathcal{U} = \{1,2,3,\ldots,9\}$. Determine the following sets:
   (a) $\{1,2,3,4\} \cap \{3,4,5,6\} =$
   (b) $\{1,2,3,4\} \cup \{3,4,5,6\} =$
   (c) $c\{1,2,3,4\} =$
   (d) $\{1,3,5,7,9\} \cap \{3,6,9\} =$
   (e) $(\{1,2,5\} \cup \{2,3,6\}) \cup \{3,4,5\} =$
   (f) $\{1,3,5,7,9\} \cap \{2,4,6,8\} =$
   (g) $c\{1,3,5,7,9\} =$
   (h) $\{1\} \cup \{2\} \cup \{3\} \cup \{4\} =$
   (i) $\{4,5,6,7\} \cap (\{1,5,9\} \cup \{4,8\}) =$
   (j) $c(\{2,3,6\} \cup \{1,2,5,7\}) =$
   (k) $\{1,6\} \cap (\{2,7\} \cup \{3,8\}) =$
2. Were each of the answers obtained in problem one subsets of $\mathcal{U}$?
3. Let $\mathcal{U} = \{0,1,2,3,4,5,6,7,8,9\}$ and let $A = \{0,2,4,6,8\}$, $B = \{1,3,5,9\}$, $C = \{0,3,6,9\}$, $D = \{2,5,8\}$, and $E = \{1,4,7\}$. Determine each of the following sets.
   (a) $C \cup (D \cup E) =$
   (b) $B \cup D =$
   (c) $A \cup C =$
   (d) $(A \cap B) \cup \emptyset =$
   (e) $c(D \cup E) =$
   (f) $c(A) \cup c(B) =$

(g) $(B \cap D) \cup A =$
(h) $c(C \cap D) =$
(i) $c(C \cup D) =$
(j) $c(\mathcal{U}) =$

4. Let $\mathcal{U} = \{1,2,3, \ldots , 10\}$, $A = \{1,2,3,5,7\}$, $B = \{1,3,5,7\}$, and $C = \{2,4,6,8\}$. Which of the following are true and which are false?

(a) $A \subseteq B$ (f) $c(A) \subseteq c(B)$
(b) $B \subseteq A$ (g) $c(B) \subseteq c(A)$
(c) $A \subset B$ (h) $B \subseteq c(C)$
(d) $B \subset A$ (i) $c(B) \subseteq C$
(e) $A \subseteq c(B)$ (j) $c(B) \subset C$

5. Let $A = \{a,b,c\}$ and $B = \{4,5\}$.
(a) Write out the set $A \times B$.
(b) Write out $B \times A$.
(c) Write $A \times A$.
(d) Write $B \times B$.
(e) Which of the previous four sets you constructed are equal?
(f) Is $(4,5) = (5,4)$?
(g) Is $\{4,5\} = \{5,4\}$?
(h) Is $(4,5) \in A \times B$?
(i) Is $\{a\} \subset \{a,b,c\}$?
(j) Is $\{a\} \subset A \times B$?
(k) Is $\{ (a,5)\} \subset A \times B$?
(l) Is $\emptyset \in A \times B$?
(m) Is $(b,4) \subset A \times B$?

6. Let $\mathcal{U}$ be the set of boys who are students at your school. Let A be the set of those who are tall and handsome, B be the set of those who are tall but not handsome, C be the set of those who are not tall but are handsome, D be the set of those who are not tall and not handsome.
(a) Is $c(A) = B$?   (d) Is $B \subseteq c(A)$?
(b) Is $c(A) = C$?   (e) Is $C \subseteq c(A)$?
(c) Is $c(A) = D$?   (f) Is $D \subseteq c(A)$?

7. Let $A = \{0,1,2\}$, $B = \emptyset$, and $C = \{1,2,3\}$.
(a) Calculate $A \times B$.   (g) Does $A \times B = B \times A$?
(b) Calculate $B \times A$.   (h) Does $A \times C = C \times A$?
(c) Calculate $B \times C$.   (i) Is $B \times C \sim C \times B$?
(d) Calculate $C \times B$.   (j) Is $B \times A \sim B \times C$?
(e) Calculate $A \times C$.   (k) Is $B \times B = \{(\emptyset,\emptyset)\}$?
(f) Calculate $C \times A$.

8. Let $A = \{0,1,2\}$, $B = \{0\}$, and $C = \{3,1,2\}$.
(a) Calculate $A \times B$.   (f) Calculate $C \times A$.
(b) Calculate $B \times A$.   (g) Does $A \times B = B \times A$?
(c) Calculate $B \times C$.   (h) Is $A \times C \sim C \times A$?
(d) Calculate $C \times B$.   (i) Is $A \times B \sim B \times A$?
(e) Calculate $A \times C$.

9. Listed below are Venn diagram representations of sets. Shade the region or regions which illustrate the set expression below each figure. If the universe is not specified, assume it to be everything inside the outer boundary of the figure.

(a)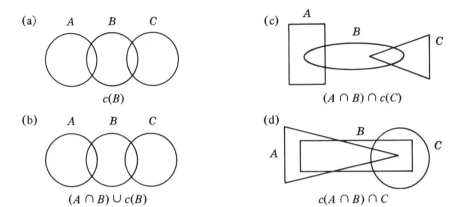

c(B)

(c)

$(A \cap B) \cap c(C)$

(b)

$(A \cap B) \cup c(B)$

(d)

$c(A \cap B) \cap C$

10. Suppose the sets $\mathcal{U}$, A, B, C, D are described by the *shaded portions* as shown.

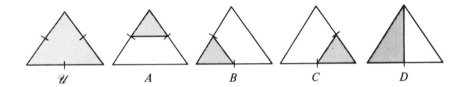

$\mathcal{U}$ A   B   C   D

I. Now sketch the following sets:
 (a) $c(A)$
 (b) $A \cup B$
 (c) $A \cap B$
 (d) $B \cap D$
 (e) $c(c(D))$
 (f) $c(A) \cup D$
 (g) $c(B) \cap c(A)$
 (h) $c(A \cup B)$
 (i) $A \cap A$
 (j) $B \cap C$

II. Decide which of the following are true:
 (a) $A \subseteq B$
 (b) $A \subseteq C$
 (c) $A \subseteq D$
 (d) $B \subset D$
 (e) $C \subseteq (c(A) \cup D)$
 (f) $C \subseteq c(A \cup B)$
 (g) $(A \cap B) \subset B$
 (h) $A \subset (c(B) \cup c(A))$
 (i) $c(A) \cap c(B) = c(A \cup B)$

11. In each of the following, shade the region described by the set expression written below the figure.

(a)   (b)   (c)

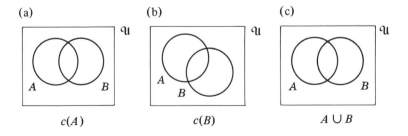

c(A)   c(B) $A \cup B$

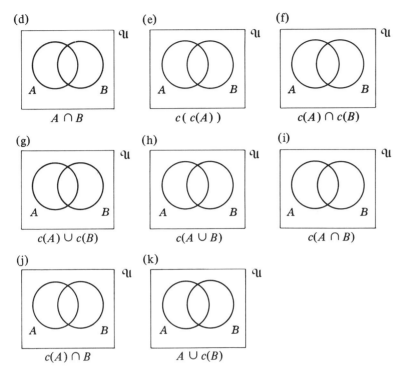

(d) $A \cap B$

(e) $c(c(A))$

(f) $c(A) \cap c(B)$

(g) $c(A) \cup c(B)$

(h) $c(A \cup B)$

(i) $c(A \cap B)$

(j) $c(A) \cap B$

(k) $A \cup c(B)$

12. Write a set expression which describes the shaded region(s) for each of the following problems. If the universe is not specified, assume it to be everything inside the outer boundary of the entire figure.

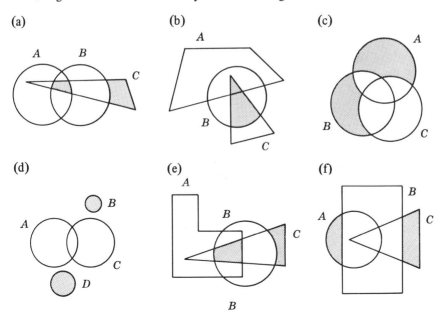

(g)   (h)   (i)

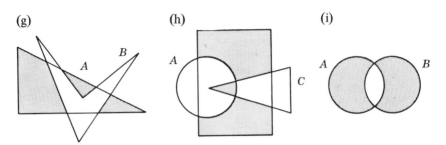

13. Draw a diagram (graph) showing $A \times B$ if $A = \{1,3,5,7\}$ and $B = \{2,4,6\}$.

5. Algebra of Sets

In the preceding section various methods were introduced by which sets may be combined in order to produce new sets. Let us now use the methods which have been described to build some new sets and see if anything of interest results.

To begin with let us consider $A \cup B$ and $B \cup A$ where A and B are any two sets. If we happen to choose

$$A = \{a,b,c,d\}$$

and

$$B = \{e,f,g\}$$

then

$$A \cup B = \{a,b,c,d,e,f,g\}$$

and

$$B \cup A = \{e,f,g,a,b,c,d\}$$

In this case we observe that $A \cup B = B \cup A$.

Now suppose we select A and B so that $A \cap B \neq \emptyset$. Choose

$$A = \{a,b,c,d\}$$

and

$$B = \{a,c,e,f\}$$

Then

$$A \cup B = \{a,b,c,d,e,f\}$$

and

$$B \cup A = \{a,c,e,f,b,d\}$$

and again we obtain the result that $A \cup B = B \cup A$.

If we use Venn diagrams, the results obtained for any two sets whatever are as follows.

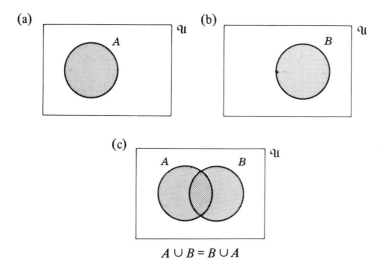

$$A \cup B = B \cup A$$

The two examples just cited and the Venn diagrams do *not* prove that $A \cup B = B \cup A$; however they do indicate the likelihood of equality.

As a second example, let us try to determine another way to represent $A \cup c(A)$ where $\mathcal{U}$ is the universal set and $A \subseteq \mathcal{U}$.

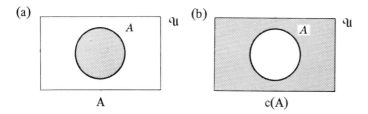

If we take the union of the shaded regions we obtain

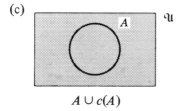

$$A \cup c(A)$$

That is, $A \cup c(A) = \mathcal{U}$. This statement is indeed true, but let us hasten to say that we have only illustrated it in this example. We have *not* proved it.

As a third example, let us see if we can determine whether it is likely that

$$A \cup (B \cap C) = (A \cup B) \cap (A \cup C)$$

by using Venn diagrams.   Parts (a) and (b) illustrate the left side of the expression.

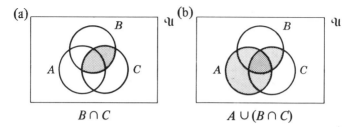

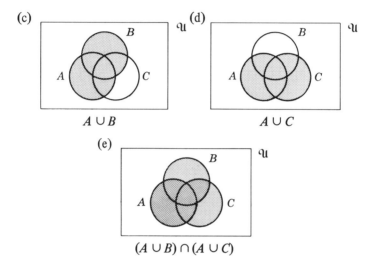

$(A \cup B) \cap (A \cup C)$

Hence we find that the darker shaded region in (e) is the region common to both $A \cup B$ and $A \cup C$. Consequently this region corresponds to

$$(A \cup B) \cap (A \cup C),$$

and we note that the region named is the same as that in (b). Therefore it appears that

$$A \cup (B \cap C) = (A \cup B) \cap (A \cup C).$$

There are many relationships, such as the above three, which always hold for the subsets of a given universal set $\mathcal{U}$. We have not proved any of them yet, but it is true that Venn diagrams or specific choices of sets lend credence to the claim that the relationships just discussed do hold. We shall now list some of the more important relationships which hold for subsets of a universal set. After having done this, we shall illustrate what must be done in order to actually prove them.

Theorem 1-2: If A, B, and C are subsets of a universal set $\mathcal{U}$, then the following laws (or relationships) hold.

(a) Identity Laws
     1. $A \cup \emptyset = A$ $1'. \ A \cap \emptyset = \emptyset$
     2. $A \cup \mathcal{U} = \mathcal{U}$ $2'. \ A \cap \mathcal{U} = A$

(b) Idempotent Laws:
     1. $A \cup A = A$ $1'. \ A \cap A = A$

(c) Complement Laws:
     1. $A \cup c(A) = \mathcal{U}$ $1'. \ A \cap c(A) = \emptyset$
     2. $c(\, c(A)\,) = A$

(d) Commutative Laws:
     1. $A \cup B = B \cup A$ $1'. \ A \cap B = B \cap A$

(e) Associative Laws:
     1. $A \cup (B \cup C) = (A \cup B) \cup C$ $1'. \ A \cap (B \cap C) = (A \cap B) \cap C$

(f) Distributive Laws:
     1. $A \cup (B \cap C) = (A \cup B) \cap (A \cup C)$
     2. $A \cap (B \cup C) = (A \cap B) \cup (A \cap C)$

(g) DeMorgan's Laws:
     1. $c(A \cup B) = c(A) \cap c(B)$ $1'. \ c(A \cap B) = c(A) \cup c(B)$

The student should draw Venn diagrams for several of the laws listed in Theorem 1-2 in order to convince himself of their validity.

Let us now select one of the laws and prove it in detail. Two methods of proof will be illustrated for a non-empty universal set,

            1) membership table proof, and
            2) element-wise proof.

We shall prove Theorem 1-3 twice, once by each method just listed.

Theorem 1-3: If $\mathcal{U}$ is a universal set and $A \subseteq \mathcal{U}$, then $A \cup c(A) = \mathcal{U}$.

1) *Outline of membership table method:* In order to prove the theorem by use of a membership table, we use primarily the definition of set equality. That is, we try to show that the sets in question have the same elements. To construct the table, we list the possibilities for membership which can occur for an arbitrary element x of $\mathcal{U}$ with respect to the sets A and $c(A)$ by using the symbols $\in$ or $\notin$. If any two columns of the table have identical entries in the same relative positions, then the column headings name the same set. We omit the cases which cannot occur from the table.

Proof: Constructing the membership table as outlined above, we obtain

A	$c(A)$	$A \cup c(A)$	$\mathcal{U}$
$\in$	$\notin$	$\in$	$\in$
$\notin$	$\in$	$\in$	$\in$

Since the last two columns to the right in the table are identical, we conclude that $A \cup c(A) = \mathcal{U}$. ∎

2) *Outline of element-wise method:*
(i) We shall choose an arbitrary element in $A \cup c(A)$ and show that the element must be an element of $\mathcal{U}$ so that $A \cup c(A) \subseteq \mathcal{U}$.
(ii) Next we shall choose an arbitrary element of $\mathcal{U}$ and show that it is in $A \cup c(A)$ so that $\mathcal{U} \subseteq A \cup c(A)$.
(iii) Finally we shall use Theorem 1-1 to conclude that $A \cup c(A) = \mathcal{U}$.

Proof: (i) Let x be an element of $A \cup c(A)$. Then by definition of $\cup$, $x \in A$ or $x \in c(A)$. Since $A \subseteq \mathcal{U}$, we have that if $x \in A$ then $x \in \mathcal{U}$ by definition of subset. Since $c(A) \subseteq \mathcal{U}$, we have that if $x \in c(A)$ then $x \in \mathcal{U}$ by definition of subset. Hence if $x \in A \cup c(A)$ then $x \in \mathcal{U}$. Thus by definition of subset, $A \cup c(A) \subseteq \mathcal{U}$.
(ii) Let y be an element of $\mathcal{U}$. Then for any subset A of $\mathcal{U}$, either $y \in A$ or $y \in A$. If $y \notin A$, then $y \in A \cup c(A)$ by definition of $\cup$. If $y \notin A$, then $y \in c(A)$ by definition of set complement. Further, if $y \in c(A)$ then $y \in A \cup c(A)$ by definition of $\cup$. Hence if $y \in \mathcal{U}$, then $y \in A \cup c(A)$. That is, $\mathcal{U} \subseteq A \cup c(A)$ by definition of subset.
(iii) From (i) we have

$$A \cup c(A) \subseteq \mathcal{U}$$

and from (ii) we have

$$\mathcal{U} \subseteq A \cup c(A).$$

Hence by Theorem 1-1 we obtain the result that

$$A \cup c(A) = \mathcal{U}$$

and the theorem is proved. ∎

It is easy to see from the two proofs of Theorem 1-3 that the membership table has the advantage of making such proofs short and concise. So that we may demonstrate its power more fully, let us next try to show that

$$A \cup (B \cap C) = (A \cup B) \cap (A \cup C).$$

Theorem 1-4: If $\mathcal{U}$ is a universal set and $A \subseteq \mathcal{U}$, $B \subseteq \mathcal{U}$, and $C \subseteq \mathcal{U}$, then $A \cup (B \cap C) = (A \cup B) \cap (A \cup C)$.

Proof:

A	B	C	$B \cap C$	$A \cup (B \cap C)$	$A \cup B$	$A \cup C$	$(A \cup B) \cap (A \cup C)$
$\in$	$\in$	$\in$	$\in$	$\in$	$\in$	$\in$	$\in$
$\in$	$\in$	$\notin$	$\notin$	$\in$	$\in$	$\in$	$\in$
$\in$	$\notin$	$\in$	$\notin$	$\in$	$\in$	$\in$	$\in$
$\in$	$\notin$	$\notin$	$\notin$	$\in$	$\in$	$\in$	$\in$
$\notin$	$\in$	$\in$	$\in$	$\in$	$\in$	$\in$	$\in$
$\notin$	$\in$	$\notin$	$\notin$	$\notin$	$\in$	$\notin$	$\notin$
$\notin$	$\notin$	$\in$	$\notin$	$\notin$	$\notin$	$\in$	$\notin$
$\notin$	$\notin$	$\notin$	$\notin$	$\notin$	$\notin$	$\notin$	$\notin$

Since columns five and eight are identical, we conclude that

$$A \cup (B \cap C) = (A \cup B) \cap (A \cup C).$$

Consequently the theorem is proved.█

It is possible to prove each of the other laws listed in Theorem 1-2 by one of the methods just described. We shall not do so here, but the reader is invited to try to prove a few of the properties. Some specific illustrations of these laws are provided for you in the exercise set at the end of the section.

If we admit some familiarity (for the moment) with numbers, there is a third alternative which can be used to illustrate the likelihood of the validity of the laws listed in Theorem 1-2. This technique involves the numbering of all possible regions formed by overlappings of the sets involved in a given law. Once this is done, we select by number the regions which describe the basic sets involved and then use the definitions of union, intersection, and complementation to determine the particular sets listed in the statement of the law under consideration.

Example: $c(A \cup B) = c(A) \cap c(B)$.

Solution: Draw a picture as indicated.

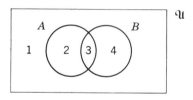

Sets Required	Regions Describing Sets
A	2, 3
B	3, 4
$A \cup B$	2, 3, 4
$c(A \cup B)$	1
$c(A)$	1, 4
$c(B)$	1, 2
$c(A) \cap c(B)$	1

Since the region numbered 1 represents both $c(A \cup B)$ and $c(A) \cap c(B)$, it appears that $c(A \cup B) = c(A) \cap c(B)$. Remember that the procedure does not constitute a proof, but rather is a helpful visual aid.

As a second example we shall select one of the laws which involves three sets.

Example: $A \cup (B \cap C) = (A \cup B) \cap (A \cup C)$.

Solution: Draw a picture as indicated.

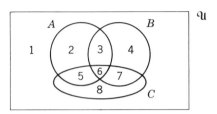

Sets Required	Regions Describing Sets
A	2, 3, 5, 6
B	3, 4, 6, 7
C	5, 6, 7, 8
$B \cap C$	6, 7
$A \cup (B \cap C)$	2, 3, 5, 6, 7
$A \cup B$	2, 3, 4, 5, 6, 7
$A \cup C$	2, 3, 5, 6, 7, 8
$(A \cup B) \cap (A \cup C)$	2, 3, 5, 6, 7

Since the regions numbered 2, 3, 5, 6, 7 represent both $A \cup (B \cap C)$ and $(A \cup B) \cap (A \cup C)$, it appears likely that $A \cup (B \cap C) = (A \cup B) \cap (A \cup C)$.

It should be noted that when one draws the pictures as in the above examples he should be sure to draw the most general picture possible. To do this use may be made of the fact that if the number of sets chosen from the universal set is n, then there should result 2^n different regions to be numbered.

In the arithmetic which we shall develop in the following chapters we shall find that time and again we shall meet some of the laws mentioned above. When we meet these laws it will be in a slightly different context (dealing with numbers), but the laws will be the same nonetheless.

EXERCISE SET 1-5

1. Using Venn Diagrams, check the following: (Some may not be true so be careful).
   (a) $c(c(A)) = A$
   (b) $c(A \cup B) = c(A) \cap c(B)$
   (c) $A \cup (B \cap C) = (A \cap B) \cup (A \cap C)$
   (d) $A \cap (B \cup C) = (A \cap B) \cup (A \cap C)$
   (e) $A \cup (B \cup C) = (A \cup B) \cup C$
   (f) $A \cap B = B \cup A$
2. Let $\mathcal{U} = \{0,1,2,3,4,5,6,7,8,9\}$. Determine the following sets.
   (a) $\{0,1,2\} \cup \{0,3,5\}$
   (b) $\{3,5,7,9\} \cap \{0,2,4,6\}$
   (c) $\{3,4,6,8\} \cap \{6,5,7,8,9\}$
   (d) $\{2,0\} \cap (\{3,4,5\} \cup \{8,9\})$ Do in two ways.
   (e) $c(c\{1,2,3,4,5\})$ Do in two ways.
   (f) $c(\{0,1,3\} \cup \{5,4\})$ Do in two ways.
   (g) $c(\{0\} \cap \{3,4,5\})$ Do in two ways.
   (h) $\emptyset \cup \{0\}$
   (i) $\emptyset \cap \{0\}$

3. Choose $\mathcal{U}$ = $\{x|x$ is a lower case letter of the English alphabet$\}$, A = $\{a,b,c,d,e\}$, $B = \{c,d,e,f,g,h,i,j\}$, and $C = \{h,i,j,k,l,m,n,o,p\}$
   (a) Calculate $c(B)$
   (b) Calculate $c(C)$
   (c) Calculate $c(B) \cap c(C)$
   (d) Calculate $c(B) \cup c(C)$
   (e) Calculate $c(B \cup C)$
   (f) Calculate $c(B \cap C)$
   (g) Are your answers to parts (c) and (e) the same?
   (h) Are your answers to parts (d) and (f) the same?
   (i) What laws of sets are illustrated in parts (g) and (h)?
   (j) Calculate $A \cup (B \cap C)$
   (k) Calculate $A \cup B$
   (l) Calculate $A \cup C$
   (m) Calculate $(A \cup B) \cap (A \cup C)$
   (n) Are your answers to parts (j) and (m) the same?
   (o) Calculate $A \cap (B \cap C)$
   (p) Calculate $(A \cap B) \cap C$
   (q) Are your answers to parts (o) and (p) the same?
4. Use membership tables to show that if A, B, and C are any three subsets of a universal set $\mathcal{U}$, then
   (a) $A \cup \emptyset = A$
   (b) $A \cap c(A) = \emptyset$
   (c) $c(c(A)) = A$
   (d) $A \cup B = B \cup A$
   (e) $A \cap B = B \cap A$
   (f) $A \cup (B \cup C) = (A \cup B) \cup C$
   (g) $A \cap (B \cup C) = (A \cap B) \cup (A \cap C)$
   (h) $c(A \cup B) = c(A) \cap c(B)$
   (i) $c(A \cap B) = c(A) \cup c(B)$
5. By means of an element-wise proof show that
   (a) $A \cup B = B \cup A$
   (b) $A \cap B = B \cap A$
   (c) $A \cup (B \cup C) = (A \cup B) \cup C$
   (d) $A \cap (B \cap C) = (A \cap B) \cap C$
   (e) $A \cap (B \cup C) = (A \cap B) \cup (A \cap C)$
   (f) $A \cup (B \cap C) = (A \cup B) \cap (A \cup C)$
   (g) $c(A \cup B) = c(A) \cap c(B)$
   (h) $c(A \cap B) = c(A) \cup c(B)$.
6. Work each part of problem five by using numbered regions in conjunction with Venn diagrams.

6. Relations

The term *relation* may at first seem to be a rather odd word to mention in a subject such as mathematics, but as we shall soon show, there is much more to say regarding this term than one might first suspect.

In every day life, if one compares any two objects, he may be trying to determine the relation of one object to the other or considering a relationship which he knows to exist between the two objects. An excellent example of such a consideration of relationships is that of a child trying to determine who are his aunts, uncles, cousins, and so forth. In this case the child is trying to pair himself with his relatives. On the other hand, one may think of pairing off objects which are apparently unrelated except for the fact that he has associated one with the other. That is, there may be no obvious way in which the objects are related one to the other, and there may have been no comparison of objects involved. A good example of this type of pairing is that of house number to houses on city blocks. Here some of the pairings appear to follow no systematic scheme since one house may be paired with 1013 while an adjacent house may be numbered 1021 instead of 1015 as might have been suspected. It is also true that there is no relation between the number used and the characteristic of the house. Yet there is a definite relationship between house and number. From these two examples one can observe that the term relation as used in the everyday sense has no well defined meaning attached to it. Because we want to use the term in the work which follows, we shall try to establish in a much more specific way what we shall mean by the term relation.

We shall concern ourselves with pairs of objects which when compared one to the other exhibit some type of relationship. Further, we shall require that in order to make a comparison of objects that the objects under consideration be members of the same set. We shall also require that both the set and relation be specified in advance. Then if given a specific relationship (or relation) and set we shall select pairs of elements of the set and try to determine if the two members of each pair have this relationship. An example of such a type of comparison would be to take as a given set the set of students in your mathematics class. From this set select members a pair at a time and see which of the pair "is taller than" the other. Now it is clear that if we select a pair, we shall choose one member first and then choose a second member. Suppose that elements a and b are chosen and that we form the ordered pair (a,b). The statement we must consider, then, is

$$a \text{ "is taller than" } b.$$

It should be clear that we are interested only in those pairs of students which can be selected for which the relation holds, for as indicated we want to know only who is taller than whom. Some of the statements which can be made regarding two elements of the set are true and some are false, the truth depending solely on which ordered pairs of students are selected. If for some pair (a,b), a and b have the relationship, we say that the relation is defined on the set.

Definition 1-18: A relation $\mathscr{R}$ **is defined on a** (non-empty) **set** S if for some two elements a and b of S the statement "a has the relation $\mathscr{R}$ to b" is true. The truth of the statement depends only on the choice of a and b.

It should be noted that Definition 1-18 implies that for every relation $\mathscr{R}$ defined on a set S there is at least one ordered pair (a,b) such that the statement "a has the relation $\mathscr{R}$ to b" is true. Such relations are usually called non-trivial relations meaning that there is such a related pair. The relations in which we will be particularly interested are of this nature. However, it is entirely possible that for a given set S and relation $\mathscr{R}$ there is no ordered pair (a,b) in which a and b are $\mathscr{R}$ related. This would be called trivial since there are no true sentences which need to be considered. As an example of a trivial relation consider the relation $\mathscr{R}$, "is taller than," on the set

$$S = \{x | x \text{ is a person who is exactly five feet tall}\}.$$

Here there are no ordered pairs which can be chosen whose members have the relation $\mathscr{R}$. Thus with regard to the relation $\mathscr{R}$ there is nothing of interest.

Depending on what set of elements and what relation we consider, the statement "a is in the relation $\mathscr{R}$ to b" may be rather lengthy. Hence we shall adopt a shorter way of writing these statements as suggested in the following definition.

Definition 1-19: If $\mathscr{R}$ is a relation defined on a set S and if for elements a and b of S, "a is in the relation $\mathscr{R}$ to b," we write $a\,\mathscr{R}\,b$. The expression $a\,\mathscr{R}\,b$ is read as "a is in the relation $\mathscr{R}$ to b," "a is $\mathscr{R}$ related to b," or simply "a are b."

As noted above, if a relation $\mathscr{R}$ is defined on a set S the set of statements of of the form "$a\,\mathscr{R}\,b$" which are true is the set in which we have a particular interest. That is, these sentences contain the members of the set which have the relation for which we tested. Hence the set of true statements may be represented by a set of *ordered* pairs (a,b) such that if we form $a\,\mathscr{R}\,b$ we obtain a true sentence. From our discussion of the Cartesian product, we find that the set $S \times S$ is the set of all ordered pairs which can be formed from the elements of S. Consequently, the set of ordered pairs (a,b) for which $a\,\mathscr{R}\,b$ is true is a subset of $S \times S$. Indeed, this is another way to describe a relation $\mathscr{R}$ defined on a set S.

Definition 1-20: A relation $\mathscr{R}$ defined on a non-empty set S is a subset of $S \times S$.

You will observe that in Definition 1-20 we have made allowance for the trivial case where there may be no members of a set which have the relation which happens to be under consideration. However, we shall not be interested in these trivial cases. Let us now consider in detail some specific relations on specific sets.

Example: Let $S = \{a,b,c,d\}$ and let $\mathscr{R}$ be the relation "is a predecessor of" (as applied to placement in the usual listing of letters of the English alphabet).

Solution: Following the procedure outlined above, we find that the possible statements are as follows:

$a\,\mathscr{R}\,a$	$a\,\mathscr{R}\,b$	$a\,\mathscr{R}\,c$	$a\,\mathscr{R}\,d$
$b\,\mathscr{R}\,a$	$b\,\mathscr{R}\,b$	$b\,\mathscr{R}\,c$	$b\,\mathscr{R}\,d$
$c\,\mathscr{R}\,a$	$c\,\mathscr{R}\,b$	$c\,\mathscr{R}\,c$	$c\,\mathscr{R}\,d$
$d\,\mathscr{R}\,a$	$d\,\mathscr{R}\,b$	$d\,\mathscr{R}\,c$	$d\,\mathscr{R}\,d$

The set of true statements is

$$\left\{\begin{matrix} a\,\mathscr{R}\,b,\, a\,\mathscr{R}\,c,\, a\,\mathscr{R}\,d, \\ b\,\mathscr{R}\,c,\, b\,\mathscr{R}\,d,\, c\,\mathscr{R}\,d \end{matrix}\right\}$$

Thus the set of associated ordered pairs,

$$\left\{\begin{matrix} (a,b),\, (a,c\,),\, (a,d), \\ (b,c),\, (b,d),\, (c,d) \end{matrix}\right\}$$

has the property that if we take any ordered pair from the set and construct from it a statement using the members from the ordered pair (in that order) along with the relation $\mathscr{R}$, that statement is true. Since this is the case, it makes sense to say that the relation $\mathscr{R}$ is this set of ordered pairs. That is,

$$\mathscr{R} = \left\{\begin{matrix} (a,b),\, (a,c\,),\, (a,d) \\ (b,c),\, (b,d),\, (c,d) \end{matrix}\right\}$$

We also note that with this interpretation it is meaningful to say that $\mathscr{R} \subseteq S \times S$, since

$$S \times S = \left\{\begin{matrix} (a,a),\, (a,b),\, (a,c),\, (a,d) \\ (b,a),\, (b,b),\, (b,c),\, (b,d) \\ (c,a),\, (c,b),\, (c,c),\, (c,d) \\ (d,a),\, (d,b),\, (d,c),\, (d,d) \end{matrix}\right\}$$

and each ordered pair of $\mathscr{R}$ is an element of $S \times S$.

Example: Let $S = \{X | X$ is a proper subset of $\{a,b\}\ \}$ and let $\mathscr{R}$ be the relation "is a proper subset of" which is defined on S.

Solution: Using the procedure outlined above and facts previously learned concerning subsets we have as our set of statements

$\emptyset\,\mathscr{R}\,\emptyset$	$\emptyset\,\mathscr{R}\,\{a\}$	$\emptyset\,\mathscr{R}\,\{b\}$
$\{a\}\,\mathscr{R}\,\emptyset$	$\{a\}\,\mathscr{R}\,\{a\}$	$\{a\}\,\mathscr{R}\,\{b\}$
$\{b\}\,\mathscr{R}\,\emptyset$	$\{b\}\,\mathscr{R}\,\{a\}$	$\{b\}\,\mathscr{R}\,\{b\}$

The set of true statements is

$$\{\emptyset\,\mathscr{R}\,\{a\},\, \emptyset\,\mathscr{R}\,\{b\}\}$$

Hence the set of ordered pairs which make true statements when used with the relation $\mathscr{R}$ is

$$\{(\emptyset, \{a\}),\, (\emptyset, \{b\})\}$$

That is

$$\mathscr{R} = \{(\emptyset, \{a\}),\, (\emptyset, \{b\})\}$$

Again, note that $\mathscr{R} \subseteq S \times S$.

Some relations defined on sets have some rather remarkable qualities. They may satisfy one or more of the following properties which many of us have used or known without fully realizing it. These properties are listed for our convenience in the following definition.

Definition 1-21: Let $\mathscr{R}$ be a relation defined on a set S.

(a) If "$a \mathscr{R} a$" for each element a of S then $\mathscr{R}$ is said to be **reflexive**.

(b) "If $a \mathscr{R} b$, then $b \mathscr{R} a$" holds for all elements a and b of S then $\mathscr{R}$ is said to be **symmetric**.

(c) "If $a \mathscr{R} b$ and $b \mathscr{R} c$, then $a \mathscr{R} c$" holds for all elements a, b, and c of S then $\mathscr{R}$ is said to be **transitive**.

In order to illustrate Definition 1-21, let us consider the following example.

Example: Let $S = \{X | X$ is a subset of $\{a,b,c\}\}$ and let $\mathscr{R}$ be the relation "is a subset of."

Solution: We first calculate the elements of S.

$$S = \{\emptyset, \{a\}, \{b\}, \{c\}, \{a,b\}, \{a,c\}, \{b,c\}, \{a,b,c\}\}$$

(a) Question: Is it true that every element (which is a set in this case) is a subset of itself?

Answer: Yes since every set is a subset of itself. Thus $a \mathscr{R} a$ holds for every $a \in S$.

(b) Question: If we choose any two elements from S such that the first is a subset of the second, is it true that the second is a subset of the first?

Answer: No, because even though $\{a\} \subseteq \{a,b\}$, $\{a,b\} \nsubseteq \{a\}$. Hence the statement "If $a \mathscr{R} b$, then $b \mathscr{R} a$" does not always hold here.

(c) Question: If any three elements of S are selected such that the first is a subset of the second and the second is a subset of the third, does it follow that the first is a subset of the third?

Answer: Yes. We shall show it in one case and leave the rest of the justification for the student.

$$\{a\} \subseteq \{a,c\} \text{ and } \{a,c\} \subseteq \{a,b,c\}$$

By definition of subset every element of $\{a,c\}$ is an element of $\{a,b,c\}$. Hence $a \in \{a,b,c\}$ and so $\{a\} \subseteq \{a,b,c\}$. Consequently the statement "If $a \mathscr{R} b$ and $b \mathscr{R} c$, then $a \mathscr{R} c$" holds.

Considering parts (a), (b), and (c) of the solution, we see by Definition 1-21 that the relation $\mathscr{R}$ discussed in this example is reflexive and transitive, but not symmetric.

It is not always possible to list all the elements of the set S, but even so, we may still be able to discuss a relation on the set.

Example: Let S be the set of all married people and let $\mathscr{R}$ be the relation "is the spouse of."

Solution: (a) No person is the spouse of himself, so that the statement $a\,\mathscr{R}\,a$ does not hold for any element a of S.

(b) If a "is the spouse of" b, then it is true that b "is the spouse of" a for every two elements a and b of S. Thus the statement "If $a\,\mathscr{R}\,b$, then $b\,\mathscr{R}\,a$" does hold.

(c) The phrase a "is the spouse of" b and b "is the spouse of" c cannot hold since married people are joined in couples. Thus $\mathscr{R}$ does not possess the transitive property.

Referring to Definition 1-21, we see that this relation is symmetric only.

There are various other relations which may be defined and we list some of these as exercises.

If a relation defined on a set satisfies all three of the properties listed in Definition 1-21, it is given a special name.

Definition 1-22: A relation $\mathscr{R}$ defined on a set S is called an **equivalence relation** if and only if it satisfies the reflexive, symmetric, and transitive properties.

Examples of equivalence relations are
 (1) "is the same height as" defined on the set of all people,
 (2) "is congruent to" defined on the set of all triangles, and
 (3) "has the same scholastic ratio as" defined on the set of students at the reader's school.

We shall see shortly that the concept of relation plays a major role in the development of number. In this respect the idea of equivalence relation will be of prime importance.

EXERCISE SET 1-6

1. Consider the following relations defined on the set of students in your college or university.
    R_1: "weighs more than"
    R_2: "is as tall as"
    R_3: "dates a boy who is dated by"
    R_4: "is in the same class as"
    R_5: "has a better grade-point ratio than"
   (a) Which of the relations is reflexive?
   (b) Which of the relations is symmetric?
   (c) Which of the relations is transitive?
   (d) Which of the relations is an equivalence relation?
2. Consider the following relations defined on the set of all living inhabitants of the United States.
    R_1: "is a descendent of"
    R_2: "is a brother of"
    R_3: "is a sister of"
    R_4: "is the father of"

R_5: "is the mother of"
R_6: "is a sibling of"
R_7: "is the spouse of"
R_8: "is younger than"
R_9: "lives next door to"
R_{10}: "is a cousin of"
R_{11}: "drives the same make car as"
R_{12}: "read a book that was also read by"

(a) Which of the relations is reflexive?
(b) Which of the relations is symmetric?
(c) Which of the relations is transitive?
(d) Which of the relations is an equivalence relation?

3. We have seen that a relation may be considered as a set of ordered pairs. Each of the following sets of ordered pairs represents a relation. Determine whether the relation is reflexive, symmetric, transitive, or an equivalence relation.

(a) $\{(2,3), (3,5), (2,5)\}$
(b) $\{(1,1), (2,2), (3,3)\}$
(c) $\{(1,4), (2,3), (4,1), (3,2)\}$
(d) $\{(1,1), (1,2), (1,3), (2,3), (2,2), (3,3), (2,1), (3,1), (3,2)\}$

4. Let $S = \{x | x$ is a finite set$\}$.
(a) Investigate what properties are satisfied by the relation "is a subset of" defined on S.
(b) Repeat part (a) for the relation "is a proper subset of."

7. Equivalent Sets and Equivalence Relations

In this section we shall consolidate some of the concepts which we have been discussing up to this point. In Section 1-2 the concept of a mapping was introduced. You will recall that in a mapping from a set A to a set B there was associated with each element of A a unique element of B called the image. It was also indicated that under such a mapping a given element of B could be the image of more than one element of A. It is of particular interest to note that the correspondence which effected the pairing of elements of A to elements of B did essentially define a set or ordered pairs such that the first member of each pair was an element of A and the second member was an element of B. The reason this is so interesting is that the set of ordered pairs thus formed is of necessity a subset of $A \times B$. Further, if one considers these ordered pairs carefully, he will find that in many such mappings the elements of the two sets are somehow related. For example a mapping of first class letters mailed at a given post office on a given day into the postage required for each letter may be interpreted as a relation where the relationship between letters and postage is the weight of the letter being sent. Thus the set of ordered pairs formed by a mapping may indeed be construed as a relation between the two sets involved. Consequently, making use of the discussion of relations (Section 1-6), mappings may be considered to be special relations between two different sets A and B. With this in mind, let us now consider just the one-to-one onto mapping from a set A to a set B and also recall (from Section 1-3) that $A \sim B$ means A is equivalent to B.

Let us consider the class of all finite sets, that is the set which has as its elements all possible finite sets. It is beyond the scope of this text to prove it, but it is a fact that this class is itself infinite. Even though we do not prove the claim made, perhaps an example of what could happen, if we assume otherwise, will shed some light on the matter.

Example: Suppose that $S = \{A,B,C\}$ is the set of all finite sets. That is suppose that A, B, C is a listing of all finite sets. Then suppose we form

$$X = \{A,B,C, \{A,B\}\}$$

Then X is finite, so $X \in S$ as well. Likewise

$$Y = \{A,B,C, \{A,C\}\} \in S$$
$$Z = \{A,B,C, \{B,C\}\} \in S$$
$$T = \{A,B,C,X\} \in S$$
$$R = \{A,B,C,Y\} \in S$$

In this way one can continue to construct finite sets from S and the possibilities for such construction are never exhausted. This example should make it a little easier to accept the fact that the set (or class) of all finite sets is indeed infinite.

Now let us consider what happens if we consider the relation $\sim$ ("is equivalent to") on the class of all finite sets. We shall do this by looking at a specific instance. Suppose we pick sets $A, B,$ and C as follows:

$$A = \{a,b,c\}$$
$$B = \{\nabla, \square, \triangle\}$$
$$C = \{\bigcirc, \ominus, \oplus\}$$

(a) Is $A \sim A$? Yes, since we have

$$\{a, \quad b, \quad c\}$$
$$\downarrow \quad \downarrow \quad \downarrow$$
$$\{a, \quad b, \quad c\}$$

(b) If $A \sim B$, is $B \sim A$? Since $A \sim B$, we have

$$\{a, \quad b, \quad c\}$$
$$\downarrow \quad \downarrow \quad \downarrow$$
$$\{\nabla, \quad \square, \quad \triangle\}$$

and so

$$\{a, \quad b, \quad c\}$$
$$\uparrow \quad \uparrow \quad \uparrow$$
$$\{\nabla, \quad \square, \quad \triangle\}$$

is possible. Hence $B \sim A$.

   (c) If $A \sim B$ and $B \sim C$, is $A \sim C$?

and

and so we could correspond A to C (one-to-one and onto) by choosing

Thus $A \sim C$.

   In other words, all three conditions of Definition 1-22 are satisfied in this case and it appears that the relation of finite sets being equivalent to each other is an equivalence relation. This is indeed true even though we shall not prove it here.

   It is proved in advanced courses in mathematics that if a relation $\mathscr{R}$ defined on a set S is an equivalence relation, then $\mathscr{R}$ sub-divides the set S into subsets which have two very important properties:

   (1) every element of S is in at least one of the subsets

   (2) no element of S is in more than one of the subsets.

This means that the subsets formed by the subdivision are mutually disjoint. Using mathematical terminology, we would say that this process is a *partitioning of S*. The subsets formed by the partition are called *equivalence classes*. It is this concept which leads us to the climax of Chapter 1.

EXERCISE SET 1-7

1. Consider the relation "lives on the same block as" defined on the set of residents of your college town.
   (a) Is this an equivalence relation?
   (b) If so, what are the equivalence classes?
2. Let $\mathscr{R}$ be the relation "is the same gender as" defined on the set of nouns of the Latin language.
   (a) Is $\mathscr{R}$ an equivalence relation?
   (b) If so, what are the equivalence classes?
3. Let $\mathscr{R}$ be the relation "is the same breed as" defined on the set of all dogs.
   (a) Is $\mathscr{R}$ an equivalence relation?
   (b) If so, what are the equivalence classes?

4. Let $\mathscr{R}$ be the relation "is the same part of speech as" defined on the set of words of the English language.
   (a) Is $\mathscr{R}$ an equivalence relation?
   (b) If so, what are the equivalence classes?
5. Consider the set of ordered pairs
   $S = \{(a,a),(a,b),(b,c),(c,a),(b,b),(c,b),(a,c),(c,c),(b,a)\}$.
   Decide if S represents an equivalence relation on the set $\{a,b,c\}$.
6. Each of the following partitions is formed by some equivalence relation on some set A. Determine the set A which is partitioned and the ordered pairs which make up the equivalence relation on A in each case.
   (a) $\{a\}, \{b,c\}$
   (b) $\{a,b\}, \{c,d\}$
   (c) $\{a\}, \{b,c,d\}$
   (d) $\{a,b\}, \{c,d,e\}$
   (e) $\{a\}, \{b,c\}, \{d\}$.

8. Cardinal Number

We now proceed to the prime objective of this chapter. To do this we again consider the set S of all finite sets. In a fairly "unjumbled form" S might appear as follows.

$$S = \left\{ \begin{array}{l} \{\ \} \\ \{a\}, \{b\}, \{c\}, \quad \cdot \quad \cdot \quad \cdot \quad \cdot \quad \cdot \quad \cdot \quad \cdot \quad \cdot \\ \{a,b\}, \{a,c\}, \{\Delta,\nabla\}, \quad \cdot \quad \cdot \quad \cdot \quad \cdot \quad \cdot \quad \cdot \\ \{a,b,c\}, \{a,\beta,\gamma\}, \{\Delta,\nabla,\square\}, \cdot \quad \cdot \quad \cdot \quad \cdot \quad \cdot \\ \{a,b,c,d\}, \{a,\beta,\gamma,\theta\}, \{\Delta,\nabla,\square,\bigcirc\}, \quad \cdot \quad \cdot \quad \cdot \\ \cdot \quad \cdot \quad \cdot \quad \cdot \quad \cdot \quad \cdot \quad \cdot \quad \cdot \quad \cdot \quad \cdot \quad \cdot \\ \{a,b,c,d,e,f,g,h,i,j,k,l,m\}, \quad \cdot \quad \cdot \quad \cdot \quad \cdot \quad \cdot \\ \cdot \quad \cdot \quad \cdot \quad \cdot \quad \cdot \quad \cdot \quad \cdot \quad \cdot \quad \cdot \quad \cdot \end{array} \right\}$$

If we now define the relation $\sim$ on S as "is equivalent to," we have an equivalence relation defined on the set. As indicated in Section 1-7, $\sim$, being an equivalence relation, subdivides S into mutually disjoint classes of sets called equivalence classes. Some of these equivalence classes might appear as follows:

$$\left\{ \{\ \} \right\}, \quad \left\{ \begin{array}{l} \{a\} \\ \{b\} \\ \{\Delta\} \\ \{\nabla\} \\ \cdot \\ \cdot \\ \cdot \end{array} \right\}, \quad \left\{ \begin{array}{l} \{a,b\} \\ \{c,d\} \\ \{\Delta,\nabla\} \\ \{a,c\} \\ \cdot \\ \cdot \\ \cdot \end{array} \right\}, \quad \left\{ \begin{array}{l} \{a,b,c\} \\ \{a,b,d\} \\ \{\Delta,\nabla,\square\} \\ \{\Delta,\square,\bigcirc\} \\ \cdot \\ \cdot \\ \cdot \end{array} \right\}, \text{ and so on.}$$

In other words, we may think of the property which we call "oneness" and (theoretically) go through the set S picking out all those sets which exhibit this property. We do this by using the relation $\sim$. In so doing we form the class of sets

$$\left\{ \begin{array}{l} \{a\} \\ \{b\} \\ \{\Delta\} \\ \{\ \ \} \\ \cdot \\ \cdot \\ \cdot \end{array} \right.$$

and since every pair of sets of this class is equivalent, they all exhibit the property which we call "oneness."

Similarly, the equivalence classes whose respective sets exhibit the properties of "twoness", or "threeness", or "fourness", and so on, can be formed by use of the relation $\sim$ on the set S. Since each of the sets in a given equivalence class exhibit the same property, we shall agree to the following:

(1) If the equivalence class has the property of "oneness", the class is called *finite cardinal number one*,

(2) If the equivalence class has the property of "twoness", the class is called *finite cardinal number two*,

(3) If the equivalence class has the property of "threeness", the class is called *finite cardinal number three*, and so on.

The special class $\{\{\ \}\}$ we shall call *finite cardinal number zero*. That is, each of the equivalence classes formed from the set S of all finite sets by the relation $\sim$, is called a *finite cardinal number*. This is why the following definition is made.

Definition 1-23: If S is the set of all finite sets and $\sim$ is the relation "is equivalent to" defined on S, then each of the resulting equivalence classes is called a **finite cardinal number.**

Oftentimes this is shortened to say that *a finite cardinal number is a class of equivalent finite sets*. When this is done, it is to be taken in the context given above. For our purposes, we shall almost always refer to a finite cardinal number simply as a cardinal number. This we do simply as a matter of convenience.

As we have indicated, the concept of cardinal number may be thought of in two ways, which are distinct but nevertheless related. That is, a cardinal number may be thought of as

(1) an equivalence class of finite sets, or

(2) the common property which is exhibited by all *finite* sets in a given equivalence class.

In the first case we speak of a set *belonging to* a cardinal number, while in the second case we speak of the cardinal number *associated with* a set (i.e., the *cardinality* of the set). In the discussion which follows, we shall feel free to use the two interchangeably. Thus if we wish to determine the cardinal number of a set such as $\{a,b,c\}$, we may either say

(1) $\{a,b,c\}$ belongs to cardinal number three, or

(2) the cardinality of $\{a,b,c\}$ is three.

It is to be understood that either statement carries the same meaning. Let us now introduce for our convenience a shorter way for denoting the cardinality of a set.

Definition 1-24: The cardinality of a set A is denoted by **n(A)**.

Thus if $A = \{a,b,c,d\}$, then $n(A)$ is four. This is not yet completely satisfactory, for as we already know, we want eventually to develop arithmetic for the numbers we have defined. Hence we shall define numerals for the cardinal numbers zero, one, two, three, and so forth in the following way.

$$n(\{\ \}) = 0$$

$$n\left(\{\{\ \}\}\right) = 1$$

$$n\left(\{\{\ \}, \{\{\ \}\}\}\right) = 2$$

$$n\left(\{\{\ \}, \{\{\ \}\}, \{\{\ \}, \{\{\ \}\}\}\}\right) = 3, \text{ and so forth}$$

These sets are called standard sets for the determination of cardinality. As you will observe, each new standard set has as elements each of the standard sets which precede it. This method of formation of standard sets is straight forward, but it is quite cumbersome at best. Perhaps a more meaningful way to form the standard sets would be the following.

$$n(\{\ \}) = 0$$
$$n(\{0\}) = 1$$
$$n(\{0,1\}) = 2$$
$$n(\{0,1,2\}) = 3$$
$$\cdot \quad \cdot \quad \cdot \quad \cdot \quad \cdot \quad \cdot \quad \cdot \quad \cdot$$
$$n(\{0,1,2,3,4,5,6,7,8\}) = 9$$

With these standard sets available, the determination of cardinality of a given set is much easier. For then given any set all we need to do is compare it with standard sets until we find a standard set which is equivalent to it. In performing such comparisons it seems to be the case that equivalent sets have the same cardinality. Indeed this is true, for if we consider any two equivalent finite sets, we find that they belong to the same equivalence class. That is, they belong to the same cardinal number. Hence we list this fact as a definition.

Definition 1-25: If A and B are equivalent finite sets, then $n(A) = n(B)$.

To illustrate how we determine the cardinality of a given set we shall work a few examples.

Example: Determine $n(A)$ if $A = \{\nabla, \triangle, \square, \ominus, \varnothing\}$.

Solution: We consider the listing of standard sets and finally note that $A \sim \{0,1,2,3,4\}$ by means of a mapping such as

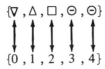

Since $n(\{0,1,2,3,4\}) = 5$ and since by Definition 1-25 $n(A) = n(\{0,1,2,3,4\})$, we conclude that $n(A) = 5$.

Example: Determine $n(B)$ if $B = \{a,b,p\}$.

Solution: Going down the list of standard sets, we have respectively,

$$\{\ \} \not\sim \{a,b,p\}$$
$$\{0\} \not\sim \{a,b,p\}$$
$$\{0,1\} \not\sim \{a,b,p\}$$

but

$$\{0,1,2\} \sim \{a,b,p\}$$

Thus, since $\{0,1,2\} \sim \{a,b,p\}$, and since $n(\{0,1,2\}) = 3$, we have by Definition 1-25 that $n(B) = 3$.

The reader will note that nothing was said regarding numerals used to represent the cardinality of sets having more than *nine* elements. We shall hold this topic in abeyance for the present. In Chapter 2 we shall discuss the concept of numeration systems and *counting*. Once this is done, we shall remove the restriction just mentioned.

As a final note, it should be pointed out that each of the equivalence classes, other than the zero equivalence class, is an infinite set of finite sets. This fact will be of some importance when we start to work with the arithmetic of cardinal numbers.

EXERCISE SET 1-8

1. Determine which of the following sets are cardinal numbers. If some sets are not cardinal numbers, tell why they are not.
   (a) a,b,c,d,e,f,g,h,i,j
   (b) $\{a\},\{b\},\{d\},\{\varnothing\},\{\Delta\},\{\square\}$
   (c) $\{a,\{a\},\{b\},\{c\},d,\{\varnothing\},\Delta,\ldots\}$
   (d) $\{\varnothing,\{a\},\{a,b\},\{a,b,c\},\{a,b,c,d\}\ \}$
   (e) $\{\ \{I\},\{a,m\},\{a\},\{s,e,t\}\ \}$
   (f) $\{\ \{\varnothing\},\{a\},\{b\},\{c\},\ldots,\{z\},\{\Delta\},\{\square\},\ldots\}$
   (g) $\{\ \{\varnothing\},\{a\},\{b\},\{c\},d,e,f\ \}$
   (h) $\{a,b,c,d,\ldots,z,\Delta,\square,\ldots\}$
   (i) $\{\ \{d,o,w,n\},\{w,i,t,h\},\{d,o,n,e\},\{\nabla,\Delta,\square,\llcorner\},\{\dashv,\top,\Delta,\nabla\},\ldots\}$
   (j) $\{\ \{f,i,v,e\},\{l,i,v,e\},\{m,i,c,e\},\{p,l,a,y\},\{w,i,t,h\},\{d,i,c,e\}\ \}$
   (k) $\{\ \{\Delta,\square,\nabla\},\{\llcorner,\square,O\},\{U,\cap,X\},\{\wedge,\vee,X\},\{a,t,e\},\{t,a,e\},\ldots\}$
   (l) $\{\ \{s,e,t\},\{e,s,t\},\{e,t,s\},\{s,t,e\},\{t,s,e\},\{t,e,s\}\ \}$

2. What is the cardinal number associated with each of the following sets?
   (a) $\{a,b,c\}$
   (b) $\{2,3\}$
   (c) $\{x|x$ is a counting number larger than 3 but smaller than 4$\}$
   (d) $\{$Joe, Sam, Oscar$\}$
   (e) $\{\triangle,*\}$
   (f) $\{$apple, orange, pear$\}$
   (g) $\{$tire, car, shovel, plate, table, cup, glass, glove, finger$\}$
3. If given the fact that $n(A) = n(B)$,
   (a) is it true that $A = B$? Always?
   (b) is it true that $A \subseteq B$? Always?
   (c) is it true that $A \subset B$? Always?
   (d) is it true that $A \sim B$? Always?
   (e) Give examples to support your answers to the above questions.
4. Show why $1 \neq 2$ even though $n(\{1\}) = n(\{2\})$.
5. Explain why no two distinct cardinal numbers are equal.

Chapter summary

The goal of Chapter 1 has been to clarify in a meaningful way the concept of number, particularly cardinal number. In order to reach this goal, we began with the basic notions of sets and set language. Next the concept of a mapping was introduced and by means of this we were able to give a more precise meaning to the terms finite and infinite than we may have had previously. Following this, some time was spent discussing relations and equivalence relations on sets. The latter were then used in conjunction with the class of all finite sets to form mutually disjoint equivalence classes. Each of these classes we defined to be a finite cardinal number. By means of this sequence of topics, we found that a finite cardinal number is in essence an abstract idea which may be associated with sets of objects in order to indicate how many objects belong to the sets. The sequence used to develop the number concept may be illustrated as follows:

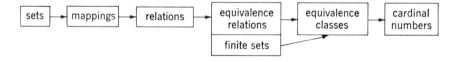

CHAPTER 2
Numeration systems

1. An Historical Note on Numeration Systems

Having defined what is meant by the cardinality of a given set, we find that if we are to assign a cardinal number to a given set, it becomes inconvenient to always refer to our basic set of comparison so often. Instead we shall use a set of symbols by means of which we can refer to the cardinality of a given set. Each of the symbols used is called a *numeral.* A *numeration system* is a set of rules (agreed upon by us) and a set of symbols by means of which a numeral can be selected to stand for the cardinal number which we associate with some particular set. Before selecting our set of numerals it would be worthwhile to take a brief look at some earlier numeration systems. The historical evolution of numeration systems is of more than just passing interest to us, since it shows how the systems developed over a long period of time. This development was influenced by economic necessity and resulted in the sophisticated system which we presently use. That system is the Hindu-Arabic system of numeration.

In primitive civilizations vocal grunts corresponding to our words "one," "two," and "many" may have sufficed, but with the progression of the civil life when trade became an important matter it was found much more convenient to have some kind of permanent record of transactions. Probably among the earliest who are of particular interest to us are the Babylonians who had a fairly well developed system at about 3000 B.C. This system was a sexigesimal (base sixty) system which made use of addition, multiplication, and some subtraction. Their numerals below two hundred used addition and in numerals above two hundred both multiplication and addition were used. Repetition was used in both. They had numerals for one, ten, and one hundred. These numerals varied somewhat in form from one clay tablet to another, but in general they appeared like those depicted below.

∇ represents one

$\triangleleft$ represents ten

$\nabla \triangleright$ represents one hundred[1]

Then for example we have numerals for numbers less than two hundred.

$\nabla \nabla \nabla \nabla$ = four $\triangleleft \triangleleft \triangleleft \nabla^\triangleright \nabla$ = twenty-nine and

$\triangleleft \nabla$ = eleven $\triangleleft \triangleleft \begin{smallmatrix} \nabla \nabla \nabla \nabla \\ \nabla \nabla \nabla \\ \nabla \nabla \end{smallmatrix}$ = twenty-nine

$\triangleleft \triangleleft \nabla \nabla \nabla$ = twenty-three

It has been found from studies of the clay tablets left by the Babylonians that if the "larger" symbol preceded the "smaller" or if symbols of the "same size" were repeated then their values were to be added. On the other hand, if "smaller" precedes "larger", then a multiplication is indicated. For example, we would write one thousand as $\triangleleft \nabla \triangleright$. If we wanted to write one thousand twenty-one, we would write the numeral $\triangleleft \nabla \triangleright \triangleleft \triangleleft \nabla$.

At about the same time (3300 B.C.) the Egyptians had a highly developed system of numerals. This system used the principles of repetition and addition and seven basic symbols to form numerals. These symbols are listed below.

one	$\rfloor$	the staff
ten	$\cap$	the heelbone or handle
one hundred	φ	scroll or coiled rope
one thousand	λ	lotus flower
ten thousand	$\mathscr{I}$	pointing finger
one hundred thousand	$\mathrm{C}\!\!\sim$	tadpole
one million	$\mathring{\mathsf{Y}}$	man in astonishment

All of the Egyptian numerals were written by using the above symbols, repetition, and addition. It might be noted that as a general rule when repetition was involved, no more than four like symbols were placed in the same grouping. Let us form a few Egyptian numerals to see how it is done.

$\rfloor$ represents one

$\rfloor\rfloor$ represents two

$\rfloor\rfloor\rfloor$ represents three

$\rfloor\rfloor\rfloor \ \rfloor\rfloor\rfloor \ \rfloor\rfloor\rfloor$ represents nine

$\cap\rfloor\rfloor$ represents twelve

$\cap\cap\rfloor\rfloor\rfloor\rfloor \ \rfloor\rfloor\rfloor\rfloor$ represents twenty-eight

---

[1] The symbol $\nabla\triangleright$ for one hundred should not be confused with $\nabla^\triangleright$ which indicates subtraction of the number named by the numeral which follows it.

For example, one thousand thirty-seven is represented by

$$\mathring{\lambda}\cap\cap\,\overset{\text{llll}}{\text{l l l}}$$

and three hundred thousand eight hundred ninety-one is represented by

$$\curvearrowright\,\curvearrowright\,\curvearrowright\,\overset{?\,?\,?\,?}{?\,?\,?\,?}\,\overset{\cap\cap\cap\cap}{\cap\cap\cap\cap}\,\cap\,\text{l}.$$

We now consider a system which resembles somewhat more closely a system which is familiar to each of us, namely that of the Greeks. It was also known as the Attic numeral system and was in use prior to 500 B.C. with the following basic symbols.

I represents one   Δ represents ten   X represents one thousand

Γ represents five   H represents one hundred   M represents ten thousand

As before, addition and repetition were used to write new numerals from these basic six. As examples, we might write two thousand three hundred fourteen as

XXHHHΔIIII

or one thousand six hundred thirty-nine as

XHHHHHHHΔΔΔΓIIII

The Greeks themselves apparently found this too cumbersome because later the principle of multiplication was introduced by use of the symbol for five in combination with the other symbols to get multiples of five as follows:

ΓΔ   represents fifty   ΓX   represents five thousand

ΓH   represents five hundred   ΓM   represents fifty thousand.

Now instead of writing 758 as

HHHHHHHΔΔΔΔΔΓIII

it could have been written as

ΓHHHΓΔΓIII

which you will agree is certainly an improvement. This system was replaced eventually by one involving some twenty-five symbols including the letters of the Greek alphabet and even though it was a very cumbersome system, it was used for some time.

In an evolutionary sense, each of the systems thus far considered has made a contribution of one type or another leading to what was then considered a better system of numerals. We now consider a system which goes one step further and is, as a matter of fact, in some use yet today. It is the system of

Roman numerals. This system employs repetition, addition, multiplication, and subtraction and eight basic symbols. They are

I representing one,
V representing five,
X representing ten,
L representing fifty,
C representing one hundred,
D representing five hundred, and
M representing one thousand.

A "bar," ‾‾‾, over a numeral means that the number represented by the numeral is to be multiplied by one thousand. We illustrate each as follows.

Repetition, Addition: VIII means eight.
Multiplication: $\overline{\text{XII}}$ means twelve thousand.
Subtraction: CD means four hundred.

The way in which addition and subtraction are used might be stated as follows. If a symbol follows another of the same or greater value, we add to find what number is represented. For example, MDCCLXV means one thousand seven hundred sixty-five. If a number is represented by a combination of symbols, and if the number represented by a given basic symbol is smaller than that of the one immediately following, we subtract it from its immediate successor to find what number the numeral represents. For example, XL stands for the number forty.

The two can be combined, of course, as is often noticed on some older public buildings. For example, one might find that a certain building was dedicated or perhaps erected in the year MDCCCCXLVIII or nineteen hundred forty-eight. Likewise, one could write the numeral for nine hundred ninety-four as DCCCCXCIV. The reader can see that even this system is not very convenient when trying to perform certain computations.

This historical discussion leads us now to consider a system of numerals with which we are all familiar. This system of which we speak is called the Hindu-Arabic system of numerals, apparently originated by the Hindus and transmitted to Europe by the Arabs who are often times given credit for its development. The original system had no numeral for zero and the basic numerals looked something like the following representations:

1 2 3 4 5 6 7 8 9

Over a considerable period of time the symbol, 0, came into use and perhaps as a result of recopying from book to book or in the course of keeping written records of trade, these symbols evolved to

0, 1, 2, 3, 4, 5, 6, 7, 8, 9.

We shall now develop our system of numeration by referring to the basic set of Hindu-Arabic numerals

$$\{0,1,2,3,4,5,6,7,8,9\}$$

and finite sets which were studied earlier.

EXERCISE SET 2-1

1. Use the Babylonian numeration system to write numerals for
   (a) thirty-two
   (b) one hundred forty-six
   (c) two hundred sixty-nine (in two ways)
   (d) eighty-six
   (e) one hundred one
2. Use the Egyptian system of numeration to write numerals for
   (a) nineteen
   (b) eighty-nine
   (c) three thousand seventy-four
   (d) one hundred forty thousand nine hundred twenty-three
   (e) two million six hundred ninety-three thousand eight hundred thirty-seven.
3. Use the Attic system of numeration to write numerals for
   (a) eighty-seven
   (b) nine hundred thirty-nine
   (c) five thousand six hundred forty-two
   (d) forty-nine
   (e) two hundred thirty-six thousand five hundred forty-eight.
4. Use the Roman system of numeration to write numerals for
   (a) four hundred sixty-nine
   (b) eight hundred ninety-eight
   (c) sixty thousand seven hundred fifty-four
   (d) one thousand nine hundred sixty-nine
   (e) two hundred thirty six thousand one hundred eleven
5. Write numerals for the cardinal numbers one to twenty by using
   (a) Babylonian numerals
   (b) Egyptian numerals
   (c) Attic numerals
   (d) Roman numerals

2. Formation of Place-Value Numerals

As noted in Section 2-1, there evolved historically nine basic numerals which are now denoted as 1, 2, 3, 4, 5, 6, 7, 8, 9. The introduction of the numeral 0 finally gave us a set of ten basic numerals with which we can denote the cardinality of sets. The obvious problem is that if we are allowed to choose an arbitrary finite set, this set may contain more than nine elements. Yet, we would like to write a numeral to represent the cardinality of such sets. This dilemma forces us to choose one of two possibilities.

   1. We must invent entirely new symbols to represent cardinalities larger than nine, or

2. we must try to devise a method by which combinations of the basic ten symbols can be used to represent cardinalities larger than nine.

We are all aware that the second choice is generally made, but it is not always clear how this can be done. We shall list two methods for achieving the results with which we are familiar and illustrate them. Each method is, in its own way, somewhat complicated, so read very carefully.

Before proceeding, we agree to call the set

$$\{0,1,2,3,4,5,6,7,8,9\}$$

our *base set* for the formation of new numerals in the base ten numeration system. We also note that when choosing our base set in a given base numeration system, the largest number named in this base set is *one* less than the base of the system. That is,

1) if the base system is *two*, the largest number named is 1,
2) if the base system is *three*, the largest number named is 2,
3) if the base system is *four*, the largest number named is 3,

and so forth. The reason for this will become clear a little later when we work some examples.

Let us now discuss the methods of formation of new numerals which we mentioned above.

Base set method:

1. Choose a base set for the base system involved.
2. Use one-to-one onto mappings to obtain
   a. all possible mutually disjoint sets that are equivalent to the base set of elements,
   b. then all possible mutually disjoint base sets of base sets,
   c. then all possible mutually disjoint base sets of base sets of base sets;
   and so on until such mappings are no longer possible.
3. Form mutually disjoint sets (work from right to left) having as elements
   a. all elements left over in 2(a)
   b. all base sets left over in 2(b)
   c. all base sets of base sets left over in 2(c)
   and so on until all of the elements and sets of part 2 have been used.
4. Determine the cardinality of each of the sets formed in 3 and write the numerals in juxtaposition either from right to left or left to right.
5. The numeral formed in step four is the place-value numeral in the given base system which represents the cardinality of the set under consideration.

The numeral formed by the base set method is called a place-value numeral because a digit may represent different sets, depending on where the digit is placed in the numeral formed.

Example: Determine a base ten numeral which represents the cardinality of the set $\{a,b,c,d,e,f,g,h,i,j,k,m,n,o,p,q\}$.

Solution:

Step 1. Choose as a base set $\{0,1,2,3,4,5,6,7,8,9\}$

Step 2. Using the one-to-one mappings discussed in 2(a) above, we might have $\{a,b,c,d,e,f,g,h,i,j\}$ with elements k, m, n, o, p, q left over. So no more such mappings are possible.

Step 3. We now form

$$\{\{a,b,c,d,e,f,g,h,i,j\}\} \text{ and } \{k,m,n,o,p,q\}$$

Step 4. $n\left(\{\{a,b,c,d,e,f,g,h,i,j\}\}\right)$ = 1 and $n(\{k,m,n,o,p,q\})$ = 6 so we write 16, where the 1 and 6 are juxtaposed, to represent the cardinality of the original set.

Example: Determine a base four numeral which represents the cardinality of the set $\{a,b,c,d,e,f,g,h,i,j,k,m,n,o,p,q,r\}$.

Solution:

Step 1. Choose as a base set $\{0,1,2,3\}$.

Step 2. Using the one-to-one mappings discussed in 2(a) above, we obtain

a. $\{a,b,c,d\}, \{e,f,g,h\}, \{i,j,k,m\}, \{n,o,p,q\}$ with r left over.

b. $\{\{a,b,c,d\}, \{e,f,g,h\}, \{i,j,k,m\}, \{n,o,p,q\}\}$ with no base sets left over and with r left over. We note that no base sets of base sets of base sets are possible and so the mapping process is complete.

Step 3. Now we form

$$\{\{\{a,b,c,d\}, \{e,f,g,h\}, \{i,j,k,m\}, \{n,o,p,q\}\}\}, \{\ \}, \text{ and } \{r\}$$

Step 4.

$$n\left(\{\{\{a,b,c,d\}, \{e,f,g,h\}, \{i,j,k,m\}, \{n,o,p,q\}\}\}\right) = 1$$

$n(\{\ \}) = 0$ and $n(\{r\}) = 1$

Hence we juxtapose the numerals to obtain 101 and so that we remember we are working in base four we write the numeral, 101_{four}, to represent the cardinality of the set.

The reader will probably agree now that the method of base sets just outlined and illustrated can be rather complicated. Let us examine a second method which, although still somewhat complicated, is more attainable for most students. We shall, for lack of a better name call it the *Bundling Method*, which we outline now.

Bundling method: [2]

1. Choose a base set for the base system involved. This base set with a closed curve drawn around it will be referred to as a *bundle*.

---

[2] The primary reason for choosing the word *bundle* is that in a physical sense sticks and colors may be chosen so that like colored sticks are actually bundled together. i.e., white sticks for singletons, blue sticks for base sets, yellow sticks for base sets of base sets, and so forth.

2. a. Form all possible mutually disjoint bundles by drawing closed curves about bundles of elements.
   b. Form all possible mutually disjoint bundles of bundles.
   c. Form all possible mutually disjoint bundles of bundles of bundles and continue this bundling process until it is no longer possible.
3. From right to left, write the juxtaposed numerals which correspond to the number of
   a. elements left over in 2(a)
   b. bundles left over in 2(b)
   c. bundles of bundles left over in 2(c)
   and so on until all elements of the original set are accounted for.
4. The numeral formed in 3 is the place-value numeral which represents the cardinality of the set being considered.

In order to illustrate this *bundling method* we shall adopt a method of denoting sets of objects which is not mathematically correct, but which lends itself quite well to the problem at hand. We have previously noted that no element of a given set should be listed more than once. However, if the finite sets involved are very large, the notation may become very complicated if we require a different symbol for each element. To avoid this problem we shall agree that we may denote all of the elements of a given finite set by a single symbol provided it is understood by everyone concerned that this is to be done for convenience only. Thus in the set

$$\{\wedge, \wedge, \wedge, \wedge, \wedge, \wedge, \wedge, \wedge, \wedge, \wedge, \wedge, \wedge, \wedge, \wedge, \wedge\}$$

it is to be clearly understood that the symbol, $\wedge$, represents a different object each time it is listed. This technique may be given some credence by the fact that young students sometimes use such things as tongue depressors for elements of sets whose cardinality is to be determined. Even though these objects look identical, they are nevertheless different. The technique we suggest is just an abstraction of this idea.

Example: Determine a base six numeral for the cardinality of the set

$$\{\wedge, \wedge, \wedge, \wedge, \wedge, \wedge, \wedge, \wedge, \wedge, \wedge, \wedge, \wedge, \wedge, \wedge, \wedge, \wedge, \wedge, \wedge, \wedge, \wedge\}$$

Solution:
Step 1. Choose the bundle to be used as

$$\boxed{0, 1, 2, 3, 4, 5}$$

Step 2. (a) We form the bundles[3]

---

[3]For the reader's convenience, we use b to denote bundle, bb to denote bundle of bundles, and so forth.

(b) Since we cannot form any bundles of bundles, we are done.

Step 3. There are three bundles and two singletons so we write 32_{six} to represent the cardinality of the given set.

Example: Determine a base two numeral for the cardinality of the set

$$\{\wedge, \wedge, \wedge, \wedge, \wedge, \wedge, \wedge, \wedge, \wedge; \wedge, \wedge, \wedge, \wedge, \wedge, \wedge, \wedge, \wedge, \wedge, \wedge, \wedge, \wedge, \wedge, \wedge\}$$

Solution:

Step 1. Choose a bundle as

Step 2. (a) Form all possible distinct bundles as follows:

(b) Now form all possible bundles of bundles.

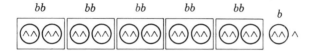

(c) Next form bundles of bundles of bundles.

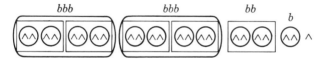

(d) Now form bundles of bundles of bundles of bundles.

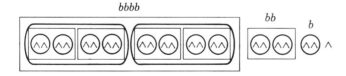

Here we observe that the matching process is complete.

Step 3. The base two numeral representing the cardinality of the given set is 10111_{two} as can be seen from the last matching.

Step 4. Thus the place value numeral for this example is 10111_{two}.

As the preceding examples illustrate, the distinguishing characteristic of the Hindu-Arabic numeration system is decidedly different from any of the other systems which were considered above. That attribute is *place-value*. In a place-value system of numeration, a given basic numeral (digit) may now mean more than one thing depending solely upon the place to which it is assigned in a numeral. For example, in the base ten numeral 68462, the left-hand six represents sixty thousand while the right-hand six represents sixty.

Now that we have a way of assigning numerals for the cardinality of a given set, we shall explore another method for the determination of cardinality. This method is motivated by the material just discussed, but is much more satisfactory for everyday use than the former. The method is that of *counting*.

EXERCISE SET 2-2

1. Given that $A = \{a,b,c,d,e,f,g,h,i,j,k,l,m,n\}$ and $B = \{p,q,r,s,t,u,v,w,x,y,z\}$, use the method of base sets to determine a numeral for the cardinality of A and B
   (a) using base two.
   (b) using base five.
   (c) using base nine.
   (d) using base twelve.

2. Given that

$$A = \{\wedge,\wedge\}$$

   use the method of bundles to determine a numeral for $n(A)$ using
   (a) base two
   (b) base three
   (c) base six
   (d) base seven
   (e) base eight
   (f) base eleven.

3. Consider the following system of enumeration.

   a - the number of elephants a fly can lift.
   β - the number of tails on a horse.
   γ - the number of ears on a cat.
   Δ - the number of wheels on a tricycle.

   Using these symbols and the method of bundles, write a numeral for the cardinality of each of the sets listed in problems one and two.

4. What is the value of seven in
   (a) 3470_{eight}?   (c) 4703_{eight}?   (e) 7304_{eight}?
   (b) 701_{twelve}?   (d) 170_{twelve}?

5. What is the value of the right-most *one* in
   (a) 1100111000_{two}?   (d) 110024_{six}?
   (b) 36102_{seven}?   (e) $601T_{twelve}$?
   (c) $411 23 20_{five}$?   (f) $1T1T9_{eleven}$?

6. Explain why there is no need for a numeral b in a base-b system of numeration when using Hindu-Arabic numerals.

7. (a) Write a single sentence using the words "zero," "nothing" and "empty." Use good English and correct mathematics.
   (b) Do the same for the words "number" and "numeral."

8. For each of the following decide whether it is true or false. Where needed, take $A = \{a,b\}$, $B = \{c,d\}$. If false, correct the statement to make it true.
   (a) $A \cup B = \{a,b,c,d\}$
   (b) $A + B = n(\{a,b,c,d\})$
   (c) $A \cup B = A + B$
   (d) $n(A \cap B) = \emptyset$

(e) $A + B = 4$
(f) $n(A \cup B) = 4$
(g) $A \cup B = 4$

3. Counting

In our daily living, it is often of interest to determine how much or how many of something there is in a given physical situation. For example, how many sheets of paper one has for a test or how many coins one has are actual occurrences in which each of us has probably been interested at one time or another. In order to determine how much or how many we often *count*.

If stripped to its bare essentials, just what does this process called counting consist of? We shall give an answer to this question in this section.

We begin by observing a point which is obvious, but which is often overlooked. This point can be illustrated by the following example. If one enters a room to see how many people are present he first notes whether or not the room is empty. If it is empty, then he knows there are zero people there. If the room isn't empty, he begins to count "one," "two," and so on until he has counted all who are present.

We shall show that this counting process can be directly related to a comparison of sets and in the following way. We have previously listed standard sets for the determination of cardinality. Now let us make a slight change and in so doing obtain even more useful standard sets.

"Old" standard sets		**"New" standard sets**
$n(\{0\}) = 1$	but $\{0\} \sim \{1\}$, so	$n(\{1\}) = 1$
$n(\{0,1\}) = 2$	but $\{0,1\} \sim \{1,2\}$, so	$n(\{1,2\}) = 2$
$n(\{0,1,2\}) = 3$	but $\{0,1,2\} \sim \{1,2,3\}$, so	$n(\{1,2,3\}) = 3$

As you can observe, this building of new standard sets can be continued as far as desired. Under either listing, however, we still have $n(\{\ \}) = 0$. Continuing this building process we obtain the list of sets which will be referred to as *standard sets* throughout the remainder of this book.

Standard Set	Cardinality
$\{1\}$	$n(\{1\}) = 1$
$\{1,2\}$	$n(\{1,2\}) = 2$
$\{1,2,3\}$	$n(\{1,2,3\}) = 3$
$\{1,2,3,4\}$	$n(\{1,2,3,4\}) = 4$
.	.
.	.
.	.
$\{1,2,3,4,5, \ldots ,k\}$	$n(\{1,2,3,4 \ldots ,k\}) = k$

where k represents some cardinal number.

Using these standard sets, it is a relatively simple matter to determine the cardinality of a given finite set by making use of *counting*. When we count we shall mean that we take a given set and compare it consecutively with each of the standard sets, in each instance naming in order the numerals listed in that standard set. We continue this process until a point is reached such that the last element of the standard set is named and our given set is exhausted simultaneously. This technique is illustrated below.

Example: Determine the cardinality of $\{a,b,c,d,e\}$.

Solution: The solid arrow is under the last element named reading from left to right.

Last name called in standard set	Elements accounted for in given set

Step 1. $\{a,b,c,d,e\} \neq \emptyset$ so $\{\ \}$ is not used.

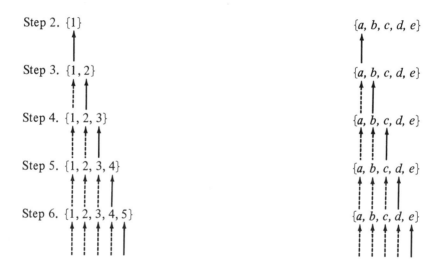

Step 2. $\{1\}$ $\{a, b, c, d, e\}$

Step 3. $\{1, 2\}$ $\{a, b, c, d, e\}$

Step 4. $\{1, 2, 3\}$ $\{a, b, c, d, e\}$

Step 5. $\{1, 2, 3, 4\}$ $\{a, b, c, d, e\}$

Step 6. $\{1, 2, 3, 4, 5\}$ $\{a, b, c, d, e\}$

Since we name *five* and exhaust the elements of the set $\{a,b,c,d,e\}$ simultaneously in step six, we say that

$$n(\{a,b,c,d,e\}) = 5$$

and we have used the process called counting to determine the cardinality.

It may also be observed that the process we call counting consists of a repeated selection of standard sets which at each stage are mapped one-to-one into the set whose cardinality is to be determined. These mappings are made repeatedly until a standard set is chosen which can be mapped *onto* the set under consideration. Hence in the example above the counting process is complete when $\{1,2,3,4,5\}$ is selected because this set is mapped one-to-one onto $\{a,b,c,d,e\}$.

Example: Determine the cardinality of $\{a,c,e,g,i,j,k\}$.

Solution: As before we list the standard sets with last number named called and the corresponding elements accounted for in the given set.

Step 1. $\{a,c,e,g,i,j,k\} \neq \emptyset$, so $\{\ \}$ is not used.

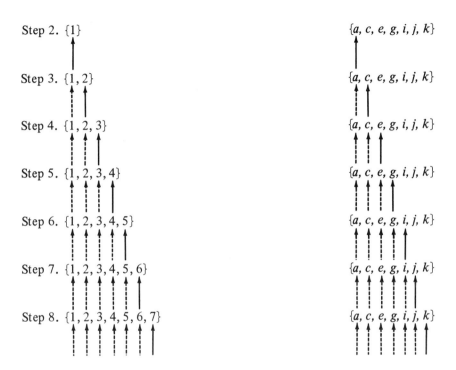

Step 2. $\{1\}$ $\{a, c, e, g, i, j, k\}$

Step 3. $\{1, 2\}$ $\{a, c, e, g, i, j, k\}$

Step 4. $\{1, 2, 3\}$ $\{a, c, e, g, i, j, k\}$

Step 5. $\{1, 2, 3, 4\}$ $\{a, c, e, g, i, j, k\}$

Step 6. $\{1, 2, 3, 4, 5\}$ $\{a, c, e, g, i, j, k\}$

Step 7. $\{1, 2, 3, 4, 5, 6\}$ $\{a, c, e, g, i, j, k\}$

Step 8. $\{1, 2, 3, 4, 5, 6, 7\}$ $\{a, c, e, g, i, j, k\}$

Since the name *seven* is named and the elements of the given set are exhausted simultaneously in step eight, we have that

$$n(\{a,c,e,g,i,j,k\}) = 7$$

Although we do not do so here, this same process of counting can be used for any base system using the numerals of that system.

The reason for stressing the process called counting is that in the work which follows it will be of basic importance. The counting required there will be somewhat more general in nature than just discussed, however the same basic idea is involved. We shall use a letter to represent the elements of a given set. In order to tell one element from another, we shall index it with a subscript which is to be one of the counting numbers. For example if we desire to consider a set A such that $n(A) = 7$, we may write

$$A = \{x_1, x_2, x_3, x_4, x_5, x_6, x_7\}$$

If $n(B) = 23$ for some set B, then we may write

$$B = \{y_1, y_2, y_3, \ldots, y_{22}, y_{23}\}$$

where the subscripts indicate that we are counting out the y's. In general then, if we are to discuss a set C such that $n(C) = c$, we may write

$$C = \{z_1, z_2, z_3, \ldots, z_c\}$$

That is, there are c elements in set C. If it happens that $c = 1001$, then we could write

$$C = \{z_1, z_2, z_3, \ldots, z_{1001}\}$$

If it happens that $c = 30986$, then we could write

$$C = \{z_1, z_2, z_3, \ldots, z_{30986}\}$$

We are saying then that c may be any counting number, and since we may not know (or care for that matter) exactly which one it is, we denote the set as

$$C = \{z_1, z_2, z_3, \ldots, z_c\}$$

where it is indicated that the elements are counted by use of the subscripts.

EXERCISE SET 2-3

1. Write out numerals (in order) for counting from one to twenty-six in
   (a) base two   (e) base seven
   (b) base three   (f) base nine
   (c) base five   (g) base eleven
   (d) base six   (h) base twelve

2. Using the results of problem one determine $n(A)$ if $A = \{x | x$ is a lower case letter of the English alphabet$\}$.

3. On planet X-101, the pages in books are numbered in order as follows:

   I, ∠, Δ, □, ▱, ⊠, I-, II, I∠, IΔ, I□, I▱, I⊠, ∠-, ∠I, etc.

   (a) What seems to be the base of the numeration system these people use?
   (b) What is the next number after ∠I   ?
   (c) Which symbol corresponds to our zero?
   (d) Write numerals for numbers from □ to □ Δ .

4. On planet $a-1$, the inhabitants count as follows:

   I, T, C, □, 己, ౽, 日, ⊠, I⊥, II, IT, IC, I□, I己, I౽, I日, I⊠, T⊥, etc.

   (a) What base system is apparently used by the a's?
   (b) What numeral corresponds to our zero?
   (c) What numeral follows next after ౽□ ?
   (d) Does ⊠ mean the same here as on planet X-101?
   (e) Write numerals for numbers from 己C to 日I .

5. If $A = \{x_1, x_2, \ldots, x_{20}\}$, determine $n(A)$ on
   (a) planet X-101
   (b) planet $a-1$

6. If $A = \{y_1, y_2, \ldots, y_{37}\}$, determine $n(A)$ on planet $\beta - 3$ if the base set for their numeration system is $\{□, I, ٧, Ч, Ӿ, Ӽ, \}$

4. Change of Base

In this section we shall illustrate how it is possible to determine different numerals in such a way that each numeral represents the cardinality of the same set. Two methods will be considered, one which involved direct matchings with bundles and one in which counting can be utilized.

Method one:

Example: Find a base five numeral which denotes the same cardinality as 201_{three}.

Solution: We note that in base three there are two bundles of bundles, no bundles, and one singleton.
    Step 1.

 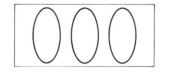

Step 2. We match the base bundle with each of the bundles putting in elements so that the bundles are equivalent.

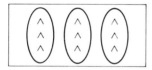 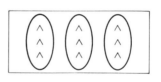

Step 3. Now re-arrange the elements in a more useable form as follows.

Step 4. Using the base bundle for base five, $\boxed{0, 1, 2, 3, 4}$, we form the numeral as in Section 2-2.
    Step 5.

               ˄˄˄

Step 6. The base five numeral is 34_{five}.

Hence we say $201_{three} = 34_{five}$ since they both represent the same cardinal number.

Example: Change 302_{four} to a base eight numeral.

Solution: We have in base four three bundles of bundles, no bundles, and two singletons.

Step 1.

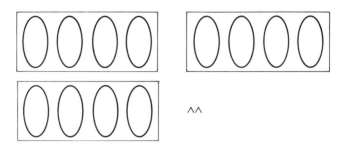

Step 2. Matching the base bundle 0, 1, 2, 3 so that we have bundles of elements, we obtain

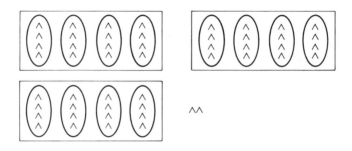

Step 3. Now rearrange the elements into a form which is more convenient.

∧ ∧

∧ ∧

Step 4. Using the base bundle 0, 1, 2, 3, 4, 5, 6, 7 for base eight we form the numeral as in Section 2-2.

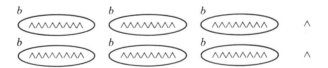

Thus the base eight numeral is 62_{eight}, so that $302_{four} = 62_{eight}$.

The second method, which involves counting, may or may not make use of the base ten numeration system. However, since most of us are more familiar with counting in base ten, we shall use it in the example which follows.

Method two:

Example: Change 241_{five} to a base four numeral.

Solution: In base five,

1 stands for a singleton in base ten,

4 stands for four bundles of five in base ten, and

2 stands for two bundles of bundles of five in base ten.

Hence in base ten we have $1 + 4 \cdot 5 + 2 \cdot 25$ or 71 elements. Next we list 71 elements by counting them off in base ten and then form a base four numeral for this set by the method discussed in Section 2-2.

This method for change of base is probably easier than method one, but we note that if one did not know any arithmetic, it would be useless because addition is involved. The advantage of *method one* is that even a small child could use it, since only matchings of sets are required.

EXERCISE SET 2-4

1. What numeral in the base seven system represents the number named by six dozen?

2. Using the symbols given in problems three and four of Exercise Set 2-3, write a new numeral for
   (a) 14_{ten} (b) 1000_{two} (c) 2121_{three}

3. Determine, by using sets or bundles directly, a
   (a) base twelve numeral for 86
   (b) base eleven numeral for 56_{seven}
   (c) base two numeral for 34_{five}
   (d) base eight numeral for 11010_{two}
   (e) base four numeral for 404_{eight}
   (f) base six numeral for 330_{four}
   (g) base five numeral for 35
   (h) base six numeral for 202_{three}
   (i) base three numeral for 22_{six}
   (j) base nine numeral for 33_{six}

4. Do parts (c), (d), (g), and (j) of problem three by converting first to base ten.

5. Show that
   (a) $23_{four} = 21_{five}$
   (b) $52_{six} = 44_{seven}$
   (c) $43_{five} = 35_{six}$
   (d) $43_{five} = 21_{seven}$

6. Show that
   (a) $43_{five} \neq 33_{seven}$
   (b) $26_{seven} \neq 26_{eight}$
   (c) $34_{five} \neq 35_{six}$
   (d) $43_{five} \neq 34_{six}$

7. The following are two-digit numerals with a, b, and c denoting Hindu-Arabic numerals zero through nine. With these conditions can the statement $ab_c = bc_a$ ever be true? Explain why it can or cannot, whichever the case may be. (Hint: Try the example $a = 2, b = 3, c = 4$ first.)

5. Operations

As a final topic of discussion prior to developing the arithmetic of cardinals, we return to consider formation of new sets from existing ones discussed in Section

1-4. In particular we shall now restrict our discussion to the set of all finite sets. That is, the universal set for this discussion is the set

$$\mathcal{U} = \{X | X \text{ is a finite set}\}$$

We shall observe the result obtained if the union, intersection, or Cartesian product of any two elements of $\mathcal{U}$ is formed. We shall not prove any general results, but will illustrate such results.

Suppose we choose $A \in \mathcal{U}$ and $B \in \mathcal{U}$ where

$$A = \{a,b,c,d,e\}$$
$$B = \{u,v,w,x\}$$

and form $A \cup B$. Doing so, we obtain

$$A \cup B = \{a,b,c,d,e,u,v,w,x\}$$

We note that A and B are both finite and so is $A \cup B$. More generally, the union of two finite sets is itself a finite set.

Similarly, if

$$C = \{a,b,c,d,e,f\}$$

and

$$D = \{a,c,e,g,h,i,j\}$$

then

$$C \cap D = \{a,c,e\}$$

Thus it appears that the intersection of two finite sets is again a finite set. This is indeed true, although we do not prove it.

If we choose

$$E = \{a,b,c\}$$

and

$$F = \{x,y,v\}$$

then

$$E \times F = \begin{Bmatrix} (a,x), (a,y), (a,v) \\ (b,x), (b,y), (b,v) \\ (c,x), (c,y), (c,v) \end{Bmatrix}$$

Once again we see that a finite set is obtained.

We have come upon a curiously interesting property which will prove to be of some significance in our later work. For sets, it is apparently possible to set up a correspondence from a set of ordered pairs of finite sets to a set of finite sets. In each of the cases above, an element from $\mathcal{U} \times \mathcal{U}$ was selected. In the first case (A,B), in the second (C,D), and in the third (E,F). Each ordered pair was associated with a single set from $\mathcal{U}$. (A,B) was associated with $A \cup B$, (C,D) with

$C \cap D$, and (E,F) with $E \times F$. This is such an important concept that we shall define it formally as follows.

Definition 2-1: If S is a set and there exists a mapping of $S \times S$ into S, then the mapping is called a **binary operation** on S.

Hence if we consider $\cup, \cap$, and $\times$ on the set of all finite sets, we see that according to Definition 2-1 these are *binary* operations since each of these maps any pair of finite sets into another finite set.

Such mappings need not be one-to-one, since for example if

$$\mathcal{U} = \{X | X \text{ is a finite set}\} \text{ and } A \in \mathcal{U},$$

then

$$A \cup A = A$$
$$A \cup \emptyset = A.$$

That is, A is the image of both $A \cup A$ and $A \cup \emptyset$.

Similarly, if A, B, and C are mutually disjoint sets and are elements of the set of all finite sets, then

$$A \cap B = \emptyset$$
$$A \cap C = \emptyset$$

and

$$B \cap C = \emptyset$$

so that $\emptyset$ is the image of $A \cap B$, $A \cap C$, and $B \cap C$.

In Chapter 3 and succeeding chapters, we shall see some more examples of binary operations when we develop the arithmetic of cardinal numbers.

EXERCISE SET 2-5

1. Let $S = \{a,b,c,d,e\}$ and let operation $\mathcal{O}$ be defined as follows: $(x,y) \rightarrow x$ for $x \in S$ and $y \in S$. Construct the table for operation $\mathcal{O}$.
2. Using the same set S as in problem one and the pairing $\mathcal{O}$ defined as follows, construct the table for $\mathcal{O}$: $\mathcal{O}$ matches with (x,y) the member of the pair which comes first in the alphabet.
3. Do problems one and two result in identical tables? Is $\mathcal{O}$ an operation?

4. Consider the table to the right and decide if it represents an operation on $S = \{i,a,b,c,d\}$.

$\circ$	i	a	b	c	d
i	i	a	b	c	d
a	a	i	d	b	c
b	b	c	i	d	a
c	c	d	a	i	b
d	d	b	c	a	i

5. Consider the table to the right and decide if it represents an operation on $S = \{a,b,c,d\}$.

∘	a	b	c	d
a	b	c	d	a
b	c	d	a	b
c	d	a	b	c
d	a	b	c	d

6. If for elements of $S = \{a,b,c\}$ we have

$$a \circ b = c = b \circ a$$
$$b \circ c = a = c \circ b$$
$$c \circ a = b = a \circ c$$

we have a partial table

∘	a	b	c
a	–	c	b
b	c	–	a
c	b	a	–

Fill in the table so that ∘ is an operation on S.

Chapter summary

Once the concept of number is understood we look forward to the eventuality of the associated arithmetic. Because of this, there is a need for symbols by means of which the ideas can be manipulated. Thus one of the main objectives of this chapter has been to devise such a set of symbols which are called numerals. We selected the familiar set of Hindu-Arabic numerals and by using these in conjunction with one-to-one onto mappings showed the mathematical meaning of the process called counting which is itself directly related to finite sets. Next we point out that the selection of numerals used to denote the cardinality of finite sets is an arbitrary selection. This observation leads us to consider the possibility of numeration systems other than base ten and consequently demonstrates that a given finite cardinal may have many names (numerals) associated with it depending upon the base system used. Schematically the sequence of events might appear

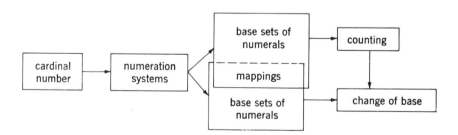

CHAPTER 3
Addition
of cardinal
numbers

---

1. Definition of Addition

Now that we have some understanding of what is meant by the *cardinal number* of a finite set and a numeral which represents this cardinal number, we shall proceed to develop a definition for addition.

As you recall from the discussion in Section 1-4, we suggested that it might be possible to define addition by using the union of sets. For example, in order to add 3 and 4 we might say

$$A = \{a,b,c\}$$

$$B = \{d,e,f,g\}$$

$$A \cup B = \{a,b,c,d,e,f,g\}$$

so that $3 + 4 = 7$.

On the other hand, we might also choose

$$A = \{a,b,c\}$$

and

$$B = \{c,d,e,f\}$$

so that

$$A \cup B = \{a,b,c,d,e,f\}.$$

In this case we would obtain $3 + 4 = 6$.

This apparent defect can be useful. Since we already know what results we want from the addition, we may be able to formulate a definition which will give us these results. As the two above examples illustrate, it is essential that we choose the sets A and B so that they are disjoint. Let us now define addition of cardinal numbers and make use of these facts.

Definition 3-1: The **sum** of two cardinal numbers, a plus b, is the cardinal number c associated with the set $C = A \cup B$ where A and B are the set representatives of a and b respectively, and $A \cap B = \emptyset$. The sum is denoted by $a + b = c$.

Thus if we wish to add $a + b$, we may proceed in the following manner.
1. Select sets A and B so that
   a. $n(A) = a, \; n(B) = b$
   b. $A \cap B = \emptyset$.
2. Form $A \cup B$.
3. Determine $n(A \cup B)$.
4. $a + b = n(A) + n(B) = n(A \cup B) = c$.

Hence to add $2 + 3$, we may proceed as follows:
1. Select $A = \{a,b\}$ and $B = \{c,d,e\}$.
   a. $n(A) = 2, \; n(B) = 3$.
   b. $\{a,b\} \cap \{c,d,e\} = \emptyset$.
2. $A \cup B = \{a,b,c,d,e\}$.
3. $n(A \cup B) = 5$.
4. $2 + 3 = n(A) + n(B) = n(A \cup B) = 5$.

That is, $2 + 3 = 5$.

This approach to addition is precisely the same as a child might use. If the child has two sets of objects and is asked how many objects he has altogether, he simply puts them in one pile and counts them. The only thing the child does not do is to check for disjointness of the original sets, but this is not necessary, since each physical object he has is distinct from the others.

There are a few things which the child may take for granted which we cannot. Two items which must be checked are existence and uniqueness of answers using Definition 3-1. If an answer does not always exist, it should be fairly clear that the arithmetic would not be of much value. Secondly, if answers do always exist, but are not unique, then it might be possible to have statements such as

$$2 + 3 = 5 \quad \text{and} \quad 2 + 3 = 4$$

both being true. With such complications, an endeavor such as bookkeeping would be an utterly impossible task. It would be very comforting to have some guarantee that such complications could not ever occur. In order to have this guarantee, we shall now prove that under Definition 3-1 sums always exist and are unique.

Theorem 3-1: Sums always exist under Definition 3-1.

Proof: In order to prove the existence of sums, we must show that the steps outlined by the definition can always be carried out. First we note from Chapter One that every cardinal number contains a finite set. Further, it is always possible to select sets for two cardinal numbers so that they are disjoint, since the equivalence classes are infinite. Next we know that set union is defined for every two sets and the union of two finite sets is a finite set which consequently belongs to a cardinal number. Hence the cardinality of the union exists. Since this latter cardinal number is the sum of the two given cardinals, the sum must always exist. ∎

The proof that sums are unique involves generalized counting, so be sure you understand this concept before proceeding.

Theorem 3-2: Sums of cardinal numbers are unique.

Proof: In order to prove the uniqueness of sums, we must show that the sum of two cardinal numbers $a + b$ is just one number regardless of what disjoint set representatives are selected for a and b.

(1) Choose sets A and B so that

$$A = \{x_1, x_2, x_3, \ldots, x_a\} \text{ with } n(A) = a$$

$$B = \{y_1, y_2, y_3, \ldots, y_b\} \text{ with } n(B) = b$$

and

$$A \cap B = \varnothing$$

Then

$$C = A \cup B$$

$$= \{x_1, x_2, x_3, \ldots, x_a, y_1, y_2, y_3, \ldots, y_b\}$$

Let us suppose that $n(C) = c$, that is, $a + b = c$.

Next we choose different set representatives for a and b. We do this as follows.

(2) Choose sets A' and B' so that

$$A' = \{x'_1, x'_2, x'_3, \ldots, x'_a\} \text{ with } n(A') = a$$

$$B' = \{y'_1, y'_2, y'_3, \ldots, y'_b\} \text{ with } n(B') = b$$

and

$$A' \cap B' = \varnothing \text{ and } A' \neq A, B' \neq B$$

Then

$$C' = A' \cup B'$$

$$= \{x'_1, x'_2, x'_3, \ldots, x'_a, y'_1, y'_2, y'_3, \ldots, y'_b\}$$

Let us suppose that $n(C') = c'$. That is, suppose that $a + b = c'$ where c' and c are not necessarily the same.

If we wish to prove uniqueness of sums, then we must show that $c = c'$. In order to show that $c = c'$ we must show that $C \sim C'$, for if we can do this, we know that equivalent sets have the same cardinality. We know that

$$A \sim A' \quad \text{so that} \quad x_i \longleftrightarrow x'_i \quad \text{for} \quad i = 1,2,3,\ldots,a$$

and

$$B \sim B' \quad \text{so that} \quad y_j \longleftrightarrow y'_j \quad \text{for} \quad j = 1,2,3,\ldots,b$$

Now consider the following correspondence:

$$C = \{x_1, x_2, x_3, \ldots, x_a, y_1, y_2, y_3, \ldots, y_b\}$$

$$\updownarrow \quad \updownarrow \quad \updownarrow \quad \cdots \quad \updownarrow \quad \updownarrow \quad \updownarrow \quad \updownarrow \quad \cdots \quad \updownarrow$$

$$C' = \{x'_1, x'_2, x'_3, \ldots, x'_a, y'_1, y'_2, y'_3, \ldots, y'_b\}$$

Using this we have C mapped one-to-one onto C' so that $C \sim C'$. Hence by Definition 1-25, $n(C) = n(C')$. That is $c = c'$ and sums are unique. ∎

Because of Theorems 3-1 and 3-2 we are assured that (1) the sum of two cardinal numbers is a cardinal number, and (2) the sum of two cardinal numbers is exactly one cardinal number.

We may also note that the set of cardinals is closed under the operation addition. That is addition is an operation which maps ordered pairs of cardinals back into the set of cardinals. The image under the mapping is a member of the original set of numbers.

EXERCISE SET 3-1

1. Let $A = \{a,b\}$, $B = \{c,d,e,f,g\}$, $A' = \{p,q\}$, and $B' = \{r,s,t,u,v\}$.
   (a) Determine $n(A)$, $n(B)$, $n(A')$, and $n(B')$
   (b) Determine $n(A \cup B)$ and $n(A' \cup B')$
   (c) Does $n(A) + n(B) = n(A \cup B)$?
   (d) Does $n(A') + n(B') = n(A' \cup B')$?
   (e) Does $n(A \cup B) = n(A' \cup B')$?
   (f) What fact of addition is illustrated?
2. In problem one,
   (a) could we have formed $n(A' \cup B)$ and $n(A \cup B')$ and still have obtained the same sums?
   (b) if we had chosen $A = \{a,p\}$, $A' = \{a,q\}$ and left B and B' as they were, would the same results have been obtained? Why or why not?
3. Show that if the requirement $A \cap B = \emptyset$ is dropped in Definition 3-1, then it is possible to have $5 + 6 = 9$.
4. Discuss (and give numerical examples) why the existence and uniqueness of sums guarantees that addition of cardinal numbers is an operation on the set of cardinals. [Hint: $(2,3) \to 5$, $(4,6) \to 10$, $(8,5) \to 13$, etc.]

2. Properties of Addition

In this section we shall consider in some detail some of the properties which addition of cardinal numbers satisfies. Some of these properties you are already familiar with; some you may find to be new. The proofs of some of the properties will make use of parts of Theorem 1-2 of Chapter 1, so be sure you are familiar with those results.

We begin by considering a type of problem which very likely was studied by you early in your career.

$$26$$
$$+\ 37$$
$$\overline{63}$$

$$\underline{63}$$
$$26$$
$$+\ 37$$
$$\overline{63}$$

Some of us were asked to check our addition problems and did so by the method illustrated above. That is, to obtain the answer, we "added down" and to check we "added up." This method of checking addition involves the commutative property which we shall now state and prove.

Theorem 3-3 (Commutative Property): If a and b are any two cardinal numbers, then $a + b = b + a.$

Proof: Choose sets

$$A = \{x_1, x_2, \ldots, x_a\} \text{ with } n(A) = a$$
$$B = \{y_1, y_2, \ldots, y_b\} \text{ with } n(B) = b$$

and

$$A \cap B = \emptyset$$

Then

$$A \cup B = \{x_1, x_2, \ldots, x_a, y_1, y_2, \ldots, y_b\}$$

and

$$n(A \cup B) = a + b$$

Next form $B \cup A = \{y_1, y_2, \ldots, y_b, x_1, x_2, \ldots, x_a\}$. Then

$$n(B \cup A) = b + a$$

Since $A \cup B = B \cup A$, $A \cup B \sim B \cup A$. By Definition 1-25

$$n(A \cup B) = n(B \cup A)$$

That is,

$$a + b = b + a$$

and the theorem is proved. ∎

The commutative property alone does not justify the check in addition problems, for often times there are more than two numbers to be added. Thus we must show that it makes no difference how numbers are grouped together when adding.

For example, does $2 + (3 + 4) = (2 + 3) + 4$? Let us show that this is indeed true. Select

$$A = \{a,b\} \text{ with } n(A) = 2$$

$$B = \{c,d,e\} \text{ with } n(B) = 3, \text{ and}$$

$$C = \{f,g,h,i\} \text{ with } n(C) = 4$$

A, B, and C are mutually disjoint as you can easily verify.
1) Form $B \cup C = \{c,d,e,f,g,h,i\}$. $n(B \cup C) = 3 + 4$.
2) Form $A \cup (B \cup C) = \{a,b,c,d,e,f,g,h,i\}$.
   $n[A \cup (B \cup C)] = 2 + (3 + 4)$.
Next form
1) $A \cup B = \{a,b,c,d,e\}$. $n(A \cup B) = 2 + 3$.
2) $(A \cup B) \cup C = \{a,b,c,d,e,f,g,h,i\}$. $n[(A \cup B) \cup C] = (2 + 3) + 4$.
Finally we note that

$$A \cup (B \cup C) = (A \cup B) \cup C$$

so that

$$n[A \cup (B \cup C)] = n[(A \cup B) \cup C]$$

That is,

$$2 + (3 + 4) = (2 + 3) + 4$$

This example illustrates the Associative Property of Addition which can be stated as follows.

Theorem 3-4 (Associative Property): If a, b, and c are any three cardinal numbers, then $a + (b + c) = (a + b) + c$.

Proof: Left as an exercise.

Both the associative and commutative properties are required to justify the checking of addition problems where three or more numbers are to be added. The associativity is required because addition is a binary operation.

There are many other useful devices which many of us use in addition of cardinal numbers, some of which we are not consciously aware. We shall look at some of these and try to justify them. One such device is that given a set of numbers such as the following, we go through the list selecting pairs whose sum is ten and mentally add tens where possible.

Example:

A formal mathematical statement of the procedure involved would appear as follows.

Theorem 3-5: If a, b, and c are any three cardinal numbers, then $a + (b + c) = (a + c) + b$.

Proof:

$$a + (b + c) = a + (c + b) \qquad \text{Thm. 3-3}$$
$$= (a + c) + b \qquad \text{Thm. 3-4.} \blacksquare$$

In the example preceding the above theorem we would have

$$7 + 9 + 3 + 8 + 1 = [7 + (9 + 3)] + (8 + 1) \qquad \text{Thm. 3-4}$$
$$= [(7 + 3) + 9] + (8 + 1) \qquad \text{Thm. 3-5}$$
$$= (7 + 3) + [9 + (8 + 1)] \qquad \text{Thm. 3-4}$$
$$= (7 + 3) + [(9 + 1) + 8] \qquad \text{Thm. 3-5}$$
$$= [(7 + 3) + (9 + 1)] + 8 \qquad \text{Thm. 3-4}$$
$$= (10 + 10) + 8 \qquad \text{Def. 3-1}$$
$$= 20 + 8 \qquad \text{Def. 3-1}$$
$$= 28 \qquad \text{Def. 3-1}$$

These handy devices or ways of working problems are called *algorisms* or *algorithms*. As can be observed, on the basis of our presently limited experience, these algorithms can be justified. That is, it is actually possible to prove that they work!

It is interesting to note that whenever we add zero to any other cardinal number, we obtain the latter cardinal number as the answer. This is common knowledge, but more interesting is the fact that we are now in a position to prove it. We shall list the fact and leave its proof to the student.

Theorem 3-6: If a is any cardinal number, then $a + 0 = a$.

Proof: Left as an exercise

Because of the fact that addition of cardinals is commutative, we may also write

$$a + 0 = 0 + a = a$$

for any cardinal number a. This property of zero is of such importance that it is given a special name.

Definition 3-2: A cardinal number z is called an **additive identity** if $z + a = a + z = a$ for every cardinal number a.

From our previous discussion, we observe that cardinal zero is an additive identity. A question which now arises is the following. Is it possible that there is more than one additive identity? If one experiments some by trying cardinals other than zero he forms the impression that zero is the only additive identity. The sad fact is, however, that such experimentation does not give us a complete answer. The reason for this is that there are infinitely many cases left untried and one of these just might work. Before showing that zero is the only additive identity for cardinals, we shall consider another property of addition and in so doing find an easy way out of our present impasse.

We turn now to a consideration of determination of solutions to number sentences. That is, we consider number sentences of the form $n + 3 = 5$ for which we want to find the number n which makes the sentence true. There are at least two ways in which this can be done.

Method 1. Guessing

Method 2. Rewrite the problem as follows:

$$n + 3 = 2 + 3$$
$$n + \cancel{3} = 2 + \cancel{3}$$
$$n = 2$$

This latter method seems reasonable since 3 appears on both sides of the equal sign and in addition to this the method appears to be systematic. This process is called cancelling. We shall soon see under what conditions it can be used. We caution you not to use it indiscriminantly. We restate the procedure formally in the following theorem.

Theorem 3-7 (Cancellation Property): If a, b, and c are cardinal numbers and if $a + c = b + c$, then $a = b$.

Proof: Select sets $A = \{x_1, x_2, \ldots, x_a\}$ with $n(A) = a$,

$$B = \{y_1, y_2, \ldots, y_b\} \text{ with } n(B) = b, \text{ and}$$

$$C = \{z_1, z_2, \ldots, z_c\} \text{ with } n(C) = c.$$

Also require $A \cap B = \emptyset$ and $B \cap C = \emptyset$. Now

$$A \cup C = \{x_1, x_2, \ldots, x_a, z_1, z_2, \ldots, z_c\}$$

$$B \cup C = \{y_1, y_2, \ldots, y_b, z_1, z_2, \ldots, z_c\}$$

and $n(A \cup C) = a + c$ and $n(B \cup C) = b + c$.

Since $a + c = b + c$, $A \cup C \sim B \cup C$ by Definition 1-25. Since $A \cup C$ can be mapped one-to-one onto $B \cup C$ and since C can be mapped one-to-one onto itself, this requires that it be possible to map A one-to-one onto B, for otherwise we could not have $A \cup C \sim B \cup C$. Thus $A \sim B$ and by Definition 1-25, $n(A) = n(B)$. That is $a = b$. ∎

Hence the procedure illustrated above for solving the number sentences is justified. More important, we can now show that zero is the only additive identity for cardinal numbers.

Theorem 3-8: There is at most one additive identity for cardinal numbers.

Proof: We know that zero is an additive identity. That is

$$0 + a = a + 0 = a$$

for every cardinal number a. Suppose that there is another additive identity z. Then by Definition 3-2

$$z + a = a + z = a.$$

Hence, combining the two we obtain

$$z + a = 0 + a$$

but then by use of the cancellation property, we obtain

$$z = 0.$$

Therefore there is no more than one additive identity. ∎

As can be seen, Theorem 3-8 was proved rather easily using cancellation. Since there is at least one additive identity (zero) and no more than one, there is precisely one, namely cardinal zero.

We have already observed some ways in which the properties of addition can be used to advantage. There are more. For example, we now consider the basic one hundred addition facts and partially construct the table in which the sum of two numbers is to be found at the intersection of row and column. (See Table 3-1.)

TABLE 3-1

+	0	1	2	3	4	5	6	7	8	9
0										
1		2								
2		3	4							
3		4	5	6						
4		5	6	7	8					
5		6	7	8	9	10				
6		7	8	9	10	11	12			
7		8	9	10	11	12	13	14		
8		9	10	11	12	13	14	15	16	
9		10	11	12	13	14	15	16	17	18

In Table 3-1, the left column and top row were not filled in because of the fact that $0 + a = a$ and so it is not necessary. The remaining blank spaces can be filled in simply by using commutativity of addition. Hence of the basic one hundred addition facts, it is only necessary to learn 45 of them. The remaining facts are gratis because of the additive identity and commutative property of addition.

We return now to complete our discussion of cancellation. We know that if

$$n + (2 + 3) = 7$$

we can solve for n by rewriting 7 as $2 + (2 + 3)$ so that

$$n + (2 + 3) = 2 + (2 + 3)$$

and

$$n = 2$$

Now suppose that we ask the following question. If $n = 4$, may we write that $n + 3 = 4 + 3$? This too appears to be reasonable. Many of us have used the fact that "equals" can be added to "equals." This process is closely related to the cancellation property and we now list the formal statement of the theorem which justifies it.

Theorem 3-9 (Converse of Cancellation): If a, b, and c are cardinal numbers, and if $a = b$, then $a + c = b + c$.

Proof: Left as an exercise.

Let us next consider the commonly used algorithm illustrated below.

$$
\begin{array}{l}
376^1 \\
+\,423 \\
\hline
\end{array}
\qquad \text{is often rewritten as} \qquad
\begin{array}{l}
300 + 70 + 6 \\
400 + 20 + 3 \\
\hline
700 + 90 + 9 = 799
\end{array}
$$

This technique is often used to make elementary students consciously think of adding hundreds, tens and units. We consider the simpler case

$$
\begin{array}{l}
35 \\
+\,44 \\
\hline
\end{array}
\qquad \text{rewritten as} \qquad
\begin{array}{l}
30 + 5 \\
40 + 4 \\
\hline
70 + 9 = 79
\end{array}
$$

and attempt to justify it. This is done in the following theorem.

Theorem 3-10: If a, b, c, and d are any four cardinal numbers, then $(a + b) + (c + d) = (a + c) + (b + d)$.

---

[1] It is to be noted that problems where "carrying" is involved have been carefully avoided. For these problems familiarity with properties of multiplication are required. Consequently these will be treated later in the book.

Proof:

$$(a + b) + (c + d) = a + [(b + c) + d] \qquad \text{Thm. 3-4}$$

$$= a + [(c + b) + d] \qquad \text{Thm. 3-3}$$

$$= (a + c) + (b + d) \qquad \text{Thm. 3-4.}\blacksquare$$

This theorem fits the problem $\begin{array}{r} 35 \\ + 44 \\ \hline \end{array}$ if we take $a = 30$, $b = 5$, $c = 40$, and $d = 4$.

The procedure for problems involving three-digit numbers can be obtained out of Theorem 3-10 and is called an *extension* of the theorem. We shall leave this latter problem as an exercise.

EXERCISE SET 3-2

1. By using the sets $A = \{a,b,c,d,e\}$ and $B = \{u,v,w\}$, show in detail why $5 + 3 = 3 + 5$. What property of addition does this illustrate?
2. By using the sets $A = \{0\}$, $B = \{1,2\}$, and $C = \{3,4,5,6\}$, show in detail why $1 + (2 + 4) = (1 + 2) + 4$. What property of addition does this illustrate?
3. By using the associative property and Theorem 3-5, find $3 + 6 + 7 + 4 + 5$.
4. Use Theorem 3-10 to determine the following sum, writing out your reasoning as in the textbook:

$$\begin{array}{r} 36 \\ + 52 \\ \hline \end{array}$$

5. (a) State a theorem which would extend Theorem 3-10 so that

$$\begin{array}{r} 342 \\ + 637 \\ \hline \end{array} \qquad \text{could be worked as} \qquad \begin{array}{r} 300 + 40 + 2 \\ 600 + 30 + 7 \\ \hline 900 + 70 + 9 = 979. \end{array}$$

   (b) Work the problem of part (a) in detail justifying each step.
   (c) Prove the theorem stated in part (a).
6. (a) Could an extension of Theorem 3-10 be stated to cover the problem

$$\begin{array}{r} 5621 \\ + 3076 \; ? \\ \hline \end{array}$$

   (b) Is there any essential difference in Theorem 3-10 and the extensions you have considered?
7. Instead of adding $\begin{array}{r} 78 \\ + 35 \\ \hline \end{array}$ a student adds $\begin{array}{r} 80 \\ + 33 \\ \hline \end{array}$ getting 113. What principles and definitions are used in order to change the problem? Is this change mathematically "legal?"
8. By using sets and generalized counting, prove Theorem 3-6.
9. By using sets and generalized counting, prove Theorem 3-9.
10. Use the cancellation property to solve the following number sentences.
    (a) $n + 6 = 5 + 7$
    (b) $n + (3 + 2) = 7$

(c) $n + 8 = 2 + (3 + 4)$

(d) $5 + 3 = 2 + (4 + n)$

11. Determine what cardinal number makes the following true if substituted for the box. Tell what properties of addition you use for each step of your solution.

(a) $3 + \square = 2 + 4$

(b) $5 + (\square + 1) = (2 + 3) + 6$

(c) $10 + 3 = (\square + 9) + 4$

(d) $5 + (2 + \square) = (3 + \square) + 4$

12. If $\square$, $\triangle$, ∇ are numerals representing cardinal numbers, tell which of the properties of cardinal addition justifies each of the following.

(a) $\square + (\nabla + \triangle) = (\square + \nabla) + \triangle$

(b) $\square + \nabla = \nabla + \square$

(c) $(\square + \nabla) + \triangle = \triangle + (\square + \nabla)$

13. Write down the property used to justify each step in each of the following.

		Step
(a)	$17 + 26 = (10 + 7) + (20 + 6)$	(a)
	$= 10 + [(7 + 20) + 6]$	(b)
	$= 10 + [(20 + 7) + 6]$	(c)
	$= (10 + 20) + (7 + 6)$	(d)
	$= 30 + 13$	(e)
	$= (30 + 0) + 13$	(f)
	$= (30 + 0) + (10 + 3)$	(g)
	$= (30 + 10) + (0 + 3)$	(h)
	$= 40 + (0 + 3)$	(i)
	$= 40 + 3$	(j)
	$= 43$	(k)

		Step
(b)	$324 + 78 = (300 + 24) + 78$	(a)
	$= 300 + (24 + 78)$	(b)
	$= 300 + [(20 + 4) + (70 + 8)]$	(c)
	$= 300 + [(20 + 70) + (4 + 8)]$	(d)
	$= 300 + [90 + 12]$	(e)
	$= 300 + [90 + (10 + 2)]$	(f)
	$= 300 + [(90 + 0) + (10 + 2)]$	(g)
	$= 300 + [(90 + 10) + (0 + 2)]$	(h)
	$= 300 + [100 + (0 + 2)]$	(i)
	$= 300 + (100 + 2)$	(j)
	$= (300 + 100) + 2$	(k)
	$= 400 + 2$	(l)
	$= 402$	(m)

		Step
(c)	$13 + (n + 20) = 45$	Given
	$(13 + n) + 20 = 45$	(a)
	$(n + 13) + 20 = 45$	(b)
	$n + (13 + 20) = 45$	(c)
	$n + [13 + (20 + 0)] = 45$	(d)
	$n + [(10 + 3) + (20 + 0)] = 45$	(e)
	$n + [(10 + 20) + (3 + 0)] = 45$	(f)

$$n + [30 + 3] = 45 \qquad \text{(g)}$$
$$n + 33 = 45 \qquad \text{(h)}$$
$$n + 33 = 33 + 12 \qquad \text{(i)}$$
$$n + 33 = 12 + 33 \qquad \text{(j)}$$
$$n = 12 \qquad \text{(k)}$$

Chapter summary

As soon as numeration systems are available, we have a tool which facilitates the study of number properties. This study involves the relationship between cardinal numbers and arithmetic operations by using the associated numeration system. In this chapter we were able to define the operation addition in a meaningful way by making use of set concepts previously discussed. Also by the use of sets we were able to justify many of the properties of addition of cardinal numbers. We showed that

(1) sums always exist and are unique,

(2) addition is commutative,

(3) addition is associative,

(4) there is a unique identity element, zero,

(5) the addition satisfies the cancellation property, and

(6) several of the well known algorithms can be justified.

Most of us were already aware of the fact that the items listed above are true. The important point to make here is that now we know, perhaps for the first time, the techniques by which we perform certain arithmetic operations are not merely rules, but rather procedures which have a firm mathematical basis.

CHAPTER 4
Subtraction of cardinal numbers

1. Preliminaries

In this chapter we shall first define subtraction in a way which would be meaningful to an elementary school student. Next, we shall show that by using the definition it is possible to give an alternate definition in a way which shows the relation between subtraction and addition.

We begin by recalling that in manipulating sets, one forms an intuitive notion of size of sets. It would appear then that since cardinal numbers are defined in terms of sets, one would form an impression regarding "size" of numbers. However, since this is to be a mathematical development, let us now deal with this matter so that there will be no ambiguity when we introduce subtraction.

Definition 4-1: If A and B are sets, then $n(A)$ **is less than** $n(B)$ if A is equivalent to a subset of B and B is equivalent to no subset of A. This is denoted $n(A) < n(B)$ or $a < b$, where $<$ is read "is less than."

Example: Decide if $5 < 6$. To make this decision, suppose we select

$$A = \{a,b,c,d,e\} \text{ with } n(A) = 5, \text{ and}$$

$$B = \{u,v,w,x,y,z\} \text{ with } n(B) = 6$$

Then $A \sim \{u,v,w,x,y\} \subseteq B$, but B is equivalent to no subset of A. Hence $n(A) < n(B)$. That is, $5 < 6$.

Definition 4-2: If A and B are sets, then $n(A)$ **is greater than** $n(B)$ if $n(B)$ is less than $n(A)$. This is denoted $n(A) > n(B)$ where $>$ is read "is greater than."

Hence $n(A) > n(B)$ if $n(B) < n(A)$. From the example above, we have $5 < 6$. By use of Definition 4-2 we may also write $6 > 5$ as an equivalent statement.

Next we shall extend the notion of the relations "is less than" and "is greater than." This extension is related to the concept of "size" of sets too and so it is a natural extension of the relations $<$ and $>$ mentioned above. The reason for this extension should be clear when subtraction is defined in Section 4-2.

Definition 4-3: If A and B are sets, then $n(A)$ **is less than or equal to** $n(B)$ if A is equivalent to a subset of B and B is equivalent to no more than one subset of A. This is denoted $n(A) \leqslant n(B)$ or $a \leqslant b$ where $\leqslant$ is read "is less than or equal to."

Similarly, we define "is greater than or equal to" as follows.

Definition 4-4: If A and B are sets, then $n(A)$ **is greater than or equal to** $n(B)$ if $n(B)$ is less than or equal to $n(A)$. This is denoted $n(A) \geqslant n(B)$.

If we want to know whether or not $5 \geqslant 3$, we proceed as follows. $5 \geqslant 3$ if $3 \leqslant 5$ by Definition 4-4. Now we can use Definition 4-3 to determine if $3 \leqslant 5$. Choose

$$A = \{a,b,c,d,e\} \text{ with } n(A) = 5$$

and

$$B = \{a,d,f\} \text{ with } n(B) = 3.$$

Then B is equivalent to a subset of A. For example we could have

$$B \sim \{a,c,d\}.$$

Further, A is equivalent to no more than one subset of B. This is obviously true since in this example, A is equivalent to no subset of B. Hence $n(B) \leqslant n(A)$ by Definition 4-3 and by Definition 4-4 we have $n(A) \geqslant n(B)$. That is, $5 \geqslant 3$.

By use of similar arguments, it can be shown for example that $5 \leqslant 5, 6 \geqslant 6, 3 \leqslant 7$, and so on.

The relations denoted by $<, >, \leqslant$, and $\geqslant$ arise so frequently in the study of mathematics that they are given a special name. They are often called *inequalities.* The relations $<$ and $>$ are sometimes called *absolute inequalities* while $\leqslant$ and $\geqslant$ are called *conditional inequalities.*

EXERCISE SET 4-1

1. Show that
   (a) $7 < 9$
   (b) $6 < 11$
   (c) $5 > 4$
   (d) $8 > 6$
   (e) $7 \leqslant 12$
   (f) $4 \leqslant 4$
   (g) $13 \geqslant 10$
   (h) $1 \geqslant 1$
2. If we know that $56 < 57$, can we write $56 \leqslant 57$ and know that it is true without checking?
3. If we know that $a < b$, is it automatically true that $a \leqslant b$? That $b \geqslant a$?
4. By careful study of Definition 4-1, see if you can devise another definition for $a < b$ where a and b are cardinal numbers.

5. Repeat problem four for $a \leqslant b$.
6. What can be said about the cardinal number a if both $a \leqslant 6$ and $a \geqslant 6$ are true?   Could such a statement $a \leqslant 0$ and $a \geqslant 0$ have meaning for us?

2. Definition of Subtraction

Now that we have considered the possible ambiguities which might arise regarding "size" of cardinal numbers we consider a situation which might concern a child. Suppose a child has a set of blocks which are labelled a, b, c, d, e, and f. Next suppose that he is asked how many he has left if he takes away this many (hold up two fingers). The child matches fingers with blocks (one-to-one onto) and removes two blocks say c and f. Then he counts those which remain and says there are four blocks left. Such a child has used sets in order to subtract. Let us formalize this procedure in the following definition.

Definition 4-5: If a and b are cardinal numbers with $a \geqslant b$, the **difference** a minus b is determined as follows;
   1) Select sets A and B such that $n(A) = a$ and $n(B) = b$.
   2) Determine a subset $\overline{A}$ of A such that $B \sim \overline{A}$.
   3) Calculate $c(\overline{A})$ in A.
   4) Determine $n[c(\overline{A})] = c$.
   5) a minus b is c. That is, $a - b = c$.

Example: Determine $5 - 3$.   Using Definition 4-4, we note first that $5 \geqslant 3$.
   1. Select $A = \{a,b,c,d,e\}$ with $n(A) = 5$ and $B = \{p,q,r\}$ with $n(B) = 3$.
   2. $B \sim \overline{A} = \{a,b,c\}$ and $\overline{A} \subseteq A$.
   3. $c(\overline{A})$ in $A = \{d,e\}$.
   4. $n[c(\overline{A})] = 2$.
   5. $5 - 3 = 2$.

Next we consider the case where both numbers are equal.

Example: Determine $5 - 5$. Using Definition 4-4, we note that $5 \geqslant 5$.
   1. Choose $A = \{a,b,c,d,e\}$ with $n(A) = 5$ and $B = \{a,b,c,x,y\}$ with $n(B) = 5$.
   2. $B \sim \overline{A} = A$ and $A \subseteq A$.
   3. $c(\overline{A})$ in $A = c(A)$ in $A = \emptyset$.
   4. $n[c(\overline{A})] = n(\emptyset) = 0$.
   5. $5 - 5 = 0$.

It should be clear from the example problems just worked why the discussion of the inequalities was so important. Without that discussion step two of Definition 4-5 could not be completed.

It should be noted that answers for subtraction do not always exist in the set of cardinal numbers. In fact, $a - b$ only exists whenever $a \geqslant b$. However, when answers do exist, they are unique as we shall now show.

Theorem 4-1: If differences of cardinal numbers exist, then they are unique.

Proof: Suppose that a and b are cardinal numbers and $a - b$ exists. Then we must show that regardless of what set representatives are selected for a and b, we obtain just one answer.

1) Choose $A = \{x_1, x_2, \ldots, x_b, x_{b+1}, \ldots, x_a\}$ with $n(A) = a$

$$B = \{y_1, y_2, \ldots, y_b\} \text{ with } n(B) = b.$$

Then $B \sim \{x_1, x_2, \ldots, x_b\} = \overline{A}$ where $\overline{A} \subseteq A$. Since

$$c(\overline{A}) \text{ in } A = \{x_{b+1}, \ldots, x_a\}$$

$$n[c(\overline{A})] = a - b \text{ by Definition 4-5}$$

Let us call $a - b = c$.

2) Now choose $A' = \{x'_1, x'_2, \ldots, x'_b, x'_{b+1}, \ldots, x'_a\}$ with $n(A') = a$

and

$$B' = \{y'_1, y'_2, \ldots, y'_b\} \text{ with } n(B') = b$$

Then $B' \sim \{x'_1, x'_2, \ldots, x'_b\} = \overline{A}'$ where $\overline{A}' \subseteq A'$. Since

$$c(\overline{A}') \text{ in } A' = \{x'_{b+1}, \ldots, x'_a\}$$

$$n[c(\overline{A}')] = a - b$$

which we call c' since we don't know that answers are unique. In order to show uniqueness then we must show that $c = c'$.

3) Checking $c(\overline{A})$ and $c(\overline{A}')$ we observe that

$$c(\overline{A}) = \{x_{b+1}, x_{b+2}, \ldots, x_a\} \sim \{x'_{b+1}, x'_{b+2}, \ldots, x'_a\} = c(\overline{A}')$$

Thus $n[c(\overline{A})] = n[c(\overline{A}')]$ by Definition 1-25. That is, $c = c'$ and the differences are unique. ∎

EXERCISE SET 4-2

1. Using Definition 4-5, determine
   (a) $7 - 5$
   (b) $8 - 8$
   (c) $6 - 2$
2. Let $n(A) = 7$ and $n(B) = 3$. Choose
   (1) $A = \{a,b,c,d,e,f,g\}$ and   (2) $A = \{a,p,s,t,u,v,z\}$
       $B = \{p,q,r\}$ $B = \{x,t,z\}$
   (a) Use Definition 4-5 and (1) to calculate $7 - 3$.
   (b) Use Definition 4-5 and (2) to calculate $7 - 3$.
   (c) Is the same result obtained?
   (d) What property is illustrated by parts (a), (b), and (c)?
3. Why is subtraction (strictly speaking) not an operation on the set of cardinal numbers? [Hint: Refer to Definition 4-5 and Definition 2-1.]
4. In choosing sets A and B in the definition of subtraction, is it necessary that $A \cap B = \emptyset$?

3. Properties of Subtraction

Two results which are used with some regularity in subtraction are the following:
1. If zero is subtracted from any cardinal number the answer is that cardinal number.
2. If any cardinal number is subtracted from itself the answer is zero.

These are easy to prove and so they will be left as exercises. However we do list them for future reference.

Theorem 4-2: If a is any cardinal number, then $a - 0 = a$.

Proof: Left as an exercise.

Theorem 4-3: If a is any cardinal number, then $a - a = 0$.

Proof: Left as an exercise.

Let us return for a moment to reconsider Definition 4-5. The definition states that if $a \geqslant b$, then $a - b$ exists. Suppose that we think of any two cardinal numbers a and b such that $a - b$ exists. Isn't it reasonable to suspect that there is a cardinal number z such that if z is added to $a - b$ the result is a? That is, is there a number z such that

$$z + (a - b) = a \ '$$

We shall show that there is such a cardinal number z, and in turn this will lead us to a rather surprising result.

Theorem 4-4: If a and b are cardinal numbers with $a \geqslant b$, then $b + (a - b) = a$.

Proof: Since $a \geqslant b$, choose

$$A = \{x_1, x_2, \ldots, x_b, x_{b+1}, \ldots, x_a\} \text{ with } n(A) = a$$

and

$$B = \{y_1, y_2, \ldots, y_b\} \text{ with } n(B) = b$$

In order to determine the cardinality $b + (a - b)$ we must form the union of set representatives of b and $(a - b)$ and these set representatives must be disjoint. We already have a set representative for b, so let us find one for $(a - b)$. By using the steps listed in Definition 4-5 we find that

$$c(A) \text{ in } A = \{x_{b+1}, x_{b+2}, \ldots, x_a\}$$

is a set representative of $(a - b)$. Hence

$$b + (a - b) = n(\ \{y_1, y_2, \ldots, y_b\} \cup \{x_{b+1}, x_{b+2}, \ldots, x_a\} \ )$$

$$= n(\ \{y_1, y_2, \ldots, y_b, x_{b+1}, x_{b+2}, \ldots, x_a\} \ )$$

$$= a.$$

Consequently $b + (a - b) = a$. ■

To illustrate the theorem, consider $a = 7$, $b = 5$. Then $5 + (7 - 5) = 5 + 2 = 7$ which is exactly what Theorem 4-4 predicts. Of even more interest from the mathematical point of view is the fact that in Theorem 4-4 there is just one cardinal which can be added to b to obtain a. We shall now prove this interesting and useful fact.

Theorem 4-5: If a and b are cardinal numbers with $a \geqslant b$, then there is at most one cardinal number z such that $b + z = a$.

Proof: We know from Theorem 4-4 that

$$b + (a - b) = a$$

Suppose that is a second number z such that

$$b + z = a$$

Then by transitivity of equality we obtain

$$b + (a - b) = b + z$$

Using the cancellation property of addition we have

$$a - b = z$$

Hence there is at most one cardinal number z such that $b + z = a$.∎

Now if we observe the results of Theorems 4-4 and 4-5, together they tell us that there is precisely one number z such that $b + z = a$, and that number is $a - b$. It is these results which give us a second way in which to perform subtraction.

Example: Determine $6 - 2$. According to Theorems 4-4 and 4-5, $6 - 2$ is the cardinal number z such that

$$z + 2 = 6$$

From addition we know that

$$4 + 2 = 6$$

hence

$$4 + 2 = z + 2$$

and by the cancellation property of addition,

$$4 = z$$

Therefore

$$6 - 2 = 4$$

We now state this result as a formal definition.

Definition 4-6 (Inverse Definition): If a and b are any two cardinal numbers with $a \geqslant b$, then a minus b $(a - b)$ is the unique cardinal number z such that $b + z = a$.

We make note of the fact that this is the definition of subtraction usually used by mathematicians. The uniqueness of differences is guaranteed by uniqueness of sums.

Now that we have a relationship between addition and subtraction we can give proofs for Theorems 4-2 and 4-3 without referring back to sets. Let us prove Theorem 4-2.

Proof: By Definition 4-6, $a - 0$ is the cardinal number z such that $a = 0 + z$. From addition we know that $a = 0 + a$. Hence

$$0 + a = 0 + z$$

so that

$$a = z.$$

Hence

$$a - 0 = a \; \blacksquare$$

We have not yet discussed how to justify the usual method for checking subtraction problems. For example, a problem and its check might appear as follows.

Problem	Check
27	13
− 13	+ 14
14	27

This method is easily verified by referring to Definition 4-5 and the details are left as an exercise.

It is rather interesting to note that if two cardinal numbers are added the resulting cardinal is larger than or equal to either of the original cardinals. Because of this it is possible to establish the following useful result which will in turn lead to another useful algorithm.

Theorem 4-6: If a, b, and c are cardinal numbers and if $a + b = c$, then $a = c - b$, and $b = c - a$.

Proof: We shall just prove one part and leave the other part as an exercise. We know that $b + (c - b) = c$ from Theorem 4-4. Also it is given that $a + b = c$, so that $b + a = c$ by the commutative property of addition. Thus $b + a = b + (c - b)$ by transitivity of equality and by then using cancellation of addition we obtain $a = c - b$. Part two is proved by an analogous argument. $\blacksquare$

The main reason the results of Theorem 4-6 are so interesting is that by using these results, we can justify an algorithm for subtraction which parallels that in Theorem 3-10 for addition. That is,

$$\begin{array}{r} 78 \\ -53 \\ \hline \end{array} \qquad \text{may be written as} \qquad \begin{array}{r} 70 + 8 \\ -(50 + 3) \\ \hline 20 + 5 = 25 \end{array}$$

so that units may be subtracted from units, tens from tens and so forth. We shall now show mathematically that these steps can be done.

Theorem 4-7: If a, b, c, and d are cardinal numbers such that $(a + b) - (c + d)$, $(a - c)$, and $(b - d)$ all exist, then $(a + b) - (c + d) = (a - c) + (b - d)$.

Proof: In order to prove this, let us say that

$$a - c = p \quad \text{and} \quad b - d = q$$

since both differences exist. Then by Definition 4-6.

$$a = c + p \quad \text{and} \quad b = d + q.$$

$$\text{Now } a + b = (c + p) + (d + q) \qquad\qquad\qquad \text{Uniq. of Add}^1$$

$$= (c + d) + (p + q) \qquad\qquad\qquad\qquad \text{Thm. 3-10}$$

$$\text{Therefore } (a + b) - (c + d) = p + q \qquad\qquad\quad \text{Thm. 4-6}$$

$$= (a - c) + (b - d) \qquad\qquad\qquad\qquad\qquad \blacksquare$$

As can be observed, if in the problem $84 - 33$ we take $a = 80$, $b = 4$, $c = 30$ and $d = 3$, we may write

$$84 - 33 = (80 + 4) - (30 + 3)$$

$$= (80 - 30) + (4 - 3)$$

$$= 50 + 1$$

$$= 51.$$

This is the same result as is obtained by rewriting

$$\begin{array}{r} 84 \\ -33 \\ \hline \end{array} \qquad \text{as} \qquad \begin{array}{r} 80 + 4 \\ -(30 + 3) \\ \hline 50 + 1 = 51 \end{array}$$

in the usual algorithm.[2]

---

[1]Here we use what is sometimes referred to as the *Principle of Substitution* which is an agreement to be free to use different names for the same object without changing the meaning. If an operation is involved (as above), then uniqueness is also involved. We shall use this fairly often from this point onward in the book.

[2]Here too we carefully avoid problems in which "borrowing" could be involved. It is not necessary to do so, but we think it would complicate matters unnecessarily to introduce it here since in practice the sets involved would become quite large.

Of particular use in several of the exercises involving subtraction is a special case of Theorem 4-7. If in Theorem 4-7, $c = 0$ we obtain the following result. It is so useful that we shall list it as a theorem for easy reference.

Theorem 4-8: If a, b, and d are cardinal numbers such that $(a + b) - d$ and $(b - d)$ exist, then $(a + b) - d = a + (b - d)$.

Proof: Left as an exercise.

We must caution the reader that even though the result of Theorem 4-8 looks very much like an associative property, it is not! Associativity is stated in terms of just one operation, not two as in Theorem 4-8.

As was the case for addition, there are other algorithms for subtraction which have not been discussed yet. However, some of these require a knowledge of multiplication in order to be meaningful. We shall discuss multiplication in the next chapter and then return to a consideration of these algorithms which have thus far been omitted.

EXERCISE SET 4-3

1. By choosing two cardinal numbers, show that subtraction does not satisfy the commutative property. For what special choices of cardinals a and b does $a - b = b - a$?
2. By choosing three cardinal numbers, show that subtraction does not satisfy the associative property.
3. Using the sets $A = \{a,b,c,d,e\}$ and $\emptyset$, show that
   (a) $5 - 0 = 5$
   (b) $5 - 5 = 0$
4. Prove by use of Definition 4-5 that for any cardinal number a,
   (a) $a - 0 = a$ and
   (b) $a - a = 0$.
   Hint: To do this one must select a general finite set A such that $n(A) = a$.
5. Use the basic 100 addition facts (preferably in table form) and Definition 4-6 to determine n if
   (a) $n - 7 = 13$ (d) $n - 11 = 5$
   (b) $6 - 3 = n$ (e) $12 - 7 = n$
   (c) $18 - n = 12$ (f) $16 - n = 7$
6. Use Definition 4-6 to show that for any cardinal number a,
   (a) $a - 0 = a$
   (b) $a - a = 0$.
7. A student works the problem $\begin{array}{r} 32 \\ -24 \\ \hline \end{array}$ as follows.

$$32 - 24 = (32 + 6) - (24 + 6)$$
$$= 38 - 30$$
$$= (30 + 8) - (30 + 0)$$
$$= 8$$

(a) Is this a valid method for subtraction?

(b) Try to generalize the method and justify it.

In problems 8 through 14 write the property which justifies each step of the solution.

	Step
8. $(17 + 9) - (13 - 2) = (17 + 9) - ([2 + 11] - 2)$	(a)
$= (17 + 9) - ([11 + 2] - 2)$	(b)
$= (17 + 9) - (11 + [2 - 2])$	(c)
$= (17 + 9) - (11 + 0)$	(d)
$= (17 + 9) - 11$	(e)
$= ([2 + 15] + 9) - 11$	(f)
$= ([15 + 2] + 9) - 11$	(g)
$= (15 + [2 + 9]) - 11$	(h)
$= (15 + 11) - 11$	(i)
$= 15 + (11 - 11)$	(j)
$= 15 + 0$	(k)
$= 15$	(l)

	Step
9. $(17 - 9) + (14 - 6) = [(9 + 8) - 9] + (14 - 6)$	(a)
$= [(8 + 9) - 9] + (14 - 6)$	(b)
$= [8 + (9 - 9)] + (14 - 6)$	(c)
$= (8 + 0) + (14 - 6)$	(d)
$= (8 + 0) + 8$	(e)
$= 8 + (0 + 8)$	(f)
$= 8 + (8 + 0)$	(g)
$= (8 + 8) + 0$	(h)
$= 16 + 0$	(i)
$= 16$	(j)

	Step
10. $(15 + 7) - 14 = (7 + 15) - 14$	(a)
$= 7 + (15 - 14)$	(b)
$= 7 + 1$	(c)
$= 8$	(d)

Step

11. $21 - (39 - 18) = 21 - [(18 + 21) - 18]$ (a)

$= 21 - [(21 + 18) - 18]$ (b)

$= 21 - [21 + (18 - 18)]$ (c)

$= 21 - (21 + 0)$ (d)

$= 21 - 21$ (e)

$= 0$ (f)

Step

12. $42 - (51 - 9) = 42 - [(9 + 42) - 9]$ (a)

$= 42 - [9 + (42 - 9)]$ (b)

$= 42 - (9 + 33)$ (c)

$= (33 + 9) - (9 + 33)$ (d)

$= (33 + 9) - (33 + 9)$ (e)

$= (33 - 33) + (9 - 9)$ (f)

$= 0 + 0$ (g)

$= 0$ (h)

Step

13. $x + 89 = 102$ (a) Given

$(x + 89) - 89 = 102 - 89$ (b)

$x + (89 - 89) = 102 - 89$ (c)

$x + 0 = 102 - 89$ (d)

$x = 102 - 89$ (e)

$x = (89 + 13) - 89$ (f)

$= (13 + 89) - 89$ (g)

$= 13 + (89 - 89)$ (h)

$= 13 + 0$ (i)

$= 13$ (j)

Step

14. $13 - x = 7$ (a) Given

$(13 - x) + x = 7 + x$ (b)

$x + (13 - x) = 7 + x$ (c)

$(x + 13) - x = 7 + x$ (d)

$(13 + x) - x = 7 + x$ (e)

$13 + (x - x) = 7 + x$ (f)

$$13 + 0 = 7 + x \qquad \text{(g)}$$

$$13 = 7 + x \qquad \text{(h)}$$

$$7 + 6 = 7 + x \qquad \text{(i)}$$

$$6 = x \qquad \text{(j)}$$

15. Prove: If a, b, and c are cardinals, and if $a - c$ and $b - c$ exist, and if $a - c = b - c$, then $a = b$. Can you find two different proofs?

16. Consider the following statement. If a, b, and c are cardinal numbers and if $a = b$, then $a - c = b - c$. Either prove that the statement is true or give an example to show that such results do not always hold.

17. Define a process on the set of cardinals by the relation

$$a \triangle b = (a - b) + 1.$$

Find the value of each of the following expressions (if it exists).

(a) $3 \triangle 2 =$

(b) $4 \triangle 2 =$

(c) $2 \triangle 3 =$

(d) Does $3 \triangle 2 = 2 \triangle 3$?

(e) Under what conditions does $a \triangle b = b \triangle a$?

Chapter summary

In this chapter the concept of subtraction was introduced by means of sets. Because of the fact that complements of sets were used we had to be sure that, in effect, we were not trying to remove more elements from a set than that set contained. For this reason the relations $<$ and $\leqslant$ were introduced. It is this problem which limits the possibilities for subtraction of cardinals and thereby guarantees that subtraction is not an operation on the set of cardinals. However, we were able to show in spite of this drawback that

(1) differences are unique when they exist,

(2) subtraction is not commutative.

(3) subtraction is not associative,

(4) there is no identity element,

(5) there can be an alternate definition of subtraction, and

(6) subtraction and addition are directly related.

In addition to these, we found that various subtraction algorithms can be justified. Thus while there are some restrictions, subtraction is still possible and very useful.

CHAPTER 5
Multiplication of cardinal numbers

1. Definition of Multiplication

The perceptive reader noticed, while reading about Cartesian product sets in Section 1-4, a striking analogy between Cartesian products and multiplication of numbers. The two are intimately related, and we shall use the concept of Cartesian product to define multiplication of cardinal numbers. Once this is done, we shall consider several properties of multiplication, some of them from a rather intuitive point of view. The reason for the intuitive approach to some of these results will be explained when we actually study them. After that is done, we shall return to a consideration of some of the algorithms which were mentioned earlier.

Definition 5-1: If a and b are any two cardinal numbers, the **product**, a times b, is the cardinality of the set $A \times B$ where A and B are set representatives of a and b respectively. The product is denoted by ab, $a \cdot b$, or $a \times b$.

The definition outlines the procedure for multiplication of cardinals a and b as follows.
1. Select sets A and B with $n(A) = a$ and $n(B) = b$.
2. Calculate $A \times B$.
3. Determine $n(A \times B) = c$.
4. $a \cdot b = c$.

Thus if we wish to determine $3 \cdot 2$, we may do so in the following fashion.
1. Select $A = \{a,b,c\}$ with $n(A) = 3$

   $B = \{c,d\}$ with $n(B) = 2$.

2.
$$A \times B = \begin{cases} (a,c), (a,d) \\ (b,c), (b,d) \\ (c,c), (c,d) \end{cases}$$

3. $n(A \times B) = 6$.

4. Therefore $3 \cdot 2 = 6$.

We may determine products of other cardinals in a similar fashion.

Again the question arises as to whether products always exist and are unique. Apparently the products do exist and are unique for we have used multiplication for a number of years without complications arising. However, we cannot afford to overlook such a possibility.

It should be rather easy to see that, based on our previous study, each step of Definition 5-1 can be done. Consequently products do exist in the set of cardinals. Since this is the case we know that multiplication is an operation defined on the set of cardinals and the set of cardinals is closed under the operation. The question of uniqueness is rather more involved and we treat it in the following theorem.

Theorem 5-1: Products of cardinal numbers are unique.

Proof: We must show that if we form the product $a \cdot b$ we can obtain just one answer. To do this we shall suppose that

$$a \cdot b = c \quad \text{and} \quad a \cdot b = c'$$

and show that c and c' name the same number. That is, we shall show that

$$c = c'$$

We do this in the following way.

1) Select $A = \{x_1, x_2, \ldots, x_a\}$ with $n(A) = a$ and

$B = \{y_1, y_2, \ldots, y_b\}$ with $n(B) = b$.

Next form

$$A \times B = \begin{cases} (x_1,y_1), (x_1,y_2), \ldots, (x_1,y_b) \\ (x_2,y_1), (x_2,y_2), \ldots, (x_2,y_b) \\ \cdot \quad \cdot \quad \cdot \quad \cdot \quad \cdot \quad \cdot \\ (x_a,y_1), (x_a,y_2), \ldots, (x_a,y_b) \end{cases}$$

Now $n(A \times B) = a \cdot b$ and we'll suppose that $a \cdot b = c$.

2) Next, we choose different set representatives for a and b as follows.

Select $A' = \{r_1, r_2, \ldots, r_a\}$ with $n(A') = a$ and

$B' = \{t_1, t_2, \ldots, t_b\}$ with $n(B') = b$.

Forming the Cartesian product of these two sets yields

$$A' \times B' = \begin{cases} (r_1, t_1), (r_1, t_2), \ldots, (r_1, t_b) \\ (r_2, t_1), (r_2, t_2), \ldots, (r_2, t_b) \\ \quad \cdot \qquad \cdot \qquad \cdot \qquad \cdot \qquad \cdot \qquad \cdot \\ (r_a, t_1), (r_a, t_2), \ldots, (r_a, t_b) \end{cases}$$

Then $n(A' \times B') = a \cdot b$ and we'll suppose that $a \cdot b = c'$ where we do not assume $c = c'$.

3) If we can show that $A \times B \sim A' \times B'$, then we will have

$$c = n(A \times B) = n(A' \times B') = c'$$

so that

$$c = c'$$

If we consider the sets $A \times B$ and $A' \times B'$ we observe that elements can be matched one-to-one column by column. Hence there is a one-to-one mapping of $A \times B$ onto $A' \times B'$ so that $A \times B \sim A' \times B'$. Then by Definition 1-25 $n(A \times B) = n(A' \times B')$ and we have $c = c'$. Thus products of cardinals are unique. ∎

The two cardinal numbers a and b which are used to form the product $a \cdot b$ have special names. Later in our discussion of multiplication, these names will be used to a considerable extent.

Definition 5-2: If a and b are cardinal numbers and if $a \cdot b = c$, then a and b are each called **factors** of c and c is called a **multiple** of a and b.

Hence if $3 \cdot 5 = 15$, 3 and 5 are both factors of 15. Likewise, 1 and 15 are factors of 15. Similarly one way also say that 15 is a multiple of 5 and a multiple of 3.

EXERCISE SET 5-1

1. By using Definition 5-1 determine
   (a) $6 \cdot 2$
   (b) $4 \cdot 4$
   (c) $2 \cdot 7$
2. By using the sets listed below, show that $5 \cdot 3$ is always 15.
   (a) $A = \{a,b,c,d,e\}$ and $B = \{x,y,z\}$
   (b) $A' = \{p,q,r,s,t\}$ and $B' = \{u,v,w\}$.
   (c) In parts (a) and (b), $A \times B \sim A' \times B'$. What can be said concerning $n(A \times B)$ and $n(A' \times B')$?
   (d) What property of multiplication has been illustrated?
3. What does uniqueness of multiplication tell us concerning the sets which are chosen for any particular product?

4. What does the fact that the Cartesian product of two finite sets is a finite set have to do with the definition of multiplication? Be specific.

5. In choosing sets A and B in the definition of multiplication, is it necessary that $A \cap B = \varnothing$?

2. Properties of Multiplication

Let us now consider some of the properties which are satisfied by multiplication of cardinal numbers.

As is the case with addition, multiplication satisfies the commutative and associative properties. However, to show it requires a somewhat higher degree of sophistication than was the case for addition. Hence we shall simply give a numerical example to illustrate what is involved.

Example: Suppose we wish to show that $2 \cdot 4 = 4 \cdot 2$.

Solution: Select $A = \{a,b\}$ with $n(A) = 2$ and
$B = \{c,d,e,f\}$ with $n(B) = 4$.

By Definition 5-1,

$$A \times B = \left\{ \begin{array}{l} (a,c), (a,d), (a,e), (a,f) \\ (b,c), (b,d), (b,e), (b,f) \end{array} \right\}$$

and

$$n(A \times B) = 2 \cdot 4$$

Similarly,

$$B \times A = \left\{ \begin{array}{l} (c,a), (c,b) \\ (d,a), (d,b) \\ (e,a), (e,b) \\ (f,a), (f,b) \end{array} \right\}$$

and

$$n(B \times A) = 4 \cdot 2$$

Since we want to show that $2 \cdot 4 = 4 \cdot 2$, we need only show that $A \times B \sim B \times A$, for we already know that equivalent finite sets have the same cardinality. Considering the Cartesian product sets we note that we match pairs which contain the same members but in the opposite order. That is,

$$(a,c) \longleftrightarrow (c,a)$$
$$(a,d) \longleftrightarrow (d,a)$$
$$(a,e) \longleftrightarrow (e,a)$$

.

.

.

$$(b,f) \longleftrightarrow (f,b)$$

Such a correspondence maps $A \times B$ one-to-one onto $B \times A$, so that $A \times B$ $\sim B \times A$. Consequently $2 \cdot 4 = 4 \cdot 2$.

The same technique proves the general commutative property for any two finite sets A and B. This result is listed for reference in the following theorem.

Theorem 5-2 (Commutative Property): If a and b are any two cardinal numbers, then $a \cdot b = b \cdot a$.

Proof: Left as an exercise.

In a similar fashion, we may illustrate the associative property for multiplication. We shall use a simple example, but even so you will observe that the work becomes rather lengthy.

Example: Show that $2 \cdot (3 \cdot 4) = (2 \cdot 3) \cdot 4$.

Solution: Let us choose

$$A = \{a,b\} \qquad \text{with } n(A) = 2$$
$$B = \{c,d,e\} \qquad \text{with } n(B) = 3$$
$$\text{and } C = \{f,g,h,i\} \qquad \text{with } n(C) = 4$$

Then

$$A \times (B \times C) = \begin{cases} [a,(c,f)], [a,(c,g)], [a,(c,h)], [a,(c,i)] \\ [a,(d,f)], [a,(d,g)], [a,(d,h)], [a,(d,i)] \\ [a,(e,f)], [a,(e,g)], [a,(e,h)], [a,(e,i)] \\ [b,(c,f)], [b,(c,g)], [b,(c,h)], [b,(c,i)] \\ [b,(d,f)], [b,(d,g)], [b,(d,h)], [b,(d,i)] \\ [b,(e,f)], [b,(e,g)], [b,(e,h)], [b,(e,i)] \end{cases}$$

and $n[A \times (B \times C)] = 2 \cdot (3 \cdot 4)$. If we calculate $(A \times B) \times C$, we have

$$\left\{ \begin{array}{l} [(a,c),f]\,,[(a,d),f]\,,[(a,e),f]\,,[(b,c),f]\,,[(b,d),f]\,,[(b,e),f] \\ [(a,c),g]\,,[(a,d),g]\,,[(a,e),g]\,,[(b,c),g]\,,[(b,d),g]\,,[(b,e),g] \\ [(a,c),h]\,,[(a,d),h]\,,[(a,e),h]\,,[(b,c),h]\,,[(b,d),h]\,,[(b,e),h] \\ [(a,c),i]\,,[(a,d),i]\,,[(a,e),i]\,,[(b,c),i]\,,[(b,d),i]\,,[(b,e),i] \end{array} \right\}$$

and $n[(A \times B) \times C] = (2 \cdot 3) \cdot 4$. If we select pairs which have the same elements of the original sets in the same order, but which are grouped differently we obtain a one-to-one onto mapping from $A \times (B \times C)$ to $(A \times B) \times C$. That is, we match

$$[a,(c,f)] \longleftrightarrow [(a,c),f]$$

.

.

.

$$[b,(c,g)] \longleftrightarrow [(b,c),g]$$

.

.

.

$$[b,(e,i)] \longleftrightarrow [(b,e),i]$$

and this maps $A \times (B \times C)$ one-to-one onto $(A \times B) \times C$ so that the two product sets are equivalent. Consequently $2 \cdot (3 \cdot 4) = (2 \cdot 3) \cdot 4$.

In general then we have the following statement of associativity of products.

Theorem 5-3 (Associative Property): If a, b, and c are any three cardinal numbers, then $a \cdot (b \cdot c) = (a \cdot b) \cdot c$.

Proof: Left as an exercise.

We note regarding the associative property that it says the manner of grouping sums and products has no effect at all on the final answer so long as the order of individual numbers is unchanged. This means that it might well be stated as

$$a + b + c = a + (b + c) = (a + b) + c$$

and

$$a \cdot b \cdot c = a \cdot (b \cdot c) = (a \cdot b) \cdot c$$

Indeed, we usually use this fact when working problems, but the left-most equality is often overlooked in the discussion of problems.

The course we shall follow in considering the possibility of çancellation in multiplication is somewhat like that used in addition. That is, if $n \cdot 5 = 35$ it makes sense to write $n \cdot 5 = 7 \cdot 5$ and conclude that $n = 7$.

But let us not jump to a conclusion too fast! For then we might obtain the result $0 = 0$ and $0 \cdot 5 = 0 \cdot 3$ so that $5 = 3!$ Hence it is apparent that if there is a cancellation property for multiplication, it does not act exactly like the one for addition. Let us now state and prove the cancellation property for multiplication of cardinal numbers.

Theorem 5-4 (Cancellation Property): If a, b, and c are cardinal numbers and if $a \cdot c = b \cdot c$, then $a = b$ provided that $c \neq 0$.

Proof: If $c = 0$ and $a \cdot c = b \cdot c$, it is not necessary that $a = b$, for then we could have

$$0 = 0$$

$$0 \cdot 1 = 0 \cdot 4$$

$$1 = 4.$$

Hence the theorem may not hold if $c = 0$.

On the other hand, if $c \neq 0$ and if $a \cdot c = b \cdot c$, then we can show that $a = b$. To do this, let us select

$$A = \{x_1, x_2, \ldots, x_a\} \quad \text{with } n(A) = a$$

$$B = \{y_1, y_2, \ldots, y_b\} \quad \text{with } n(B) = b, \text{ and}$$

$$C = \{z_1, z_2, \ldots, z_c\} \quad \text{with } n(C) = c \neq 0$$

This means that $C \neq \emptyset$, and since $a \cdot c = b \cdot c$, $A \times C \sim B \times C$. That is

$$\left\{\begin{array}{l} (x_1,z_1),(x_1,z_2), \ldots, (x_1,z_c) \\ (x_2,z_1),(x_2,z_2), \ldots, (x_2,z_c) \\ \cdot \quad \cdot \quad \cdot \quad \cdot \quad \cdot \quad \cdot \\ (x_a,z_1),(x_a,z_2), \ldots, (x_a,z_c) \end{array}\right\} \sim \left\{\begin{array}{l} (y_1,z_1),(y_1,z_2), \ldots, (y_1,z_c) \\ (y_2,z_1),(y_2,z_2), \ldots, (y_2,z_c) \\ \cdot \quad \cdot \quad \cdot \quad \cdot \quad \cdot \quad \cdot \\ (y_b,z_1),(y_b,z_2), \ldots, (y_b,z_c) \end{array}\right\}$$

Since the same elements z appear as second members of the ordered pairs and since the ordered pairs of $A \times C$ can be mapped one-to-one onto those of $B \times C$, this means that $A \sim B$, for otherwise there could not be a one-to-one mapping of $A \times C$ onto $B \times C$. Further, since $A \sim B$, we have $n(A) = n(B)$. That is, $a = b$. ∎

The cancellation property may be used to solve problems of the following type.

Example: Determine n if $\qquad 2n + 6 = 10$

Solution:
$$2n + 6 = 4 + 6$$
$$2n = 4$$
$$2n = 2 \cdot 2$$
$$n = 2$$

Example: Determine n if $3n - 2 = 4.$

Solution:
$$(3n - 2) + 2 = 4 + 2$$
$$2 + (3n - 2) = 4 + 2$$
$$(2 + 3n) - 2 = 4 + 2$$
$$(3n + 2) - 2 = 4 + 2$$
$$3n + (2 - 2) = 4 + 2$$
$$3n + 0 = 4 + 2$$
$$3n = 6$$
$$3n = 3 \cdot 2$$
$$n = 2$$

It is now easy to show that cardinal number one is the only multiplicative identity. This is done quickly by using Theorem 5-4 to show that there is at most one multiplicative identity.

Theorem 5-5: There is at most one multiplicative identity.

Proof: We know that $1 \cdot a = a \cdot 1 = a$ for every cardinal number a. Suppose there is a second cardinal number z such that

$$z \cdot a = a \cdot z = a$$

and such that $z \neq 1$. By transitivity of equality,

$$z \cdot a = 1 \cdot a$$

so that if $a \neq 0$, $z = 1$

Since there is no such second cardinal number z this means that there is at most one multiplicative identity. ∎

Since cardinal one is a multiplicative identity and since there is at most one, there is precisely one multiplicative identity. It is cardinal number one.

We have already seen that if equals are added to equals, the results are equal. We explored this when discussing the converse of cancellation for addition. It is of interest to note that the same holds true for multiplication and we shall state it in the following theorem and outline its proof.

Theorem 5-6 (Converse of Cancellation): If a, b, and c are cardinal numbers and if $a = b$, then $a \cdot c = b \cdot c$.

Outline of Proof: If $a = b$, and if A, B, and C are chosen so that $n(A) = a$, $n(B) = b$, and $n(C) = c$, then $A \times C \sim B \times C$. The reason for this is that the same number of ordered pairs can be formed since A and B have the same number of elements. This then gives a one-to-one mapping of $A \times C$ onto $B \times C$ so that $n(A \times C) = n(B \times C)$. That is, $a \cdot c = b \cdot c$. ∎

It might be noted that Theorem 5-6 is not of particular use to us at this time; however its parallel in the rational number system is quite valuable. Since this is the first place it appears we do mention it. It might also be noted that as in addition the converse of cancellation is equivalent to uniqueness of products.

The next consideration will be one of the most important made in multiplication. The reason it is of such importance is that it is very useful in the study of addition and subtraction problems. The property to be considered is called the *distributive property* of multiplication with respect to addition. The general proof of this property, like those of Theorems 5-2 and 5-3, becomes rather lengthy, so we shall illustrate it with a numerical example. It might be noted however that the general proof is not very difficult.

Theorem 5-7 (Distributive Property): If a, b, and c are cardinal numbers, then $a \cdot (b + c) = a \cdot b + a \cdot c$.

Proof: Left as an exercise.

Example: Show that $2 \cdot (3 + 4) = 2 \cdot 3 + 2 \cdot 4$.

Solution: Select $A = \{a,b\}$ with $n(A) = 2$,

$$B = \{c,d,e\} \text{ with } n(B) = 3,$$

$$C = \{f,g,h,i\} \text{ with } n(C) = 4,$$

and $B \cap C = \emptyset$. Then

$$B \cup C = \{c,d,e,f,g,h,i\}$$

and $n(B \cup C) = 3 + 4$.

Now

$$A \times (B \cup C) = \left\{ \begin{matrix} (a,c),(a,d),(a,e),(a,f),(a,g),(a,h),(a,i) \\ (b,c),(b,d),(b,e),(b,f),(b,g),(b,h),(b,i) \end{matrix} \right\}$$

and by Definition 5-1, $n[A \times (B \cup C)] = 2 \cdot (3 + 4)$.

Next form

$$A \times B = \left\{ \begin{array}{l} (a,c),(a,d),(a,e) \\ (b,c),(b,d),(b,e) \end{array} \right\} \text{ with } n(A \times B) = 2 \cdot 3.$$

Similarly $A \times C = \left\{ \begin{array}{l} (a,f),(a,g),(a,h),(a,i) \\ (b,f),(b,g),(b,h),(b,i) \end{array} \right\}$ and $n(A \times C) = 2 \cdot 4.$

Since $(A \times B) \cap (A \times C) = \emptyset,$

$$(A \times B) \cup (A \times C) = \left\{ \begin{array}{l} (a,c),(a,d),(a,e),(b,c),(b,d),(b,e),(b,f), \\ (a,f),(a,g),(a,h),(a,i),(b,g),(b,h),(b,i) \end{array} \right\}$$

and

$$n[(A \times B) \cup (A \times C)] = 2 \cdot 3 + 2 \cdot 4$$

Note that $A \times (B \cup C) = (A \times B) \cup (A \times C)$. Since this is so, we automatically have that $A \times (B \cup C) \sim (A \times B) \cup (A \times C)$ and consequently,

$$n[A \times (B \cup C)] = n[(A \times B) \cup (A \times C)]$$

That is, $2 \cdot (3 + 4) = 2 \cdot 3 + 2 \cdot 4$. We have now distributed the factor 2 over the sum $3 + 4$. This example is actually somewhat misleading, since even though the general proof is more abstract, it is not much longer at all.

Of equal interest is the fact that if the difference of two cardinal numbers exists, then multiplication is distributive with respect to subtraction. This too can be proved by using sets, but there is also a rather easy proof available which does not make direct use of sets. This proof is as follows.

Theorem 5-8: If a, b, and c are cardinal numbers and if $b - c$ exists, then $a \cdot (b - c) = a \cdot b - a \cdot c$.

Proof: As stated in the theorem, $b - c$ exists. Also, $b = b$ by the reflexive property of equality. Now

$(b - c) + c = b$	Thm. 4-4
$a \cdot [(b - c) + c] = a \cdot b$	Thm. 5-6
$a \cdot (b - c) + a \cdot c = a \cdot b$	Thm. 5-7
$a \cdot (b - c) = a \cdot b - a \cdot c$	Thm. 4-6 ∎

Thus we may work such problems as $5 \cdot (6 - 4)$ in two ways and be assured that either method yields the correct answer.

Examples: (a) $5 \cdot (6 - 4) = 5 \cdot 2 = 10$
(b) $5 \cdot (6 - 4) = 5 \cdot 6 - 5 \cdot 4 = 30 - 20 = 10$

In working numerical problems we often need the distributive property in slightly altered forms.   These forms are called extensions of the distributive property.

Theorem 5-9: If a, b, c, and d are cardinal numbers, then $a \cdot (b + c + d) = a \cdot b + a \cdot c + a \cdot d$.

Proof:

$$a \cdot (b + c + d) = a \cdot [(b + c) + d] \qquad \text{Thm. 3-4}$$
$$= a \cdot (b + c) + a \cdot d \qquad \text{Thm. 5-7}$$
$$= (a \cdot b + a \cdot c) + a \cdot d \qquad \text{Thm. 5-7}$$
$$= a \cdot b + a \cdot c + a \cdot d \qquad \text{Thm. 3-4} \blacksquare$$

Another form sometimes needed is the following.

Theorem 5-10: If a, b, c, and d are cardinal numbers, then $(a + b) \cdot (c + d) = a \cdot c + b \cdot c + a \cdot d + b \cdot d$.

Proof: Left as an exercise.

EXERCISE SET 5-2

1. See if you can determine cardinal numbers which satisfy the following. (The numbers may be different for each problem.)
   (a) $a + b = a - b$ (c) $3 \cdot a = a$
   (b) $a + b = a \cdot b$ (d) $a \cdot b = a - b$
2. Prove that $a \cdot 1 = a$ where a and 1 are cardinal numbers.   Remember that to do this you must select a general finite set A.
3. By using the definition of addition and the distributive property, show that
   (a) $3 \cdot 2 = 3 + 3$
   (b) $4 \cdot 3 = 3 + 3 + 3 + 3$.
   (c) Judging from parts (a) and (b), what is the relationship between multiplication and addition?
4. An *even* cardinal number is one which has a factor 2.   That is, if n is even we may write $n = 2k$ where k is some cardinal number.   Using this fact, show that if a and b are even, then
   (a) $a + b$ is even
   (b) $a - b$ is even provided $a \geqslant b$
   (c) $a \cdot b$ is even
   (d) $a \cdot a$ is even.
5. If a cardinal number n is not even, it is *odd* and can be written $n = 2k + 1$ where k is some cardinal number.   Using this fact, show that if a and b are odd, then
   (a) $a + b$ is even
   (b) $a - b$ is even provided $a \geqslant b$
   (c) $a \cdot b$ is odd
   (d) $a \cdot a$ is odd.
6. If a is odd and b is even, show that
   (a) $a + b$ is odd
   (b) $a \cdot b$ is even

7. Fill in the blanks in each of the following exercises so that the resulting statement is true.
   (a) $8 \cdot (9 + 7) = $ _____ $\cdot 9 + 8 \cdot$ _____
   (b) $5 \cdot ($_____$+ 3) = 5 \cdot 2 + $ _____ $\cdot 3$
   (c) _____ $\cdot (4 + 6) = 12 + $ _____

8. (a) Decide as *true* or *false* by means of a *specific* example whether $A \times (B \cup C)$ is the same set as $A \times (C \cup B)$. [Since your decision is based on only one example bear in mind that it could be false.]
   (b) Now find $n[A \times (B \cup C)]$ and $n[A \times (C \cup B)]$. Are they the same cardinal number? If they are equal cardinals, what would be another way of writing this property?

9. Let $A = \{x,y,z\}$, $B = \{u,v\}$ and $C = \{y,z,v\}$. Then $a = n(A) = 3$, $b = n(B) = 2$, and $c = n(C) = 3$.
   (a) Find $n(B \cup C)$.
   (b) Write out $A \times (B \cup C)$.
   (c) Find $n[A \times (B \cup C)]$.
   (d) Find $n(A \times B)$.
   (e) Find $n(A \times C)$.
   (f) In this example is
   $$a \cdot (b + c) = a \cdot b + a \cdot c?$$
   (g) If your answer to (f) was NO, what could be done to remedy the situation?

10. Let $A = \{\Box, \bigcirc, \triangle\}$, $B = \{a,b\}$, and $C = \{7,8,9,6\}$.
    (a) If $n(A) = a$, $n(B) = b$, and $n(C) = c$, does $a \cdot (b - c) = a \cdot b - a \cdot c$? If not, explain why not. If so, show how.
    (b) Does $a \cdot (b + c + a) = a \cdot b + a \cdot c + a \cdot a$ here? If not, explain why not. If so, show how.

11. (a) Show by means of a numerical example that it is not always true for cardinals that $a + (b \cdot c) = (a + b) \cdot (a + c)$.
    (b) See if you can find at least one example for which the equality in part (a) does hold.
    (c) What name would we give to the equality exhibited in problem 7?

12. Using any of the number properties now available, find the solution to each of the following.
    (a) $2n + 3 = 7$
    (b) $3n - 1 = 17$
    (c) $2n + 3n + 4 = 24$
    (d) $12n - 3n - 4 = 77$
    (e) $5n + 2 = 2n + 17$
    (f) $7n - 3 = 4n + 18$

13. Suppose we have a process called "triangle," $\triangle$, as follows: $4 \triangle 3 = 15$, $8 \triangle 6 = 54$, $0 \triangle 5 = 5$, $4 \triangle 9 = 45$.
    (a) After establishing how $\triangle$ works, determine

$6 \triangle 6$	$8 \triangle 5$	$12 \triangle 8$
$9 \triangle 7$	$10 \triangle 7$	$5 \triangle 0$
$5 \triangle 8$	$6 \triangle 11$	$(4 \triangle 6) \triangle 3$
$4 \triangle (6 \triangle 3)$		

    (b) Does an answer always exist for $\triangle$? Is it unique?
    (c) Does $\triangle$ have an identity element? If so, what is it?

(d) Is $a \triangle b = b \triangle a$?

(e) Is $a \triangle (b \triangle c) = (a \triangle b) \triangle c$?

(f) If $a \triangle c = b \triangle c$, does $a = b$?

(g) Is $\triangle$ an operation on the set of cardinals?

14. Suppose we define $\oplus$ and $\odot$ by the tables shown below where sums and products are found at intersection of rows and columns.

$\oplus$	A	B	C	D	E
A	E	C	F	A	B
B	C	G	D	B	F
C	F	D	A	C	G
D	A	B	C	D	E
E	B	F	G	E	C

$\odot$	A	B	C	D	E
A	D	E	B	C	A
B	C	D	A	E	B
C	E	A	D	B	C
D	B	C	E	A	D
E	A	B	C	D	E

(a) Does $\oplus$ have an identity element? If so, what is it?

(b) Is $\odot$ commutative?

(c) Is $\odot$ commutative?

(d) Does $\odot$ have an identity element? If so, what is it?

(e) Is $\odot$ associative? If not, give an example to support your answer.

(f) Is $B \odot (C \odot D) = (B \odot C) \oplus (B \odot D)$? If not, show how you made your decision. Conclusion to this?

(g) Is $\oplus$ an operation on the set $\{A,B,C,D,E\}$?

(h) Is $\odot$ an operation on the set $\{A,B,C,D,E\}$?

Justify each step of problems 15 and 16 below.

15.

$$8[7 + (8 - 4)] - 4[3 + 2(5 - 3)] = 8(7 + 4) - 4(3 + 2 \cdot 2) \qquad \text{(a)}$$

$$= 8 \cdot 11 - 4(3 + 2 \cdot 2) \qquad \text{(b)}$$

$$= 8 \cdot 11 - 4(3 + 4) \qquad \text{(c)}$$

$$= 8 \cdot 11 - 4 \cdot 7 \qquad \text{(d)}$$

$$= 8(4 + 7) - 4 \cdot 7 \qquad \text{(e)}$$

$$= (8 \cdot 4 + 8 \cdot 7) - 4 \cdot 7 \qquad \text{(f)}$$

$$= (32 + 56) - 28 \qquad \text{(g)}$$

$$= 32 + (56 - 28) \qquad \text{(h)}$$

$$= 32 + [(28 + 28) - 28] \qquad \text{(i)}$$

$$= 32 + [28 + (28 - 28)] \qquad \text{(j)}$$

$$= 32 + (28 + 0) \qquad \text{(k)}$$

$$= 32 + 28 \qquad \text{(l)}$$

$$= (30 + 2) + 28 \qquad \text{(m)}$$

$$= 30 + (2 + 28) \qquad \text{(n)}$$

$$= 30 + [2 + (20 + 8)] \qquad \text{(o)}$$
$$= 30 + [2 + (8 + 20)] \qquad \text{(p)}$$
$$= 30 + [(2 + 8) + 20] \qquad \text{(q)}$$
$$= 30 + (10 + 20) \qquad \text{(r)}$$
$$= 30 + 30 \qquad \text{(s)}$$
$$= 3 \cdot 10 + 3 \cdot 10 \qquad \text{(t)}$$
$$= (3 + 3)10 \qquad \text{(u)}$$
$$= 6 \cdot 10 \qquad \text{(v)}$$
$$= 60 \qquad \text{(w)}$$

Step

16. $15(34 + 23) - 750 = 15[(30 + 4) + (20 + 3)] - 750$ (a)
$$= 15[(30 + 20) + (4 + 3)] - 750 \qquad \text{(b)}$$
$$= 15(50 + 7) - 750 \qquad \text{(c)}$$
$$= 15(57) - 750 \qquad \text{(d)}$$
$$= 15(30 + 27) - 750 \qquad \text{(e)}$$
$$= (15 \cdot 30 + 15 \cdot 27) - 750 \qquad \text{(f)}$$
$$= (450 + 15 \cdot 27) - 750 \qquad \text{(g)}$$
$$= (450 + 15[27 + 0]) - 750 \qquad \text{(h)}$$
$$= (450 + 15[(27 + 3) - 3]) - 750 \qquad \text{(i)}$$
$$= (450 + 15[30 - 3]) - 750 \qquad \text{(j)}$$
$$= (450 + [15 \cdot 30 - 15 \cdot 3]) - 750 \qquad \text{(k)}$$
$$= (450 + [450 - 45]) - 750 \qquad \text{(l)}$$
$$= ([450 + 450] - 45) - 750 \qquad \text{(m)}$$
$$= (900 - 45) - 750 \qquad \text{(n)}$$
$$= ([855 + 45] - 45) - 750 \qquad \text{(o)}$$
$$= (855 + [45 - 45]) - 750 \qquad \text{(p)}$$
$$= (855 + 0) - 750 \qquad \text{(q)}$$
$$= 855 - 750 \qquad \text{(r)}$$
$$= (750 + 105) - 750 \qquad \text{(s)}$$
$$= 105 \qquad \text{(t)}$$

3. Exponents

In Section 5-1, we defined a factor of a cardinal number. Some products of cardinal numbers have factors which may be repeated and are of special interest. We shall soon see that the consideration of such factors leads us to a very useful and important concept of arithmetic.

Definition 5-3: If a is any cardinal number and n is any non-zero cardinal number, then a^n means n factors a.
That is, $a^n = \underbrace{a \cdot a \cdot a \cdots a \cdot a.}_{n \text{ factors}}$

The number a is called the *base* and n is called the *exponent*. For example,

$$3 \cdot 3 \cdot 3 \cdot 3 = 3^4,$$
$$5 \cdot 5 \cdot 5 = 5^{3}{}^{1},$$
$$2 \cdot 2 = 2^2,$$
$$7 \cdot 7 \cdot 7 \cdot 7 \cdot 7 = 7^5, \text{ and so forth.}$$

If the bases are the same, some interesting results occur. For example,

$$5^3 \cdot 5^4 = (5 \cdot 5 \cdot 5) \cdot (5 \cdot 5 \cdot 5 \cdot 5)$$
$$= 5 \cdot 5 \cdot 5 \cdot 5 \cdot 5 \cdot 5 \cdot 5$$
$$= 5^7$$
$$= 5^{3+4}.$$

On the basis of examples similar to that just worked, it appears that the following theorem is true.

Theorem 5-11: If a is a cardinal number, then $a^n \cdot a^m = a^{n+m}$ where $n \neq 0, m \neq 0$.

The proof of Theorem 5-11 requires what is called mathematical induction and so will be omitted. However, the student should work some examples such as that which precedes the theorem to convince himself of its validity.

Another useful result concerning exponents is the following.

Theorem 5-12: If a is a cardinal number and m and n are non-zero cardinal numbers, then $(a^m)^n = a^{mn}$.

Again we omit the proof which requires induction.

---

[1] It is important that (for example) $5 \cdot 5 \cdot 5$ be read as "three factors five" rather than "three fives," for the former means 125 and the latter means 15 — quite a difference!

Example:

$$(2^4)^3 = (2^4) \cdot (2^4) \cdot (2^4)$$
$$= (2 \cdot 2 \cdot 2 \cdot 2) \cdot (2 \cdot 2 \cdot 2 \cdot 2) \cdot (2 \cdot 2 \cdot 2 \cdot 2)$$
$$= 2 \cdot 2 \cdot 2 \cdot 2 \cdot 2 \cdot 2 \cdot 2 \cdot 2 \cdot 2 \cdot 2 \cdot 2 \cdot 2$$
$$= 2^{12}$$
$$= 2^{4 \cdot 3}$$

Up to this point you may have observed that we have avoided zero exponents. Let us now consider this possibility. Since one is the multiplicative identity, we may write for example that

$$2^5 = 2 \cdot 2 \cdot 2 \cdot 2 \cdot 2$$
$$= 1 \cdot 2 \cdot 2 \cdot 2 \cdot 2 \cdot 2, \quad \text{i.e., factor 1 and five factors 2.}$$

Similarly

$$2^4 = 1 \cdot 2 \cdot 2 \cdot 2 \cdot 2, \qquad \text{i.e., factor 1 and four factors 2}$$
$$2^3 = 1 \cdot 2 \cdot 2 \cdot 2, \qquad \text{i.e., factor 1 and three factors 2}$$
$$2^2 = 1 \cdot 2 \cdot 2, \qquad \text{i.e., factor 1 and two factors 2}$$
$$2^1 = 1 \cdot 2, \qquad \text{i.e., factor 1 and one factor 2}$$

What, then, is 2^0? In order to be consistent it appears that we should write

$$2^0 = 1 \qquad \text{i.e., factor 1}$$

As an alternative approach for defining a^0, where a is a cardinal number, consider the following. Since $4 = 0 + 4$,

$$a^4 = a^{0 + 4} \qquad \qquad \text{Thm. 3-6}$$
$$= a^0 \cdot a^4 \qquad \qquad \text{Thm. 5-11}$$

Since one is the multiplicative identity,

$$1 \cdot a^4 = a^4$$

and by transitivity of equality we obtain the fact that

$$1 \cdot a^4 = a^0 \cdot a^4$$

If $a \neq 0$, then the only way in which we may still use the cancellation property of multiplication is to define $a^0 = 1$. Hence we make the following definition.

Definition 5-4: If a is a non-zero cardinal number, then $a^0 = 1$.

The problem of evaluating 0^0 is a very special problem whose solution can be obtained only by use of some rather sophisticated mathematics. For this reason, we shall not consider 0^0 at all.

Directly related to the concept of exponent is another important concept, namely that of *square root.* Since

$$2 \cdot 2 = 4$$

we say that 2 is the square root of 4. That is, 2 is the number such that if multiplied by itself gives 4. Similarly, 3 is the square root of 9 since 3 times 3 yields 9. In general, we define the square root of a cardinal number as follows.

Definition 5-5: If n is a cardinal number and if there is a cardinal number a such that $a^2 = n,$ then a is the **square root** of $n.$ This is denoted $a = \sqrt{n}.$

Note that the square root of a cardinal number may not exist. For example, there is no cardinal number a such that $a^2 = 3$ because $1^2 = 1$ and $2^2 = 4.$ On the other hand, if the square root does exist, then we have

$$a^2 = (\sqrt{n})^2$$

$$= n.$$

Example: If $n = 16,$ then $a = \sqrt{16} = 4$ and

$$a^2 = (\sqrt{16})^2$$

$$= 4^2$$

$$= 16$$

$$= n.$$

EXERCISE SET 5-3
1. Since $2^2 = 2 \cdot 2,$ can we conclude that $3^2 = 2 \cdot 3$? Why or why not?
2. Write each of the following products so as to make use of exponents.
    (a) $4 \cdot 4 \cdot 4 \cdot 4 \cdot 4$ (d) 100
    (b) $5 \cdot 5 \cdot 3 \cdot 3 \cdot 3$ (e) $10^3 \cdot 10 \cdot 10 \cdot 10 \cdot 10$
    (c) $8 \cdot 2$ (f) $18 \cdot 8$
3. Determine
    (a) $3^2 \cdot 3^4$
    (b) $7^4 \cdot 7^3$
    (c) $4^2 \cdot 2^4$
    (d) $8^3 \cdot 4^1$
    (e) $5^3 \cdot 2^3$
4. Is it true that
    (a) $2^4 \cdot 3^4 = 6^4$?
    (b) $5^3 \cdot 6^3 = 30^3$?
    (c) $4^2 \cdot 3^2 = 12^2$?
    (d) $4^3 \cdot 5^3 = 20^3$?
5. State a theorem which would justify the results in problem four.
6. Show that
    (a) $(\sqrt{4})^4 = 4^2$

(b) $(\sqrt{9})^3 = 27$

(c) $(\sqrt{16})^3 = 2^6$

7. If b and c are "perfect squares" (that is, cardinals obtained by multiplying cardinals by themselves, such as 1, 4, 9, 16, 25, . . .) then is it true that $b \cdot c$ is a perfect square? If not, illustrate by an example.

4. Prime Factors and the Fundamental Theorem of Arithmetic

Certain of the cardinal numbers which may appear as factors are of special usefulness in arithmetic and consequently are given a special name.

Definition 5-6: If p is a cardinal number such that

(1) $p > 1$ and

(2) the only factors of p are 1 and p, then p is called a **prime** cardinal number.

Definition 5-7: If n is a cardinal number such that

(1) $n > 1$ and

(2) n is not a prime, then n is called a **composite** cardinal number.

Some primes are 2, 3, 5, 7, 11, 13, 17, 19, 23, and 29. One way to determine whether or not a number is prime is by trial and error. However, there is a more systematic method for the determination of some of the prime numbers. This method makes use of the *Sieve of Eratosthenes.* Using this method one simply lists a set of cardinal numbers, then proceeds to mark out all "proper" multiples of two, three, five, and so on. By a proper multiple of a number n we mean $2n$, $3n$, $4n$, and so forth. We illustrate in the following example.

Example: Determine all primes which are less than or equal to 30.

Solution: We list the cardinals 2 through 30 and mark out proper multiples as illustrated in Figure 5-1.

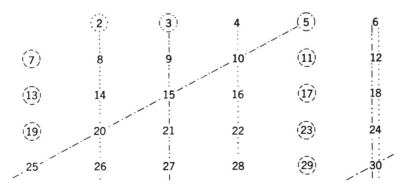

FIGURE 5-1

Step 1:   2 is prime so mark out all multiples of 2 (. . . . .).
Step 2:   The next number larger than 2 which has not been marked out is
3 and 3 is a prime. Hence we now mark out all multiples of 3 (— .. — .. — .. —).
Step 3:   The next number larger than 3 which has not been marked out is
5 and 5 is a prime. Hence we now mark out all multiples of 5 (— . — . — . — .—).
The question now arises as to how one can tell when he need *not* mark out any
more cardinal numbers in the array. The answer to this is discussed in the theory
of numbers at an advanced level. It is shown there that if all proper multiples of
primes $p \leqslant \sqrt{n}$ (where n is the last entry of the array) are eliminated, the
numbers which remain are all primes. Here, again proper multiples means
multiples two or greater of the primes involved. Thus $2p$, $3p$, $4p$, and so forth
are the proper multiples of the prime p.

In our example, $n = 30$ and the largest prime p such that $p \leqslant \sqrt{30}$ is 5.
Hence if we mark out all proper multiples of 2, 3, and 5, only primes remain.
Therefore the prime cardinals less than or equal to 30 are 2, 3, 5, 7, 11, 13, 17,
19, 23, and 29.

Using a similar technique, we find the primes less than or equal to 50 to be
those circled in Figure 5-2.

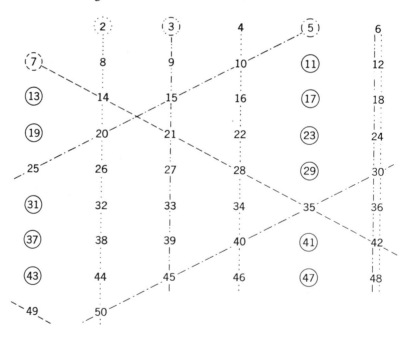

FIGURE 5-2

It should be observed that the use of the sieve itself can become a rather
lengthy process. For our purposes, however, it will suffice, since we are not
generally interested in extremely large numbers for practical arithmetic problems.

The main purpose we have in mind for the introduction of the Sieve of Eratosthenes is so that it can be used in discussing the determination of prime factors of given cardinal numbers. Using the sieve we are able to illustrate the following very important result.

Theorem 5-13 (Fundamental Theorem of Arithmetic[2]): If n is any cardinal number greater than one, n can be expressed as a product of prime factors. The expression is unique (except possibly for the order in which the factors occur).

Even though the Fundamental Theorem of Arithmetic is very important, its proof is beyond the scope of this exposition. For this reason the proof is omitted.

To illustrate what the Fundamental Theorem of Arithmetic states note that $78 = 2 \cdot 3 \cdot 13 = 2 \cdot 13 \cdot 3 = 3 \cdot 2 \cdot 13 = 3 \cdot 13 \cdot 2 = 13 \cdot 2 \cdot 3 = 13 \cdot 3 \cdot 2$. The only difference in the above expressions is the order in which the factors occur. In each case however, precisely the same factors do occur, and this is what the Fundamental Theorem guarantees.

To illustrate the relation of the Sieve of Eratosthenes to the Fundamental Theorem of Arithmetic, let us consider the following example.

Example: Determine the prime factors of 36.

Solution: We make use of the Sieve of Eratosthenes as illustrated in Figure 5-3 by finding primes which are factors of 36.

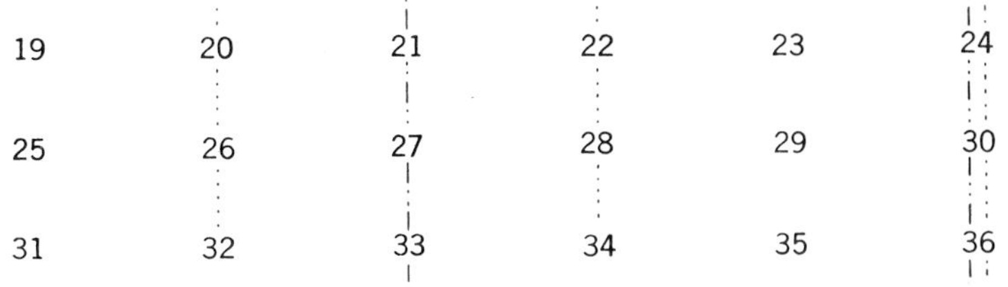

FIGURE 5-3

Hence both 2 and 3 are factors of 36 and consequently

$$36 = 2 \cdot 3 \cdot 6$$

Another application of the sieve yields the fact that

$$6 = 2 \cdot 3.$$

[2]The Fundamental Theorem of Arithmetic is also sometimes referred to as the Unique Factorization Theorem.

Thus

$$36 = 2 \cdot 3 \cdot 2 \cdot 3$$
$$= (2 \cdot 2)(3 \cdot 3)$$
$$= 2^2 \cdot 3^2.$$

Using the language of sets, the set of prime factors of 36 is $\{2,3\}$. The prime factorization of 36 is $2 \cdot 2 \cdot 3 \cdot 3$ and since products are commutative, the order of the factors is immaterial. Later, after division has been discussed, we shall see that there is another (and often easier) way in which prime factors of a given cardinal number can be determined.

It is sometimes of interest to determine the smallest number which is a multiple of a given set of numbers. This is of prime importance in certain problems which involve rational numbers as we shall see later. Let us now state this idea formally and try to determine a method which will yield the desired result.

Definition 5-8: If a and b are two cardinal numbers, then the smallest cardinal number which is a non-zero multiple of both is called the **least common multiple** of a and b. This is often denoted as l.c.m. (a,b) or L.C.M. (a,b).

Example: Suppose we attempt to determine the L.C.M. of 24 and 36. Since we are to determine the L.C.M., it would apparently be useful to consider the common multiples of each and consequently the multiples of each. Let us agree to the following terminology in order to make our task easier.

(1) $M(a) = \{x \mid x$ is a non-zero multiple of $a\}$
(2) $CM(a,b) = \{x \mid x$ is a common multiple of a and $b\}$.

Then

$$M(24) = \{24,48,72,96,120,144,168,192,216, \ldots\}$$

and

$$M(36) = \{36,72,108,144,180,216, \ldots\}.$$

Then

$$CM(24,36) = M(24) \cap M(36)$$
$$= \{72,144,216,288,360, \ldots\}.$$

Since the L.C.M. is the smallest of the common multiples, we have that

$$\text{L.C.M.}(24,36) = 72$$

Hence, 72 is the smallest cardinal number which has both 24 and 36 as factors.

Example: Determine L.C.M.$(28,42)$.

Solution: $M(28) = \{28,56,84,112,140,168,196,224,252, \ldots\}$

and

$$M(42) = \{42,84,126,168,210,252, \ldots\}$$

Hence

$$CM(28,42) = M(28) \cap M(42)$$

$$= \{84,168,252, \ldots\}$$

The smallest element of $CM(28,42)$ is 84 and consequently

$$\text{L.C.M.}(28,42) = 84 \ [3]$$

Let us now consider the same two examples by making use of the Fundamental Theorem of Arithmetic which guarantees that each of the numbers listed does have a set of prime factors.

TABLE 5-1

	Number	Prime factorization
	24	$2^3 \cdot 3$
Example 1.	36	$2^2 \cdot 3^2$
	L.C.M.(24,36) = 72	$2^3 \cdot 3^2$
	28	$2^2 \cdot 7$
Example 2.	42	$2 \cdot 3 \cdot 7$
	L.C.M.(28,42) = 84	$2^2 \cdot 3 \cdot 7$

Using Table 5-1, if one studies carefully the prime factors of 24 and 36 in relation to those of 72, and those of 28 and 42 in relation to the prime factors of 84, he observes the following very important principle:

The least common multiple of two cardinals a and b is the product of the highest powers of the prime factors which occur in the prime factorization of a or b.

Since this method of determining the L.C.M. is based on the use of prime factors, the Fundamental Theorem of Arithmetic is of considerable use.

Closely related to the concept of least common multiple is that of *greatest common factor* which we shall now define and discuss.

---

[3]One is assured that it is always possible to determine both the L.C.M. and G.C.F. (see Definition 5-9). The existence of the L.C.M. rests on the fact that the set of cardinals is a *well-ordered* set. The existence of the G.C.F. rests on the fact that if a set has an upper bound then it has a least upper bound. Both of these concepts require more sophistication than we wish to use.

Definition 5-9: The **greatest common factor** of two cardinal numbers, a and b, is the largest cardinal number which is a factor of both a and b. This is often denoted g.c.f.(a,b) or G.C.F.(a,b).

If the G.C.F. of two cardinals is to be determined, then we must necessarily use the common factors and consequently the factors. By use of the following two examples we shall attempt to devise a systematic method for the determination of the G.C.F. of two cardinal numbers.

Example: Determine the G.C.F. of 24 and 36.

Solution: Let us agree (for convenience) to the following terminology:
(1) $F(a) = \{x \mid x$ is a factor of $a\}$
(2) $CF(a,b) = \{x \mid x$ is a common factor of a and $b\}$.

Then

$$F(24) = \{1,2,3,4,6,8,12,24\}$$

and

$$F(36) = \{1,2,3,4,6,9,12,18,36\}$$

Then

$$CF(24,36) = F(24) \cap F(36)$$
$$= \{1,2,3,4,6,12\}$$

Consequently, by Definition 5-9, we have

$$G.C.F(24,36) = 12$$

That is, 12 is the largest cardinal which is a factor of both 24 and 36.

Example: Determine G.C.F.$(28,42)$.

Solution: Proceeding as in the preceding example, we have

$$F(28) = \{1,2,4,7,14,28\}$$

and

$$F(42) = \{1,2,3,6,7,14,21,42\}$$

Hence

$$CF(28,42) = F(28) \cap F(42)$$
$$= \{1,2,7,14\}, \text{ and}$$
$$G.C.F.(28,42) = 14$$

Thus 14 is the largest cardinal which is a factor of both 28 and 42.

If one again studies the prime factors listed in Table 5-1, he can observe the following important principle:

The greatest common factor of two cardinal numbers a and b is the product of the lowest powers of the prime factors which occur in the prime factorization of both a and b.

If one investigates the concept of G.C.F. a little farther, he can observe that there are some cardinal numbers a and b such that G.C.F.$(a,b) = 1$. For example, G.C.F.$(2,3) = 1$, G.C.F.$(4,9) = 1$, G.C.F.$(3,4) = 1$, and so forth. Such pairs of cardinal numbers occur frequently in the study of rational numbers and are called *relatively prime* numbers.

Definition 5-10: If a and b are cardinal numbers and the G.C.F.$(a,b) = 1$, then a and b are called **relatively prime.**

This is how one tells if a numeral for a rational number is in reduced form, by checking to see if numerator and denominator are relatively prime.

We have now discussed several important aspects of multiplication of cardinal numbers and are now ready to proceed to the climax of this chapter.

EXERCISE SET 5-4

1. Use the Sieve of Eratosthenes to determine all primes p such that
   (a) $p \leqslant 25$
   (b) $p \leqslant 50$
   (c) $p \leqslant 75$
   (d) $p \leqslant 100$

2. (a) Give a definition for a set $\{a,b,c\}$ of relatively prime numbers.
   (b) Using the results of part (a), decide which of the following are sets of relatively prime numbers.

   $\{3,4,10\}$ $\{26,39,65\}$
   $\{63,77,105\}$ $\{17,18,34\}$
   (c) Could the definition of relative primeness be extended to include any arbitrary finite set of cardinals?

3. Write the prime factorization of each of the following.
   (a) 26   (e) 252
   (b) 48   (f) 225
   (c) 625   (g) 540
   (d) 375   (h) 576

4. Use sets and show in detail how to determine the L.C.M. and G.C.F. for each of the following pairs of cardinal numbers.
   (a) 24 and 48
   (b) 36 and 48
   (c) 44 and 66
   (d) 38 and 52
   (e) 42 and 98

5. Work problem four by making use of the Prime Factorization Theorem.

6. (a) Give a Definition for the L.C.M. of a set $\{a,b,c\}$ of three cardinal numbers.
   (b) Using the result of part (a), determine the L.C.M. of each of the following sets.
   $\{24,36,54\}, \{16,48,96\}, \{39,52,54\}$
   (c) Give a definition for the G.C.F. of a set $\{a,b,c\}$ of three cardinal numbers.
   (d) Using the result of part (c), determine the G.C.F. of each of the following sets.
   $\{48,54,72\}, \{16,24,72\}, \{20,50,125\}$
   (e) Could the definitions given by you in parts (a) and (c) be extended to cover any arbitrary finite set of cardinals?

5. Positional Notation and Multiplication

We shall begin by returning to a consideration of positional notation and by doing so relate the place-value numeral to multiplication. Once this has been done, we shall consider some algorithms dealing with addition, subtraction, and multiplication.

Let us begin by rewriting (in a special way) the numeral 374698.

$374698 = 300000 + 70000 + 4000 + 600 + 90 + 8$ Def. 3-1

$\qquad = 3 \cdot 100000 + 7 \cdot 10000 + 4 \cdot 1000 + 6 \cdot 100 + 9 \cdot 10 + 8$ Def. 5-1

$\qquad = 3 \cdot (10 \cdot 10 \cdot 10 \cdot 10 \cdot 10) + 7 \cdot (10 \cdot 10 \cdot 10 \cdot 10) +$

$\qquad\quad 4 \cdot (10 \cdot 10 \cdot 10) + 6 \cdot (10 \cdot 10) + 9 \cdot 10 + 8$ Def. 5-1

$\qquad = 3 \cdot 10^5 + 7 \cdot 10^4 + 4 \cdot 10^3 + 6 \cdot 10^2 + 9 \cdot 10^1 + 8$ Def. 5-3

Similarly, we find that

$\qquad 78621 = 7 \cdot 10^4 + 8 \cdot 10^3 + 6 \cdot 10^2 + 2 \cdot 10^1 + 1,$

$\qquad 5982 = 5 \cdot 10^3 + 9 \cdot 10^2 + 8 \cdot 10^1 + 2, \text{ and}$

$\qquad 6789447 = 6 \cdot 10^6 + 7 \cdot 10^5 + 8 \cdot 10^4 + 9 \cdot 10^3 + 4 \cdot 10^2 + 4 \cdot 10^1 + 7.$

In each case, the numeral on the right side of the equals sign is called the *expanded form* of the numeral for the given cardinal number. In each of the examples listed we note that the largest exponent on 10 is one less than the number of digits in the original place-value numeral. Hence it is apparently possible to simply count the number of digits in the given numeral, and start writing the expanded form, decreasing the exponent on 10 by one in each term to the right. In the general case we define the expanded form as follows.

Definition 5-11: If $d_n d_{n-1} \ldots d_2 d_1 d_0$ is a place-value numeral for a cardinal number n, then the **expanded form** of the numeral for n is $d_n \cdot 10^n + d_{n-1} \cdot 10^{n-1} + \ldots + d_2 \cdot 10^2 + d_1 \cdot 10^1 + d_0$. Since both numerals name n, we also write $d_n d_{n-1} \ldots d_2 d_1 d_0 = d_n \cdot 10^n + d_{n-1} \cdot 10^{n-1} + \ldots + d_2 \cdot 10^2 + d_1 \cdot 10^1 + d_0$.

In some problems, it may be convenient to use $d_0 \cdot 10^0$ instead of d_0, but this is permissible since we have by Definition 5-4 that $10^0 = 1$ and 1 is the multiplicative identity.

We are now in a position to investigate the algorithms which were mentioned in Sections 3-2, 4-3, and 5-1. We shall begin by considering addition problems in which "carrying" is involved.

a. An addition algorithm

Since "carrying" is used as a convenience in many addition problems, let us try to determine what is meant by the process, and further, let us try to see what properties of arithmetic justify the process. We shall consider the following example.

Example:

$$
\begin{array}{r}
876 \\
+\,659 \\
\end{array}
\quad \text{often worked as} \quad
\begin{array}{r}
11 \\
876 \\
+\,659 \\
\hline
1535 \\
\end{array}
$$

Solution: We shall use the expanded form (Definition 5-11) to investigate the algorithm.

$876 + 659 = (8 \cdot 10^2 + 7 \cdot 10^1 + 6) + (6 \cdot 10^2 + 5 \cdot 10^1 + 9)$ Def. 5-11

$\quad = (8 \cdot 10^2 + 7 \cdot 10^1) + \left([6 + (6 \cdot 10^2 + 5 \cdot 10^1)] + 9\right)$ Thm. 3-4

$\quad = (8 \cdot 10^2 + 7 \cdot 10^1) + \left([(6 \cdot 10^2 + 5 \cdot 10^1) + 6] + 9\right)$ Thm. 3-3

$\quad = (8 \cdot 10^2 + 7 \cdot 10^1) + [(6 \cdot 10^2 + 5 \cdot 10^1) + (6 + 9)]$ Thm. 3-4

$\quad = \left(8 \cdot 10^2 + [7 \cdot 10^1 + (6 \cdot 10^2 + 5 \cdot 10^1)]\right) + (6 + 9)$ Thm. 3-4

$\quad = \left(8 \cdot 10^2 + [(6 \cdot 10^2 + 5 \cdot 10^1) + 7 \cdot 10^1]\right) + (6 + 9)$ Thm. 3-3

$\quad = (8 \cdot 10^2 + 6 \cdot 10^2) + [(5 \cdot 10^1 + 7 \cdot 10^1) + (6 + 9)]$ Thm. 3-4

$\quad = (8 + 6) \cdot 10^2 + [(5 + 7) \cdot 10^1 + (6 + 9)]$ Thm. 5-7

$\quad = (8 + 6) \cdot 10^2 + [(5 + 7) \cdot 10^1 + 15]$ Def. 3-1

$\quad = (8 + 6) \cdot 10^2 + [(5 + 7) \cdot 10^1 + (1 \cdot 10^1 + 5)]$ Def. 5-11

$\quad = (8 + 6) \cdot 10^2 + \left([(5 + 7) \cdot 10^1 + 1 \cdot 10^1] + 5\right)$ Thm. 3-4

$\quad = (8 + 6) \cdot 10^2 + \left([(5 + 7) + 1] \cdot 10^1 + 5\right)$ [4]   Thm. 5-7

$\quad = (8 + 6) \cdot 10^2 + [(12 + 1) \cdot 10^1 + 5]$ Def. 3-1

$\quad = (8 + 6) \cdot 10^2 + [13 \cdot 10^1 + 5]$ Def. 3-1

$\quad = (8 + 6) \cdot 10^2 + [(1 \cdot 10^1 + 3) \cdot 10^1 + 5]$ Def. 5-11

[4] Here, one ten has been "carried" to the tens column.

$$= (8 + 6) \cdot 10^2 + [(1 \cdot 10^1) \cdot 10^1 + (3 \cdot 10^1 + 5)] \qquad \text{Thm. 5-7}$$

$$= (8 + 6) \cdot 10^2 + [1 \cdot (10^1 \cdot 10^1) + (3 \cdot 10^1 + 5)] \qquad \text{Thm. 5-3}$$

$$= (8 + 6) \cdot 10^2 + [1 \cdot 10^2 + (3 \cdot 10^1 + 5)] \qquad \text{Thm. 5-11}$$

$$= [(8 + 6) \cdot 10^2 + 1 \cdot 10^2] + (3 \cdot 10^1 + 5) \qquad \text{Thm. 3-4}$$

$$= [(8 + 6) + 1] \cdot 10^2 + (3 \cdot 10^1 + 5)\,^5 \qquad \text{Thm. 5-7}$$

$$= (14 + 1) \cdot 10^2 + (3 \cdot 10^1 + 5) \qquad \text{Def. 3-1}$$

$$= 15 \cdot 10^2 + (3 \cdot 10^1 + 5) \qquad \text{Def. 3-1}$$

$$= (1 \cdot 10^1 + 5) \cdot 10^2 + (3 \cdot 10^1 + 5) \qquad \text{Def. 5-11}$$

$$= [(1 \cdot 10^1) \cdot 10^2 + 5 \cdot 10^2] + (3 \cdot 10^1 + 5)\,^6 \qquad \text{Thm. 5-7}$$

$$= [1 \cdot (10^1 \cdot 10^2) + 5 \cdot 10^2] + (3 \cdot 10^1 + 5) \qquad \text{Thm. 5-3}$$

$$= (1 \cdot 10^3 + 5 \cdot 10^2) + (3 \cdot 10^1 + 5) \qquad \text{Thm. 5-11}$$

$$= 1 \cdot 10^3 + 5 \cdot 10^2 + 3 \cdot 10^1 + 5 \qquad \text{Thm. 3-4}$$

$$= 1535 \qquad \text{Def. 5-11}$$

In the example just worked we have gone into considerable detail in order to show what properties and definitions are required in order to "carry" in addition. If one studies the solution he can observe the important fact that in particular, "carrying" necessarily relies directly on the distributive property. Further, we observe that the answer obtained when the problem is worked step by step is precisely that which results by use of the algorithm. The chief advantage of being able to explain such a problem in detail is that we may now work such problems without having to work with sets and still be assured that the results are valid.

b. A subtraction algorithm

Let us now work a subtraction problem to see what, exactly, takes place when "borrowing" is involved. Again, we shall make use of the expanded form of numerals. From this point on we shall begin to combine steps and occasionally leave it to the reader to decide what properties are used.

Example:

$$
\begin{array}{r} 86 \\ -49 \\ \hline \end{array}
\qquad \text{often worked as} \qquad
\begin{array}{r} {}^{1}\!86 \\ -49 \\ \hline 37 \end{array}
$$

---

[5] Here, one hundred has been "carried" to the hundreds column.
[6] Here, one thousand has been "carried" to the thousands column.

Solution:

$$86 - 49 = (8 \cdot 10^1 + 6) - (4 \cdot 10^1 + 9) \qquad \text{Def. 5-11}$$
$$= [(7 + 1) \cdot 10^1 + 6] - (4 \cdot 10^1 + 9) \qquad \text{Def. 3-1}$$
$$= [(7 \cdot 10^1 + 1 \cdot 10^1) + 6] - (4 \cdot 10^1 + 9) \qquad \text{Thm. 5-7}$$
$$= [7 \cdot 10^1 + (1 \cdot 10^1 + 6)] - (4 \cdot 10^1 + 9) \qquad \text{Thm. 3-4}$$
$$= (7 \cdot 10^1 + 16) - (4 \cdot 10^1 + 9) \qquad \text{Def. 5-11}$$
$$= (7 \cdot 10^i - 4 \cdot 10^1) + (16 - 9) \qquad \text{Why?}$$
$$= (7 - 4) \cdot 10^1 + (16 - 9) \qquad \text{Thm. 5-8}$$
$$= 3 \cdot 10^1 + 7 \qquad \text{Def. 4-6}$$
$$= 37 \qquad \text{Def. 5-11}$$

The remarks concerning distributivity and the addition algorithm hold for the subtraction problem just worked except that here we are concerned with distributivity with respect to differences. The reader will note that Theorem 4-7 was also used, but that in order to do so we had to "borrow" in order to guarantee the existence of the difference $16 - 9$. Indeed, this is the crux of the problem — to be able to guarantee that all differences involved do, in fact, exist.

c. A multiplication algorithm

By this stage, the reader has observed the importance of the distributive property in numerical problems. We shall now work a multiplication problem and leave it to the reader to supply all justification required.

Example:

$$
\begin{array}{r}
^{21}\\
26\\
\times\,42\\
\hline
52\\
104\\
\hline
1092
\end{array}
$$

Solution: Using the expanded forms of numerals, we have

$$26 \cdot 42 = (2 \cdot 10^1 + 6) \cdot (4 \cdot 10^1 + 2)$$
$$= [(2 \cdot 10^1) \cdot (4 \cdot 10^1) + (2 \cdot 10^1) \cdot 2] + [6 \cdot (4 \cdot 10^1) + 6 \cdot 2]$$
$$= (2 \cdot 4) \cdot 10^2 + \left([(2 \cdot 2) \cdot 10^1 + (6 \cdot 4) \cdot 10^1] + 6 \cdot 2 \right)$$
$$= 8 \cdot 10^2 + [(4 + 24) \cdot 10^1 + 12]$$
$$= 8 \cdot 10^2 + (28 \cdot 10^1 + 12)$$
$$= (8 \cdot 10^2 + 2 \cdot 10^2) + [8 \cdot 10^1 + (1 \cdot 10^1 + 2)]$$

$$= (8 \cdot 10^2 + 2 \cdot 10^2) + [(8 \cdot 10^1 + 1 \cdot 10^1) + 2]$$
$$= (8 + 2) \cdot 10^2 + [(8 + 1) \cdot 10^1 + 2]$$
$$= 10 \cdot 10^2 + (9 \cdot 10^1 + 2)$$
$$= 10^1 \cdot 10^2 + (9 \cdot 10^1 + 2)$$
$$= 10^3 + (9 \cdot 10^1 + 2)$$
$$= 1 \cdot 10^3 + (9 \cdot 10^1 + 2)$$
$$= (1 \cdot 10^3 + 0 \cdot 10^2) + (9 \cdot 10^1 + 2)$$
$$= 1 \cdot 10^3 + 0 \cdot 10^2 + 9 \cdot 10^1 + 2$$
$$= 1092$$

Here again, we note that the distributive property is of extreme importance in the justification of the algorithm.

There are, besides the algorithms already discussed, several others which are useful and interesting. Some of these are listed for your consideration in the problem set below.

EXERCISE SET 5-5

1. Change each of the following place-value numerals to a numeral in expanded form.
   (a) 576
   (b) 35,892
   (c) 6,770,158
   (d) 9,283,034,832

2. Change each of the following from expanded form to a place-value numeral.
   (a) $2 \cdot 10^5 + 0 \cdot 10^4 + 7 \cdot 10^3 + 6 \cdot 10^2 + 8 \cdot 10^1 + 1$
   (b) $7 \cdot 10^7 + 8 \cdot 10^6 + 0 \cdot 10^5 + 0 \cdot 10^4 + 2 \cdot 10^3 + 9 \cdot 10^2 + 5$
   (c) $5 \cdot 10^6 + 6 \cdot 10^5 + 0 \cdot 10^4 + 4 \cdot 10^3 + 0 \cdot 10^2 + 8 \cdot 10^1 + 0$
   (d) $4 \cdot 10^4 + 3 \cdot 10^3 + 0 \cdot 10^2 + 0 \cdot 10^1 + 9$

   Justify each step of problems 3 through 9 below.

	Step
3. $29 + 73 = (2 \cdot 10 + 9) + (7 \cdot 10 + 3)$	(a)
$= 2 \cdot 10 + [(9 + 7 \cdot 10) + 3]$	(b)
$= 2 \cdot 10 + [(7 \cdot 10 + 9) + 3]$	(c)
$= (2 \cdot 10 + 7 \cdot 10) + (9 + 3)$	(d)
$= (2 + 7) \cdot 10 + (9 + 3)$	(e)
$= 9 \cdot 10 + 12$	(f)
$= 9 \cdot 10 + (10 + 2)$	(g)
$= (9 \cdot 10 + 10) + 2$	(h)
$= (9 \cdot 10 + 1 \cdot 10) + 2$	(i)
$= (9 + 1) \cdot 10 + 2$	(j)

$$= 10 \cdot 10 + 2 \qquad \text{(k)}$$
$$= 10^2 + 2 \qquad \text{(l)}$$
$$= 1 \cdot 10^2 + 2 \qquad \text{(m)}$$
$$= (1 \cdot 10^2 + 2) + 0 \qquad \text{(n)}$$
$$= 1 \cdot 10^2 + (2 + 0) \qquad \text{(o)}$$
$$= 1 \cdot 10^2 + (0 + 2) \qquad \text{(p)}$$
$$= 1 \cdot 10^2 + (0 \cdot 10 + 2) \qquad \text{(q)}$$
$$= 1 \cdot 10^2 + 0 \cdot 10 + 2 \qquad \text{(r)}$$
$$= 102 \qquad \text{(s)}$$

Step

4. $37 + 84 = (3 \cdot 10 + 7) + (8 \cdot 10 + 4)$ (a)
$$= 3 \cdot 10 + [(7 + 8 \cdot 10) + 4] \qquad \text{(b)}$$
$$= 3 \cdot 10 + [(8 \cdot 10 + 7) + 4] \qquad \text{(c)}$$
$$= (3 \cdot 10 + 8 \cdot 10) + (7 + 4) \qquad \text{(d)}$$
$$= (3 + 8) \cdot 10 + (7 + 4) \qquad \text{(e)}$$
$$= 11 \cdot 10 + 11 \qquad \text{(f)}$$
$$= (10 + 1) \cdot 10 + (10 + 1) \qquad \text{(g)}$$
$$= [(10 \cdot 10) + 1 \cdot 10] + (10 + 1) \qquad \text{(h)}$$
$$= 10 \cdot 10 + [(1 \cdot 10 + 10) + 1] \qquad \text{(i)}$$
$$= 10^2 + [(1 \cdot 10 + 10) + 1] \qquad \text{(j)}$$
$$= 1 \cdot 10^2 + [(1 \cdot 10 + 1 \cdot 10) + 1] \qquad \text{(k)}$$
$$= 1 \cdot 10^2 + [(1 + 1) \cdot 10 + 1] \qquad \text{(l)}$$
$$= 1 \cdot 10^2 + (2 \cdot 10 + 1) \qquad \text{(m)}$$
$$= 1 \cdot 10^2 + 2 \cdot 10 + 1 \qquad \text{(n)}$$
$$= 121 \qquad \text{(o)}$$

Step

5. $39 - 27 = (3 \cdot 10 + 9) - (2 \cdot 10 + 7)$ (a)
$$= (3 \cdot 10 - 2 \cdot 10) + (9 - 7) \qquad \text{(b)}$$
$$= (3 - 2) \cdot 10 + (9 - 7) \qquad \text{(c)}$$
$$= 1 \cdot 10 + 2 \qquad \text{(d)}$$
$$= 12 \qquad \text{(e)}$$

Step

6. $57 - 39 = (5 \cdot 10 + 7) - (3 \cdot 10 + 9)$ (a)
$$= [(4 + 1) \cdot 10 + 7] - (3 \cdot 10 + 9) \qquad \text{(b)}$$
$$= [(4 \cdot 10 + 1 \cdot 10) + 7] - (3 \cdot 10 + 9) \qquad \text{(c)}$$
$$= [4 \cdot 10 + (1 \cdot 10 + 7)] - (3 \cdot 10 + 9) \qquad \text{(d)}$$
$$= [4 \cdot 10 + (10 + 7)] - (3 \cdot 10 + 9) \qquad \text{(e)}$$
$$= (4 \cdot 10 + 17) - (3 \cdot 10 + 9) \qquad \text{(f)}$$
$$= (4 \cdot 10 - 3 \cdot 10) + (17 - 9) \qquad \text{(g)}$$
$$= (4 - 3) \cdot 10 + (17 - 9) \qquad \text{(h)}$$
$$= 1 \cdot 10 + 8 \qquad \text{(i)}$$
$$= 18 \qquad \text{(j)}$$

Step

7. $37 \cdot 8 = (3 \cdot 10 + 7) \cdot 8$ (a)

$= (3 \cdot 10) \cdot 8 + 7 \cdot 8$ (b)

$= 8 \cdot (3 \cdot 10) + 7 \cdot 8$ (c)

$= (8 \cdot 3) \cdot 10 + 7 \cdot 8$ (d)

$= 24 \cdot 10 + 56$ (e)

$= (2 \cdot 10 + 4) \cdot 10 + (5 \cdot 10 + 6)$ (f)

$= [(2 \cdot 10) \cdot 10 + 4 \cdot 10] + (5 \cdot 10 + 6)$ (g)

$= [2 \cdot (10 \cdot 10) + 4 \cdot 10] + (5 \cdot 10 + 6)$ (h)

$= [2 \cdot 100 + 4 \cdot 10] + (5 \cdot 10 + 6)$ (i)

$= 2 \cdot 100 + [(4 \cdot 10 + 5 \cdot 10) + 6]$ (j)

$= 2 \cdot 10^2 + [(4 \cdot 10 + 5 \cdot 10) + 6]$ (k)

$= 2 \cdot 10^2 + [(4 + 5) \cdot 10 + 6]$ (l)

$= 2 \cdot 10^2 + (9 \cdot 10 + 6)$ (m)

$= 2 \cdot 10^2 + 9 \cdot 10 + 6$ (n)

$= 296$ (o)

Step

8. $14 \cdot 16 = 14 \cdot (1 \cdot 10 + 6)$ (a)

$= 14 \cdot (1 \cdot 10) + 14 \cdot 6$ (b)

$= 14 \cdot 10 + 14 \cdot 6$ (c)

$= (1 \cdot 10 + 4) \cdot 10 + (1 \cdot 10 + 4) \cdot 6$ (d)

$= [(1 \cdot 10) \cdot 10 + 4 \cdot 10] + [(1 \cdot 10) \cdot 6 + 4 \cdot 6]$ (e)

$= [1 \cdot (10 \cdot 10) + 4 \cdot 10] + [1 \cdot (10 \cdot 6) + 4 \cdot 6]$ (f)

$= (1 \cdot 100 + 4 \cdot 10) + [1 \cdot (10 \cdot 6) + 24]$ (g)

$= (1 \cdot 100 + 4 \cdot 10) + [1 \cdot (6 \cdot 10) + 24]$ (h)

$= (1 \cdot 100 + 4 \cdot 10) + [(1 \cdot 6) \cdot 10 + 24]$ (i)

$= (1 \cdot 100 + 4 \cdot 10) + [6 \cdot 10 + 24]$ (j)

$= (1 \cdot 100 + 4 \cdot 10) + [6 \cdot 10 + (2 \cdot 10 + 4)]$ (k)

$= [1 \cdot 100 + (4 \cdot 10 + 6 \cdot 10)] + (2 \cdot 10 + 4)$ (l)

$= [(1 \cdot 100 + (4 + 6) \cdot 10] + (2 \cdot 10 + 4)$ (m)

$= (1 \cdot 100 + 100) + (2 \cdot 10 + 4)$ (n)

$= (1 \cdot 100 + 1 \cdot 100) + (2 \cdot 10 + 4)$ (o)

$= (1 + 1) \cdot 100 + (2 \cdot 10 + 4)$ (p)

$= 2 \cdot 100 + (2 \cdot 10 + 4)$ (q)

$= 2 \cdot 10^2 + (2 \cdot 10 + 4)$ (r)

$= 2 \cdot 10^2 + 2 \cdot 10 + 4$ (s)

$= 224$ (t)

$$\begin{array}{lll}
& & Step \\
9. \ 68 \cdot 100 = (6 \cdot 10 + 8) \cdot 100 & & (a) \\
 = (6 \cdot 10) \cdot 100 + 8 \cdot 100 & & (b) \\
 = 6 \cdot (10 \cdot 100) + 8 \cdot 100 & & (c) \\
 = 6 \cdot 1000 + 8 \cdot 100 & & (d) \\
 = 6 \cdot 10^3 + 8 \cdot 10^2 & & (e) \\
 = 6 \cdot 10^3 + 8 \cdot 10^2 + 0 & & (f) \\
 = 6 \cdot 10^3 + 8 \cdot 10^2 + 0 + 0 & & (g) \\
 = 6 \cdot 10^3 + 8 \cdot 10^2 + 0 \cdot 10 + 0 & & (h) \\
 = 6800 & & (i)
\end{array}$$

10. We are aware that if we multiply a cardinal number n
    (a) by 10, the answer consists of the digits of n with a zero juxtaposed on the right
    (b) by 10^2, the answer consists of the digits of n with two zeros juxtaposed on the right
    (c) by 10^3, the answer consists of the digits of n with three zeros juxtaposed on the right, and so forth.
    (d) Prove that for a given cardinal number k,

$$(d_n d_{n-1} \ldots d_1 d_0) \cdot 10^k = d_n d_{n-1} \ldots d_1 d_0 \underbrace{000 \ldots 000.}_{k \text{ zeros}}$$

11. Apply the algorithm of problem ten to calculate each of the following products.
    (a) $32 \cdot 100$
    (b) $436 \cdot 10^4$
    (c) $26 \cdot 3000$
    (d) $200 \cdot 400$

12. Some of us are familiar with the algorithm for multiplying a number which ends in five by itself. Prove that this is a valid algorithm.
    (Hint: $65 \cdot 65$: $6 \cdot 7 = 42$ and $5 \cdot 5 = 25$, so $65 \cdot 65 = 4225$
    $75 \cdot 75$: $7 \cdot 8 = 56$ and $5 \cdot 5 = 25$, so $75 \cdot 75 = 5625$ etc.)

13. Each of the following problems involves at least two distinct algorithms. Work the problems and identify the algorithm used.
    (a) $25 \cdot 250$
    (b) $350 \cdot 350$
    (c) $450 \cdot 4500$
    (d) $34 \cdot 80$
    (e) $42 \cdot 250$

14. A student is asked to find the product $52 \cdot 44$. Instead of thinking

$$\begin{array}{r}
52 \\
\times 44 \\
\hline
208 \ , \\
208 \\
\hline
2288
\end{array}$$ the student thinks -- fifty 44's and two 44's

would be 2200 and 88 or 2288. What property of multiplication did this student use? Is this always a valid method of multiplication? Why or why not?

15. Another student is asked to find 49·68. He reasons that fifty 68's less one 68 would be 3400 less 68. So his answer is 3332. The teacher, not having had much mathematics could not understand how the student obtained his answer. What didn't this teacher know about mathematics?

Chapter summary

In this chapter we used Cartesian product sets to define multiplication of cardinals. As soon as this was done we proceeded to establish the familiar properties of multiplication. In particular we were able to show that

(1) products always exist and are unique,

(2) multiplication is commutative,

(3) multiplication is associative,

(4) multiplication is distributive with respect to addition and subtraction,

(5) there is a unique identity element, one, and

(6) cancellation and the converse of cancellation are possible.

Having established these, we next introduced exponents in order to discuss with greater clarity certain types of factors. This lead to a consideration of prime factors of cardinals and culminated in the Fundamental Theorem of Arithmetic. The Fundamental Theorem was then used in conjunction with the Sieve of Eratosthenes to discuss least common multiples and greatest common factors of sets of cardinal numbers. In this connection it was possible to show the interrelation of the Fundamental Theorem, the Sieve of Eratosthenes, and sets to the concepts of multiples and factors. The final topic of discussion concerned the relationship of multiplication to addition and subtraction. Using expanded notation we were able to use properties of multiplication to give a more detailed description of the concepts often referred to as "carrying" and "borrowing" and thus complete the discussion of addition and subtraction algorithms.

CHAPTER 6
Division
of cardinal
numbers

1. Definition of Division

In this chapter we shall introduce by use of sets the concept of division of cardinals and then discuss some of its properties which are of particular interest.

We begin by considering what might occur if a child is told to share a certain collection of objects with his playmates. The child may proceed to pass out the objects in various ways, but one way to make the sharing as fair as possible is to pass out the objects one at a time until he no longer has enough for another time around. If the child was to share seven cookies with two playmates, he finds that if he passes the cookies one at a time, each of the three children involved has two cookies and there is one cookie left over. In distributing the cookies the child went twice-around, each time giving one cookie to each of the three involved in the sharing. If we now abstract such situations as just mentioned we find a reasonable way to define division of cardinal numbers.

Definition 6-1: If a and b are cardinal numbers and $b \neq 0$, then a divided by b yields an ordered pair of cardinal numbers (q,r) which is determined as follows:

1. Select A and B with $n(A) = a$ and $n(B) = b$ respectively.
2. Map B one-to-one onto mutually disjoint subsets, $A_1, A_2, \ldots, A_q$ of A until such a mapping is no longer possible.
3. Form $Q = \{A_1, A_2, \ldots, A_q\}$ and $R = c(A_1 \cup A_2 \cup \ldots \cup A_q)$.
4. Define $n(Q) = q$ and $n(R) = r$.
5. Form (q,r).

The division is denoted $a \div b$ yields (q,r). q is called the **quotient** and r is called the **remainder**.

Each of the disjoint subsets formed in part (2) corresponds to one time around, giving each person one object. The numbers of times around taken to distribute the objects corresponds to $n(Q)$ in part (4) of the definition. R contains the elements left over after the completion of the one-to-one mappings of part (2) of the definition and $n(R)$ is the cardinality of this set.

Example: Determine $8 \div 3$.

Solution: 1. Select $A = \{a,b,c,d,e,f,g,h\}$ with $n(A) = 8$ and
$\qquad\qquad$ $B = \{p,q,r\}$ with $n(B) = 3$.
$\quad\quad$ 2. Form by means of one-to-one onto mappings

$$B \sim \{a,b,c\} = A_1$$

$$B \sim \{d,e,f\} = A_2$$

$\qquad$ No further such mapping is possible.
$\quad\quad$ 3. Form $Q = \{A_1, A_2\}$ and
$\qquad\qquad$ $R = c(A_1 \cup A_2) = c\{a,b,c,d,e,f\} = \{g,h\}$.
$\quad\quad$ 4. $n(Q) = 2$ and $n(R) = 2$
$\quad\quad$ 5. $(q,r) = (2,2)$
Thus $8 \div 3$ yields $(2,2)$.

As a second example, consider the following:

Example: Determine $12 \div 2$.

Solution: 1. Select $A = \{a,b,c,d,e,f,g,h,i,j,k,l\}$ with $n(A) = 12$ and
$\qquad\qquad$ $B = \{y,z\}$ with $n(B) = 2$.
$\quad\quad$ 2. Form by means of one-to-one onto mappings

$$B \sim \{a,b\} = A_1$$

$$B \sim \{c,d\} = A_2$$

$$B \sim \{e,f\} = A_3$$

$$B \sim \{g,h\} = A_4$$

$$B \sim \{i,j\} = A_5$$

$$B \sim \{k,l\} = A_6$$

$\qquad$ No further such mapping is possible.
$\quad\quad$ 3. Form $Q = \{A_1, A_2, A_3, A_4, A_5, A_6\}$ and
$\qquad\qquad$ $R = c(A_1 \cup A_2 \cup A_3 \cup A_4 \cup A_5 \cup A_6)$
$\qquad\qquad\quad$ $= c\{a,b,c,d,e,f,g,h,i,j,k,l\}$
$\qquad\qquad\quad$ $= \emptyset$
$\quad\quad$ 4. $n(Q) = 6$ and $n(R) = 0$
$\quad\quad$ 5. $(q,r) = (6,0)$
Hence $12 \div 2$ yields $(6,0)$.

It appears that Definition 6-1 does give the results to which we are accustomed. However, it might be profitable to discuss the existence and uniqueness of the quotient and remainder in order to be assured that Definition 6-1 is a workable definition in all of the cases we wish to consider.

Theorem 6-1: The quotient and remainder of Definition 6-1 always exist.

Proof: Note that since a and b are cardinal numbers, it is always possible to select finite sets A and B with $n(A) = a$ and $n(B) = b$. Next, note that A, the selected representative of cardinal number a, is empty or it is not. If $A = \emptyset$, then no mapping of B onto A is possible and therefore $Q = \emptyset$, and $R = \emptyset$. Q and R are both finite and hence belong to a cardinal number, namely zero. Thus $n(Q) = 0$ and $n(R) = 0$ and we form $(0,0)$.

If A is not empty, there are three cases to consider. $(1)\, a > b$, $(2)\, a = b$, and $(3)\, a < b$. We shall discuss case (1) and leave cases (2) and (3) for the reader to complete.

Case (1): Since both A and B are finite sets, and $n(A) > n(B)$, B is equivalent to at least one subset of A, so that there is a set A_1, such that $B \sim A_1$ and $A_1 \subset A$. Now if $n[c(A_1)] \geqslant n(B)$, then B is equivalent to at least one subset of $c(A_1)$. Hence there is a set A_2 such that $B \sim A_2$ and $A_2 \subset A$. Continuing this process, we see that by using one-to-one onto mappings, sets $A_1\ A_2, \ldots, A_q$, can be constructed until the onto mappings are no longer possible. Since we have a finite number of sets $A_1, A_2, \ldots, A_q$, these sets are elements of a finite set, call it Q. The set of elements left over after the completion of the mapping process is finite since we started with a finite set A. Hence sets Q and R of step (3) exist and are finite. Because Q and R are finite, they each belong to a cardinal number. Consequently $n(Q) = q$ and $n(R) = r$ can be determined. Once it is known that q and r exist, it is always possible to form (q,r). ∎

It should be pointed out that Definition 6-1 guarantees $r < b$, for if not, then step (2) of the definition has not been completed. Furthermore, the "remainder set," R, is either empty or not empty so that $r \geqslant 0$. Thus, once we have completed a division problem it is always necessary to have a remainder r which satisfies the condition

$$0 \leqslant r < b.$$

Let us now show that if the sets selected for a division problem satisfy (1) of Definition 6-1, then the choice of selection has no effect on q and r. That is, we shall show that answers are unique.

Theorem 6-2: The quotient and remainder of Definition 6-1 are unique.

Proof: The three cases which require consideration are $(1)\, a > b$, $(2)\, a = b$, and $(3)\, a < b$. We shall consider case (1) and leave the other two cases for the reader.

Part 1: 1. Select $A = \{x_1, \ldots, x_b, x_{b+1}, \ldots, x_{2b}, x_{2b+1}, \ldots, x_{3b}, \ldots, x_{qb+1}, \ldots, x_a\}$ and
$B = \{y_1, y_2, \ldots, y_b\}$ so that $n(A) = a$ and $n(B) = b$.

2. $B \sim \{x_1, \ldots, x_b\} = A_1$
$B \sim \{x_{b+1}, \ldots, x_{2b}\} = A_2$
$B \sim \{x_{2b+1}, \ldots, x_{3b}\} = A_3$
. . . .
$B \sim \{x_{(q-1)b+1}, \ldots, x_{qb}\} = A_q$
and elements $x_{qb+1}, \ldots, x_a$ are left over when the mappings are complete.
3. Form $Q = \{A_1, A_2, \ldots, A_q\}$ and $R = \{x_{qb+1}, x_{qb+2}, \ldots, x_a\}$.
4. $n(Q) = q$ and $n(R) = r$ where it is assumed that $0 \leqslant r \leqslant b$.

Part 2: Now select different set representatives for a and b.

1. Select $\overline{A} = \{s_1, \ldots, s_b, s_{b+1}, \ldots, s_{2b}, s_{2b+1}, \ldots, s_{3b}, \ldots, s_{qb+1}, \ldots, s_a\}$ and
$\overline{B} = \{t_1, t_2, \ldots, t_b\}$.
2. Then $\overline{B} \sim \{s_1, \ldots, s_b\} = \overline{A}_1$
$\overline{B} \sim \{s_{b+1}, \ldots, s_{2b}\} = \overline{A}_2$
$\overline{B} \sim \{s_{2b+1}, \ldots, s_{3b}\} = \overline{A}_3$
. . . .
$\overline{B} \sim \{s_{(q-1)b+1}, \ldots, s_{qb}\} = \overline{A}_q$
and elements $s_{qb+1}, \ldots, s_a$ are left over when the mappings are complete.
3. Form $\overline{Q} = \{\overline{A}_1, \overline{A}_2, \ldots, \overline{A}_q\}$ and $\overline{R} = \{s_{qb+1}, \ldots, s_a\}$.
4. $n(\overline{Q}) = \overline{q}$ and $n(R) = \overline{r}$ where it is assumed that $0 \leqslant \overline{r} < b$.

Now by comparing Q and $\overline{Q}$, and R and $\overline{R}$ respectively, we see that $Q \sim \overline{Q}$ and $R \sim \overline{R}$. Consequently $q = \overline{q}$ and $r = \overline{r}$ so that q and r as determined by Definition 6-1 are unique. ∎

Thus we have a workable definition for division of cardinal numbers. That is, the quotient and remainder always exist and are unique under Definition 6-1.

EXERCISE SET 6-1

1. Using Definition 6-1, determine the quotient and remainder for each of the following.
   (a) $17 \div 3$
   (b) $32 \div 14$
   (c) $23 \div 5$
   (d) $13 \div 4$
2. Give an example of a division problem which will show that the set R might be $\emptyset$.
3. If one allows remainders r such that $r \leqslant b$ instead of $r < b$, does this have any effect on the uniqueness of answers for division? Explain your answer and give numerical examples to support your claim.
4. In Definition 6-1, do sets A and B have to be chosen so that $A \cap B = \emptyset$?
5. Explain what might happen in division if in part (2) of Definition 6-1 we omit the words *mutually disjoint*.

2. Properties of Division

We have found that using Definition 6-1 gives the results

$$8 \div 3 \text{ yields } (2,2)$$

and

$$12 \div 2 \text{ yields } (6,0)$$

Similarly we find that

$$27 \div \ 4 \text{ yields } (6,3)$$
$$39 \div 16 \text{ yields } (2,7)$$
$$0 \div \ 5 \text{ yields } (0,0)$$
$$4 \div \ 9 \text{ yields } (0,4)$$

and in general,

$$a \div b \text{ yields } (q,r)$$

It is of interest to note that corresponding to these examples we have the results

$$8 = 3 \cdot 2 + 2$$
$$12 = 2 \cdot 6 + 0$$
$$27 = 4 \cdot 6 + 3$$
$$39 = 16 \cdot 2 + 7$$
$$0 = 5 \cdot 0 + 0$$

and

$$4 = 9 \cdot 0 + 4$$

so that in general it appears that if $a \div b$ yields (q,r) then

$$a = b \cdot q + r$$

This is exactly the property which is used to check division problems. Let us now prove that this property holds.

Theorem 6-3: If a, b, q, and r are cardinal numbers with $b \neq 0$, and if $a \div b$ yields (q,r), then $a = b \cdot q + r$.

Proof: For convenience we shall assume that $a > b$ and leave the other two cases for the reader to investigate. The definition of division assures us that there were sets A, B, Q, and R such that

$$A = \{x_1, x_2, \ldots, x_b, x_{b+1}, \ldots, x_{2b}, x_{2b+1}, \ldots, x_{3b}, \ldots,$$
$$x_{qb}, x_{qb+1}, \ldots, x_a\} \quad \text{with } n(A) = a,$$

$$B = \{y_1, y_2, \ldots, y_b\} \quad \text{with } n(B) = b$$

$$Q = \{A_1, A_2, \ldots, A_q\} \quad \text{with } n(Q) = q$$

and

$$R = \{x_{qb+1}, \ldots, x_a\} \quad \text{with } n(R) = r$$

We must show that $A \sim [(B \times Q) \cup R]$ so that $n(A) = b \cdot q + r$. Now

$$B \times Q = \begin{Bmatrix} (y_1, A_1), (y_1, A_2), \ldots, (y_1, A_q) \\ (y_2, A_1), (y_2, A_2), \ldots, (y_2, A_q) \\ \cdot \quad \cdot \quad \cdot \quad \cdot \quad \cdot \quad \cdot \quad \cdot \quad \cdot \quad \cdot \quad \cdot \quad \cdot \\ (y_b, A_1), (y_b, A_2), \ldots, (y_b, A_q) \end{Bmatrix}$$

and since $(B \times Q) \cap R = \emptyset$,

$$(B \times Q) \cup R = \begin{Bmatrix} (y_1, A_1), (y_1, A_2), \ldots, (y_1, A_q) \\ (y_2, A_1), (y_2, A_2), \ldots, (y_2, A_q) \\ \cdot \quad \cdot \quad \cdot \quad \cdot \quad \cdot \quad \cdot \quad \cdot \quad \cdot \quad \cdot \quad \cdot \\ (y_b, A_1), (y_b, A_2), \ldots, (y_b, A_q) \\ x_{qb+1}, x_{qb+2}, \ldots, x_a \end{Bmatrix}$$

By the definitions of multiplication and addition we have

$$n[(B \times Q) \cup R] = b \cdot q + r$$

According to the division, there are in A, q mutually disjoint subsets each containing b elements and some elements left over after the mappings are completed. Hence if we map the elements of these disjoint subsets of A with the ordered pairs of $(B \times Q) \cup R$, taken column-wise, the only elements not used are x_{qb+1}, x_{qb+2}, $\ldots$, x_a, and these can be mapped onto themselves since they occur in both sets. Therefore there is a one-to-one mapping of A onto $(B \times Q) \cup R$ so that $A \sim (B \times Q) \cup R$. Consequently $a = b \cdot q + r$ because equivalent sets have the same cardinality. ∎

Equally interesting is the following result for which, because of its rather sophisticated nature, we shall not present the proof.

Theorem 6-4: If a, b, q, and r are cardinal numbers with $b \neq 0$ and $0 \leqslant r < b$ and if $a = b \cdot q + r$, then $a \div b$ yields (q, r).

That is, a division problem is equivalent to a corresponding statement in terms of multiplication and addition. Thus, for example,

if $26 \div 3$ yields $(8, 2)$, then $26 = 3 \cdot 8 + 2$ and conversely

if $26 = 3 \cdot 8 + 2$, then $26 \div 3$ yields $(8, 2)$ since $0 \leqslant 2 < 3$.

Let us illustrate how Theorem 6-4 may be used in a typical division problem.

Example: Consider 29 $\overline{)3671}$.

Solution: (1) By means of the usual division algorithm we have

$$
\begin{array}{r}
126 \\
29 \overline{)3671} \\
29 \\
\hline
77 \\
58 \\
\hline
191 \\
174 \\
\hline
17
\end{array}
$$

That is, (126,17).

(2) Making use of addition of cardinal numbers, we obtain

$$3671 = 3000 + [(600 + 70) + 1]$$
$$= (2900 + 100) + [(600 + 70) + 1]$$
$$= 2900 + [(100 + 600) + (70 + 1)]$$
$$= 2900 + [700 + (70 + 1)]$$
$$= 2900 + [(580 + 120) + (70 + 1)]$$
$$= (2900 + 580) + [(120 + 70) + 1]$$
$$= (2900 + 580) + (190 + 1)$$
$$= (2900 + 580) + [(174 + 16) + 1]$$
$$= (2900 + 580) + [174 + (16 + 1)]$$
$$= [(2900 + 580) + 174] + 17$$
$$= (2900 + 580 + 174) + 17$$
$$= (29 \cdot 100 + 29 \cdot 20 + 29 \cdot 6) + 17$$
$$= 29 \cdot (100 + 20 + 6) + 17$$
$$= 29 \cdot 126 + 17$$

Since $0 \leqslant 17 < 29$, we have by Theorem 6-4 that $3671 \div 29$ yields (126,17).

In the next to last step of part (2) of the above example, the numbers represented by (100 + 20 + 6) are called *partial quotients*, and as can be observed by comparing with the usual algorithm, a quotient may be obtained by adding partial quotients. Thus perhaps one of the more important results to be obtained from Theorem 6-4 is that division may be thought of as a repeated subtraction. In this case, the quotient would be the total number of multiples of the divisor which could be subtracted from the dividend and could be determined by adding partial quotients.

Example: Determine $29 \overline{)3671}$.

Solution:

$$
\begin{array}{r|l}
29 \overline{)3671} & \text{Partial quotients} \\
\underline{2900} & 100 \\
771 & \\
\underline{290} & 10 \\
481 & \\
\underline{290} & 10 \\
191 & \\
\underline{145} & 5 \\
46 & \\
\underline{29} & \underline{1} \\
17 & 126 = \text{sum of partial quotients}
\end{array}
$$

Hence $3671 \div 29$ yields $(126,17)$.

The example just completed might provide a first introduction for division, since long division usually requires that the solver make estimates and here the estimates need not be extremely accurate. However, as is usually the case, the child should be encouraged to make more accurate estimates as his work in arithmetic progresses.

EXERCISE SET 6-2

1. Fill in each blank below so that the resulting statement is true.
    (a) $42 \div 5$ yields $(\_\_,2)$
    (b) $67 \div \_\_$ yields $(7,4)$
    (c) $\_\_ \div 13$ yields $(4,1)$
    (d) $89 \div 14$ yields $(6,\_\_)$
    (e) $78 = 6 \cdot \_\_ + 0$
    (f) $\_\_ = 15 \cdot 6 + 3$
    (g) $57 = 17 \cdot 3 + \_\_$
    (h) $45 = \_\_ \cdot 3 + 0$

2. In problem one, rewrite
    (a) parts (a) through (d) in the form $a = b \cdot q + r$
    (b) parts (e) through (h) in the form $a \div b$ yields (q,r).

3. It was noted that Theorem 6-3 forms the basis for checking division problems. Ferdy uses the check but still has his answer counted wrong on a test.

Explain what he has done wrong.

Solution	Check
343	28
28) 8615	x 343
74	74
121	112
112	74
95	8594
74	+ 21
21	8615

4. Show by numerical example that
   (a) $a \div b \neq b \div a$
   (b) $(a \div b) \div c \neq a \div (b \div c)$.
5. If $a \div b$ yields (q_1, r_1) and $c \div b$ yields (q_2, r_2) is it
   (a) always true that $(a + c) \div b$ yields $(q_1 + q_2, r_1 + r_2)$?
   (b) ever true that $(a + c) \div b$ yields $(q_1 + q_2, r_1 + r_2)$?
   [Hint: Try some numerical examples.]
6. By making use of Theorem 6-4, show in detail that
   (a) $876 \div 37$ yields $(23, 25)$
   (b) $932 \div 45$ yields $(20, 32)$
   (c) $784 \div 21$ yields $(37, 7)$
7. By treating division as repeated subtraction, find
   (a) $417 \div 14$
   (b) $386 \div 42$
   (c) $879 \div 37$
   (d) $652 \div 28$

3. Divisibility and Its Properties

In Section 6-2 we determined a workable definition for division. During the general discussion we avoided any lengthy consideration of quotient and remainder for the case $a = b$. If one does consider the cases suggested there he finds that if $a = b$ then $a \div b$ yields $(1,0)$. Similarly, if a is a non-zero multiple of b, say $a = bq$, then $a \div b$ yields $(q,0)$. This is of considerable importance in arithmetic and consequently the following definition is usually made to describe the situation.

Definition 6-2: If a and b are cardinal numbers with $b \neq 0$, then a **is divisible by** b if there exists a cardinal number c such that $a = b \cdot c$. The number c is called the quotient. Divisibility of a by b is denoted $b \mid a$ and is read as "a is divisible by b" or "b divides a."

It is easy to see that answers do *not* always exist under divisibility. For example, it is false that $3 \mid 8$, since there is no cardinal c such that $3 \cdot c = 8$. However, if an answer does exist, it must be unique because multiplication gives unique products. If $b \mid a$ is false we write this as $b \nmid a$, read "b does not divide a" or "a is not divisible by b."

It is easy to show that, like division, divisibility does not satisfy the commutative and associative properties, and so this is left as an exercise. However, divisibility does have some rather useful properties which we now illustrate.

Example: If $3 \mid 27$ and $3 \mid 15$, does $3 \mid 42$?

Solution: We know that $3 \mid 42$, since $3 \cdot 14 = 42$. That is, there is a unique cardinal, 14, such that $3 \cdot 14 = 42$. But we need to show that this can be made to depend on $3 \mid 27$ and $3 \mid 15$. Now since

$$3 \mid 27, \text{ we have } 3 \cdot 9 = 27$$

and since

$$3 \mid 15, \text{ we have } 3 \cdot 5 = 15$$

Adding, we obtain

$$3 \cdot 9 + 3 \cdot 5 = 27 + 15$$

or

$$3 \cdot 9 + 3 \cdot 5 = 42$$

By the distributive property,

$$3 \cdot (9 + 5) = 42$$

or

$$3 \cdot 14 = 42$$

and it has been shown that $3 \mid 42$ depends on the fact that $3 \mid 27$ and $3 \mid 15$.

Of course if the numbers involved are small, then not much is gained, however this does not guarantee that such procedures always give valid results. In addition to this it turns out that the results do have some fairly important applications. For these reasons let us prove the following theorem.

Theorem 6-5: If a, b, and c are cardinal numbers with $b \neq 0$, and if $b \mid a$ and $b \mid c$, then $b \mid (a + c)$.

Proof: The method of proof is much like that of the preceding example. Since

$$\begin{bmatrix} b \mid a \\ \text{and} \\ b \mid c \end{bmatrix}, \quad \text{we have} \quad \begin{bmatrix} a = b \cdot m \\ \text{and} \\ c = b \cdot n \end{bmatrix}$$

by Definition 6-2. Now

$$a + c = b \cdot m + b \cdot n \qquad \text{Thm. 3-9}$$

$$= b \cdot (m + n) \qquad \text{Thm. 5-7}$$

Since sums are unique, $m + n$ is a unique cardinal number and since products are unique, there is just one number $m + n$ such that

$$a + c = b \cdot (m + n)$$

Thus according to Definition 6-2, $b \mid (a + c)$. ∎

Theorem 6-5 will be of particular utility in Section 6-4 where we shall discuss some of the tests for divisibility. As a companion to Theorem 6-5 to strengthen these tests for divisibility it will be useful to have the following result. Be sure you understand these results because we shall use them repeatedly when the tests for divisibility are discussed.

Theorem 6-6: If a, b, and c are cardinal numbers with $b \neq 0$ and $b \mid a$ but $b \nmid c$, then $b \nmid (a + c)$.

Outline of Proof: We shall assume that $b \mid a$ and $b \mid (a + c)$ and try to show that with these assumptions $b \mid c$. If we can do this, we will have contradicted one of the hypotheses of the theorem which then indicates the falsity of our original assumption. That is, we will have shown that $b \mid (a + c)$ must be false and therefore the theorem holds.

Proof: Since

$$\begin{bmatrix} b \mid a \\ \text{and} \\ b \mid (a + c) \end{bmatrix} \quad \text{there are cardinals } m \text{ and } n \text{ such that} \quad \begin{bmatrix} a = b \cdot m \\ \text{and} \\ a + c = b \cdot n \end{bmatrix}$$

by Definition 6-2. Because of the fact that $a + c \geqslant a$ for every cardinal number c, the principle of substitution yields $b \cdot n \geqslant b \cdot m$. Thus $b \cdot n - b \cdot m$ exists and by Theorem 5-8 $b \cdot n - b \cdot m = b \cdot (n - m)$. Using uniqueness of differences this may be rewritten as

$$b \cdot (n - m) = b \cdot n - b \cdot m$$
$$= (a + c) - a$$
$$= c$$

Thus $b \mid c$ which is a contradiction and the theorem is proved. ∎

Along the lines of Theorem 6-5, it can also be shown that, for example, if $4 \mid 100$ and $4 \mid 64$, then $4 \mid (100 - 64)$. That is $4 \mid 36$. Thus if a cardinal number divides each of two given cardinals, it divides their difference whenever the difference is defined. The formal statement of this fact is in Theorem 6-7 below. However since the proof of this theorem is quite similar to that of Theorem 6-5, we shall not prove it.

Theorem 6-7: If a, b, and c are cardinal numbers with $b \neq 0$, $b \mid a$, $b \mid c$, and $a - c$ exist, then $b \mid (a - c)$.

Proof: Left as an exercise.

It is also interesting to observe that if $b \mid (a + c)$ or if $b \mid (a - c)$, it is not necessarily true that $b \mid a$ or $b \mid c$.

Examples: (a) $20 + 22 = 42$ and $6 \mid 42$,   but $6 \nmid 20$ and $6 \nmid 22$.
  (b) $15 - 3 = 12$ and $6 \mid 12$,   but $6 \nmid 15$ and $6 \nmid 3$.

Thus Theorems 6-5, 6-6, and 6-7 do not give us a great deal of latitude in spite of their usefulness.

EXERCISE SET 6-3

1. Show that
   (a) $13 \mid 52$ (f) $13 \nmid 42$
   (b) $43 \mid 86$ (g) $19 \nmid 48$
   (c) $25 \mid 175$ (h) $27 \nmid 36$
   (d) $16 \mid 80$ (i) $2 \nmid 3$
   (e) $24 \mid 120$ (j) $4 \nmid 27$
2. By constructing appropriate numerical examples, decide if
   (a) $a \mid b = b \mid a$ is always true.
   (b) $a \mid b = b \mid a$ is ever true.
3. Determine each of the following.
   (a) If $2 \mid 4$ and $4 \mid 100$, does $2 \mid 100$?
   (b) If $7 \mid 14$ and $14 \mid 196$, does $7 \mid 196$?
   (c) If $5 \mid 35$ and $35 \mid 140$, does $5 \mid 140$?
   (d) Write a general theorem which appears to justify problems of the type given in parts (a), (b), and (c).
   (e) Prove or disprove the theorem stated in part (d).
4. Determine each of the following.
   (a) If $2 \mid 18$ and $2 \mid 8$, does $2 \mid 144$?
   (b) If $6 \mid 24$ and $6 \mid 12$, does $6 \mid 288$?
   (c) If $9 \mid 18$ and $9 \mid 63$, does $9 \mid 1134$?
   (d) Write a general theorem which appears to justify the problems of parts (a), (b), and (c).
   (e) Prove or disprove the theorem stated in part (d).
5. Determine each of the following.
   (a) If $2 \mid 24$ and $3 \mid 24$, does $6 \mid 24$?
   (b) If $4 \mid 120$ and $5 \mid 120$, does $20 \mid 120$?
   (c) If $3 \mid 72$ and $4 \mid 72$, does $12 \mid 72$?
   (d) Write a general theorem which appears to justify the problems of parts (a), (b), and (c).
   (e) Prove or disprove the theorem stated in part (d).
6. By using Definition 6-2, give an alternate definition (in terms of divisors) for
   (a) prime cardinal number
   (b) two relatively prime cardinal numbers

(c) L.C.M. of two cardinal numbers
(d) G.C.F. of two cardinal numbers.
7. Prove that for any non-zero cardinal number a,
   (a) $a \mid a$
   (b) $a \mid 0$
   (c) $1 \mid a$.
8. Prove Theorem 6-7.
9. Show by numerical example that if $b \nmid (a + c)$ it is not necessary that $b \mid a$ and $b \nmid c$. That is, show that the converse of Theorem 6-6 is not valid.

4. Tests for Divisibility

In this section we shall show how Theorems 6-5 and 6-6 can be used to devise some tests for divisibility of cardinal numbers. In order to establish these tests we shall also make considerable use of properties of arithmetic which we have discussed in previous chapters. In each case we let N be the cardinal number to be tested and assume $N = a_n \cdot 10^n + a_{n-1} \cdot 10^{n-1} + \ldots + a_2 \cdot 10^2 + a_1 \cdot 10 + a_0$.

Divisibility by Two: Rewrite N as follows:

$$N = 10(a_n \cdot 10^{n-1} + a_{n-1} \cdot 10^{n-2} + \ldots + a_2 \cdot 10 + a_1) + a_0$$

This is possible by the associative property of addition and an extension of the distributive property. Then

$$N = 2 \cdot [5 \cdot (a_n \cdot 10^{n-1} + a_{n-1} \cdot 10^{n-2} + \ldots + a_2 \cdot 10 + a_1)] + a_0$$

Since

$$2 \mid 2 \cdot [5 \cdot (a_n \cdot 10^{n-1} + a_{n-1} \cdot 10^{n-2} + \ldots + a_2 \cdot 10 + a_1)],$$

we have by Theorem 6-5 that $2 \mid N$ if $2 \mid a_0$. On the other hand, if $2 \nmid a_0$ then by Theorem 6-6 it is not possible for N to be divisible by 2.

Example: Determine if $2 \mid 2896$.

Solution: $2 \mid 6$, so by the test for divisibility for two, $2 \mid 2896$.

Example: Determine if $2 \mid 8375$.

Solution: $2 \nmid 5$, hence by the test for divisibility for two, $2 \nmid 8375$.

For divisibility by three, we use a slightly different approach.

Divisibility by Three: Rewrite N in the following way.

$$N = a_n \cdot [(10^n - 1) + 1] + a_{n-1} \cdot [(10^{n-1} - 1) + 1] + \ldots +$$
$$a_2 \cdot [(10^2 - 1) + 1] + a_1 \cdot [(10 - 1) + 1] + a_0$$

This is possible since for any cardinal number $a \geqslant 1, a = (a - 1) + 1$. By the associative property of addition and the distributive property,

$$N = a_n \cdot (10^n - 1) + a_n + a_{n-1} \cdot (10^{n-1} - 1) + a_{n-1} + \ldots +$$
$$a_2 \cdot (10^2 - 1) + a_2 + a_1 \cdot (10 - 1) + a_1 + a_0$$

Using the general associative and commutative properties of addition we obtain

$$N = [a_n \cdot (10^n - 1) + a_{n-1} \cdot (10^{n-1} - 1) + \ldots + a_2 \cdot (10^2 - 1) +$$
$$a_1 \cdot (10 - 1)] + (a_n + a_{n-1} + \ldots + a_2 + a_1 + a_0)$$

Since for $n \geqslant 1$, $10^n - 1 = \underbrace{999\ldots9}_{n \text{ digits}}$, and this is divisible by 3. Consequently

$$3 \mid [a_n \cdot (10^n - 1) + a_{n-1} \cdot (10^{n-1} - 1) + \ldots + a_2 \cdot (10^2 - 1) + a_1 \cdot (10 - 1)]$$

Hence by Theorem 6-5, if $3 \mid [a_n + a_{n-1} + \ldots + a_0)$, then $3 \mid N$. As in the test for divisibility by two, we note by use of Theorem 6-6 that if $3 \nmid (a_n + a_{n-1} + \ldots + a_0)$ then 3 cannot divide N. Thus to test N for divisibility by three, we add the digits of N and to see if that sum is divisible by 3.

Example: Determine if $3 \mid 23511$.

Solution: $2 + 3 + 5 + 1 + 1 = 12$ and $3 \mid 12$, so by the test for divisibility by three, $3 \mid 23511$.

Example: Determine if $3 \mid 2453$.

Solution: $2 + 4 + 5 + 3 = 14$ and $3 \nmid 14$, so by the test for divisibility by three, $3 \nmid 2453$.

Divisibility by Four: Rewrite N as follows:

$$N = 10^2 \cdot [a_n \cdot 10^{n-2} + a_{n-1} \cdot 10^{n-3} + \ldots + a_2] + (a_1 \cdot 10 + a_0)$$

This again is made possible by associativity of addition and the distributive property. Now

$$N = 2^2 \cdot [5^2 \cdot (a_n \cdot 10^{n-2} + a_{n-1} \cdot 10^{n-3} + \ldots + a_2)] + (a_1 \cdot 10 + a_0)$$

and

$$4 \mid [5^2 \cdot (a_n \cdot 10^{n-2} + a_{n-1} \cdot 10^{n-3} + \ldots + a_2)]$$

Hence, by Theorems 6-5 and 6-6 if $4 \mid (a_1 \cdot 10 + a_0)$ then $4 \mid N$ and if $4 \nmid (a_1 \cdot 10 + a_0)$ then $4 \nmid N$. That is, if 4 divides the number named by the last two digits of N, then $4 \mid N$.

Example: Determine if $4 \mid 73964$.

Solution: $4 \mid 64$. Hence by the test for divisibility by four, $4 \mid 73964$.

Example: Determine if $4 \mid 8377$.

Solution: $4 \nmid 77$, so by the test for divisibility by four, $4 \nmid 8477$.

There are several other tests for divisibility which are useful and convenient to know. Some of these may be obtained by making use of the following information and are left as exercises.

1. Divisibility by 5 can be derived by altering the test for divisibility by 2.
2. Divisibility by 6 is immediate from those for 2 and 3.
3. Divisibility by 8 can be derived by using the technique of that used for 4 except we first extract the factor 10^3 instead of 10^2.
4. Divisibility by 9 just requires an alteration of the test for 3.
5. Divisibility by 10 can be derived by an alteration of the test used for 2 and 5.

Oddly enough there is no easy test for divisibility by seven. If one uses a test he soon finds that it is usually just as easy to try division of the original number by seven as it is to use the test. We list a test below, but make no attempt to show its derivation.

Divisibility by Seven: If $N = a_n \cdot 10^n + a_{n-1} \cdot 10^{n-1} + \ldots + a_5 \cdot 10^5 + a_4 \cdot 10^4 + a_3 \cdot 10^3 + a_2 \cdot 10^2 + a_1 \cdot 10 + a_0$, then $7 \mid N$ if $7 \mid (a_0 + 3a_1 + 2a_2 - a_3 - 3a_4 - 2a_5 + a_6 + 3a_7 + 2a_8 - a_9 - \ldots)$.

EXERCISE SET 6-4

1. Check each of the following for divisibility by two and five.
   (a) 824
   (b) 7921
   (c) 1012
   (d) 375
   (e) 4,216
   (f) 531
2. Check each of the following for divisibility by three and nine.
   (a) 1,101
   (b) 36,747
   (c) 5,642
   (d) 21,027
   (e) 9,684
   (f) 36,721
3. Check each of the following for divisibility by four.
   (a) 1,896
   (b) 3,762
   (c) 8,634
   (d) 5,712
   (e) 29,368
   (f) 7,856
4. State and derive a test for divisibility by
   (a) five
   (b) six
   (c) eight
   (d) nine
   (e) ten
5. Check each of the following for divisibility by six.
   (a) 318
   (b) 471
   (c) 432
   (d) 726
   (e) 1176
   (f) 1,350
6. Check each of the following for divisibility by eight.
   (a) 1,896
   (d) 18,884

(b) 592   (e) 11,664
(c) 3,244   (f) 6,423,816

7. Explain why each of the following is true or false for a cardinal number N.
   (a) If $2 \mid N$ and $4 \mid N$, then $8 \mid N$.
   (b) If $3 \mid N$ and $4 \mid N$, then $12 \mid N$.
   (c) If $8 \mid N$, then $4 \mid N$.
   (d) If $9 \mid N$ and $8 \mid N$, then $6 \mid N$.

Chapter summary

In Chapter 6 we have shown that division can be defined in terms of sets. We also showed that while this division is always possible, the result is not a single cardinal number, but rather an ordered pair of cardinals. Even though an ordered pair results from the division, the ordered pair is unique. Division is not commutative, nor associative and there is no identity element. However, we do find that it is related in some way to multiplication, addition, and to subtraction. That is, division may be thought of in terms of repeated subtraction, and $a \div b$ yields (q,r) if and only if $a = b \cdot q + r$ where q is frequently called the quotient and r the remainder.

By reconsidering division for the case when the remainder is zero, it is possible to define divisibility and do so in terms of multiplication. Here we found that the procedure is not always possible, but even so, by using the facts available we were able to construct several useful tests for divisibility. The relation between divisibility and multiplication then allows a reinterpretation of prime factorization, least common multiples, and greatest common factors in terms of divisors of the numbers involved. Thus even though division and divisibility at first appear somewhat restrictive in nature, we can find considerable use for the two concepts.

CHAPTER 7 The order relation and cardinal numbers

1. Order Relations

In Section 1-6 the concept of relations was discussed. There we showed that if $\mathscr{R}$ is a relation defined on a set S, then $\mathscr{R}$ can be expressed as a set of ordered pairs and is a subset of $S \times S$. Further, we showed that some relations satisfy the reflexive, symmetric, or transitive properties. Relations which satisfied all three properties, we called equivalence relations. In particular, we discussed the importance and usefulness of the equivalence relation, "is equivalent to," in the development of cardinal number. In some problems however, we found that there are relations which do not satisfy the reflexive and symmetric properties for any choices, but which do satisfy the transitive property. Such properties are very important.

Definition 7-1: A relation $\mathscr{R}$ defined on a set S is called an **order relation** on S if and only if
  (1) for all $a \in S$, $\mathscr{R}$ is not reflexive,
  (2) for all $a, b \in S$, $\mathscr{R}$ is not symmetric, and
  (3) $\mathscr{R}$ is transitive.

We shall soon show that the relation, $<$, is an order relation on the set of cardinal numbers. However, before we proceed with our discussion of this, let us reconsider the definitions for $<$, $>$, $\leqslant$, and $\geqslant$ which were given in terms of sets in Section 4-1. In Definition 4-1 we said that

$$a = n(A) < n(B) = b$$

if A was equivalent to a subset of B and B was equivalent to no subset of A. Since A and B represent finite sets, this means that B has more elements than

A. Hence there is a non-empty set *C* such that $n(A) + n(C) = n(B)$. That is, there is a set *C* such that

$$a + c = b$$

where $n(C) = c$, and $c \neq 0$. Hence we may make the following definition.

Definition 7-2: If *a* and *b* are cardinal numbers, then $a < b$ if there is a non-zero cardinal number *k* such that $a + k = b$.

Example: Determine if $7 < 12$.

Solution: From addition $7 + 5 = 12$ and $5 \neq 0$. Therefore there is a non-zero cardinal *k* such that $7 + k = 12$. That *k* is 5. Hence by Definition 7-2, $7 < 12$.

One can observe on the basis of the preceding example that our new definition is much easier to use than the former. By proceeding in a similar fashion, we could obtain the following definition for $\leqslant$.

Definition 7-3: If *a* and *b* are cardinal numbers, then $a \leqslant b$ if there is a cardinal number *k* such that $a + k = b$.

In this case it is possible that $k = 0$.

Example: Show that $6 \leqslant 6$.

Solution: From addition, $6 + 0 = 6$. Hence there is a cardinal number *k* such that $6 + k = 6$. In this case, $k = 0$. By Definition 7-3, then, $6 \leqslant 6$.

We still define the relations, $>$ and $\geqslant$, as in Definitions 4-2 and 4-4 respectively.

Let us now show that the relation, $<$, is an order relation on the set of cardinal numbers.

Theorem 7-1: The relation $<$ is an order relation on the set of cardinal numbers.

Proof: We must show that $<$ is (1) nowhere reflexive, (2) nowhere symmetric, and (3) transitive.

(1) Let *a* be any cardinal number. Then we consider the statement $a < a$ where *a* is any cardinal number. Is there a cardinal number *k* such that $a = a + k$? We know from addition that $a = a + 0$, and since the additive identity is unique, it must be the case that $k = 0$. But by Definition 7-2, $k \neq 0$ must hold in order that $a < a$. Hence for every cardinal number *a*, $a \nleqslant a$ and consequently $<$ does not satisfy the reflexive property.

(2) Let *a* and *b* be any two cardinal numbers such that $a < b$. From this we must show that $b < a$ if $<$ is to be symmetric. Since $a < b$, we have by Definition

7-2 that there is a non-zero cardinal k such that $b = a + k$. The only way in which $a = b + k$ might be obtained is to write

$$b = a + k$$

$$b - k = (a + k) - k$$

$$b - k = a + (k - k)$$

$$b - k = a$$

But then, Definition 7-2 is not satisfied so that we must conclude $b \leqslant a$. That is, the relation $<$ does not satisfy the symmetric property.

(3) Suppose a, b, and c are any three cardinal numbers such that $a < b$ and $b < c$. Then we need to show that $a < c$ in order to show that $<$ is an order relation. Now since

$$a < b, \qquad \text{we obtain} \qquad b = a + k \text{ where } k \neq 0$$

and since

$$b < c, \qquad \text{we obtain} \qquad c = b + m \text{ where } m \neq 0$$

both by Definition 7-2. Making a substitution for b in the latter equation, we have

$$\begin{aligned} c &= b + m &\qquad &\text{why?} \\ &= (a + k) + m &\qquad &\text{why?} \\ &= a + (k + m). &\qquad &\text{why?} \end{aligned}$$

Since $k + m \neq 0$, we have by Definition 7-2 that $a < c$.

Taking parts (1), (2), and (3) into account, we have by Definition 7-1 that the relation $<$ is an order relation on the set of cardinal numbers.∎

The fact that $<$ is an order relation on the set of cardinals means that given a set of cardinals, we can theoretically arrange them from smallest to largest. This is sometimes referred to as placing the cardinals in a *linear* order. This seemingly simple concept plays a very important role in mathematics at advanced levels. It is used a great deal in such areas as algebra, analysis, geometry, topology, and applied mathematics.

We return now to subtraction of cardinals to see if any other relation exists between subtraction and the order besides that implied in Definition 7-2. There we may note that if $a + k = b$, then by Theorem 4-6 an equivalent statement is $b - a = k$ where k is non-zero. However if any two cardinals are considered there are exactly three possibilities which may arise, namely

(1) $b - a = k$,

(2) $b - a = 0$, or

(3) $a - b = n$

where k and n are non-zero. If case (1), then by Definition 7-2 we obtain that $a < b$. In case (2) of course, $a = b$, while for case (3) Definition 7-2 yields $b < a$ or equivalently $a > b$. Thus for any two cardinal numbers exactly one of three things can occur. These possibilities together are called the Trichotomy Property for cardinal numbers and it is of frequent usefulness. A formal statement is as follows.

Trichotomy Property: If a and b are any two cardinal numbers, then one and only one of the following holds: $a < b$; $a = b$; or $a > b$.

EXERCISE SET 7-1

1. Determine which of the following are order relations if defined on the set listed.
    (a) R_1: "is taller than" ;
        $S_1 = \{x | x$ is a student in your mathematics class$\}$.
    (b) R_2: "is as tall as" ; $S_2 = S_1$
    (c) R_3: "is a descendent of" ;
        $S_3 = \{x | x$ is a living inhabitant of the U.S.$\}$.
    (d) R_4: "is less than or equal to" ;
        $S_4 = \{x | x$ is a cardinal number$\}$.
    (e) R_5: "is greater than" ; $S_5 = S_4$
2. Decide which of the following statements are true and which are false. Be able to support your judgement with examples.
    (a) If $a < b$, then $a \leqslant b$.   (e) If $a \leqslant b$, then $a < b$.
    (b) If $a > b$, then $b \leqslant a$.   (f) If $a \geqslant b$, then possibly $a = b$.
    (c) If $a < b$, then $b \geqslant a$.   (g) If $a \geqslant b$, then $b < a$.
    (d) If $a \leqslant b$, then $b \geqslant a$.
3. Might a small child who has little knowledge of number concepts make use of the concept of order? If so given an example.
4. By using Definition 7-2 or 7-3 show that
    (a) $6 < 8$ (e) $13 < 21$
    (b) $9 > 2$ (f) $14 > 7$
    (c) $16 \leqslant 20$ (g) $10 \leqslant 10$
    (d) $30 \geqslant 19$ (h) $24 \geqslant 24$
5. Show that if $a \leqslant b$ and $b \leqslant a$, then $b = a$.

2. Properties of Order Relations

It was noted at the end of the previous section that the relation $<$ is of considerable consequence in the study of mathematics at advanced levels. One should not suppose that its only use is in very sophisticated mathematical problems however. Very often it is of considerable value in trying to determine solutions to number sentences. In this section we shall examine a few of the properties which $<$ satisfies, then show how the relation can be put to use to solve problems.

We have already shown in Chapter 3 that by using the converse of cancellation or uniqueness it is possible to add the same cardinal to both sides of a statement of equality and still have a statement of equality. Our first consideration here will be to show that a similar result holds for inequalities.

Theorem 7-2: If a, b, and c are cardinal numbers and $a < b$, then $a + c < b + c$.

Proof: Since $a < b$, we have for some $k \neq 0$,

	$b = a + k$	Def. 7-2
	$b + c = (a + k) + c$	Thm. 3-9
	$b + c = a + (k + c)$	Thm. 3-4
	$b + c = a + (c + k)$	Thm. 3-3
	$b + c = (a + c) + k.$	Thm. 3-4
Since $k \neq 0$,	$a + c < b + c.$	Def. 7-2 ∎

To see how Theorem 7-2 can be used, consider the following example.

Example: Find all cardinals n such that $n - 4 < 6$.

Solution:		
	$n - 4 < 6$	given
	$(n - 4) + 4 < 6 + 4$	Thm. 7-2
	$4 + (n - 4) < 6 + 4$	Thm. 3-3
	$(4 + n) - 4 < 6 + 4$	Why?
	$(n + 4) - 4 < 6 + 4$	Thm. 3-3
	$n + (4 - 4) < 6 + 4$	Why?
	$n + 0 < 6 + 4$	Why?
	$n < 10.$	Why?

Hence the set, N, of numbers, n, such that $n - 4 < 6$ is

$$N = \{4,5,6,7,8,9\}$$

The reason 0, 1, 2, and 3 were omitted is that in those instances, $n - 4$ does not exist. When working with inequalities you should keep such a possibility in mind.

Theorem 7-2 also suggests the possibility of subtracting the same cardinal number from both sides of an inequality. With some restriction this can be done. The restriction required for this is given in the following theorem and as you may have suspected it is that the differences must exist.

Theorem 7-3: If a, b, and c are cardinal numbers and if $c \leqslant a$ and $a < b$, then $a - c < b - c$.

Proof: Left as an exercise.

Example: Determine the set N of cardinal numbers n such that $2n < n + 5$.

Solution: Since $n \leqslant 2n$, $2n - n$ exists. Thus we have

$2n < n + 5$	given
$2n - n < (n + 5) - n$	Thm. 7-3
$2 \cdot n - 1 \cdot n < (n + 5) - n$	Why?
$(2 - 1)n < (n + 5) - n$	Why?
$1 \cdot n < (n + 5) - n$	Why?
$n < (n + 5) - n$	Why?
$n < (5 + n) - n$	Thm. 3-3
$n < 5 + (n - n)$	Thm. 4-8
$n < 5 + 0$	Why?
$n < 5$	Why?

Hence $N = \{0,1,2,3,4\}$ is the solution set.

Example: Determine the set N of cardinal numbers n such that $n + 5 < 17$.

Solution:

$n + 5 < 17$	given
$n + 5 < 12 + 5$	Def. 3-1
$(n + 5) - 5 < (12 + 5) - 5$	Thm. 7-3
$n + (5 - 5) < 12 + (5 - 5)$	Thm. 4-8
$n + 0 < 12 + 0$	Thm. 4-3
$n < 12$	Why?

Hence the solution set is $N = \{0,1,2,3,...,11\}$.

It might be observed from the latter example that Theorem 7-3 yields results very similar to the cancellation property of addition. The similarity is quite striking.

As might be suspected, it is also possible to multiply both sides of an inequality by the same cardinal number c provided that $c \neq 0$. We shall now state this fact formally and prove it.

Theorem 7-4: If a, b, and c are cardinal numbers such that $a < b$ and $c \neq 0$, then $ac < bc$.

Proof: Since $a < b$, we have

$$a + k = b$$

where $k \neq 0$. Then

$$(a + k) \cdot c = b \cdot c \qquad \text{Thm. 5-6}$$

$$ac + kc = bc \qquad \text{Thm. 5-7}$$

Since $k \neq 0$ and $c \neq 0$, $kc \neq 0$ and so by Definition 7-2 we obtain $ac < bc$. ∎

A more useful result is the following one which allows us to divide out factors common to both sides of an inequality.

Theorem 7-5: If a, b, and c are cardinal numbers such that $ac < bc$ and $c \neq 0$, then $a < b$.

Proof: Since $ac < bc$, there is a cardinal $k \neq 0$ such that

$$ac + k = bc$$

Then

$$k = bc - ac \qquad \text{Thm. 4-6}$$

$$k = (b - a) \cdot c \qquad \text{Thm. 5-8}$$

Hence by Definition 6-2, $c|k$ and there is a cardinal number $m \neq 0$ such that $k = m \cdot c$. Consequently we may write

$$ac + mc = bc \qquad \text{Subs.}$$

$$(a + m)c = bc \qquad \text{Thm. 5-7}$$

Since $c \neq 0$, we have by Theorem 5-4 that

$$a + m = b$$

Finally by Definition 7-2, $a < b$. ∎

This result is especially useful for problems of the following type. We shall see later when rational numbers are discussed that there is a very useful extension of this theorem which alleviates the inherent drawback in Theorem 7-5.

Example: Find the set N of cardinal numbers n for which $2n - 5 < 7$.

Solution:

$$2n - 5 < 7 \qquad \text{given}$$

$$(2n - 5) + 5 < 7 + 5 \qquad \text{Thm. 7-2}$$

$$5 + (2n - 5) < 7 + 5 \qquad \text{Thm. 3-3}$$

$$(5 + 2n) - 5 < 7 + 5 \qquad \text{Thm. 4-8}$$

$$(2n + 5) - 5 < 7 + 5 \qquad \text{Thm. 3-3}$$

$$2n + (5 - 5) < 7 + 5 \qquad \text{Thm. 4-8}$$
$$2n + 0 < 7 + 5 \qquad \text{Thm. 4-3}$$
$$2n < 7 + 5 \qquad \text{Why?}$$
$$2n < 12 \qquad \text{Def. 3-1}$$
$$2n < 2 \cdot 6 \qquad \text{Def. 5-1}$$
$$n < 6 \qquad \text{Thm. 7-5}$$

Hence $N = \{3,4,5\}$ since for 0, 1, and 2, $2n - 5$ does not exist.

EXERCISE SET 7-2

1. For each of the following use Theorem 7-2 or 7-3 to determine the set N of cardinal numbers n which make the sentence true.
   - (a) $n - 3 < 7$
   - (b) $n + 5 < 13$
   - (c) $(n + 5) - 3 < 12$
   - (d) $(2n + 11) - 4 < 21 + n$
   - (e) $n - 2 < 4$
   - (f) $n + 7 < 10$
   - (g) $(n - 3) + 2 < 6$
   - (h) $(3n + 2) - (n + 1) < 4 + n$

2. Show that Theorem 7-2 remains true if $<$ is changed to $>$, $\leqslant$, or $\geqslant$.

3. Using the results of problem two, determine the solution set for each of the following.
   - (a) $x - 5 > 2$
   - (b) $2x - 5 \leqslant x + 2$
   - (c) $7 - 2x \geqslant 5 - x$
   - (d) $3 > 11 - x$
   - (e) $15 + x \geqslant 4 + 2x$
   - (f) $5 \leqslant 2x + (5 - x)$

4. Show that Theorem 7-5 remains true if $<$ is replaced by $>$, $\leqslant$, or $\geqslant$.

5. Determine the solution set for each of the following.
   - (a) $2x - 5 < 4 - x$
   - (b) $(5x - 4) - 2x \leqslant (5 - x) + (3 - 2x)$
   - (c) $3y - 9 \geqslant 15$
   - (d) $2y - 7 > 15 - 9y$

6. Determine the solution set for each of the following.
   - (a) $\{n | n + 2 \geqslant 5\} \cap \{n | 2n + 3 \leqslant 12 - 3n\}$
   - (b) $\{x | 2x - 4 \leqslant 6\} \cap \{x | 2x - 4 \geqslant 6\}$
   - (c) $\{y | y - 4 < 7\} \cup \{y | 2y - 3 > 5\}$
   - (d) $\{y | y - 4 > 7\} \cap \{y | 2y - 3 > 5\}$
   - (e) $\{n | 3n + 4 \geqslant 22\} \cap \{n | n - 2 \leqslant 10 - 2n\}$

7. Show that if $a < b$ and $c < d$, then $a + c < b + d$.

Chapter summary

When subtraction was discussed we recall that it was necessary to consider the relations $<$ and $\leqslant$ in order to make subtraction meaningful. In the present chapter we considered the relations again and showed that $<$ is an order relation. This means that given a set of cardinals we may select any finite subset and arrange them in a linear fashion from smallest to largest. Next we showed that the order relation possesses some properties very similar in nature to those already known for statements of equality. Primary among these are the results which parallel cancellation and its converse.

By a reconsideration of the definition for "is less than" we showed a close relationship between the order relation and subtraction which led directly to the statement of the Trichotomy Property for cardinal numbers.

Finally we noted how some number sentences involving inequalities may be solved by making use of the properties derived earlier. The culmination of these concepts will be found in Chapter Eighteen.

CHAPTER 8 Other systems of arithmetic

1. Base Six Arithmetic

In Chapters One through Seven we have developed, with the aid of the set concept, an arithmetic of cardinal numbers. In doing so, many properties were proved or pointed out to the reader and several algorithms were discussed. In practically all of the illustrations of these properties and algorithms base ten numerals were used primarily because these are the most familiar ones. However, because of the fact that counting was discussed with some generality, it would have been possible to use counting in some base other than ten and consequently illustrate the properties and algorithms in that base. This points out the fact that the properties of the arithmetic which we developed are independent of the base of the numeration system used. The object of this chapter, then, is to illustrate the system of arithmetic of cardinal numbers by using a numeration system with base different from ten. To do this, we shall use a base *six* system of numeration.

For the base set, we shall use

$$B = \{0,1,2,3,4,5\}.[1]$$

In Chapter Two we learned how to form place-value numerals for several bases and as we did we made the following agreement.

Agreement: If $d_n d_{n-1} \ldots d_2 d_1 d_0$ is a numeral in the base b system of numeration, where $b \geqslant 2$, we agree to write $d_n d_{n-1} \ldots d_2 d_1 d_{0_{\text{base } b}}$ for every base b except ten. In this case no subscript is written.

We also make the following agreement regarding the naming of numerals for any base b other than ten.

---

[1] Other sets equivalent to B could be used, but our choice of B is the one commonly taken.

Agreement: In so far as is possible, base ten names will be used for numerals of members of the original base set. All numerals which are combinations of original base set members will be named by combining the names of those members used to form the new numerals.

This is illustrated for base six in Table 8-1 below.

TABLE 8-1

Numeral	Name of Numeral
0_{six}	zero, base six
1_{six}	one, base six
2_{six}	two, base six
3_{six}	three, base six
4_{six}	four, base six
5_{six}	five, base six
10_{six}	one-zero, base six
25_{six}	two-five, base six
31_{six}	three-one, base six
401_{six}	four-zero-one, base six
523_{six}	five-two-three, base six
2014_{six}	two-zero-one-four, base six
34211_{six}	three-four-two-one-one, base six

It is very interesting to observe the "nice" carry-over of the expanded form of a place-value numeral. With a minimum of adaptation this works quite well. We recall that in base ten we defined

$$d_n d_{n-1} \ldots d_2 d_1 d_0 = d_n \cdot 10^n + d_{n-1} \cdot 10^{n-1} + \ldots + d_2 \cdot 10^2 + d_1 \cdot 10^1 + d_0$$

and that in the expanded form the factors 10 represented base sets of ten members. Hence for some general base b we could have

$$d_n d_{n-1} \ldots d_2 d_1 d_{0_b} = d_n \cdot b^n + d_{n-1} \cdot b^{n-1} + \ldots + d_1 \cdot b^1 + d_0$$

or equivalently

$$d_n d_{n-1} \ldots d_2 d_1 d_{0_b} = d_n \cdot (\text{base})^n + d_{n-1} \cdot (\text{base})^{n-1} + \ldots + d_1 \cdot (\text{base}) + d_0.$$

Making use of the fact that for any base b, $b_{10} = 10_b$, we may make the following general definition.

Definition 8-1: If $d_n d_{n-1} \ldots d_2 d_1 d_{0_b}$ is a place-value numeral in a base $b \geqslant 2$, then the **expanded form** of the numeral is $d_n \cdot (10_b)^n + d_{n-1} \cdot (10_b)^{n-1} + \ldots + d_1 \cdot (10_b)^1 + d_0$ where $d_n, d_{n-1}, \ldots, d_2, d_1, d_0$, and n are base b numerals. This is denoted $d_n d_{n-1} \ldots d_2 d_1 d_0 = d_n \cdot (10_b)^n + d_{n-1} \cdot (10_b)^{n-1} + \ldots + d_1 \cdot (10)^1 + d_0$.

Example: Write the expanded form of 2134205_{six}.

Solution:

$$2134205_{six} = 2\cdot10^{10} + 1\cdot10^5 + 3\cdot10^4 + 4\cdot10^3 + 2\cdot10^2 + 0\cdot10^1 + 5$$

where it is understood that 10 as well as all of the other numerals are base six numerals.

Example: Write the expanded form of $te8932t_{twelve}$.

Solution: A base set for base twelve is $\{0,1,2,3,4,5,6,7,8,9,t,e\}$.

$$te8932t_{twelve} = t\cdot10^6 + e\cdot10^5 + 8\cdot10^4 + 9\cdot10^3 + 3\cdot10^2 + 2\cdot10^1 + t$$

where each of the numerals used is a base twelve numeral.

   If addition and multiplication tables are constructed for base six arithmetic it can be observed that the usual algorithms do indeed hold. First we consider base six addition. In doing this we shall refer to Table 8-2 for the basic addition facts needed and make use of the expanded form of numerals.

TABLE 8-2

+	0	1	2	3	4	5
0	0	1	2	3	4	5
1	1	2	3	4	5	10
2	2	3	4	5	10	11
3	3	4	5	10	11	12
4	4	5	10	11	12	13
5	5	10	11	12	13	14

Example: Determine $54_{six} + 33_{six}$.

Solution: Using the expanded form of the given numerals, we have (temporarily omitting the subscript six):

$$54_{six} + 33_{six} = (5\cdot10^1 + 4) + (3\cdot10^1 + 3) \qquad \text{Def. 8-1}$$
$$= 5\cdot10^1 + [(4 + 3\cdot10^1) + 3] \qquad \text{Thm. 3-4}$$
$$= 5\cdot10^1 + [(3\cdot10^1 + 4) + 3] \qquad \text{Thm. 3-3}$$
$$= (5\cdot10^1 + 3\cdot10^1) + (4 + 3) \qquad \text{Thm. 3-4}$$
$$= (5 + 3)\cdot10^1 + (4 + 3) \qquad \text{Thm. 5-7}$$

$$= 12 \cdot 10^1 + 11 \qquad\qquad\qquad \text{Table 8-2}$$

$$= (1 \cdot 10^1 + 2) \cdot 10^1 + (1 \cdot 10^1 + 1) \qquad \text{Def. 8-1}$$

$$= [(1 \cdot 10^1) \cdot 10^1 + 2 \cdot 10^1] + (1 \cdot 10^1 + 1) \qquad \text{Thm. 5-7}$$

$$= [1 \cdot (10^1 \cdot 10^1) + 2 \cdot 10^1] + (1 \cdot 10^1 + 1) \qquad \text{Thm. 5-3}$$

$$= (1 \cdot 10^2 + 2 \cdot 10^1) + (1 \cdot 10^1 + 1) \qquad \text{Def. 5-3}$$

$$= 1 \cdot 10^2 + [(2 \cdot 10^1 + 1 \cdot 10^1) + 1] \qquad \text{Thm. 3-4}$$

$$= 1 \cdot 10^2 + [(2 + 1) \cdot 10^1 + 1] \qquad \text{Thm. 5-7}$$

$$= 1 \cdot 10^2 + [3 \cdot 10^1 + 1] \qquad \text{Table 8-2}$$

$$= 1 \cdot 10^2 + 3 \cdot 10^1 + 1 \qquad \text{Thm. 3-4}$$

$$= 131_{\text{six}} \qquad\qquad\qquad \text{Def. 8-1}$$

As can be observed the answer is identical to that obtained by using the usual algorithm as illustrated in the following example. In either case use is made of Table 8-2.

Example: By use of the usual addition algorithm determine $54_{\text{six}} + 33_{\text{six}}$.

Solution: By use of the algorithm we have

$$
\begin{array}{r}
54_{\text{six}} \\
33_{\text{six}} \\
\hline
131_{\text{six}}
\end{array}
$$

In order to do subtraction problems we must make sure that differences are defined. This requires an application of associative and distributive properties in some cases, but as we observed in Chapter 4, this can be done if the difference of the original two numbers exists. Expanded form of the numerals could be used to justify the usual algorithm, but since it is essentially the same as that for addition we omit it here. Instead, we illustrate the algorithm.

Example: Determine $5432_{\text{six}} - 455_{\text{six}}$.

Solution:
$$
\begin{array}{r}
5432_{\text{six}} \\
-\ 455_{\text{six}} \\
\hline
4533_{\text{six}}
\end{array}
$$

Table 8-2 and the inverse definition are used as well as "borrowing." Checking, we obtain

$$455_{six}$$
$$+ 4533_{six}$$
$$5432_{six}.$$

Hence the resulting answer of 4533_{six} is correct by the definition of subtraction as the inverse of addition. Once again we should observe that the algorithms developed in the preceding materials are independent of the base of the numeration system being used.

Next we illustrate multiplication in a base six system of numeration. In doing this we shall refer to Table 8-3 for the determination of the required basic products or multiplication facts (all base six).

TABLE 8-3

·	0	1	2	3	4	5
0	0	0	0	0	0	0
1	0	1	2	3	4	5
2	0	2	4	10	12	14
3	0	3	10	13	20	23
4	0	4	12	20	24	32
5	0	5	14	23	32	41

Example: Determine 54_{six} times 33_{six}.

Solution: We shall temporarily drop the sub-six and use the expanded form of the numerals.

$54_{six} \cdot 33_{six}$

$= (5 \cdot 10^1 + 4) \cdot (3 \cdot 10^1 + 3)$ Def. 8-1

$= (5 \cdot 10^1) \cdot (3 \cdot 10^1) + (5 \cdot 10^1) \cdot 3 + 4 \cdot (3 \cdot 10^1) + 4 \cdot 3$ Thm. 5-10

$= [5 \cdot (10^1 \cdot 3) \cdot 10^1] + (5 \cdot 10^1) \cdot 3 + (4 \cdot 3) \cdot 10^1 + 4 \cdot 3$ Thm. 5-3

$= [5 \cdot (3 \cdot 10^1) \cdot 10^1] + 3 \cdot (5 \cdot 10^1) + (4 \cdot 3) \cdot 10^1 + 4 \cdot 3$ Thm. 5-2

$= [(5 \cdot 3) \cdot (10^1 \cdot 10^1)] + [(3 \cdot 5) \cdot 10^1 + (4 \cdot 3) \cdot 10^1] + 4 \cdot 3$ Thm. 5-3

$= (5 \cdot 3) \cdot 10^2 + [(3 \cdot 5) \cdot 10^1 + (4 \cdot 3) \cdot 10^1] + 4 \cdot 3$ Def. 5-3

$= (5 \cdot 3) \cdot 10^2 + [3 \cdot 5 + 4 \cdot 3] \cdot 10^1 + 4 \cdot 3$ Thm. 5-7

$= 23 \cdot 10^2 + (23 + 20) \cdot 10^1 + 20$ Table 8-3

$= 23 \cdot 10^2 + 43 \cdot 10^1 + 20$ Table 8-2

$= (2 \cdot 10^1 + 3) \cdot 10^2 + (4 \cdot 10^1 + 3) \cdot 10^1 + (2 \cdot 10^1 + 0)$ Def. 8-1

$= [(2 \cdot 10^1) \cdot 10^2 + 3 \cdot 10^2] + [(4 \cdot 10^1) \cdot 10^1 + 3 \cdot 10^1] + (2 \cdot 10^1 + 0)$ Thm. 5-7

$= [2 \cdot (10^1 \cdot 10^2) + 3 \cdot 10^2] + [4 \cdot (10^1 \cdot 10^1) + 3 \cdot 10^1] + (2 \cdot 10^1 + 0)$ Thm. 5-3

$= (2 \cdot 10^3 + 3 \cdot 10^2) + (4 \cdot 10^2 + 3 \cdot 10^1) + (2 \cdot 10^1 + 0)$ Def. 5-3

$= 2 \cdot 10^3 + (3 \cdot 10^2 + 4 \cdot 10^2) + [(3 \cdot 10^1 + 2 \cdot 10^1) + 0]$ Thm. 3-4

$= [2 \cdot 10^3 + (3 + 4) \cdot 10^2] + [(3 + 2) \cdot 10^1 + 0]$ Thm. 5-7

$= [2 \cdot 10^3 + 11 \cdot 10^2] + [5 \cdot 10^1 + 0]$ Table 8-2

$= [2 \cdot 10^3 + (1 \cdot 10^1 + 1) \cdot 10^2] + (5 \cdot 10^1 + 0)$ Def. 8-1

$= 2 \cdot 10^3 + [(1 \cdot 10^1) \cdot 10^2 + 1 \cdot 10^2] + (5 \cdot 10^1 + 0)$ Thm. 5-7

$= 2 \cdot 10^3 + [1 \cdot (10^1 \cdot 10^2) + 1 \cdot 10^2] + (5 \cdot 10^1 + 0)$ Thm. 5-3

$= 2 \cdot 10^3 + (1 \cdot 10^3 + 1 \cdot 10^2) + (5 \cdot 10^1 + 0)$ Def. 5-3

$= (2 \cdot 10^3 + 1 \cdot 10^3) + 1 \cdot 10^2 + (5 \cdot 10^1 + 0)$ Thm. 3-4

$= (2 + 1) \cdot 10^3 + 1 \cdot 10^2 + (5 \cdot 10^1 + 0)$ Thm. 5-7

$= 3 \cdot 10^3 + 1 \cdot 10^2 + 5 \cdot 10^1 + 0$ $\left\{\begin{array}{l}\text{Table 8-2} \\ \text{Thm. 3-4}\end{array}\right.$

$= 3150_{six}$ Def. 8-1

According to the usual multiplication algorithm, we obtain

$$
\begin{array}{r}
54_{six} \\
\times\ 33_{six} \\
\hline
250 \\
250 \\
\hline
3150_{six}
\end{array}
$$

Hence, apparently the usual multiplication algorithm does indeed work. Again, the most important point to bear in mind when working in a base other than ten is that 10_b means one base set in base b and $b_{10} = 10_b$.

The addition and multiplication facts can be used to solve division problems in base six just as they are in base ten.

Example: Determine $3452_{six} \div 25_{six}$.

Solution:

$$
\begin{array}{r}
120\phantom{_{six}} \\
25_{six}\ \overline{)\ 3452_{six}} \\
25\phantom{52_{six}} \\
\hline
55\phantom{2_{six}} \\
54\phantom{2_{six}} \\
\hline
12\phantom{_{six}} \\
0\phantom{_{six}} \\
\hline
12\phantom{_{six}}
\end{array}
$$

Checking, we have

$$120_{six}$$
$$\times\ 25_{six}$$
$$\overline{1040}$$
$$240$$
$$\overline{3440_{six}}$$
$$+\ 12_{six}$$
$$\overline{3452_{six}}$$

The algorithms which we have just discussed and illustrated in a base six numeration system are equally valid in any other base $b \geqslant 2$. The only difference is in the representation of the numbers. The cardinal numbers and their properties do not vary with a change of name. Thus the numerals used to represent the numbers in no way later the basic properties of the numbers involved.

EXERCISE SET 8-1

1. Construct appropriate addition tables and work the following problems.

(a) 110010_{two}
  $+\ 11110_{two}$

(e) 21304_{five}
  $-\ 4432_{five}$

(b) 2102_{three}
  $+\ 1221_{three}$

(f) 764_{eight}
  $+\ 537_{eight}$

(c) 1032_{four}
  $+\ 3213_{four}$

(g) $t969_{eleven}$
  $+\ 85t4_{eleven}$

(d) 4331_{five}
  $+\ 3421_{five}$

(h) $6te8_{twelve}$
  $+\ 75e9_{twelve}$

2. Determine each of the following differences by use of an appropriate addition table.

(a) 3421_{six}
  $-\ 534_{six}$

(d) 21304_{five}
  $-\ 4432_{five}$

(b) 784_{nine}
  -675_{nine}

(e) 3675_{eight}
  $-\ 2766_{eight}$

(c) $1t3e_{twelve}$
  $-\ 98t_{twelve}$

(f) $35t7_{eleven}$
  $-\ 98t_{eleven}$

3. Construct appropriate multiplication tables and work each of the following problems.

(a) 76_{nine}
  $\times\ 54_{nine}$

(c) 2012_{three}
  $\times\ \ 122_{three}$

(b) $9t_{twelve}$
  $\times\ 3e_{twelve}$

(d) $89t_{eleven}$
  $\times\ \ t6_{eleven}$

4. With help of appropriate addition and multiplication tables, work each of the following division problems.
   (a) $3211_{four} \div 23_{four}$ (d) $8345_{nine} \div 46_{nine}$
   (b) $4320_{five} \div 21_{five}$ (e) $9tt4_{eleven} \div 86_{eleven}$
   (c) $5643_{seven} \div 206_{seven}$ (f) $ett9_{twelve} \div 2t_{twelve}$

5. Determine which of the following statements are true.
   (a) $675_{eight} < 576_{eight}$ (e) $543_{eight} < 534_{nine}$
   (b) $5te6_{twelve} \geqslant 5et6_{twelve}$ (f) $3tt_{eleven} \leqslant 3ee_{twelve}$
   (c) $46t_{eleven} \leqslant 4t9_{eleven}$ (g) $t95_{eleven} \geqslant et5_{twelve}$
   (d) $821_{nine} > 832_{nine}$ (h) $563_{nine} > 653_{eight}$

   Problems 6 and 7 are worked in base seven. List the justification for each step.

6.

		Step
$160 - 26$	$= (150 + 10) - (20 + 6)$	(a)
	$= (150 - 20) + (10 - 6)$	(b)
	$= (15 \cdot 10 - 2 \cdot 10) + (10 - 6)$	(c)
	$= (15 - 2) \cdot 10 + (10 - 6)$	(d)
	$= 13 \cdot 10 + 1$	(e)
	$= (10 + 3) \cdot 10 + 1$	(f)
	$= 10 \cdot 10 + 3 \cdot 10 + 1$	(g)
	$= 10^2 + 3 \cdot 10 + 1$	(h)
	$= 1 \cdot 10^2 + 3 \cdot 10 + 1$	(i)
	$= 131$	(j)

7.

		Step
$160 + 26$	$= (1 \cdot 10^2 + 6 \cdot 10 + 0) + (2 \cdot 10 + 6)$	(a)
	$= (1 \cdot 10^2 + 6 \cdot 10) + [(0 + 2 \cdot 10) + 6]$	(b)
	$= (1 \cdot 10^2 + 6 \cdot 10) + [(2 \cdot 10 + 0) + 6]$	(c)
	$= 1 \cdot 10^2 + [(6 \cdot 10 + 2 \cdot 10) + (0 + 6)]$	(d)
	$= 1 \cdot 10^2 + [(6 + 2) \cdot 10 + (0 + 6)]$	(e)
	$= 1 \cdot 10^2 + [(11) \cdot 10 + 6]$	(f)
	$= 1 \cdot 10^2 + [(10 + 1) \cdot 10 + 6]$	(g)
	$= 1 \cdot 10^2 + [(10 \cdot 10 + 1 \cdot 10) + 6]$	(h)
	$= (1 \cdot 10^2 + 10 \cdot 10) + (1 \cdot 10 + 6)$	(i)
	$= (1 \cdot 10^2 + 10^2) + (1 \cdot 10 + 6)$	(j)
	$= (1 \cdot 10^2 + 1 \cdot 10^2) + (1 \cdot 10 + 6)$	(k)
	$= (1 + 1) \cdot 10^2 + (1 \cdot 10 + 6)$	(l)
	$= 2 \cdot 10^2 + (1 \cdot 10 + 6)$	(m)
	$= 2 \cdot 10^2 + 1 \cdot 10 + 6$	(n)
	$= 216$	(o)

8. Suppose someone writes $\begin{array}{r} 34 \\ + \ 44 \\ \hline 133 \end{array}$.

    (a) What base are they using so that this is correct?

    (b) With this same base what is $\begin{array}{r} 102 \\ + \ 424 \\ \hline \end{array}$?

9. An elementary schoolteacher from Mars visits a classroom in which you teach arithmetic. One of the problems you work for the class that day is $\begin{array}{r} 32 \\ + \ 35 \\ \hline \end{array}$ for which you write $\begin{array}{r} 32 \\ + \ 35 \\ \hline 67 \end{array}$. Being a good sport, the Martian teacher waits until school is out for the day to tell you that the answer to the problem was quite obviously 111. How many digits per hand is it likely that the Martian has? On what do you base your answer?

10. (a) If one works the following problem and gets the indicated answer, what base system must the answer be written in so that the answer is correct?

$$\begin{array}{r} 10_{\text{eight}} \\ + \ 10_{\text{ten}} \\ \hline 20 \end{array}$$

    (b) What about

$$\begin{array}{r} 10_{\text{ten}} \\ + \ 10_{\text{six}} \\ \hline 20 \qquad ? \end{array}$$

    (c) Would addition using numerals from two different base systems hold in general as it did for the two examples? Give a numerical example to support your answer.

2. Modular (Clock) Number Systems

Consider a simple two position "off-on" switch and the following related problem. If the switch is in the off position and someone changes its position exactly three times, is the switch in the "on" or the "off" position?

A solution to the above problem could be found by the following method: starting with the switch in the "off" position, the first position change places it in the "on" position, the second returns it to the "off" position, and the third places it in the "on" position. The switch occupies the following sequence of positions, off-on-off-on. This implies that starting with the switch in the "off" position three changes would leave it in the "on" position. Below is a table which would solve a similar problem in the situations where zero to six position changes were made.

TABLE 8-4

No. of Changes	Sequence	Final Position
0	off	off
1	off-on	on
2	off-on-off	off
3	off-on-off-on	on
4	off-on-off-on-off	off
5	off-on-off-on-off-on	on
6	off-on-off-on-off-on-off	off

This method of solution becomes cumbersome as the number of position changes increases. For this reason one might study the table to see if some pattern exists which would give some insight to a general solution when n position changes are to be made. From the table it appears that the switch will be in the "off" position if the number of position changes is even and in the "on" position if the number of position changes is odd. So one could associate the set of even numbers $A = \{0,2,4,6,8,...\}$ with the "off" position of the switch and the set of odd numbers $B = \{1,3,5,7,9,...\}$ with the "on" position. The solution to the problem in general is that the switch will be in the "off" position if $n \in A$ and in the "on" position if $n \in B$.

In the above situation we solved a physical problem by replacing it with a mathematical model which depended on properties of numbers rather than upon the physical movement of the switch. The properties of the cardinal numbers to which we appealed were the concepts of even and odd numbers. Previously, an even cardinal number was defined to be a number having two as a factor, that is, n is an even number if $n = 2k$ for some cardinal k. Another way of saying this is that n is even if one obtains the remainder zero when dividing n by two. A number n is odd if one gets the remainder one when dividing n by two. These remainders can be utilized in the solution of the above switch problem to determine the final position of the switch since all numbers giving remainder zero are associated with "off" and are in A while all numbers giving remainder one are associated with "on" and are in B.

As an extension of the preceding switch problem consider a three-position rotary switch having the positions off-low-high (see Figure 8-1). Again starting with the switch in the off position determine its position after n changes. For the purpose of the problem assume that the switch can be rotated in a clockwise direction only.

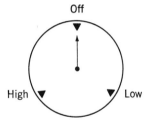

FIGURE 8-1

As before a solution could be obtained for the problem by physically rotating the switch through the given number of position changes and observing the results. However, let us approach the problem by substituting a mathematical model for the physical situation as we did in the case of the two position switch. To do this we should first observe that any cardinal number gives the remainder 0, 1, or 2 when divided by three. The set of numbers giving the remainder zero is $A = \{0,3,6,9,...\}$, the multiples of three, and so each can be expressed as $3k$, where k is some cardinal number. If the switch is rotated from the "off" position through any number n of position changes, where $n \in A$, the switch will be moved through some number of complete revolutions with the resulting positions of the switch being at "off". Since each member of the set $\{0,3,6,9,...\}$ gives the remainder zero when divided by three and the results of changing the position of the switch n-times, $n \in A$, places the switch in the "off" position let us rename this set by $\bar{0}$. In other words

$$\bar{0} = \{0,3,6,9,12,...\}.$$

Similarly the set $\{1,4,7,10,13,...\}$ is the set of numbers which give the remainder one when divided by three, and consequently each element of this set can be expressed in the form $3k + 1$ where k is some cardinal number. Now if a number is selected from this set and the switch is to be changed this number of times from the "off" position the resulting position will be "low." This follows from the fact that each number in the set is of the form $3k + 1$ and so the switch would be rotated through k complete revolutions placing it at "off" followed by one additional change placing the switch at the "low" position. Since each of these numbers yields the same result as one position change, let us use the following notation:

$$\bar{1} = \{1,4,7,10,13,...\}.$$

Since all of the cardinal numbers *not* listed in set $\bar{0}$ or set $\bar{1}$ must give the remainder of 2 when divided by three they are of the form $3k + 2$, where k is some cardinal number. This means that if the switch were moved through any number of changes where the number is of the form $3k + 2$ the switch would be rotated through some complete number of revolutions followed by two additional position changes. In each case the switch would be in the "high" position. As above, let us denote this set of numbers by $\bar{2}$, to indicate that each number of the set yields the same result as the number two. Then $\bar{2} = \{2,5,8,11,14,...\}$.

The general solution to the problem proposed is that after n position changes the switch is in the "off" position if $n \in \bar{0}$, in the "low" position if $n \in \bar{1}$, and in the "high" position if $n \in \bar{2}$.

Suppose the question now arises as to where the switch would be positioned if starting at "off" one makes 32 position changes followed by 16 position changes. Since $32 \in \bar{2}$ the switch would be in the "high" position after the initial 32 changes. Now $16 \in \bar{1}$ and so gives a remainder of one when divided by three. This means that starting at the "high" position where the switch was positioned by the 32 initial changes, one would make 5 complete revolutions with the switch (15 position changes) which would again position it at "high" followed by one more change necessary to make 16 changes. This would position the switch in the "off" position. One could have determined this simply by observing that $32 + 16 = 48$ and $48 \in \overline{0}$. This illustration suggests that for any $m \in \overline{2}$ and $n \in \overline{1}$ that $(n + m) \in \overline{0}$. To prove this in general observe that if $n \in \overline{2}$ then $m = 3k_1 + 2$ for some cardinal k_1 and if $n \in \overline{1}$ then $n = 3k_2 + 1$ for some cardinal k_2. Now

$$m + n = (3k_1 + 2) + (3k_2 + 1)$$
$$= (3k_1 + 3k_2) + (2 + 1)$$
$$= 3(k_1 + k_2) + 3$$
$$= 3[(k_1 + k_2) + 1]$$

Since k_1, k_2, and 1 are cardinal numbers $(k_1 + k_2) + 1$ is a cardinal, say k, and so $m + n = 3k$. This implies that $m + n$ is a multiple of three and so gives the remainder zero when divided by three. Therefore $m + n \in \overline{0}$.

By similar arguments one can establish the following "addition" table where this "addition" will be denoted by the symbol $\oplus$.

$\oplus$	$\overline{0}$	$\overline{1}$	$\overline{2}$
$\overline{0}$	$\overline{0}$	$\overline{1}$	$\overline{2}$
$\overline{1}$	$\overline{1}$	$\overline{2}$	$\overline{0}$
$\overline{2}$	$\overline{2}$	$\overline{0}$	$\overline{1}$

As an example of the interpretation that should be given to the information contained in the table, consider the tabulated fact that $\overline{1} \oplus \overline{2} = \overline{0}$. This fact implies that if any number contained in the set $\overline{1} = \{1,4,7,10,...\}$ is added to any number in the set $\overline{2} = \{2,5,8,11,...\}$ the sum will be in the set $\overline{0} = \{0,3,6,9,12,...\}$. Stated in terms of remainders this fact states that if a cardinal number which gives the remainder one when divided by three is added to a cardinal number which gives the remainder two when divided by three the sum is always a cardinal number that gives the remainder zero when divided by three.

In the preceding discussion a mathematical system has been constructed in which the operation $\oplus$ has been defined on the set with elements $\overline{0}$, $\overline{1}$, and $\overline{2}$. Since these elements were the sets of cardinal numbers which gave remainders of 0, 1, and 2 respectively when divided by three, similar systems could be constructed using other cardinal numbers for the divisor. In any case, the number of elements involved in the system would depend on the number of possible remainders. The mathematical system defined by the preceding table is frequently referred to as the system of cardinal numbers modulo 3 under addition. For this reason the arithmetic is usually referred to as modular arithmetic.

Another mathematical system could be constructed by considering the operation of multiplication of cardinals rather than addition as in the preceding example. If the operation is denoted by $\odot$ in such a system, one would have that $\overline{2} \cdot \overline{2} = \overline{1}$ indicating the fact that if any two cardinal numbers which give the remainder two when divided by three are multiplied together the product is a cardinal number which gives the remainder one when divided by three. The following is a table of the system of cardinal numbers modulo 3 under multiplication.

$\odot$	$\bar{0}$	$\bar{1}$	$\bar{2}$
$\bar{0}$	$\bar{0}$	$\bar{0}$	$\bar{0}$
$\bar{1}$	$\bar{0}$	$\bar{1}$	$\bar{2}$
$\bar{2}$	$\bar{0}$	$\bar{2}$	$\bar{1}$

EXERCISE SET 8-2

1. Construct the tables for the operations addition and multiplication of cardinal numbers modulo 5.
2. A set with an associative operation defined upon it is a mathematical system called a group if there exists an identity for the operation and if each element has an inverse. Show that the cardinal numbers under addition modulo 5 is a group. Are the cardinal numbers under modulo 5 multiplication a group?
3. If subtraction is defined by

$$a - b = c \text{ if } c + b = a,$$

   construct a table for the subtraction of cardinal numbers modulo 7 from the corresponding addition table.
4. In modulo 7 multiplication $\bar{4} \cdot \bar{3} = \bar{5}$ and so one could say that $\bar{5} \div \bar{3} = \bar{4}$. Construct a table of division facts for the cardinal numbers modulo 7.
5. Discuss the following argument for division by zero in modulo 7 arithmetic. Since $\bar{0} \cdot \bar{1} = \bar{0}$ then $\bar{0} \div \bar{0} = \bar{1}$. This implies that division by zero is possible in modulo 7 arithmetic.
6. A number b is called a *perfect square* number if there exists a number a such that $a \cdot a = b$. Find the perfect square numbers in the arithmetic of the cardinal numbers modulo 3; modulo 7; modulo 10.

3. Natural Numbers (Optional)

In the materials preceding this chapter, the cardinal number system with the operations of addition and multiplication has been constructed using the ideas of sets and set operations as a basis. This approach parallels that which a child uses in his first efforts to understand the meaning of the abstract concept of number. In this development the properties of the cardinal numbers, as well as the cardinal numbers themselves, were based upon some underlying property or properties of sets. The greatest advantage of this approach for the beginning student is that he can utilize sets of concrete objects to help master certain basic properties of numbers before progressing to the more abstract notions associated with further study. Since the cardinal number system was literally constructed from sets, this process is called a constructive approach to the concept of number. An alternate method is called a postulational approach to number and the resulting system is usually referred to as the system of natural numbers.[2] Mathematicians generally prefer this second approach where the numbers are postulated into existence since it eliminates any argument concerning the primitive concepts utilized in our development. In any event both methods of approach yield number systems that have the same mathematical properties. It is the postulational approach to numbers that we wish to discuss very briefly in the remaining paragraphs of this section.

The set of postulates upon 'which we shall base our discussion contains essentially those first stated by G. Peano (1858-1932) in his studies of number systems. Since Peano was the first mathematician to state these postulates, they are frequently referred to as Peano's Postulates.

Peano's postulates:

The system of natural numbers is a set N and a mapping σ having the following properties:
1. There exists an element denoted by 0 in N.
2. The mapping σ is a one-to-one mapping of N into N (if $n \in N$, the image $\sigma(n)$ of the element n is called the successor of n).
3. The element 0 is the image of no $n \in N$ under the mapping σ.
4. If S is a subset of N such that:
   (a) $0 \in S$
   (b) $\sigma(n) \in S$ whenever $n \in S$,
   then S is the set N of natural numbers.

Having stated the above postulates we shall first investigate intuitively the role that each postulate is to play in the development of the natural number system. Postulate 1 simply assures us that there exists at least one natural number, namely zero, while postulate 3 can be interpreted to imply that this number zero is the smallest natural number. Postulates 2 and 3 tell us that there is no last natural number, or equivalently that the set of natural numbers is an infinite set. This fact can be realized by noting that the mapping σ is one-to-one and so distinct natural numbers have distinct images. Since by postulate 3, 0 is the image of no natural number $\sigma(0) \neq 0$. Hence $\sigma(0)$ must be a natural number other than 0, say 1. Now since $\sigma(1) \neq 0$ by postulate 3, and $\sigma(1) \neq 1$ because σ is a one-to-one mapping and $\sigma(0) = 1$, $\sigma(1)$ must be a third natural number. Following this line of reasoning we see that N must be an infinite set. The role that postulate 4 plays in the development of the natural numbers is that it provides a method of proof for establishing properties of the natural numbers. In the constructive method utilized in our development of the cardinal number system, many properties of the cardinal numbers were established by first proving a related property for sets. The desired property of the cardinal numbers then followed from this related set property. Since we can no longer resort to this method of proof with the natural numbers, an alternate method must be realized and that is essentially the purpose of postulate 4. This postulate plays such an important role in the postulational development of the number system that it has been given a name: The Principle of Mathematical Induction. Because of the importance of The Principle of Mathematical Induction we shall consider this postulate in some detail before progressing further with our development of the natural number system.

In the discussion that follows it should be clearly understood that properties of the natural numbers that have not been developed at this point will be utilized. However, The Principle of Mathematical Induction is the prime method of proof used in the development and so we should first understand this method before attempting to continue. Among those properties that will be used without proof is that the successor of any natural number n under the mapping σ will be denoted by $n + 1$, that is $\sigma(n) = n + 1$. With this in mind, let us use The Principle of Mathematical Induction to prove that the subset of natural numbers S for which the proposition P(n): $1 + 2 + \ldots + n = \frac{1}{2} n(n + 1)$ is true is indeed the entire set of natural numbers. That is, $S = N$.

The first step in our inductive proof that the proposition P(n) is true for all natural numbers is to establish its validity for the number zero. In other words we must prove that P(0) is true. Now if $n = 0$, upon replacing n by 0 in the statement of P(n), we have:

$$P(0): \ 0 = \frac{1}{2} (0) (0 + 1)$$

$$= 0$$

Hence $0 \in S$, that is P(n) is true for the natural number 0. Next we must show that whenever $n \in S$ then $\sigma(n) \in S$ where $\sigma(n)$ is the successor of n. Since $\sigma(n) = n + 1$, this implies that P($n + 1$) must be true whenever P(n) is true if S is to be the entire set of natural numbers. To this end, suppose that $k \in S$, then P(k) is true. This assumption is usually referred to as the induction hypothesis. This induction hypothesis assumes that P(k) is true, hence

$$P(k): \ 1 + 2 + \ldots + k = \frac{1}{2} k(k + 1).$$

Now consider P(k)+ 1). If $k + 1 \in S$ then we must show that P($k + 1$) is true whenever P(k) is true. That is we should be able to prove that $1 + 2 + \ldots + k + (k + 1) = \frac{1}{2} (k + 1)[(k + 1) + 1]$ using the induction hypothesis P(k) as a tool. Now

$$1 + 2 + \ldots + k + (k + 1) = [1 + 2 + \ldots + k] + [k + 1] \quad \text{Associative Property}$$

$$= \frac{1}{2} k(k + 1) + (k + 1) \quad \text{Induction Hypothesis}$$

$$= \frac{1}{2} k(k + 1) + (\frac{1}{2} \cdot 2)(k + 1) \quad \text{Multiplicative Identity}$$

$$= \frac{1}{2}(k+1)(k+2) \qquad\qquad \text{Distributive Property}$$

$$= \frac{1}{2}(k+1)(k+1+1) \qquad\qquad \text{Addition fact}$$

$$= \frac{1}{2}(k+1)[(k+1)+1] \qquad\qquad \text{Associative Property}$$

So if one considers the natural number $\sigma(n) = n + 1$ the above proof states that

$$1 + 2 + \ldots + n + \sigma(n) = \frac{1}{2}[\sigma(n)][\sigma(n)+1]$$

which is $P(n + 1)$. Hence whenever $P(n)$ is true, that is whenever $n \in S$, then $P(\sigma(n)) = P(n + 1)$ is true so that $\sigma(n) \in S$. The Principle of Mathematic Induction now assures us that the subset S of natural numbers for which $P(n)$ is true is the entire set N of natural numbers. Therefore $S = N$.

This type of proof can be compared in a limited sense to the physical task of climbing a ladder. To prove that zero belongs to S can be compared to establishing the ability of the climber to reach a first rung on the ladder. If the ability of the climber enables him to reach rung number $n + 1$ every time he can get to rung number n then he can climb the entire ladder. One should notice that if either of these abilities is refused the climber he will be unable to climb the ladder. If he cannot reach a first rung he cannot even start up the ladder. On the other hand, if he cannot reach rung number $n + 1$ whenever he reaches rung number n for some n, then he will fail to reach the top of the ladder because he cannot get beyond rung number n.

Having postulated the set N of natural numbers, including a method of proof called mathematical induction, we now wish to consider the question of how the operations of addition and multiplication are introduced into the natural number system. In each case we must utilize the mapping σ and the concept of the successor, or image, of the natural number n, $\sigma(n)$. It also becomes necessary at this time to assign names to the elements of N in order to be able to refer to these elements as needed. The assigning of these names can be made quite arbitrarily, however, we shall utilize names with which we are already familiar. For example we have already used the symbol "0" to represent the element of N which is the image of no natural number under the mapping σ. Suppose we agree to call $\sigma(0) = 1$, $\sigma(1) = 2$, $\sigma(2) = 3$, $\sigma(3) = 4$, $\sigma(4) = 5$, and so forth. This now enables one to make repeated applications of the mapping σ on a given natural number. For example: $\sigma(\sigma(\sigma(1))) = \sigma(\sigma(2)) = \sigma(3) = 4$. To facilitate the writing of such repeated applications of σ we will use the following notation:

$$\sigma^2(1) = \sigma(\sigma(1)) = \sigma(2) = 3$$
$$\sigma^3(1) = \sigma(\sigma(\sigma(1))) = \sigma^2(2) = \sigma(3) = 4$$

To generalize we make the following definition.

Definition 8-2: $\sigma^n(\kappa) = \underbrace{(\sigma\ \sigma\ \ldots\ \sigma)}_{n}(k) = \underbrace{\sigma\Big(\sigma\ \ldots\ \big(\sigma(k)\big)\Big)}_{n}$ for any natural num-

bers n and k.

A special situation arises in regard to the meaning of the symbol σ^0. Previously the fact has been pointed out that it is very convenient to define $a^0 = 1$ if a is any non-zero number. That is, a^0 is associated with the identity element for multiplication. Since σ is a mapping and not a cardinal number this definition cannot be used to give meaning to the symbol σ^0. However, the definition does suggest that we might wish to define the mapping σ^0 to be the identity mapping or that mapping which identifies each natural number with itself. Indeed this is the meaning we wish to assign to the symbol σ^0, that is, $\sigma^0(n) = n$ for each natural number n.

Using the above notation we can now return to the problem of defining the operation of addition for natural numbers.

Definition 8-3: Let m and n be two natural numbers. The sum of m and n, denoted by $m + n$, is given as

$$m + n = \sigma^n(m).$$

To illustrate how this definition can be used to find the sum of two natural numbers, consider the problem of finding the sum $3 + 2$.

$3 + 2 = \sigma^2(3)$	Definition of addition
$\quad = \sigma\Big(\sigma(3)\Big)$	Definition of σ^2
$\quad = \sigma(4)$	Application of the mapping σ
$\quad = 5$	Application of the mapping σ

Since σ is a one-to-one mapping of the natural numbers N into the natural numbers N, it possesses the following basic properties which can be established by inductive proofs.

Theorem 8-1: $\sigma^m\Big(\sigma^n(k)\Big) = \sigma^{m+n}(k)$ and $(\sigma^m\sigma^n)(k) = (\sigma^n\sigma^m)(k)$.

Although these properties are very important to the development of the arithmetic of natural numbers we will not give proofs of these. Nevertheless we will feel free to use Theorem 8-1 to establish some of those properties of natural numbers which are similar to previously discussed properties of cardinals.

The following theorem is proven because of its basic importance in the succeeding development and as another illustration of an inductive proof. The theorem states that the mth successor of 0 is the natural number m.

Theorem 8-2: $\sigma^m(0) = m$.

Proof: The proof is by induction on the number m of repeated applications of the successor function σ. Let P(n) represent the statement $\sigma^n(0) = n$, and let S be the subset of natural numbers for which P(n) is true.

By definition of σ^0, $0 \in S$ since $\sigma^0 = 0$. Hence part (a) of postulate 4 is satisfied. Now suppose $k \in S$, that is $\sigma^k(0) = k$, and consider $P\big(\sigma(k)\big) = P(k + 1)$.

$$\sigma^{k+1}(0) = \sigma^{1+k}(0) \qquad\qquad \sigma^{n+1} = \sigma^{1+n}$$

$$= \sigma\big(\sigma^k(0)\big) \qquad\qquad \text{Definition of } \sigma^{1+n}$$

$$= \sigma(k) \qquad\qquad n \in S \text{ by assumption so } \sigma^n(0) = n$$

$$= k + 1 \qquad\qquad \text{Definition of } \sigma$$

We have demonstrated that $\sigma(n) \in S$ whenever $n \in S$ and so part (b) of postulate 4 has been verified for P(n). Hence S is the set of all natural numbers. ∎

Theorem 8-3: Addition of natural numbers is commutative, that is $m + n = n + m$, for all natural numbers m and n.

Proof: $m + n = \sigma^n(m)$ Def. of addition

$$= \sigma^n\big(\sigma^m(0)\big) \qquad\qquad \text{Thm. 8-2}$$

$$= \big(\sigma^n\sigma^m\big)(0) \qquad\qquad \text{Property of } \sigma \text{ as a mapping}$$

$$= \big(\sigma^m\sigma^n\big)(0) \qquad\qquad \text{Thm. 8-1}$$

$$= \sigma^m\big(\sigma^n(0)\big) \qquad\qquad \text{Property of } \sigma$$

$$= \sigma^m(n) \qquad\qquad \text{Thm. 8-2}$$

$$= n + m \qquad\qquad \text{Definition of addition.} ∎$$

One can now establish the fact that zero is the additive identity element.

Furthermore suppose the natural number a is also an identity element for addition, than $a + n = n + a$ for all natural numbers n. In particular $a + 0 = 0 + a$. But by the definition of addition $a + 0 = \sigma^0(a)$ and $0 + a = \sigma^a(0)$. By assumption a is an identity, so $0 + a = \sigma^a(0) = 0$. But $\sigma^a(0) = a$ by Theorem 8-2. Since σ is a one-to-one map, the ath successor of 0 is unique and so $a = 0$.

All the properties of cardinal numbers that were discussed in Chapters 3-7 have corresponding analogues in the natural number system and could be developed from the four basic postulates stated at the beginning of this section. Many of these properties depend on properties of the mapping σ and thus illustrate the usefulness of the concept of mappings discussed briefly in Chapter 1.

Let us now consider briefly the problem of how the operation of multiplication can be defined for the set of natural numbers. Similar to the operation of addition, multiplication is defined in terms of the mapping σ. The definition illustrates the fact that multiplication can be interpreted as repeated addition since the definition is iterative in nature.

Definition 8-4: Let m and n be two natural numbers. The product of m and n, denoted by $m \cdot n$, is given as $m \cdot n = (\sigma^m)^n(0)$.

As an illustration of how this definition can be used, consider the problem of finding the product of 3 and 2.

$$3 \cdot 2 = (\sigma^3)^2(0) \qquad\qquad \text{Definition 8-4}$$

$$= [(\sigma^3)(\sigma^3)](0) \qquad\qquad \text{Definition 8-2}$$

$$= \sigma^{3+3}(0) \qquad\qquad \text{Theorem 8-1}$$

$$= \sigma^6(0) \qquad\qquad \text{Definition 8-3}$$

$$= 6 \qquad\qquad \text{Theorem 8-2}$$

Using Definition 8-4, the postulates, and the properties of σ as a one-to-one mapping, all the properties of multiplication of natural numbers analogous to those developed for the cardinal numbers in Chapter 5 can be established. Since a complete development of the natural number system is not the purpose of this section no further details will be presented. However, some of the exercises in the following list are proposed to challenge the student to pursue this development.

EXERCISE SET 8-3

1. Using the definitions of addition and multiplication of natural numbers prove the following equalities.
   (a) $4 + 3 = 7$
   (b) $(3 + 2) + 2 = 7$
   (c) $4 \cdot 2 = 8$
   (d) $3 \cdot 2 + 4 = 10$
   (e) $4 \cdot (3 + 2) = 4 \cdot 3 + 4 \cdot 2$
   (f) $(5 \cdot 2) \cdot 2 = 5 \cdot (2 \cdot 2)$
2. Using The Principle of Mathematical Induction prove the following statements are valid for all natural numbers.
   (a) $1 + 2 + 3 + \ldots + n = \dfrac{1}{2} n \cdot (n + 1)$
   (b) $4 + 8 + 12 + \ldots + 4n = 2n(n + 1)$
   (c) $3 + 6 + 9 + \ldots + 3n = \dfrac{3}{2} n(n + 1)$
   (d) $1 + 3 + 5 + \ldots + 2n - 1 = n^2$
3. Prove that addition of natural numbers is an associative operation.
4. Prove that $a + m = b + m$ implies that $a = b$ for all natural numbers m.
5. Prove $m \cdot 0 = 0$ for all natural numbers m.
6. Prove that $\sigma(0) = 1$ is a multiplicative identity for natural numbers.
7. Prove that multiplication of natural numbers is a commutative operation.

Chapter summary

This chapter is the climax of the work with cardinal numbers. Here we constructed two different systems of arithmetic each having as its basis the set of cardinals. The main point to note regarding arithmetic in bases other than ten is that the number properties are identical with those of base ten. In other words the properties in no way depend upon the numerals used to represent the numbers.

The modular systems have many of the same properties that ordinary arithmetic has, and in addition to this, these systems have only a finite number of elements. Many of the properties in which we are interested can therefore be demonstrated with much more ease than with the ordinary base ten system.

For the sake of completeness we also introduced a system of numbers from an axiomatic point of view, the natural number system. This is often preferred by mathematicians because of its conceptual simplicity. In any case, this system acts exactly like the system of finite cardinals and because of this the two types of numbers are often used interchangeably in nontechnical discussions. Also used by some as synonyms for cardinal or natural numbers are the terms whole number and counting number.

PART II Integers rational numbers and real numbers

CHAPTER 9 Integers

1. The Concept of Integers

One of the major reasons for the development of mathematical concepts has been to describe physical phenomena in a meaningful way. Often times physical problems give rise to a mathematical model and the investigation of the mathematical properties of this model yields a means of interpreting similar physical problems or of predicting outcomes of related phenomena. This being the case, it might be useful to determine whether the cardinal numbers are sufficient to describe the physical world as we know it.

It is not difficult to find many instances where the concepts of "positive" or "negative," or "opposites" are used. In nature, there is often a difference of electrical potential between the earth and the clouds over-head. Occasionally during thunderstorms there is an equalizing discharge between these bodies of different polarity, namely lightning.

Similarly, if one studies magnets he finds that a natural magnet has two poles which have different magnetic properties. Like poles repel while unlike poles attract each other.

In an electrolytic cell there are two poles, one called a cathode or negative pole, and one called the positive pole or anode. Another topic common to both physics and chemistry is charged particles. Perhaps three of the most common are electrons, protons, and neutrons. To the electron a charge of negative one has been assigned and to the proton a charge of positive one has been assigned. Interestingly enough, if a proton and electron join, they form a neutron which has no electrical charge.

If one studies the movement of particles or other physical entities, he finds that the rate of change of velocity with respect to time is called acceleration. If the velocity increases we say that there is a positive acceleration, while a decrease in velocity means that a negative acceleration has occurred or is occurring.

Other examples of phenomena which are described in terms of positive and negative numbers are the degree scales for recording temperatures in Fahrenheit, Centigrade, Kelvin, and Rankine. Also, for those who may have an interest in space exploration, we mention the recording of time during the final count-down phase of the rocket launching sequence.

What has been pointed out, then, is the occurrence of positive and negative and also positive and negative numbers in describing physical situations. A case can also be made for the need of negative numbers from the mathematical point of view. That is that we would like to have a number system in which subtraction is always possible. As you will recall, it was not always possible to subtract in the system of cardinal numbers. As you are also aware, signed numbers do exist. Let us therefore see how certain signed numbers, namely the set of integers, may be constructed. This construction will be somewhat abstract, but many of the concepts learned in Part One will be used again.

Let us consider ordered pairs of cardinals and associate with each ordered pair a point (as illustrated in Figure 9-1). We determine a point named by the ordered pair of cardinals, say (a,b), as follows: We go to the right to the vertical line labelled a and up to the horizontal line labelled b. The point where these lines cross is the point associated with the ordered pair (a,b).

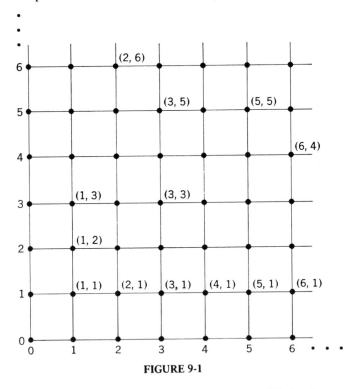

FIGURE 9-1

As you can see, in Figure 9-1 some of the names have been filled in for you. Be sure you understand how we have agreed to name such points as those illustrated in Figure 9-1. If this process of associating ordered pairs of cardinals with points on this grid (or graph) is continued, we readily observe that we have a vast array of such ordered pairs of cardinals. Let us make one more agreement before we consider this infinite set further. We shall replace the cardinals listed in Figure 9-1 by ordered pairs of cardinals, one of whose members is cardinal zero.

(See Figure 9-2). This replacement is a direct consequence of the method used to form Cartesian products in Section 1-4.

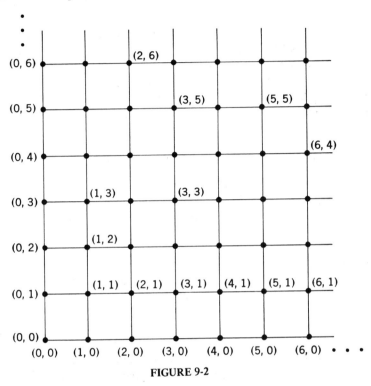

FIGURE 9-2

What we have formed then is a pictorial representation of $C \times C$ where C is the set of cardinal numbers.

Let us now consider this set of ordered pairs which were just constructed to see if we can find any useful relation which might be defined on the set. If this is done, we find a relation, which we denote by $\mathcal{I}$, can be defined as follows.[1]

Definition 9-1: If (a,b) and (c,d) are members of $C \times C$, then $(a,b) \mathcal{I} (c,d)$, [read (a,b) is in the relation "$\mathcal{I}$" to (c,d)] if and only if $a + d = b + c$.

Note that the addition in Definition 9-1 is cardinal addition.

Examples:
(a) (2,3) and (4,5): Now $2 + 5 = 3 + 4$, so by Definition 9-1 it must be the case that $(2,3) \mathcal{I} (4,5)$.

---

[1]Other relations are possible. A very useful one is that which is defined on $\{0,1,...\} \times \{1,2,...\}$. The relation is $(a,b) \mathcal{R} (c,d)$ iff $ad = bc$. This leads to the set of unsigned rational numbers.

(b) (3,7) and (13,17): Here $3 + 17 = 7 + 13$, so we have again by Definition 9-1 that $(3,7).\mathscr{I}(13,17)$.

(c) (0,5) and (2,7): Here we have that $0 + 7 = 5 + 2$ so that $(0,5).\mathscr{I}(2,7)$.

The student should study the three examples just given and then try to work out a few for himself. Some more problems of this type will be listed in the exercise set at the end of this section.

We already know from the work with sets and cardinal numbers that some relations are equivalence relations and that the latter may be very useful. Let us now prove that the relation which we defined in Definition 9-1 is an equivalence relation.

Theorem 9-1: The relation $\mathscr{I}$ in Definition 9-1 is an equivalence relation.

Proof: Recall that to prove the theorem, we must show that $\mathscr{I}$ is reflexive, symmetric, and transitive.

(1) Let (a,b) be any ordered pair of cardinals. We must show that

$$(a,b).\mathscr{I}(a,b).$$

But this is true by Definition 9-1 provided that we can show that $a + b = b + a$. From cardinal arithmetic we know that such sums exist, are unique, and that the addition is commutative. That is, $a + b$ exists, the sum is unique, and

$$a + b = b + a.$$

Hence by Definition 9-1, we conclude that $(a,b).\mathscr{I}(a,b)$.

(2) Let (a,b) and (c,d) be any two ordered pairs of cardinal numbers. We must show that if $(a,b) \mathscr{I} (c,d)$, then $(c,d) \mathscr{I} (a,b)$. That is, we need to show that if $a + d = b + c$, then it is also true that $c + b = d + a$. But from cardinal arithmetic we have that

$$b + c = c + b \text{ and } a + d = d + a.$$

Hence we have that

$$d + a = a + d = b + c = c + b.$$

By transitivity of equality, $d + a = c + b$ and by the symmetric property $c + b = d + a$. Then using Definition 9-1 we obtain the fact that $(c,d) \mathscr{I}(a,b)$ and the relation, $\mathscr{I}$, is therefore symmetric.

(3) Let (a,b), (c,d), and (e,f) be any three ordered pairs of cardinals. We want to show that if $(a,b).\mathscr{I}(c,d)$ and $(c,d).\mathscr{I}(e,f)$, then $(a,b).\mathscr{I}(e,f)$. From $(a,b).\mathscr{I}(c,d)$ we have $a + d = b + c$, and from $(c,d).\mathscr{I}(e,f)$ we have $c + f = d + e$, all by Definition 9-1. We need to show that $a + f = b + e$, then use Definition 9-1 to obtain the result $(a,b).\mathscr{I}(e,f)$.

We start with $a + d = b + c$ and $c + f = d + e$. Adding, we obtain

$$(a + d) + (c + f) = (b + c) + (d + e).$$

Then $\qquad\qquad (a + f) + (c + d) = (b + e) + (c + d).$ **Why?**

Using the cancellation property of cardinal addition, we obtain

$$a + f = b + e.$$

Hence by Definition 9-1 we obtain the fact that $(a,b)\,\mathcal{I}\,(e,f)$. Thus the relation $\mathcal{I}$ is transitive and we can now conclude that it is indeed an EQUIVALENCE relation. ∎

As in the work with sets, because of the fact that $\mathcal{I}$ is an equivalence relation, it partitions (i.e., "cuts up") this infinite set of ordered pairs of cardinals into mutually disjoint classes called EQUIVALENCE CLASSES. Three of the equivalence classes are

$$\begin{Bmatrix} (1,0) \\ (2,1) \\ (3,2) \\ (4,3) \\ (5,4) \\ \cdot \\ \cdot \\ \cdot \end{Bmatrix} , \quad \begin{Bmatrix} (0,0) \\ (1,1) \\ (2,2) \\ (3,3) \\ (4,4) \\ \cdot \\ \cdot \\ \cdot \end{Bmatrix} , \text{ and } \begin{Bmatrix} (0,1) \\ (1,2) \\ (2,3) \\ (3,4) \\ (4,5) \\ \cdot \\ \cdot \\ \cdot \end{Bmatrix}$$

Note that in any particular class, any two of the ordered pairs are equivalent with respect to the relation $\mathcal{I}$. These equivalence classes which were just formed are what we shall call integers.

Definition 9-2: A class of equivalent ordered pairs of cardinal numbers (i.e., an equivalence class as obtained from the relation $\mathcal{I}$ above) is an **integer**.

Notice that in the three equivalence classes listed, each class has one ordered pair which has at least one member *zero*. This characteristic is always the case. The student should construct a few additional equivalence classes and satisfy himself that this is true. That is, in every equivalence class there is an ordered pair which has one of the forms $(0,k)$, $(0,0)$, or $(k,0)$ where k is a non-zero cardinal number. This observation will become important when we name the integers.

Theorem 9-2: Every integer contains an element of the form $(0,k)$, $(0,0)$, or $(k,0)$ where $k \neq 0$.

Proof: Every ordered pair of cardinals (a,b) belongs to some integer. By the Trichotomy Law for cardinal numbers there are just three possibilities for the relation of a to b:

1) $a = b$,
2) $a > b$, or
3) $a < b$.

(1) If $a = b$, then $(a,b) \mathcal{I} (0,0)$ since a + 0 = 0 + b. Hence the integer must also contain (0,0).

(2) If $a > b$, then there is a cardinal number $m \neq 0$ such that

$$b + m = a$$

Then

$$a + 0 = b + m \qquad \text{(Why?)}$$

so that $(a,b) \mathcal{I} (m,0)$ and consequently $(m,0)$ belongs to the integer.

(3) If $a < b$, then there is a cardinal number $n \neq 0$ such that

$$a + n = b$$

Since

$$a + n = 0 + b$$

we have by Definition 9-1 that $(a,b) \mathcal{I} (0,n)$ and consequently $(0,n)$ belongs to the integer. ∎

Furthermore, it is never possible for any integer to contain more than one of the types $(0,k)$, $(0,0)$, and $(k,0)$, $k \neq 0$, as we shall now show.

Theorem 9-3: No two of the types $(0,k)$, $(0,0)$, and $(k,0)$ can be elements of the same integer.

Proof: This will be proved by directly considering the possibilities.

(1) Suppose that $(0,k)$ and $(0,0)$ belong to the same integer. Then $(0,k) \mathcal{I} (0,0)$ so that $0 + 0 = k + 0$. That is, $k = 0$. But this is *not* possible since we specified $k \neq 0$ previously.

(2) Suppose that $(0,k)$ and $(k,0)$ belong to the same integer. Then $(0,k) \mathcal{I} (k,0)$ so that $0 + 0 = k + k$. That is, $2k = 0$ and consequently $k = 0$. Again, we contradict the fact that $k \neq 0$ as specified.

(3) Suppose that $(0,0)$ and $(k,0)$ belong to the same integer. The proof is similar to that in part (1) above and we leave it for the student to try. ∎

Finally, it is never true that we can have $(0,k)$ and $(0,n)$ in the same class with $k \neq 0$, $n \neq 0$, and $k \neq n$. We now state this fact formally as a theorem and prove it.

Theorem 9-4: If $k \neq 0$, $n \neq 0$, and $k \neq n$, then $(0,k)$ and $(0,n)$ cannot be in the same equivalence class.

Proof: Suppose that $(0,k)$ and $(0,n)$ are in the same equivalence class. Then

$$(0,n) \, \mathcal{S} \, (0,k)$$

so that

$$0 + k = n + 0$$

or

$$k = n.$$

But this contradicts the fact that $k \neq n$ and so the theorem is proved. ∎

The student might at this point enjoy making up a theorem similar to Theorem 9-4 which concerns the elements $(k,0)$ and $(n,0)$. Its proof would be similar to that of Theorem 9-4. We invite you to try it.

Since the equivalence classes will be quite unhandy (if not impossible) to work with, we shall introduce some simplifying notation for them.

Definition 9-3: An equivalence class (i.e., the integer) which contains the element (a,b) will be denoted by $[a,b]$.

Thus if an element $(3,5)$ belongs to an integer (equivalence class), we shall denote the integer by $[3,5]$. Apparently, since $(4,6) \, \mathcal{S} \, (3,5)$, $[4,6]$ also denotes the class which contains $(3,5)$. Thus it appears that several symbols may be used to denote a given integer.

Furthermore, since by previous discussion each integer contains an element of one and only one of the forms $(0,k)$, $(0,0)$, or $(k,0)$, $k \neq 0$, we may denote any integer by one of the forms $[0,k]$, $[0,0]$, or $[k,0]$ where k is a non-zero cardinal.

Definition 9-4: The numerals $[0,k]$, $[0,0]$, and $[k,0]$ are called **standard forms** for representing integers.

These standard forms will be exceedingly useful when we discuss some of the properties of integers.

As a final note on terminology and notation, we shall now list synonyms for the standard forms which were mentioned above.

Definition 9-5: 1) $[0,k]$ means the same as **negative k**, denoted ^-k
2) $[0,0]$ means the same as **zero**, denoted 0
3) $[k,0]$ means the same as **positive k**, denoted ^+k or k.

Example:

1) $[0,2]$ is negative two (i.e., $^-2$),
2) $[0,0]$ is zero (i.e., 0),
3) $[5,0]$ is positive five (i.e., $^+5$), or 5.

We shall feel free to use the type of numeral which is most convenient during the ensuing discussions, but we will eventually end up with numerals of the type suggested in Definition 9-5. If you find the bracketed pairs confusing, feel free to use the type $\bar{k}$, 0, or ^+k.

The designation of integers as being positive or negative (excluding zero) is not entirely arbitrary, as we shall now show. In Figure 9-3 we have drawn diagonal lines through certain sets of points on the grid representing $C \times C$. Notice that each of these lines is associated with one of the equivalence classes which were developed earlier. This is of special significance as we shall soon illustrate.

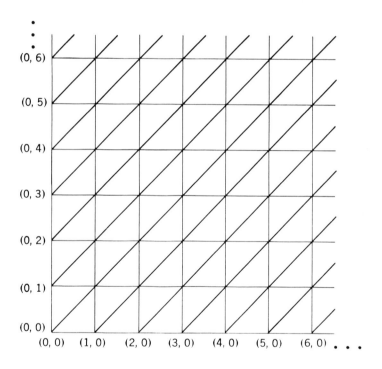

FIGURE 9-3

If on the lower horizontal line we choose the direction to the right of the main vertical line as being positive, we could associate with the points (1,0), (2,0), ... the integers $^+1$, $^+2$, and so forth as in Figure 9-4, since the names of those points are members of the respective integers.

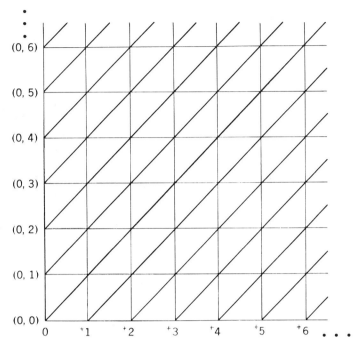

FIGURE 9-4

Now if we extend the lower horizontal line to the left and also extend the diagonals which intersect the left hand vertical, we determine points to the left of that vertical and on the extended horizontal. These are in the opposite direction from the main vertical line as those already listed to the right. Thus in this context it makes sense to call these integers *negative*. We illustrate this in Figure 9-5 and Figure 9-6 which follow.

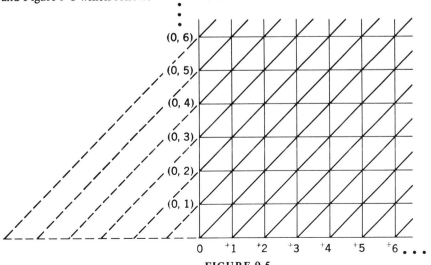

FIGURE 9-5

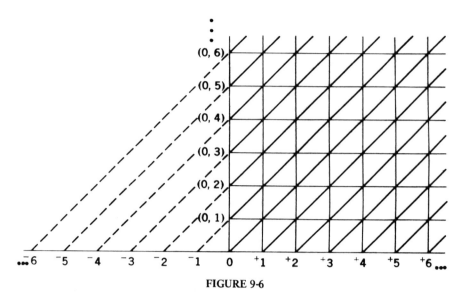

FIGURE 9-6

We shall also need to know when two integers are equal in order to develop our arithmetic in the ensuing chapters. We shall define equality in the following way because of the implications of Definition 9-3.

Definition 9-6: Two integers are **equal** if they contain the same ordered pairs of cardinal numbers. That is, $[a,b] = [c,d]$ if and only if $a + d = b + c$.

As you may observe, this is analogous to saying that two cardinals are equal if their numerals name the same class of equivalent sets. Equivalently we can say that two integers are equal if they can be represented by the same standard form. For example, $[3,4] = [21,22]$ since both can be represented by $[0,1]$.

Now that we have discussed the concept of integer, we are ready to try to develop an arithmetic for the set of integers.

EXERCISE SET 9-1

1. Determine the names (ordered pairs) for the remaining points of Figure 9-1.
2. Check each of the following pairs of ordered pairs to see if the relation. ✗ holds.
   (a) (3,2) and (2,3)   (d) (7,7) and (3,3)
   (b) (5,7) and (1,3)   (e) (8,9) and (10,9)
   (c) (6,5) and (3,4)   (f) (9,8) and (9,7)
3. Are the equivalence classes consisting of equivalent ordered pairs of cardinals infinite classes? A simple "yes" or "no" is not sufficient. Support your answer. [Hint: Can the elements of one of these equivalence classes be mapped 1-1 onto those of the set of cardinals?]
4. Write *three* numerals each for
   (a) [2,3]   (b) [7,3]   (c) [1,1]
5. You are probably familiar with the statement "zero is neither positive nor negative." From what you have learned in Section 9-1, is there any basis for this statement? If so, what?

6. Test the following pairs for equality by using the standard forms mentioned in Definition 9-4.

(a) [3,2] and [2,3]

(b) [7,9] and [2,4]

(c) [6,4] and [4,3]

(d) [4,4] and [1,1]

(e) [7,8] and [8,7]

(f) [9,8] and [9,7]

7. Prove that if $k \neq 0$, $n \neq 0$, and $k \neq n$, then $(k,0)$ and $(n,0)$ cannot be in the same equivalence class.

Chapter summary

If one reflects upon the system of cardinal numbers developed in Part One, he finds that mathematical model to be lacking in some respects. For one thing, it is found that the concept of cardinal number is not sufficient to describe certain phenomena. Secondly, the system is not completely acceptable from the point of view of the mathematician because of the fact that subtraction is not always possible. For these reasons we try to develop a new system of numbers with the hope that these deficiencies do not exist in this new system.

In this chapter we set as our task the development of a new kind of number, the integer. In the development of the concept of integer the idea of *equivalence relation* again plays an important role. We find that each integer is an equivalence class, and thus it appears even at this early stage that we may meet many of the concepts of Part One again.

Relative to the concepts of positive and negative it should be emphasized that our choice was an arbitrary one. However, in addition to the intuitive geometric approach used above, it might be pointed out that the grid representing the Cartesian product of the cardinals cross the cardinals must be of the type shown because of the original agreement regarding the graphing of product sets.

CHAPTER 10 Addition and subtraction of integers

1. Definition of Addition

The object of this section is to define addition of integers, show that the resulting arithmetic satisfies all of the properties which cardinal addition satisfies, and show that integers have certain other desirable properties as well.

When we define addition of integers, we want the cardinal sum, $a + b$, to correspond to the integer sum, $[a,0] \oplus [b,0]$. That is, if in cardinal addition we have $2 + 3$, what would be a "natural" way to define $[2,0] \oplus [3,0]$? It is easy to see that we might form $[2 + 3,0]$ as the sum. This is made somewhat acceptable if we refer to Figures 9-1 and 9-2 of Section 9-1, for there we set up a correspondence between cardinals and integers as follows:

Cardinal	Integer
$a \longleftrightarrow$	$[a,0]$

Hence if $\quad 2 \longleftrightarrow [2,0]$

and $\quad 3 \longleftrightarrow [3,0]$,

it seems we should want the correspondence

$$2 + 3 \longleftrightarrow [2 + 3,0].$$

That is, $\quad 5 = 2 + 3 \longleftrightarrow [2 + 3,0] = [5,0].$

There are several possibilities for forming combinations of 2, 3, 0, 0, but we list only those having some combination of 2 and 3 for first members since we are trying to obtain 5 as a first member in order that we can obtain the desired correspondence between cardinals and integers.

Case 1): $\quad [2,0] \oplus [3,0] = [2 + 3, 0 + 0]$

Case 2): $\quad [2,0] \oplus [3,0] = [2 \cdot 3, 0 + 0]$

Case 3): $[2,0] \oplus [3,0] = [2+3, 0\cdot 0]$

Case 4): $[2,0] \oplus [3,0] = [2\cdot 3, 0\cdot 0]$

Note that only cases 1 and 3 are possibilities if we require the preservation of the correspondence which we decided upon.   Hence all that we must decide is whether to take the sum or the product of the second members of the integers. Since using second elements both zero does not decide the issue, let us select

$$[2,0] \oplus [4,1]$$

Note that $[4,1]$ is still the integer three. Note also that we are ignoring for the moment the question of uniqueness of sums. But for now this is acceptable since the definition we shall form is only a tentative one. Once we have formed our tentative definition of addition, we shall discuss the questions of existence and uniqueness in some detail.

Now the two possibilities are

$$[2,0] \oplus [4,1] = [2+4, 0+1]$$

and

$$[2,0] \oplus [4,1] = [2+4, 0\cdot 1]$$

From these, we obtain $[6,1]$ and $[6,0]$ respectively. Since only $[6,1] = [5,0]$, we must choose Case 1 as the way in which to add integers. Again, this is done in order to preserve the desired correspondence with cardinal addition. If several examples of this type are worked, we are led to the following as a tentative definition for addition of integers.

Definition 10-1: The **sum** of two integers $[a,b]$ and $[c,d]$ is the integer $[a+c, b+d]$. That is, $[a,b] \oplus [c,d] = [a+c, b+d]$ where $\oplus$ denotes addition of integers.

Note that in Definition 10-1 we have differentiated symbolically between integer addition and cardinal addition. This is important since we are defining a new operation in terms of one which is already available, and this new operation is on a different set. There is actually an important mapping which exists between a subset of the set of integers and the set of cardinals, but we shall defer discussion of this important aspect until a later section. By that time, we will have developed multiplication of integers which we also need prior to that discussion.

Although we now have a definition for addition of integers, it will not be useful unless we know that under the operation $\oplus$ an answer always exists and is unique. Hence our definition must possess these two properties.

It should be clear that if we select the cardinals as instructed in Definition 10-1, we always obtain an ordered pair of cardinal numbers, since the sum of two cardinal numbers is certainly a cardinal number. Consequently, the result of using $\oplus$ on two integers *is* always an integer. That is, the set of integers is closed under $\oplus$.

Uniqueness is somewhat more involved and so we shall state it as a theorem and prove it.

Theorem 10-1 (Uniqueness): If $[a,b] = [e,f]$ and $[c,d] = [g,h]$, then $[a,b] \oplus [c,d] = [e,f] \oplus [g,h]$.

Proof: $[a,b] \oplus [c,d] = [a + c, b + d]$ and $[e,f] \oplus [g,h] = [e + g, f + h]$ by Definition 10-1. We want to show that

$$[a + c, b + d] = [e + g, f + h]$$

and this is the case provided that

$$(a + c) + (f + h) = (b + d) + (e + g) \text{ by Definition 9-6}$$

From $[a,b] = [e,f]$ we have $a + f = b + e$ and from $[c,d] = [g,h]$ we have $c + h = d + g$ by Definition 9-6.

Then by the uniqueness of cardinal addition, we obtain

$$(a + f) + (c + h) = (b + e) + (d + g)$$

Using commutativity and associativity for cardinal addition, we obtain

$$(a + c) + (f + h) = (b + d) + (e + g)$$

Consequently, we have finally obtained the result that

$$[a,b] \oplus [c,d] = [e,f] \oplus [g,h] \text{ by Definition 9-6}$$

That is, addition of integers is unique. ∎

Thus if we want to add the integers five and negative seven, we are assured that we can choose any representative for five and any representative for negative seven and obtain the same integer as our sum. Thus for example we could select

$$5 \oplus {}^-7$$

$$[5,0] \oplus [0,7]$$

$$[6,1] \oplus [7,14]$$

$$[14,9] \oplus [2,9], \text{ or}$$

$$[26,21] \oplus [42,49]$$

and we would always obtain the same sum, namely negative two. The only differences which would exist would be in the numerals representing negative two.

EXERCISE SET 10-1

1. Using Definition 10-1 determine the sum for each of the following.

   (a) $[4,3] \oplus [3,4]$ (d) $[7,5] \oplus [5,8]$
   (b) $[5,2] \oplus [6,4]$ (e) $[8,3] \oplus [9,7]$
   (c) $[3,5] \oplus [6,5]$ (f) $[2,4] \oplus [6,1]$

2. When $\oplus$ was defined we claimed that it was an operation on the set of integers. Discuss why you think $\oplus$ *is* or *is not* an operation on this set.

3. Why is the set of integers closed under $\oplus$?
4. Show that in each of the following parts the same integer is named by both sums.
   (a) $[1,2] \oplus [3,4]$ and $[5,6] \oplus [10,11]$.
   (b) $[8,2] \oplus [6,1]$ and $[12,6] \oplus [7,2]$.
   (c) $[9,4] \oplus [4,7]$ and $[12,7] \oplus [16,19]$.
   (d) $[1,5] \oplus [9,7]$ and $[4,8] \oplus [4,2]$.
5. Does each part of problem four illustrate the idea of uniqueness of sums? Explain why or why not.
6. Since $^-7 \oplus {}^+15 = {}^+8$ and $^+5 \oplus {}^+3 = {}^+8$, can it be concluded that answers are *not* always unique under $\oplus$?

2. Properties of Addition

Now that we know that sums are unique, we want to check to see if the commutative and associative properties hold and if there is an identity element for addition. The main reason we want these properties is because we are trying to construct a system which has more utility in describing physical phenomena than the cardinal numbers but which retains as many of the desirable properties of the system of cardinals as possible.

Theorem 10-2 (Commutative): If $[a,b]$ and $[c,d]$ are integers, then $[a,b] + [c,d] = [c,d] + [a,b]$.

Proof: $[a,b] + [c,d] = [a+c, b+d]$ Def. 10-1

$\qquad\qquad\quad = [c+a, d+b]$ Comm. (+)

$\qquad\qquad\quad = [c,d] + [a,b]$ Def. 10-1

Hence it makes no difference in which order we add integers. That is, addition of integers is commutative. ∎

Example: $[2,7] \oplus [5,3] = [2+5, 7+3]$

$\qquad\qquad\qquad\quad = [7,10]$

and

$\qquad [5,3] \oplus [2,7] = [5+2, 3+7]$

$\qquad\qquad\qquad\quad = [7,10]$

Hence $[2,7] \oplus [5,3] = [5,3] \oplus [2,7]$. That is, $^-4 \oplus {}^+2 = {}^+2 \oplus {}^-4$.

As is true for the system of cardinal numbers, the commutative property provides a basis for the method of checking addition problems which we commonly use. Of course we also need the associative property in order to use this method of checking, for we often have more than two numbers in an addition problem.

Example: $[2,1] \oplus ([5,8] \oplus [6,3]) = [2,1] \oplus [5 + 6, 8 + 3]$ Def. 10-1

$$= [2 + (5 + 6), 1 + (8 + 3)]$$ Def. 10-1

$$= [(2 + 5) + 6, (1 + 8) + 3]$$ Assoc. (+)

$$= [2 + 5, 1 + 8] \oplus [6,3]$$ Def. 10-1

$$= ([2,1] \oplus [5,8]) \oplus [6,3]$$ Def. 10-1

That is, $^+1 \oplus (^-3 \oplus {}^+3) = (^+1 \oplus {}^-3) \oplus {}^+3$ since

$$^+1 \oplus (^-3 \oplus {}^+3) = {}^+1 \oplus 0 \qquad (^+1 \oplus {}^-3) \oplus {}^+3 = {}^-2 \oplus {}^+3$$

$$\text{and}$$

$$= {}^+1 \qquad\qquad\qquad\qquad = {}^+1.$$

The formal statement of this result is given in Theorem 10-3 below.

Theorem 10-3 (Associative): If $[a,b]$, $[c,d]$, and $[e,f]$ are integers, then $[a,b] \oplus ([c,d] \oplus [e,f]) = ([a,b] \oplus [c,d]) \oplus [e,f]$.

Proof: The proof parallels the justification of the preceding example. We leave it as an exercise.

Addition of integers is associative, and now the usual method of checking addition of integers is now completely justified.

If one now asks himself whether or not an additive identify exists for integers, he is very likely to guess that it is the integer zero, since cardinal zero is the identity for the addition of cardinal numbers. Let us see if this is the case by finding the sum of the integer zero and an arbitrary integer $[a,b]$.

$$[a,b] \oplus [0,0] = [a + 0, b + 0]$$

$$= [a,b].$$

Using commutativity of addition, we have that

$$[0,0] \oplus [a,b] = [a,b] \oplus [0,0] = [a,b]$$

so that integer zero is indeed an additive identity. We can be even more precise than this, for as might be suspected by now, zero is the only additive identity for the system of integers.

Theorem 10-4: There is at most one additive identity for integers.

Proof: We leave this as an exercise. [Hint: Refer to Theorem 3-8.]

Consequently, since there is an additive identity and there is at most one additive identity, there is precisely one, namely $[0,0]$, the integer zero.

In the solving of certain arithmetic problems, we are sometimes confronted with sentences of the form

$$[x,y] \oplus [2,3] = [4,1] \oplus [2,3]$$

and are asked to determine the number $[x,y]$. Our intuition may lead us to conclude that $[x,y] = [4,1]$. This seems to be reasonable, so let us see if we can prove that some such result can be obtained.

Theorem 10-5 (Cancellation): If $[a,b]$, $[c,d]$, and $[e,f]$ are integers, and if $[a,b] \oplus [e,f] = [c,d] \oplus [e,f]$, then $[a,b] = [c,d]$.

Proof: Since $[a,b] \oplus [e,f] = [c,d] \oplus [e,f]$,
we have

$$[a + e, b + f] = [c + e, d + f] \qquad \text{Def. 10-1}$$

$$(a + e) + (d + f) = (b + f) + (c + e) \qquad \text{Def. 9-6}$$

$$(a + d) + (e + f) = (b + c) + (e + f) \qquad \text{Why?}$$

$$a + d = b + c \qquad \text{Why?}$$

$$[a,b] = [c,d] \qquad \text{Def. 9-6} \blacksquare$$

Thus in this case our intuition was correct and cancellation behaves for integers just as it did for cardinals. But *beware*, don't rely too heavily on your intuition, for if you do, it will eventually get you into mathematical difficulties!

Another useful result is the Converse of the Cancellation Property, which is sometimes useful in determining solutions for number sentences, as we shall see in the succeeding discussion.

Theorem 10-6 (Converse of Cancellation): If $[a,b]$ and $[c,d]$ are integers and $[a,b] = [c,d]$, then for any integer $[e,f]$, $[a,b] \oplus [e,f] = [c,d] \oplus [e,f]$.

Proof: From $[a,b] = [c,d]$ we obtain

$$a + d = b + c \qquad \text{Def. 9-6}$$

Then

$$(a + d) + (e + f) = (b + c) + (e + f) \qquad \text{Why?}$$

$$(a + e) + (d + f) = (b + f) + (c + e) \qquad \text{Why?}$$

so that

$$[a + e, b + f] = [c + e, d + f] \qquad \text{Def. 9-6}$$

$$[a,b] \oplus [e,f] = [c,d] \oplus [e,f] \qquad \text{Def. 10-1} \blacksquare$$

Here again we note that to use the converse of cancellation is mathematically equivalent to using the concept of uniqueness. It is the latter which allows one to say "If equals are added to equals, the results are equal."

Consider now an addition problem such as $^-2 \oplus {}^+3 \oplus {}^+2 \oplus {}^+7$. As in cardinal arithmetic, it is natural to try to group by tens, but it may also be the case that some pairs of integers will add to give the integer zero as their sum. The following theorem justifies omitting these pairs from the actual computation, thus reducing the problem to one which is easier to work.

Theorem 10-7: If a, b, c, and d are integers, then
$(a \oplus b) \oplus (c \oplus d) = (a \oplus c) \oplus (b \oplus d)$.

Proof: Recall the proof for the corresponding theorem (Theorem 3-10) in cardinal addition. The proof of this one is nearly identical and so is omitted. We invite you to try it.

Using Theorem 10-7 and the additive identity, we can solve the example problem mentioned above as follows:

Example: $^-2 \oplus {}^+3 \oplus {}^+2 \oplus {}^+7 = ({}^-2 \oplus {}^+2) \oplus ({}^+3 \oplus {}^+7)$ Step (1)

$= 0 \oplus ({}^+3 \oplus {}^+7)$ (2)

$= {}^+3 \oplus {}^+7$ (3)

$= {}^+10$ (4)

In practice, we would usually omit steps one and two, so that there is some considerable saving on the part of the *informed* problem solver.

In working with sums of integers as in the preceding example, one finds that there are some pairs which yield the integer zero when added. In fact, if one reflects on this and recalls that on the number line certain pairs are symmetrically positioned relative to the integer zero, this phenomenon is expected at the intuitive level. It is possible to show that this does hold for special pairs of integers, and we shall do this in the following theorem.

Theorem 10-8: $[a,b] \oplus [b,a] = [0,0]$ for every integer $[a,b]$.

Proof: $[a,b] \oplus [b,a] = [a + b, b + a]$ Def. 10-1

$= [a + b, a + b]$ Comm. (+)

$= [0,0]$ Why? ∎

That is, for every integer, there exists another integer such that the sum of the two is the integer zero. We shall make considerable use of this in working with subtraction of integers.

Definition 10-2 (Additive Inverse): If $[a,b] \oplus [c,d] = [0,0]$, then $[c,d]$ is called an **additive inverse** of $[a,b]$ and $[a,b]$ is called an additive inverse of $[c,d]$.

As a matter of fact, each integer has one and only one additive inverse. From Theorem 10-8, each integer has an additive inverse, so all we need to show is that it has just one.

Theorem 10-9: An integer $[a,b]$ has only one additive inverse, $[b,a]$.

Proof: We leave this as an exercise. As a hint, suppose that there is another additive inverse $[m,n]$. Then use Theorem 10-8, Definition 10-1, and Definition 9-6.

Theorem 10-8 states that $^+6 \oplus {}^-6 = 0$ and Theorem 10-9 states that $^-6$ is the only integer that can be added to $^+6$ and obtain 0.

a. Rules of signs for addition

Most of us are familiar with the rules for adding signed numbers. We may have memorized them when they were first introduced to us. However, the validity may not have been discussed at that time and consequently it would be of considerable value for us to investigate the formulation of those rules. What we seek then, is to determine *why* results such as the following are true.

$$(1) \quad {}^+6 \oplus {}^+5 = {}^+11$$

$$(2) \quad {}^-7 \oplus {}^-2 = {}^-9$$

$$(3) \quad {}^+17 \oplus {}^-13 = {}^+4$$

$$(4) \quad {}^+12 \oplus {}^-18 = {}^-6$$

As we shall see, the results can be obtained fairly easily by reverting back to the use of numerals in *standard form.* These are the results of Theorems 10-10 through 10-13 below.

Theorem 10-10: $[a,0] \oplus [b,0] = [a + b, 0]$.

Proof:

$$[a,0] \oplus [b,0] = [a + b, 0 + 0] \qquad \text{Def. 10-1}$$
$$= [a + b, 0] \qquad \text{Add. Ident.} \blacksquare$$

This states that to add two positive integers, one may add as in cardinal addition and use the common sign.

Examples:

(a) $\qquad {}^+6 \oplus {}^+5 = {}^+(6 + 5)$
$$= {}^+11.$$

(b) $\qquad {}^+8 \oplus {}^+21 = {}^+(8 + 21)$
$$= {}^+29.$$

Theorem 10-11: $[0,a] \oplus [0,b] = [0, a + b]$.

Proof: If the student studies the proof of Theorem 10-10, he will find that the proof of this theorem can be constructed very easily. Try it!

To illustrate Theorem 10-11, consider the following example.

Example: $\qquad {}^-2 \oplus {}^-5 = {}^-(2 + 5)$
$$= {}^-7$$

Again, as in the preceding example, one can add as in cardinals and then use the common sign.

Theorem 10-12: $[a,0] \oplus [0,b] = [a - b, 0]$ where for cardinals $a \geqslant b$.

Proof:

$$[a,0] \oplus [0,b] = [a + 0, 0 + b] \qquad \text{Why?}$$
$$= [a,b] \qquad \text{Why?}$$

Now if $a \geqslant b$, then there is a cardinal k such that $b + k = a$, but this means that $k = a - b$. Hence

$$[a,b] = [b + k, b] \qquad \text{Why?}$$
$$= [k,0] \qquad \text{Why?}$$
$$= [a - b, 0] \qquad \text{Why?}$$

Consequently, by the transitive property of equality, we have that $[a,b] \oplus [0,b] = [a - b, 0]$. ∎

Example:
$$^{+}6 \oplus {}^{-}2 = {}^{+}(6 - 2)$$
$$= {}^{+}4$$

Theorem 10-13: $[a,0] \oplus [0,b] = [0, b - a]$ where for cardinals $a \leqslant b$.

Proof: This proof parallels that of Theorem 10-12 and is left as an exercise.

Example:
$$^{+}5 \oplus {}^{-}11 = {}^{-}(11 - 5)$$
$$= {}^{-}6$$

By means of the above theorems we see that the rules for addition of signed numbers are not so very mysterious after all. In fact, the rules are a direct consequence of our definition of addition of integers.

EXERCISE SET 10-2
1. (a) Calculate $[2,4] \oplus [8,5]$.
   (b) Calculate $[11,8] \oplus [5,7]$.
   (c) Do the results of parts (a) and (b) illustrate that $\oplus$ is commutative?
2. What is (a) $[6,2] \oplus [7,3]$?
   (b) $[8,5] \oplus [7,2]$?
   (c) $[9,6] \oplus [6,3]$?
   (d) What theorem about integer addition is illustrated?
3. What is (a) $[2,7] \oplus [3,5]$?
   (b) $[4,9] \oplus [5,9]$?
   (c) $[6,8] \oplus [5,6]$?
   (d) What theorem about integer addition is illustrated?

4. Work the following problems by first changing them to *standard form.*

(a) $[2,3] \oplus [4,2]$
(b) $[5,1] \oplus [1,6]$
(c) $[8,4] \oplus [3,9]$
(d) $[10,3] \oplus [7,12]$

(e) If you scrutinize your work in the first four parts of this problem, you find that a procedure emerges which gives a quick method for adding integers when one is positive and the other is negative. Describe this procedure.

5. Using the rules for addition of signed numbers, determine each of the following sums.

(a) $^+7 \oplus {}^+5$
(b) $^+4 \oplus {}^+3$
(c) $^-6 \oplus {}^-2$
(d) $^-5 \oplus {}^-9$
(e) $^+12 \oplus {}^-9$
(f) $^+7 \oplus {}^-5$
(g) $^+2 \oplus {}^-5$
(h) $^+3 \oplus {}^-4$

6. Change each of the numerals in problem five to *standard form* and work each part according to one of the Theorems 10-10, 10-11, 10-12, or 10-13. Write each problem out in detail. You need not list reasons.

7. Determine the additive inverse for each of the following. Use the same form as the numeral listed.

(a) $^+2$
(b) $^-11$
(c) $^+7$
(d) $^-8$
(e) 0
(f) $[2,3]$
(g) $[4,0]$
(h) $[4,1]$
(i) $[5,8]$
(j) $[4,4]$

8. What is the only integer which is its own additive inverse?

9. Determine the solution to each of the following number sentences.

(a) $x \oplus {}^-3 = {}^-2$
(b) $y \oplus {}^+7 = {}^+7$
(c) $n \oplus ({}^+7 \oplus {}^-5) = {}^-2$
(d) $t \oplus ({}^-9 \oplus {}^+9) = {}^-5$
(e) $k \oplus ({}^-2 \oplus {}^-3 \oplus {}^+8) = {}^+1$
(f) $t \oplus ({}^+5 \oplus {}^-2) = {}^-4 \oplus {}^-2.$

10. Make use of the converse of cancellation, additive inverse, or additive identity in solving each of the following number sentences.

(a) $[a,b] \oplus [7,3] = [2,6]$
(b) $[3,8] \oplus [n,m] = [2,12]$
(c) $[x,2] \oplus [5,1] = [3,7]$
(d) $[3,y] \oplus [x,5] = [2,6]$
(e) $[4,y] \oplus [10,8] = [7,16]$

3. Definition of Subtraction for Integers

Let us now consider how we might define subtraction for integers. As for addition, let us agree that whatever definition we decide upon, we shall require that we keep the same type of correspondence with differences in cardinals as we did for sums. Thus, if we have the correspondences

	Cardinal	Integer
	5 ⟷	[5,0]
and	3 ⟷	[3,0]
we want	5 − 3 ⟷	[2,0]

Now one way would be to take

$$[5,0] \ominus [3,0] = [5 - 3, 0] = [2,0]$$

However, we must also demand that our definition give us the correct answer even if the numerals are *not* in standard form. For example we could have

$$[8,3] \ominus [5,2]$$

But note that

$$[5,3] = [5 - 0, 3 - 0] \qquad (1)$$
$$= [5 + 0, 3 - 0] \qquad (2)$$
$$= [5 - 0, 3 + 0] \qquad (3)$$
$$= [5 + 0, 3 + 0] \qquad (4).$$

Will one of the above four choices work for numerals not in standard form? Remember that the method we select must work for *all* choices of numerals. Perhaps the most reasonable approach is to try a few examples to see if some of the four possible choices can be eliminated.

To this end, instead of [5,0] and [3,0], let us use [6,1] and [4,1], since [5,0] = [6,1] and [3,0] = [4,1].

$$[6,1] \ominus [4,1] = [6 - 1, 4 - 1] = [5,3] = [2,0]$$

so choice (1) still works.

Now $$[6,1] \ominus [4,1] = [6 + 1, 4 - 1] = [7,3] = [4,0]$$

Consequently, under choice (2), the desired correspondence with cardinals does not hold. Hence, we eliminate choice (2). Now we consider

$$[6,1] \ominus [4,1] = [6 - 1, 4 + 1] = [5,5] = [0,0]$$

Hence under choice (3) the correspondence with cardinals is not kept and we eliminate choice (3). Next consider

$$[6,1] \ominus [4,1] = [6 + 1, 4 + 1] = [7,5] = [2,0]$$

So choice (4) still works.

We have now narrowed our choices to (1) and (4). Let us now use [6,1] and [5,2] instead of [5,0] and [3,0] respectively. Under choice (1) we have

$$[6,1] \ominus [5,2] = [6 - 5, 1 - 2]$$

but $1 - 2$ is not a cardinal number, so that choice (1) is eliminated. Furthermore,

$$[6,1] \ominus [5,2] = [6 + 2, 1 + 5] = [8,6] = [2,0]$$

which still maintains the desired correspondence with cardinal subtraction. This leaves us with possibility (4) as a tentative way for subtracting integers. Let us formalize this in the following definition and then check to see if the consequences of the definition are those properties which we desire based on our knowledge of cardinal subtraction.

Definition 10-3: The **difference** $[a,b]$ minus $[c,d]$ is the integer $[a + d, b + c]$. Symbolically, $[a,b] \ominus [c,d] = [a + d, b + c]$.

Note that Definition 10-3 always assures that we obtain an integer as the difference, since each of the members of the order pair $(a + d, b + c)$ is a cardinal number and every such pair belongs to an integer. Next we must check to see if differences of integers are unique.

Theorem 10-14: Subtraction of integers yields unique differences.

Proof: Choose $[a,b] = [u,v]$ and $[c,d] = [x,y]$. Then we want to show that

$$[a,b] \ominus [c,d] = [u,v] \ominus [x,y]$$

By Definition 10-3

$$[a,b] \ominus [c,d] = [a + d, b + c]$$

and

$$[u,v] \ominus [x,y] = [u + y, v + x]$$

Hence

$$[a,b] \ominus [c,d] = [u,v] \ominus [x,y]$$

if and only if

$$[a + d, b + c] = [u + y, v + x]$$

But the latter statement is true if and only if

$$(a + d) + (v + x) = (b + c) + (u + y)$$

by Definition 9-6 of equality. Since $[a,b] = [u,v]$ and $[c,d] = [x,y]$,

$$\left. \begin{cases} a + v = b + u \\ c + y = d + x \end{cases} \right\} \qquad \text{by Definition 9-6.}$$

Adding the two equations, we obtain

$$(a + v) + (d + x) = (b + u) + (c + y)$$

Then

$$(a + d) + (v + x) = (b + c) + (u + y)$$

by commutativity and associativity of cardinal addition. Therefore, if the above steps are reversed, we obtain the result

$$[a,b] \ominus [c,d] = [u,v] \ominus [x,y]$$

Consequently, subtraction gives unique answers. ∎

EXERCISE SET 10-3

1. Use Definition 10-3 to determine each of the following differences.
    (a) $[4,3] \ominus [6,7]$ (d) $[2,5] \ominus [0,1]$
    (b) $[8,2] \ominus [4,1]$ (e) $[8,5] \ominus ([5,8] \ominus [6,4])$
    (c) $[4,13] \ominus [12,9]$ (f) $([8,5] \ominus [5,8]) \ominus [6,4]$.
2. Calculate each of the following pairs of differences.
    (a) $[2,6] \ominus [5,4]$ and $[5,9] \ominus [2,1]$
    (b) $[8,3] \ominus [11,5]$ and $[11,6] \ominus [13,7]$
    (c) $[5,8] \ominus [2,9]$ and $[8,11] \ominus [12,19]$
    (d) $[13,4] \ominus [1,4]$ and $[15,6] \ominus [15,18]$
    (e) Does each of the preceding parts illustrate the uniqueness of differences? Why or why not?
3. (a) Is $\ominus$ defined on the set of integers an operation? How does this compare with differences of cardinal numbers?
    (b) Is the set of integers closed with respect to $\ominus$?
4. If subtraction of integers had been defined as follows, would the desired correspondence with cardinals have been maintained?
    Definition: $[a,b] \ominus [c,d] = [ac,bd]$.

4. Properties of Integer Subtraction

Now that we have a workable definition for subtraction, let us consider more closely the difference $[a,b] \ominus [c,d]$. We shall obtain a rather surprising result to say the least.

Theorem 10-15: $[a,b] \ominus [c,d] = [a,b] \oplus [d,c]$.

Proof: $[a,b] \ominus [c,d] = [a + d, b + c]$ Def. 10-3

                               $= [a,b] \oplus [d,c]$ Def. 10-1. ∎

This theorem states, then, that any subtraction problem involving integers can be transformed to an equivalent problem in addition. In fact, Theorem 10-15 is stronger than that. To subtract $[c,d]$ from $[a,b]$, we add the additive inverse of $[c,d]$ to $[a,b]$ and that sum is the difference $[a,b] \ominus [c,d]$.

Example: Calculate $[7,3] \ominus [2,6]$.

Solution: (a) By Definition 10-3

$$[7,3] \ominus [2,6] = [7 + 6, 3 + 2]$$

$$= [13,5]$$

(b) By Theorem 10-15,

$$[7,3] \ominus [2,6] = [7,3] \oplus [6,2]$$

$$= [7 + 6, 3 + 2]$$

$$= [13,5]$$

As can be observed, the same answer results by using either method.

It is interesting to note that a relationship between addition and subtraction was also established for cardinals even though it was not this general. Furthermore, this again shows that subtraction gives unique answers because we already know that sums of integers are unique.

Theorem 10-16: If $[a,b]$ and $[c,d]$ are any two integers, then
$([a,b] \oplus [d,c]) \oplus [c,d] = [a,b]$.

Proof: $([a,b] \oplus [d,c]) \oplus [c,d] = [a,b] \oplus ([d,c] \oplus [c,d])$ Thm. 10-3

$\qquad\qquad\qquad\qquad\quad = [a,b] \oplus [0,0]$ Thm. 10-13

$\qquad\qquad\qquad\qquad\quad = [a,b]$ Thm. 10-4. ∎

Theorems 10-15, 10-16, and properties of addition enable us to prove that we have found a unique integer, namely $[a,b] \ominus [c,d]$, such that if added to $[c,d]$ yields the integer $[a,b]$. Thus we are now justified in forming an alternative definition for subtraction of integers.

Definition 10-4 (Inverse Definition): The difference $[a,b] \ominus [c,d]$ is the unique integer $[x,y]$ such that $[c,d] \oplus [x,y] = [a,b]$.

Using properties of integer addition and Theorem 10-15, we find that with regard to Definition 10-4,

$$[x,y] = [a,b] \ominus [c,d]$$
$$= [a,b] \oplus [d,c]$$

Examples: (a) $^+6 \ominus {}^-2 = {}^+6 \oplus {}^+2 = {}^+(6 + 2) = {}^+8,$
(b) $^+7 \ominus {}^+5 = {}^+7 \oplus {}^-5 = {}^+(7 - 5) = {}^+2,$
(c) $^-5 \ominus {}^+3 = {}^-5 \oplus {}^-3 = {}^-(5 + 3) = {}^-8.$

This explains the rule "change the sign and add as in signed numbers" which is often used when one subtracts signed numbers. As you can see, this rule is not so very mysterious if approached from this point of view.

Theorem 10-17: If $[a,b]$ is any integer, then $[a,b] \ominus [0,0] = [a,b]$.

Proof: This is left as an exercise for the student.

Theorem 10-18: If $[a,b]$ is any integer, then $[a,b] \ominus [a,b] = [0,0]$.

Proof: This is also left as an exercise for the student.

We have already observed that the difference of any two integers exists. Of particular interest is the result obtained if any integer whatever is subtracted from zero.

Examples: (a) $[0,0] \ominus [3,5] = [0,0] \oplus [5,3]$

$= [0+5, 0+3]$

$= [5,3]$

(b) $[0,0] \ominus [7,4] = [0,0] \oplus [4,7]$

$= [0+4, 0+7]$

$= [4,7]$

It appears from the examples above that if one subtracts a given integer from zero, the result is the additive inverse of the original. This fact may be stated formally as in Theorem 10-19 below.

Theorem 10-19: $[0,0] \ominus [a,b] = [b,a]$ for every integer $[a,b]$.

Proof: $[0,0] \ominus [a,b] = [0,0] \oplus [b,a]$ Thm. 10-15

$= [0+b, 0+a]$ Def. 10-1

$= [b,a]$ Add. Ident. (+).∎

Let us consider Theorem 10-19 more closely by using the standard form of a numeral for an integer.
Case 1: $[0,0] \ominus [k,0]$, where $k \neq 0$.
Solution: $[0,0] \ominus [k,0] = [0,k]$ by Theorem 10-19.
Therefore, if we calculate $0 \ominus {}^{+}5$, we obtain $^{-}5$. If we calculate $0 \ominus {}^{+}7$, we obtain $^{-}7$. That is, if we subtract the integer ^{+}n from zero, we always obtain ^{-}n as the difference.
Case 2: $[0,0] \ominus [0,k]$, where $k \neq 0$.
Solution: $[0,0] \ominus [0,k] = [k,0]$ by Theorem 10-19.
Hence if we calculate $0 \ominus {}^{-}3$, we obtain $^{+}3$ and if we calculate $0 \ominus {}^{-}8$, we obtain $^{+}8$. We see then that if we subtract an integer ^{-}n from zero, we always obtain ^{+}n as the difference.
Case 3: $[0,0] \ominus [0,0]$.
Solution: Left as an exercise.
It is also true in integer subtraction, as it was in subtraction of cardinals, that neither the commutative nor associative properties hold. The proofs of these facts can be established by selecting numerical counter-examples and so are left to the student as exercises.
The student will recall that for cardinal numbers a, b, c, and d, the following theorem was true.

Theorem: If $(a+b)-(c+d)$, $a-c$, and $b-d$ are defined, then
$(a+b)-(c+d) = (a-c)+(b-d)$.

This justified an algorithm commonly used in subtraction problems. There is a corresponding theorem for integer subtraction, except that we need no longer be concerned about the existence of the differences involved.

Theorem 10-20: If $[a,b]$, $[c,d]$, $[e,f]$, and $[g,h]$ are integers, then
$$([a,b] \oplus [c,d]) \ominus ([e,f] \oplus [g,h]) = ([a,b] \ominus [e,f]) \oplus ([c,d] \ominus [g,h]).$$

Proof: Since the difference of integers is always defined,

set
$$\begin{cases} [x,y] = [a,b] \ominus [e,f] \\ \text{and} \\ [u,v] = [c,d] \ominus [g,h] \end{cases}.$$

Then
$$\begin{cases} [a,b] = [x,y] \oplus [e,f] \\ \text{and} \\ [c,d] = [u,v] \oplus [g,h] \end{cases}.$$

Adding these equations we obtain
$$[a,b] \oplus [c,d] = ([x,y] \oplus [e,f]) \oplus ([u,v] \oplus [g,h])$$
$$= ([x,y] \oplus [u,v]) \oplus ([e,f] \oplus [g,h]).$$

Therefore,
$$([a,b] \oplus [c,d]) \ominus ([e,f] \oplus [g,h]) = [x,y] \oplus [u,v]$$
$$= ([a,b] \ominus [e,f]) \oplus ([c,d] \ominus [g,h]). \blacksquare$$

This theorem would be useful for working problems such as

$$\begin{array}{r} {}^+28 \\ \ominus\ {}^-26 \\ \hline \end{array}$$

or

$$({}^+7 \oplus {}^-5) \ominus ({}^+8 \oplus {}^-2).$$

Examples: (a)
$$\begin{array}{r} {}^+28 \\ \ominus\ {}^-26 \\ \hline \end{array}$$
yields
$$\begin{array}{r} {}^+20 \oplus {}^+8 \\ \ominus ({}^-20 \oplus {}^-6) \\ \hline {}^+40 \oplus {}^+14 = {}^+54 \end{array}$$

(b) $({}^+7 \oplus {}^-5) \ominus ({}^+8 \oplus {}^-2) = ({}^+7 \ominus {}^+8) \oplus ({}^-5 \ominus {}^-2)$
$$= {}^-1 \oplus {}^-3$$
$$= {}^-(1 + 3)$$
$$= {}^-4$$

EXERCISE SET 10-4

1. Use Definition 10-4 to determine each of the following differences.
   (a) $[5,6] \ominus [8,2]$ (d) $[3,7] \ominus [9,11]$
   (b) $[3,5] \ominus [5,2]$ (e) $[12,5] \ominus [2,6]$
   (c) $[11,1] \ominus [9,5]$

2. Show that
    (a) $[2,1] \ominus [0,0] = [2,1]$ (c) $[3,5] \ominus [0,0] = [3,5]$
    (b) $[2,1] \ominus [2,2] = [2,1]$ (d) $[3,5] \ominus [5,5] = [3,5]$
    (e) Prove that $[a,b] \ominus [0,0] = [a,b]$.
3. Show that
    (a) $[2,8] \ominus [2,8] = [0,0]$ (c) $[5,2] \ominus [5,2] = [0,0]$
    (b) $[2,8] \ominus [5,11] = [0,0]$ (d) $[5,2] \ominus [9,6] = [0,0]$
    (e) Prove that $[a,b] \ominus [a,b] = [0,0]$.
4. Calculate each of the following differences.
    (a) $[0,0] \ominus [5,3]$ (d) $[3,3] \ominus [5,3]$
    (b) $[2,2] \ominus [5,3]$ (e) $[0,0] \ominus [0,0]$
    (c) $[5,5] \ominus [5,3]$
5. Show that subtraction of integers does not satisfy
    (a) the commutative property.
    (b) the associative property.
6. Show in detail (with reasons) why
    $([x,y] \oplus [e,f]) \ominus ([u,v] \oplus [g,h]) = ([x,y] \ominus [u,v]) \oplus ([e,f] \ominus [g,h])$
    in proof of Theorem 10-20.
7. Apply Theorem 10-20 to each of the following problems.

    (a) $^+36$ (b) $^+49$ (c) $^+57$ (d) $^+66$
         $\ominus\,^+23$ $\ominus\,^+35$ $\ominus\,^-25$ $\ominus\,^-35$

    (e) $^-87$ (f) $^-85$ (g) $^-79$ (h) $^-47$
         $\ominus\,^-22$ $\ominus\,^-14$ $\ominus\,^+18$ $\ominus\,^+32$

8. See if you can formulate a theorem which would allow an "easy" solution to
   the following problem. $^+37$

    $$\ominus\,^+\,7$$

    [Hint: Consider Theorem 10-20 and try to find a special case which fits the
    conditions of the given problem.]
9. Determine a solution for each of the following number sentences and write
   your answers in *standard form*.
    (a) $[x,y] \oplus [2,3] = [5,3]$
    (b) $[x,y] \ominus [7,4] = [3,2]$
    (c) $([3,8] \oplus [5,2]) \ominus [7,5] = [x,y]$
    (d) $([9,2] \oplus [3,7]) \ominus [2,4] = [x,y]$
    (e) $([9,7] \ominus [3,7]) \oplus [2,1] = [x,y]$
    (f) $([9,5] \ominus [7,3]) \ominus [x,y] = [2,2]$
    (g) $([x,y] \oplus [3,2]) \ominus [1,3] = [0,0]$
    (h) $([x,y] \ominus [9,2]) \oplus [3,4] = [5,6]$
    (i) $([7,9] \ominus [x,y]) \ominus [4,1] = [4,1]$
    (j) $([8,5] \ominus [x,y]) \oplus [5,3] = [3,7]$

10. Define Δ on the set of integers as follows.

    $$[a,b] \, \Delta \, [c,d] = [b,a] \oplus [c,d]$$

    (a) Is Δ an operation on the set of integers?
    (b) Is there an identity with respect to Δ?

(c) Does $[a,b] \triangle [c,d] = [c,d] \triangle [a,b]$?

(d) Does $([a,b] \triangle [c,d]) \triangle [e,f] = [a,b] \triangle ([c,d] \triangle [e,f])$?

(e) Is there a cancellation property for $\triangle$?

11. Define $*$ on the set of integers as in the following examples.

e.g., $[2,3] * [5,4] = [8,15]$, $[7,3] * [6,4] = [28,18]$

Determine each of the following.

(a) $[3,5] * [7,6]$ (e) $[2,4] * ([3,7] * [8,2])$

(b) $[8,3] * [2,0]$ (f) $([2,4] * [3,7]) * [8,2]$

(c) $[7,9] * [3,3]$ (g) $[3,7] * ([2,5] \ominus [6,4])$

(d) $[7,6] * [3,5]$ (h) $([3,7] * [2,5]) \ominus ([3,7] * [6,4])$

(i) On the basis of the above parts, would you say that $*$ is commutative?

(j) Would you say that $*$ is associative?

(k) Is there an identity element?

(l) Does $*$ appear to be distributive over $\ominus$?

Chapter Summary

In Chapter 10 we were able to define sums and differences of integers by making certain requirements on the outcome. That is, we insisted that, in so far as possible, there be a direct correspondence between cardinal arithmetic and that being developed for the integers. In doing this, we find many properties of cardinals give rise to identical properties for integers. In particular, for sums

1. uniqueness of sums of integers depends directly upon uniqueness of sums of cardinals,

2. commutativity and associativity of sums of integers depend directly upon the corresponding properties for cardinals,

3. the additive identity for integers is a direct consequence of the additive identity for cardinals, and so forth.

One concept which distinguishes the system of integers from the system of cardinals was also discovered during the course of discussing properties of integer addition, namely that of *additive inverse*. Later, when subtraction of integers was studied, we found that by using the concept of additive inverse we could restate *every* subtraction problem in terms of an equivalent problem in addition and conversely. Thus, subtraction in the system of integers *is an operation* and one of the main deficiencies with the system of cardinals is now corrected.

CHAPTER II
Multiplication of integers

1. Definition of Multiplication

Now that we have developed a meaningful way to add and subtract integers, we shall try to obtain a method for the determination of products of integers. As before, we want to determine a method by which the desired correspondence with cardinals will be maintained. That is, since in cardinals we have $4 \cdot 2 = 8$, in integers we want $[4,0] \odot [2,0] = [8,0]$. One way in which this result can be obtained is to define multiplication as

$$[4,0] \odot [2,0] = [4 \cdot 2, 0] = [8,0]$$

Hence we shall require that in the product $[a,b] \odot [c,d]$, the product $a \cdot c$ must appear as the first member of the resulting ordered pair.

Now suppose we consider the numerals [5,1] and [3,1] instead of [4,0] and [2,0] respectively. After all, we want to be able to use any numerals we wish in order to determine products of integers. Possibilities which might be considered are

1) $[5 \cdot 3 + 5 \cdot 1, 1 \cdot 1 + 1 \cdot 3]$,
2) $[5 \cdot 3 + 1 \cdot 3, 1 \cdot 1 + 5 \cdot 1]$, and
3) $[5 \cdot 3 + 1 \cdot 1, 1 \cdot 3 + 5 \cdot 1]$; these because of our requirement that $5 \cdot 3$ be part of the first member.

We need not worry about trying to use differences (where sums have been used above) since we cannot guarantee that the differences of cardinals will always exist. Hence we shall rule those cases out.

Let us see if anything useful results from the three choices listed above.
Choice 1): $[5 \cdot 3 + 5 \cdot 1, 1 \cdot 1 + 1 \cdot 3] = [15 + 5, 1 + 3]$
$$= [20,4]$$
$$= [16,0]$$
But $[16,0] \neq [8,0]$, so this possibility must be ruled out.

Choice 2): $[5 \cdot 3 + 1 \cdot 3, 1 \cdot 1 + 5 \cdot 1] = [15 + 3, 1 + 5]$
$$= [18,6]$$
$$= [12,0].$$

Again, since $[12,0] \neq [8,0]$, we must rule out this possibility as well.

Choice 3): $[5 \cdot 3 + 1 \cdot 1, 1 \cdot 3 + 5 \cdot 1] = [15 + 1, 3 + 5]$
$$= [16,8]$$
$$= [8,0].$$

We observe that the third choice works *in this particular case.* Let us try a few more choices for numerals before we make a decision as to what our tentative definition will be.

Example: $[10,6] \odot [11,9] = [10 \cdot 11 + 6 \cdot 9, 10 \cdot 9 + 6 \cdot 11]$
$$= [110 + 54, 90 + 66]$$
$$= [164, 156]$$
$$= [8, 0].$$

Example: $[6,2] \odot [7,5] = [6 \cdot 7 + 2 \cdot 5, 6 \cdot 5 + 2 \cdot 7]$
$$= [42 + 10, 30 + 14]$$
$$= [52,44]$$
$$= [8,0]$$

Apparently, this method of determining products of integers is a useful one because it satisfies all conditions we have required thus far. Let us now formalize the definition for convenient reference.

Definition 11-1: The **product** of two integers, $[a,b]$ times $[c,d]$, is the integer $[ac + bd, ad + bc]$. Symbolically we write $[a,b] \odot [c,d] = [ac + bd, ad + bc]$.

We hasten to note that at this point we cannot guarantee the utility of the definition for products of all integers. After all, we have only obtained desired results in a few cases thus far. As a second step in establishing the usefulness of Definition 11-1, let us show that its use always results in an integer, and that integer is unique.

It should be clear from the definition of multiplication that the result is *always* an integer, for each member of the ordered pairs in the class is a cardinal number — this because products and sums of cardinals are cardinals. Hence multiplication, as we have defined it, is an operation on the set of integers. The uniqueness of products is not so obvious and so we shall prove it as a theorem.

Theorem 11-1 (Uniqueness): If $[a,b] = [e,f]$ and $[c,d] = [g,h]$, then $[a,b] \odot [c,d] = [e,f] \odot [g,h]$.

Proof: To show that $[a,b] \odot [c,d] = [e,f] \odot [g,h]$, we must show that

$$[ac + bd, ad + bc] = [eg + fh, eh + fg]$$

since these are the respective products. According to the definition of equality, we must show that

$$(ac + bd) + (eh + fg) = (ad + bc) + (eg + fh)$$

If we can show that the latter statement of equality holds, we will be done with the proof. Now we know that

$$\left.\begin{cases} [a,b] = [e,f] \\ \text{and} \\ [c,d] = [g,h] \end{cases}\right\} \quad \text{so that} \quad \left.\begin{cases} a + f = b + e \\ \text{and} \\ c + h = d + g \end{cases}\right\} \qquad \begin{aligned} &(1) \\ &\\ &(2) \end{aligned}$$

Multiplying equation $\begin{cases} (1) \text{ by } g, \text{ we obtain } ag + fg = bg + eg, \\ (2) \text{ by } b, \text{ we obtain } bc + bh = bd + bg, \\ (1) \text{ by } h, \text{ we obtain } ah + fh = bh + eh, \\ (2) \text{ by } a, \text{ we obtain } ac + ah = ad + ag. \end{cases}$

Now $(\mathbf{ac} + ah) + (\mathbf{bd} + bg) + (\mathbf{bh} + eh) + (\mathbf{ag} + fg) =$

$$(\mathbf{ad} + ag) + (\mathbf{bc} + bh) + (\mathbf{ah} + \mathbf{fh}) + (bg + \mathbf{eg})$$

Hence $(ac + bd) + (eh + fg) + (ah + bg + bh + ag) =$

$$(ad + bc) + (eg + fh) + (ah + bg + bh + ag). \text{ Why?}$$

By the cancellation property of cardinal addition we obtain

$$(ac + bd) + (eh + fg) = (ad + bc) + (eg + fh)$$

Therefore, we conclude that multiplication of integers is unique. ∎

As in Chapter 10, the uniqueness property states that if the product of two integers is formed, it makes no difference which of their names are used to represent them.

Example: Determine $^{+}5 \odot {}^{-}3$.

Solution: (a) $^{+}5 \odot {}^{-}3 = {}^{-}15$.

(b) $[5,0] \odot [0,3] = [5 \cdot 0 + 0 \cdot 3, 5 \cdot 3 + 0 \cdot 0]$
$\qquad\qquad\qquad\quad = [0 + 0, 15 + 0]$
$\qquad\qquad\qquad\quad = [0,15]$.

(c) $[7,2] \odot [7,10] = [7 \cdot 7 + 2 \cdot 10, 7 \cdot 10 + 2 \cdot 7]$
$\qquad\qquad\qquad\quad = [49 + 20, 70 + 14]$
$\qquad\qquad\qquad\quad = [69,84]$.

(d) $[14,9] \odot [5,8] = [14 \cdot 5 + 9 \cdot 8, 14 \cdot 8 + 9 \cdot 5]$
$\qquad\qquad\qquad\quad = [70 + 72, 112 + 45]$
$\qquad\qquad\qquad\quad = [142,157]$.

In each case different names have been used for the integers to be multiplied, and each final result is a name for the same integer, namely negative fifteen.

EXERCISE SET 11-1

1. Use Definition 11-1 to determine each of the following products.

   (a) $[8,3] \odot [5,3]$ (e) $[10,2] \odot [9,9]$
   (b) $[6,1] \odot [3,7]$ (f) $[5,5] \odot [3,5]$
   (c) $[2,5] \odot [7,2]$ (g) $[7,4] \odot [6,11]$
   (d) $[1,4] \odot [3,10]$ (h) $[6,14] \odot [13,8]$

2. Show that in each of the parts (a) through (d), the indicated products name the same integer.

   (a) $[3,2] \odot [7,4]$ and $[6,5] \odot [10,7]$
   (b) $[2,5] \odot [1,7]$ and $[7,10] \odot [8,14]$
   (c) $[7,4] \odot [2,5]$ and $[9,6] \odot [3,6]$
   (d) $[1,8] \odot [4,2]$ and $[4,11] \odot [8,6]$
   (e) What property of multiplication is illustrated in parts (a) through (d)?

3. Why is the set of integers closed under $\odot$?

2. Properties of Multiplication

Now that we have a workable definition for multiplication, we need to check to determine if the multiplication is commutative, associative, and distributive over addition and subtraction as was the multiplication of cardinals.

Theorem 11-2 (Commutative): If $[a,b]$ and $[c,d]$ are integers, then $[a,b] \odot [c,d] = [c,d] \odot [a,b]$.

Proof: $[a,b] \odot [c,d] = [ac + bd, ad + bc]$ Def. 11-1
                   $= [ca + db, da + cb]$ Comm. $(\cdot)$
                   $= [c,d] \odot [a,b]$ Def. 11-1. ∎

Example: $^{+}4 \odot {}^{-}5 = [4,0] \odot [0,5]$ and $^{-}5 \odot {}^{+}4 = [0,5] \odot [4,0]$
                   $= [4 \cdot 0 + 0 \cdot 5, 4 \cdot 5 + 0 \cdot 0]$ $= [0 \cdot 4 + 5 \cdot 0, 0 \cdot 0 + 5 \cdot 4]$
                   $= [0 + 0, 20 + 0]$ $= [0 + 0, 0 + 20]$
                   $= [0,20]$ $= [0,20]$
                   $= {}^{-}20$ $= {}^{-}20$

Hence by transitivity of equality, $^{+}4 \odot {}^{-}5 = {}^{-}5 \odot {}^{+}4$.

It would be instructive for the reader to attempt a general proof of commutativity of products using the same approach as that used in the preceding example.

Theorem 11-3 (Associative): If $[a,b]$, $[c,d]$, and $[e,f]$ are integers, then $[a,b] \odot ([c,d] \odot [e,f]) = ([a,b] \odot [c,d]) \odot [e,f]$.

Proof: A proof of this is very much like that in the preceding example. We omit it here, but the student should illustrate the result of the theorem with numbers to satisfy himself of its validity.

We shall now show that multiplication is distributive with respect to addition. These results are all important, so be sure you understand what each allows us to do in the arithmetic we are developing.

Theorem 11-4 (Distributive): If $[a,b]$, $[c,d]$, and $[e,f]$ are integers, then $[a,b] \odot ([c,d] \oplus [e,f]) = ([a,b] \odot [c,d]) \oplus ([a,b] \odot [e,f])$.

Proof: We shall calculate both sides and then show that they are equal.

$[a,b] \odot ([c,d] \oplus [e,f]) = [a,b] \odot [c + e, d + f]$ Why?

$= [a(c + e) + b(d + f), a(d + f) + b(c + e)]$ Why?

$= [ac + ae + bd + bf, ad + af + bc + be]$ Why?

For the expression on the right side we have

$([a,b] \odot [c,d]) \oplus ([a,b] \odot [e,f]) = [ac + bd, ad + bc] +$

$[ae + bf, af + be]$ Why?

$= [(ac + bd) + (ae + bf)$

$(ad + bc) + (af + be)]$ Why?

$= [ac + ae + bd + bf, ad + af + bc + be]$ Why?

Since the two results are identical, the symmetric and transitive properties of equality assure us that

$[a,b] \odot ([c,d] \oplus [e,f]) = ([a,b] \odot [c,d]) \oplus ([a,b] \odot [e,f])$.

That is, multiplication is distributive with respect to addition. ∎

Example: Show that $^+2 \odot (^-3 \oplus {}^+5) = (^+2 \odot {}^-3) \oplus (^+2 \odot {}^+5)$.

Solution:

$^+2 \odot (^-3 \oplus {}^+5) = {}^+2 \odot {}^+2$ and $(^+2 \odot {}^-3) \oplus (^+2 \odot {}^+5) = {}^-6 \oplus {}^+10$

$= {}^+4$ $= {}^+4$

Therefore

$^+2 \odot (^-3 \oplus {}^+5) = (^+2 \odot {}^-3) \oplus (^+2 \odot {}^+5)$

Hence we may add first and then multiply, or multiply first and then add with the assurance that we will obtain the same result by either method.

If indeed this arithmetic is to satisfy all of the properties of the arithmetic of cardinals, it is natural to ask if there is a multiplicative identity for integers. As you might suspect, $^+1$ is an identity element for multiplication. Theorem 11-5 and commutativity establish this fact.

Theorem 11-5: $[1,0] \odot [a,b] = [a,b]$ for every integer $[a,b]$.

Proof: $[1,0] \odot [a,b] = [1 \cdot a + 0 \cdot b, \ 1 \cdot b + 0 \cdot a]$ Def. 11-1

$\qquad\qquad\quad = [a + 0, b + 0]$ Why?

$\qquad\qquad\quad = [a,b]$ Why? ∎

Hence $^+1$ times any integer n is the integer n. Commutativity of multiplication is all that is required now to justify calling $^+1$ a multiplication identity. This multiplicative identity is unique, but before we show this, it will be useful to obtain a cancellation property for multiplication. As was true in cardinal arithmetic, this will provide us with a very useful tool which can be used to solve number sentences. It will also give us an easy way to prove that $^+1$ is the unique multiplicative identity.

Theorem 11-6 (Cancellation): If $[a,b] \odot [e,f] = [c,d] \odot [e,f]$ and $[e,f] \neq [0,0]$, then $[a,b] = [c,d]$.

Proof: Since we are assuming that $[e,f] \neq [0,0]$, we only need consider the two cases

$$(1) \quad [e,f] = [k,0] , k \neq 0$$

and

$$(2) \quad [e,f] = [0,k] , k \neq 0$$

Case (1): Assume that $[a,b] \odot [k,0] = [c,d] \odot [k,0]$. Then

$[a \cdot k + b \cdot 0, a \cdot 0 + b \cdot k] = [c \cdot k + d \cdot 0, c \cdot 0 + d \cdot k]$ Def. 11-1

$\qquad\quad [a \cdot k, b \cdot k] = [c \cdot k, d \cdot k]$ Card.$(\cdot),(+)$

Consequently

$a \cdot k + d \cdot k = b \cdot k + c \cdot k$ Def. 9-6

$(a + d) \cdot k = (b + c) \cdot k$ Why?

$a + d = b + c$ Why?

Thus we obtain

$[a,b] = [c,d]$ Def. 9-6

Case (2): The proof of this part is essentially just a repetition of that of part (1) and so we omit it. However, the student should work through it before reading on. ∎

Example: Find the solution set for the number sentence

$$3n \oplus {}^-4 = 8$$

Solution:

$$(3n \oplus {}^-4) \oplus {}^+4 = 8 \oplus {}^+4 \qquad \text{Thm. 10-6}$$

$$3n \oplus ({}^-4 \oplus {}^+4) = 8 \oplus {}^+4 \qquad \text{Thm. 10-3}$$

$$3n \oplus 0 = 8 \oplus {}^+4 \qquad \text{Thm. 10-12}$$

$$3n = 8 \oplus {}^+4 \qquad \text{Def. 10-2}$$

$$3n = 12 \qquad \text{Def. 10-1}$$

$$3n = 3 \odot 4 \qquad \text{Def. 11-1}$$

$$n = 4 \qquad \text{Thm. 11-6}$$

Therefore the solution set is {4}.

We do note that if in Theorem 11-6, it had been the case that $[e,f] = [0,0]$, we could not have guaranteed the equality of $[a,b]$ and $[c,d]$ even though $[a,b] \odot [0,0] = [c,d] \odot [0,0]$. So you can see that the requirement placed on $[e,f]$ was a necessary one.

Now that a cancellation property is available, it is a relatively simple matter to show that the multiplicative identity is indeed unique.

Theorem 11-7: $[1,0]$ is the unique multiplicative identity for integers.

Proof: Suppose there is a second multiplicative identity, say $[m,n] \neq [1,0]$. Then we have

$$[m,n] \odot [a,b] = [a,b]$$

and

$$[1,0] \odot [a,b] = [a,b]$$

By use of the symmetric and transitive properties of equality we obtain that

$$[m,n] \odot [a,b] = [1,0] \odot [a,b]$$

If $[a,b] \neq [0,0]$, then Theorem 11-6 applied to the above statement gives

$$[m,n] = [1,0]$$

which contradicts the assumption that there is a second identity. Therefore there is no other multiplicative identity besides $[1,0]$. ∎

It is useful to observe that $^-1 \odot 5 = {}^-5$, $^-1 \odot {}^-3 = 3$, and in general that $^-1 \odot n = {}^-n$ for each integer n. This fact is proved in Theorem 11-8.

Theorem 11-8: If $[a,b]$ is any integer, then $[0,1] \odot [a,b] = [b,a]$.

Proof: $[0,1] \odot [a,b] = [0 \cdot a + 1 \cdot b, \ 0 \cdot b + 1 \cdot a]$ Def. 11-1

$$= [1 \cdot b, \ 1 \cdot a] \qquad \text{Why?}$$

$$= [b,a] \qquad \text{Why?} \ ∎$$

Example: $^-1 \odot {}^-7 = [0,1] \odot [0,7]$

$$= [0 \cdot 0 + 1 \cdot 7, 0 \cdot 7 + 1 \cdot 0]$$

$$= [0 + 7, 0 + 0]$$

$$= [7,0]$$

$$= {}^+7$$

If we refer to Figure 11-1 below and recall that in Chapter 9 we assigned a "positive" and "negative" direction along the number line, it makes sense to say that $^-1$ times an integer n yields the negative of the integer, namely ^-n.

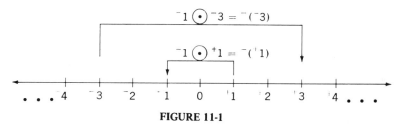

FIGURE 11-1

If one refers to Figure 9-6, he may observe that the class which belongs to $^-3$ is, in a sense, directly opposite the class belonging to $^+3$ relative to the zero class. That is, $^-3$ and $^+3$ are symmetrically positioned relative to zero. This lends some credence to calling ^-n the opposite of ^+n. One may also note that the negative of an integer n is just the additive inverse of n. That is,

$$[a,b] \oplus [b,a] = [a,b] \oplus ([0,1] \odot [a,b])$$

For convenience, we shall denote the negative of an integer as follows.

Definition 11-2; If $[a,b]$ is any integer, then the **negative of** $[a,b]$ is given by $[0,1] \odot [a,b] = {}^-[a,b]$. That is, $^-1 \odot n = {}^-n$. ^-n is also called the **opposite** of n.

By using Theorem 11-8 and Definition 11-2 it is easy to show that the following result holds.

Corollary 11-1: If $[a,b]$ is any integer, then $^-[a,b] = [b,a]$.

Proof: Left as an exercise. Use the hint given prior to the statement of the corollary.

Consider the following example.

Example: Solve the number sentence for $[x,y]$ if

$$[x,y] \oplus ([0,1] \odot [2,3]) = [4,1]$$

Solutions:

(1)

$[x,y] \oplus {}^-[2,3] = [4,1]$	Def. 11-2
$[x,y] \oplus [3,2] = [4,1]$	Thm. 11-8
$[x,y] = [4,1] \ominus [3,2]$	Def. 10-4
$[x,y] = [4 + 2, 1 + 3]$	Def. 10-3
$[x,y] = [6,4]$	Def. (+)

So that $[x,y] = [2,0]$, i.e., ${}^+2$

(2) The example could also have been written as

$$n \oplus ({}^-1 \odot {}^-1) = {}^+3.$$

Then

$$n \oplus {}^+1 = {}^+3$$

$$n = {}^+3 \ominus {}^+1$$

$$= {}^+(3 \ominus 1)$$

$$= {}^+2$$

(3)

$[x,y] \oplus {}^-[2,3] = [4,1]$	Def. 11-2
$([x,y] \oplus {}^-[2,3]) \oplus [2,3] = [4,1] \oplus [2,3]$	Thm. 10-6
$[x,y] \oplus ({}^-[2,3] \oplus [2,3]) = [4,1] \oplus [2,3]$	Thm. 10-3
$[x,y] \oplus [0,0] = [4,1] \oplus [2,3]$	Def. 10-2
$[x,y] = [4,1] \oplus [2,3]$	Thm. 10-4
$[x,y] = [4 + 2, 1 + 3]$	Def. 10-1
$[x,y] = [6,4]$	Def. (+)

Analogous to Corollary 11-1 are the following. The proofs are simple and are left to the reader to complete.

Corollary 11-2: The negative of a negative integer, ${}^-n$, is the positive integer ${}^+n$. That is, ${}^-({}^-n) = {}^+n$.

Corollary 11-3: The negative of a positive integer, ${}^+n$, is the negative integer ${}^-n$. That is, ${}^-({}^+n) = {}^-n$.

Along these same lines, many of us are familiar with the rule that the negative of the negative of any integer is the integer itself. That is, ${}^-({}^-3) = {}^+3$, ${}^-({}^-5) = {}^+5$, and so on. While this makes good intuitive sense, we are now in a position to prove that this is always the case.

Theorem 11-9; ${}^-({}^-[a,b]) = [a,b]$ for every integer $[a,b]$.

Proof: By Corollary 11-1, $^-[a,b] = [b,a]$. Hence

$$^-(^-[a,b]) = [0,1] \odot {}^-[a,b] \qquad \text{Def. 11-2}$$
$$= [0,1] \odot [b,a] \qquad \text{Cor. 11-1}$$
$$= {}^-[b,a] \qquad \text{Def. 11-2}$$
$$= [a,b] \qquad \text{Cor. 11-1.}$$

Hence the negative of the negative of any integer is that integer.∎

Another interesting fact is that if one adds two integers and takes the negative of the sum, he obtains the same result as if he forms the negatives of the integers individually and then adds the results.

Example: $\quad^-([3,1] \oplus [2,5]) = {}^-[3,1] \oplus {}^-[2,5]$

Solution: It is not difficult to convince ourselves of this, for

(1) $\qquad\qquad ^-([3,1] \oplus [2,5]) = {}^-([2,0] \oplus [0,3])$
$$= {}^-[0,1]$$
$$= [1,0]$$

and

(2) $\qquad\qquad ^-[3,1] \oplus {}^-[2,5] = {}^-[2,0] \oplus {}^-[0,3]$
$$= [0,2] \oplus [3,0]$$
$$= [1,0]$$

We see that in this example we obtain the same integer for our answer. But will such a procedure always work? We shall answer this question in the affirmative by means of the following theorem.

Theorem 11-10: If $[a,b]$ and $[c,d]$ are any two integers, then $^-([a,b] \oplus [c,d]) = {}^-[a,b] \oplus {}^-[c,d]$.

Proof: We shall do the proof just as we did the example problem preceding the theorem.

(1) $\qquad\quad ^-([a,b] \oplus [c,d]) = {}^-[a+c, b+d] \qquad \text{Def. 10-1}$
$$= [b+d, a+c] \qquad \text{Cor. 11-1}$$
(2) $\qquad\quad ^-[a,b] \oplus {}^-[c,d] = [b,a] + [d,c] \qquad \text{Cor. 11-1}$
$$= [b+d, a+c] \qquad \text{Def. 10-1}$$

Then using (1) and (2) and transitivity of equality, we have

$$^-([a,b] \oplus [c,d]) = {}^-[a,b] \oplus {}^-[c,d].∎$$

That is, the negative of the sum of two integers is the same as the sum of the negatives of the two integers. Further, problems such as the example we listed are always workable and statements of that form are true without exception.

As in addition and subtraction of signed numbers, many of us memorized *rules of signs* for multiplication. This was perhaps an unfortunate circumstance, but it too can now be remedied. We shall investigate some of these rules in detail. As usual, we shall make use of ordered pairs to facilitate the work and the interpretation of results.

Theorem 11-11: $[a,0] \odot [b,0] = [a \cdot b, 0]$ where $a \neq 0$ and $b \neq 0$.

Proof:

$$[a,0] \odot [b,0] = [a \cdot b + 0 \cdot 0, a \cdot 0 + 0 \cdot b] \qquad \text{Def. 11-1}$$
$$= [a \cdot b + 0, 0 + 0] \qquad \text{Def. } (\cdot)$$
$$= [a \cdot b, 0] \qquad \text{Identity } (+)$$

That is, $^+a \odot {}^-b = {}^+(a \cdot b)$, or in other words, the product of two positive integers is a positive integer. ▮

Example: Determine $^+3 \odot {}^+6$.

Solution: By use of ordered pairs, we obtain

$$[3,0] \odot [6,0] = [3 \cdot 6 + 0 \cdot 0, 3 \cdot 0 + 0 \cdot 6]$$
$$= [18 + 0, 0 + 0]$$
$$= [18,0]$$

That is, $^+3 \odot {}^+6 = {}^+18$.

It is an easy matter to show that the product of two negative integers is always a positive integer. The following example illustrates this fact by use of ordered pair notation.

Example: Determine the product $^-4 \odot {}^-5$.

Solution: Using the ordered pair notation we find that

$$[0,4] \odot [0,5] = [0 \cdot 0 + 4 \cdot 5, 0 \cdot 5 + 4 \cdot 0]$$
$$= [0 + 20, 0 + 0]$$
$$= [20,0]$$

Hence $^-4 \odot {}^-5 = {}^+20$.

The statement of the general result is contained in Theorem 11-12 below.

Theorem 11-12: $[0,a] \odot [0,b] = [a \cdot b, 0]$ where $a \neq 0$ and $b \neq 0$.

Proof: Left as an exercise.

In a similar fashion, one can determine the result of multiplying a negative integer by a positive integer.

Theorem 11-13: $[0,a] \odot [b,0] = [0, a \cdot b]$ where $a \neq 0$ and $b \neq 0$.

Proof:

$$[0,a] \odot [b,0] = [0 \cdot b + a \cdot 0, 0 \cdot 0 + a \cdot b] \qquad \text{Why?}$$
$$= [0 + 0, 0 + a \cdot b] \qquad \text{Why?}$$
$$= [0, a \cdot b] \qquad \text{Why?}$$

This result says that a negative integer times a positive integer is a negative integer. Hence, $^-a \odot {}^+b = {}^-(a \cdot b)$. ∎

Example: Determine $^-5 \odot {}^+7$.

Solution: Changing to ordered pair notation, we obtain

$$[0,5] \odot [7,0] = [0 \cdot 7 + 5 \cdot 0, 0 \cdot 0 + 5 \cdot 7]$$
$$= [0 + 0, 0 + 35]$$
$$= [0,35]$$

Consequently, $^-5 \odot {}^+7 = {}^-35$.

Theorem 11-14: $[a,0] \odot [0,b] = [0, a \cdot b]$ where $a \neq 0$ and $b \neq 0$.

Proof: This proof is left for the student. The proof will work out easily if you model it after that of theorem 11-13.

On the basis of the above theorems the student can see that there is really no mystery concerning the rules for multiplication of signed numbers. The rules are quite "natural" and follow as direct consequences of the definition which we took for multiplication.

There is another useful and important result which has not yet been considered. This result states that if one takes the negative of the product of two integers, the same number is obtained if the negative of either one of the factors (but not both) is used instead.

Example:
   (a) $^-(^+2 \odot {}^-4) = {}^-(^-8) = {}^+8$.   i.e., negative of a product.
   (b) $^-(^+2) \odot {}^-4 = {}^-2 \odot {}^-4 = {}^+8$. i.e., negative of the first factor multiplied by the second factor.
   (c) $^+2 \odot {}^-(^-4) = {}^+2 \odot {}^+4 = {}^+8$.   i.e., first factor multiplied by the negative of the second factor.

In each of the three possibilities, the same answer results. This fact has many applications, especially in the algebra of signed numbers. It is considered in some detail in Theorem 11-15 below.

Theorem 11-15; $^-(a \odot b) = \ ^-a \odot b = a \odot \ ^-b$ for every two integers a and b.

Proof: Since we could consider several cases here, let us revert to ordered pair notation to avoid this problem. Let the integer a be represented by $[m,n]$ and the integer b be represented by $[r,t]$. Then we want to show that $^-([m,n] \odot [r,t]) = \ ^-[m,n] \odot [r,t] = [m,n] \odot \ ^-[t,y]$, this by use of the Principle of Substitution of Equals. Just two cases need be considered:

1) $^-([m,n] \odot [r,t]) = \ ^-[m,n] \odot [r,t]$.

Now
$$^-(a \odot b) = \ ^-([m,n] \odot [r,t]) \qquad \text{Prin. Subs.}$$
$$= [0,1] \odot ([m,n] \odot [r,t]) \qquad \text{Def. 11-2}$$
$$= ([0,1] \odot [m,n]) \odot [r,t] \qquad \text{Thm. 11-2}$$
$$= \ ^-[m,n] \odot [r,t] \qquad \text{Def. 11-2}$$

That is,
$$^-(a \odot b) = \ ^-a \odot b$$

2) $^-[m,n] \odot [r,t] = [m,n] \odot \ ^-[r,t]$.

Here we have
$$^-a \odot b = \ ^-[m,n] \odot [r,t] \qquad \text{Prin. Subs.}$$
$$= ([0,1] \odot [m,n]) \odot [r,t] \qquad \text{Def. 11-2}$$
$$= ([m,n] \odot [0,1]) \odot [r,t] \qquad \text{Thm. 11-2}$$
$$= [m,n] \odot ([0,1] \odot [r,t]) \qquad \text{Thm. 11-3}$$
$$= [m,n] \odot \ ^-[r,t] \qquad \bullet \text{ Def. 11-2}$$

Thus,
$$^-a \odot b = a \odot \ ^-b$$

By transitivity of equality, we obtain the result that $^-(a \odot b) = a \odot \ ^-b$. Then combining these relations with the results of part (1), we obtain

$$^-(a \odot b) = \ ^-a \odot b = a \odot \ ^-b \quad \blacksquare$$

Theorems 11-15 and 11-10 together provide a means of solving number sentences of the type illustrated in the following example.

Example: Solve the number sentence $x \ominus (2x \ominus \ ^-4) = 3$.

Solution:
$$x \ominus (2x \oplus \ ^-4) = 3 \qquad \text{Given}$$
$$x \oplus \ ^-(2x \oplus \ ^-4) = 3 \qquad \text{Thm. 10-15}$$
$$x \oplus \ ^-(2x) \oplus \ ^-(^-4) = 3 \qquad \text{Thm. 11-10}$$
$$x \oplus [^-2x \oplus \ ^-(^-4)] = 3 \qquad \text{Thm. 11-15}$$

$$x \oplus \ulcorner 2x \oplus {}^+4 \urcorner = 3 \qquad \text{Thm. 11-9}$$

$$(x \oplus {}^-2x) \oplus {}^+4 = 3 \qquad \text{Thm. 10-3}$$

$$(1 \odot x \oplus {}^-2 \odot x) \oplus {}^+4 = 3 \qquad \text{Thm. 11-5}$$

$$(1 \oplus {}^-2)x \oplus {}^+4 = 3 \qquad \text{Thm. 11-4}$$

$$({}^-1 \odot x) \oplus {}^+4 = 3 \qquad \text{Thm. 10-13}$$

$$[{}^-1 \odot ({}^-x)] \oplus {}^+4 = 3 \qquad \text{Thm. 11-15}$$

$${}^-x \oplus {}^+4 = 3 \qquad \text{Thm. 11-5}$$

$${}^-x = 3 \ominus 4 \qquad \text{Def. 10-4}$$

$${}^-x = 3 \oplus {}^-4 \qquad \text{Thm. 10-15}$$

$${}^-x = {}^-1 \qquad \text{Thm. 10-11}$$

$${}^-1 \odot x = {}^-1 \odot 1 \qquad \text{Why?}$$

$$x = 1$$

We showed in the arithmetic of cardinals that if $a \cdot b = 0$, then $a = 0$ or $b = 0$. Is the same theorem true if a and b are integers? Most of us would probably suspect that the answer is YES, but let us show that this is in fact true.

Theorem 11-16: If a and b are integers and $a \odot b = 0$, then $a = 0$ or $b = 0$.

Proof: In $a \odot b = 0$, suppose that $a \neq 0$ and note that for any integer a, $0 = a \odot 0$. By transitivity of equality we have

$$a \odot b = a \odot 0$$

Using the cancellation property of multiplication, we obtain

$$b = 0$$

Similarly, by noting that $0 = 0 \odot b$ for any integer b, we have, if we assume that $b \neq 0$,

$$a \odot b = 0 \odot b$$

Using cancellation, we obtain

$$a = 0 \quad\blacksquare$$

The above theorem is useful in solving number sentences of the following type.

Example: Solve the number sentence $a \oplus (a \odot b) = 0$.

Solution: Using Theorem 11-16, we obtain

$$(a \odot 1) \oplus (a \odot b) = 0$$

$$a \odot (1 \oplus b) = 0$$

so that

$$a = 0$$

or

$$1 \oplus b = 0.$$

That is,

$$a = 0$$

or

$$b = {}^-1.$$

Then 0 or $^-1$ will make the original sentence true when substituted in for a or b respectively.

EXERCISE SET 11-2

1. Perform the multiplications $[5,6] \odot [7,2]$ and $[7,2] \odot [5,6]$. What answers do you obtain? Is this result expected? Why or why not?

2. Work $[3,1] \odot ([5,2] \odot [3,7])$ and $([3,1] \odot [5,2]) \odot [3,7]$ out individually. Do these numerals represent the same integer? Why or why not?

3. Ferdy Snicklefritz asks Grunella Garble to work the problem $[2,3] \odot ([4,1] \oplus [5,3])$ for him in two ways. Is there a well-known property illustrated here? If so, which one?

4. Would you say that multiplication is distributive over subtraction of integers? [Hint: Before answering, try a few examples using numbers in the relation

$$[a,b] \odot ([c,d] \ominus [e,f]) = ([a,b] \odot [c,d]) \ominus ([a,b] \odot [e,f]).$$

5. Make use of the cancellation property of multiplication of integers to find the solution to each of the following number sentences. [Rules of signed numbers may also be needed.]
   (a) $[m,n] \odot [7,1] = [3,0] \odot [3,1]$
   (b) $[x \cdot 3 + y \cdot 1, x \cdot 1 + y \cdot 3] = [8,0]$
   (c) $[u,v] \odot [2,3] = [u,v] \odot [x,y]$, where $[u,v] \neq [0,0]$
   (d) $[x,y] \odot [0,4] = [13,1]$
   (e) $[x \cdot 1 + y \cdot 3, x \cdot 3 + y \cdot 1] = [1,7]$
   (f) $n \odot {}^-({}^+2 \oplus {}^-5) = {}^-6$
   (g) $(x \odot {}^-2) \oplus (x \odot {}^+4) = {}^+18$
   (h) $({}^-4 \odot x) \oplus ({}^+3 \odot x) = {}^-3$
   (i) $[({}^+2 \odot n) \oplus ({}^+5 \odot n)] \odot {}^-3 = {}^+42$

6. In Theorem 11-6 use $[a,b] = [3,1]$, $[c,d] = [6,4]$ and $[e,f] = [5,0]$. Work it through as shown in the proof to conclude that if $[3,1] \odot [5,0] = [6,4] \odot [5,0]$, then $[3,1] = [6,4]$.

7. Show by actual computation that $[2,0] \odot [1,2] \neq [2,0]$. This shows that what integer is *not* a multiplicative identity?

8. Show by using Definition 11-2 and then Definition 11-1 that
   (a) $^-[2,5] = [5,2]$
   (b) $^-[6,1] = [1,6]$

9. (a) Choose an ordered pair for $^-5$ and show by actual computation that
   $^-(^-5) = 5$.
   (b) Choose an ordered pair for $^+7$ and show by actual computation that
   $^-(^+7) = ^-7$.
10. Show that Theorem 11-9 holds if we choose $[a,b]$ to be
    (a) $^-3$
    (b) $^+5$
11. Show that $^-(^-2 \oplus ^+4) = ^+2 \oplus ^-4 = ^-2$ in two ways.
12. Show by actual computation that
    (a) $[2,0] \odot [3,0]$ is a positive integer.
    (b) $[0,3] \odot [0,4]$ is a positive integer.
    (c) $[2,0] \odot [0,3]$ is a negative integer.
    (d) $[0,3] \odot [4,0]$ is a negative integer.
13. Compute each of the following:
    (a) $^-([2,3] \odot [4,1])$
    (b) $^-[2,3] \odot [4,1]$.
    (c) $[2,3] \odot ^-[4,1]$.
    (d) Do you get the same answer for parts (a), (b), and (c)?
    (e) What theorem is illustrated?
14. Find the solution *set* for each of the following.
    (a) $x^2 \oplus 2x = 0$
    (b) $a^2 \ominus b^2 = 0$
    (c) $x^2 \oplus x \ominus 2 = 0$
    (d) $3n^2 \ominus ^+11 = ^+1$
    (e) $2n(n \ominus 2) \oplus 6(n \ominus 2) = 0$
15. In cardinal arithmetic we had the theorem $(a + b) + (c + d) = (a + c) +$
    $(b + d)$. Does this same theorem hold if a, b, c, and d are integers and the
    operation is $\oplus$? Before you decide on your answer, work through the
    following problems.
    (a) $^+26 \oplus ^+13 =$
    (b) $^+32 \oplus ^-11 =$
    (c) $^+46 \oplus ^-28 =$
    (d) $^-29 \oplus ^-32 =$
    (e) Explain how multiplication may be involved in parts (c) and (d).
    [Hint: Devise an expanded notation for integer numerals.]
16. The sum of two consecutive integers is $^+15$. Determine their product.
17. Show that if $[a,b] = [c,d]$, then $[a,b] \odot [e,f] = [c,d] \odot [e,f]$ for every
    integer $[e,f]$. What property is this? Does this work if $[e,f] = [0,0]$?
18. Define $a \triangle b$ on integers as in the following examples. Examples: $2 \triangle 3 =$
    $8, 5 \triangle 7 = 40, ^-4 \triangle 2 = ^-12, ^-5 \triangle ^-3 = 10$. Calculate each of the following.
    (a) $4 \triangle 6$
    (b) $6 \triangle 4$
    (c) $2 \triangle (3 \triangle 4)$
    (d) $(2 \triangle 3) \triangle 4$
    (e) $^-3 \triangle (4 + 5)$
    (f) $(^-3 \triangle 4) + (^-3 \triangle 5)$
    (g) $1 \triangle 7$
    (h) $^-4 \triangle 0$

19. Is Δ (a) commutative? (b) associative? (c) distributive? (d) Show that if $a \Delta c = b \Delta c$, then $a = b$ or else show that there is no cancellation property for Δ.

3. Similarity of Cardinal Numbers and Integers

Throughout the development of integer arithmetic we have observed several striking similarities. This parallelism, though striking, should not come as a complete surprise, for we have purposely attempted to construct the system of integers so that the desirable characteristics of cardinal arithmetic were retained. In order to observe this strong similarity between the systems of cardinal numbers and integers, we shall consider both sets of numbers and their corresponding operations. First we note that the set of cardinal numbers is equivalent to the set of non-negative integers under the one-to-one onto mapping

$$C = \{ 0, 1, 2, 3, \ldots, k, \ldots \}$$
$$\updownarrow \; \updownarrow \; \updownarrow \; \updownarrow \qquad \updownarrow$$
$$I^+ = \{ 0, {}^+1, {}^+2, {}^+3, \ldots, {}^+k, \ldots \}.$$

Secondly, we have been successful in constructing the arithmetic for integers in such a way that if we select the correspondences

$$\begin{array}{ccc} \text{Cardinals} & & \text{Integers} \\ a & \longleftrightarrow & [a,0] \\ b & \longleftrightarrow & [b,0], \end{array}$$

then the correspondences

$$a + b \longleftrightarrow [a,0] \oplus [b,0] = [a + b, 0]$$
$$a \cdot b \longleftrightarrow [a,0] \odot [b,0] = [a \cdot b, 0]$$

were obtained.

Thus the systems of cardinal numbers and integers exhibit three very important characteristics:

(1) a one-to-one onto mapping exists between the cardinals and non-negative integers.

(2) sums of cardinals correspond to sums of non-negative integers, and

(3) products of cardinals correspond to products of non-negative integers.

When two systems such as these are found in mathematics, they are referred to as *isomorphic systems*. As is indicated by the name, isomorphic, this means that the systems are similarly structured. For the systems we are studying, this means that everything which involves only addition or multiplication of cardinal numbers can be transformed to addition or multiplication of corresponding non-negative integers and the results are equally valid. If you will reflect on this state of affairs, you may reach the conclusion (and properly so) that there is no real advantage to having both systems to contend with. Thus if a problem arises which may properly be solved by use of cardinal numbers, it can now be transformed to the corresponding integer problem, solved, and then reinterpreted in terms of cardinals. Since we have already observed that the system of integers does have some addition desirable properties not found in the system of cardinal numbers, we shall now work with the extended and more convenient system of integers even in those cases where cardinals would suffice. In doing so, nothing is lost and in several instances some advantages are realized.

Now that we have made our decision to use integers in place of cardinals and because of the isomorphism between the two systems, we can agree to use the symbols $+$, $-$, $\cdot$, instead of $\oplus$, $\ominus$, $\odot$, for addition, subtraction, and multiplication respectively. This is possible because there will be no ambiguity arising from problems in which these operations are involved. The only real chance for ambiguity would be in the use of ordered pairs, but we don't need these any longer either, since we have already developed the operations on integers and their properties.

EXERCISE SET 11-3

1. It was noted that sums and products of cardinals correspond to those of non-negative integers. Does this correspondence hold for differences?
2. The sum of two consecutive odd integers is 44. What are the integers? Is a similar result true in the system of cardinal numbers? Explain.
3. The sum of two consecutive odd integers is $^-24$. Determine these integers. Can the isomorphism between cardinals and integers be used to obtain a corresponding result in the system of cardinals?
4. The product of two integers is 54 and their difference is three. What is their sum?
5. Consider the cardinals modulo 4 and a new system which has elements A, B, C, D. If $A \longleftrightarrow \overline{3}$, $C \longleftrightarrow \overline{2}$, $B \longleftrightarrow \overline{1}$, and $D \longleftrightarrow \overline{0}$, and it is known that the systems are isomorphic, construct "addition" and "multiplication" tables for the new system.
6. Referring to Section 8-2 where modular arithmetic was introduced, explain how the concept of isomorphic systems could have been utilized in the discussions presented.
7. (a) Investigate how a modulo 3 system might be constructed from the set of integers and construct an addition table.
   (b) In relation to part (a), how might "positive" and "negative" be interpreted if a three position rotary switch is used as a physical model?

Chapter summary

In this chapter we continued our efforts to obtain results which correspond to those determined for cardinal numbers. For the operation multiplication we were successful and found once more that many integer properties depend very heavily upon the corresponding properties for cardinal numbers. That is, uniqueness of products depends on uniqueness in cardinals, commutativity depends on commutativity, associativity depends on associativity, and so forth.

During the discussion of multiplication of integers we also found that the "rules of signs" arise very naturally as a result of defining integers in terms of ordered pairs. In fact, these results might have been suspected once the corresponding rules were obtained in Chapter 10.

Because of the initial correspondence which we established between the cardinals and the non-negative integers, we were able to demonstrate that the system of cardinal numbers is isomorphic to the system of non-negative integers. Because of this we often use the latter to solve certain problems rather than maintaining separate systems for different types of problems. The fact that the cardinal numbers are occasionally referred to as a subset of the integers is based on the existence of the isomorphism between the two systems.

CHAPTER 12 Division divisibility and order

1. Division of Integers

In Chapter 11 the similarity of the systems of cardinal numbers and integers was discussed. This similarity was restricted to problems in addition and multiplication, but it does not end there. Since in both systems it was possible to give an inverse definition for subtraction, it should be clear that there is some similarity here as well. On the basis of similarity in addition, subtraction, and multiplication, one might suspect that division in the two systems too exhibits some striking similarities. The student will recall that for division of cardinals the following correspondence was obtained:

$$a \div b \text{ yields } (q,r) \longleftrightarrow a = b \cdot q + r$$

As the following examples illustrate, this same type of correspondence can be obtained for long division in the system of integers.

Examples: (a)

$$
\begin{array}{r|l}
^-26 \overline{)5347} & \\
5200 & ^-200 \\
\hline
147 & \\
130 & ^-5 \\
\hline
17 & ^-205 \\
\end{array}
$$

Hence $5347 \div {}^-26$ yields $(^-205,17) \longleftrightarrow 5347 = {}^-26 \cdot \underline{{}^-205} + \underline{17}$.

(b)

$$
\begin{array}{r|l}
^-27 \overline{)^-5683} & \\
^-5400 & 200 \\
\hline
^-283 & \\
^-270 & 10 \\
\hline
^-13 & 210 \\
\end{array}
$$

Thus $^-5683 \div {}^-27$ yields $(210,^-13) \longleftrightarrow {}^-5683 = {}^-27 \cdot \underline{210} + {}^-13$.

In division problems where the system of cardinal numbers is sufficient to effect a solution, there is no real advantage to using integers. However, from the mathematical point of view, the system of integers gives one more latitude in applications, particularly in problems of a more theoretical nature. It is in cases such as this that the student can begin to become aware of the evolution of this area of mathematics. As can be observed, we have tried to build a system of mathematics in order to describe the world in which we live. In doing this, we find that our mathematical model possesses some characteristics which seem to have no meaningful physical interpretation. It is here that the mathematician begins to study the model itself and its internal structure and extensions. In many such studies, results have been derived which seemed useless at the time but many years later were found to have further important physical applications.

We shall pursue these theoretical considerations only far enough to try to obtain the results which are of interest to us in the development of arithmetic. For our purposes, then, we shall not be overly interested in the division of one integer by another, since it does not appear to add a great deal to the knowledge we already have concerning division. As we shall see in the next section, however, those division problems which yield a remainder $r = 0$ will prove to be of considerable interest.

EXERCISE SET 12-1

1. Determine the quotient and remainder for $a \div b$ if
   (a) $a = 346, b = {}^-9$
   (b) $a = {}^-4539, b = 62$
   (c) $a = 6892, b = 74$
   (d) $a = {}^-92814, b = {}^-83$
2. Complete each of the following statements by filling in the appropriate number.
   (a) $3476 = 36 \cdot$ _____ $+ 20$
   (b) ${}^-5231 = {}^-37 \cdot 140 +$ _____
   (c) _____ $= 26 \cdot {}^-38 + {}^-14$
   (d) $\overline{1250} =$ _____ $\cdot {}^-43 + 3$
3. Write each of the parts of problem 2 in terms of division.

2. Divisibility of Integers

As we have indicated, the case where $r = 0$ in the division process is of considerable interest, for then we can define divisibility for integers much as we did divisibility for cardinal numbers.

Definition 12-1: If a and b are integers with $a \neq 0$, then b is **divisible by** a (or a **divides** b) if there is an integer c such that $b = a \cdot c$. This division is denoted $a \mid b$ and is read "a divides b" or "b is divisible by a."

As before in cardinal numbers, if $a \mid b$, then the integer c is unique because the multiplication of integers yields unique products. We also note that occasionally it is convenient to denote divisibility by use of the symbol $\div$ as well as $\mid$.

We shall have occasion to use ÷ in this context when division of rational numbers is discussed in Section 15-3.

Every result which holds true for cardinal numbers holds for integers as well. In addition to this, there are a few new results which one might expect because of the fact that integers appear to satisfy a wider range of properties than do cardinal numbers. We shall now discuss and prove some of these and by doing so, find that the discussion leads in a "natural" way to a consideration of prime integers, L.C.M. of integers and the Fundamental Theorem of Arithmetic as applied to integers.

The first result we consider is that every non-zero integer divides both itself and its opposite as the following example illustrates.

Example: (a) $5 \mid 5$ since $5 = 5 \odot 1$, and

(b) $5 \mid {}^-5$ since $5 = {}^-5 \odot {}^-1$. Thus 5 divides both itself and its negative.

The proof of the fact in general is just as straightforward.

Theorem 12-1: If n is any non-zero integer, then $n \mid n$ and ${}^-n \mid n$.

Proof: From properties of multiplication we observe that

$$n = n \odot 1 \text{ and } n = {}^-n \odot {}^-1$$

Thus by Definition 12-1 $n \mid n$ and ${}^-n \mid n$ as claimed.∎

Of equal interest, as we shall soon see, is the fact that ${}^+1$ and ${}^-1$ both divide every integer. The proof of this fact is quite straightforward and is much like that for Theorem 12-1. For these reasons we shall just state the result and leave its proof for the reader to complete.

Theorem 12-2: If n is any integer, then $1 \mid n$ and ${}^-1 \mid n$.

Proof: Left as an exercise.

There are several other results concerning divisibility of integers which could be derived. Some of these parallel the results in the system of cardinal numbers and as we have now observed, some of the results are new. We shall list some of these as exercises at the end of this section for student study.

We observe that if for integers it is known that $a \cdot b = c$, then a and b are *factors* or *divisors* of c. Because of the isomorphism between the cardinal numbers and non-negative integers, we may consider the L.C.M. and G.C.F. of sets of non-negative integers. This may be done by considering the sets of common multiples and common factors and then selecting the largest or smallest members of these respective sets. Thus the same techniques can be used as were used in cardinal arithmetic. Note however that this cannot always be done if one allows the inclusion of negative integers.

Example: Determine the L.C.M. of ⁻24 and 36.

Solution: Using the type of notation agreed upon for cardinals, we obtain

$M(^-24) = \{\ldots, 96, 48, 24, ^-24, ^-48, ^-96, ^-120, ^-144, ^-168, ^-192, ^-216, ^-240, ^-264, \ldots\}$

and

$M(36) = \{\ldots, 108, 72, 36, ^-36, ^-72, ^-108, ^-144, ^-180, ^-216, ^-252, ^-288, \ldots\}$

Then C.M. $(^-24, 36) = M(^-24) \cap M(36)$ or

C.M.$(^-24, 36) = \{\ldots, ^-288, ^-216, ^-144, ^-144, ^-216, ^-288, \ldots\}$

As one can observe C.M. $(^-24,36)$ contains no smallest member, so that if one includes negative integers, the existence of the L.C.M. cannot be assured. It is important to note, however, that if we restrict our discussion to the set of common multiples whose members are positive, then the L.C.M. does exist just as it did for cardinal numbers. We shall see later, when rational numbers are discussed, that this will be quite important in the determination of least common denominators.

On the other hand, the G.C.F. of any two integers does always exist because of the fact that the set of factors of every integer is a finite set and so has a largest member.

Example: Determine the G.C.F. of ⁻54 and 48.

Solution: If the same type of notation agreed upon for cardinal numbers is used here, we have

$F(^-54) = \{^-54, ^-27, ^-18, ^-9, ^-6, ^-3, ^-2, ^-1, 1, 2, 3, 6, 9, 18, 27, 54\}$

and

$F(48) = \{^-48, ^-24, ^-16, ^-12, ^-8, ^-6, ^-4, ^-3, ^-2, ^-1, 1, 2, 3, 4, 6, 8, 12, 16, 24, 48\}$

Then

C.F. $(^-54, 48) = F(^-54) \cap F(48)$

or

C.F. $(^-54, 48) = \{^-6, ^-3, ^-2, ^-1, 1, 2, 3, 6\}$

Therefore G.C.F. $(^-54, 48) = 6$ is the largest of the common factors.

In the arithmetic of cardinals it was found that the use of prime factors facilitated the determination of the L.C.M. and G.C.F. of two numbers. Thus it might be useful to try such an approach for integers. In order to do this we must first determine what a prime integer is. One might be tempted to use the same definition as was used for cardinal numbers, but if he considers Theorems 12-1 and 12-2 he finds that for every non-zero integer n there are at least four distinct integers which are factors of n. Those factors (or divisors) are $^+1, ^-1, n$, and ^-n. Therefore, in order to have essentially an extension of the definition of primeness, it seems appropriate to define a prime integer as follows.

Definition 12-2: A non-zero integer p is called a **prime** integer if $p \neq 1, p \neq ^-1$ and if the only divisors of p are $1, ^-1, p$, and ^-p. Integers other than $^+1$ and $^-1$ which are not prime are called **composite** integers.

Thus $2, 3, 5, 7, 11, 13, 17, ^-2, ^-3, ^-5, ^-7, ^-11, ^-13$, and $^-17$ are prime but $^-15, ^-12$, $^-8, ^-6, 4, 10, 12, 14$, and 15 are composite integers. As indicated in Definition 12-2, the integer zero is composite.

Because of the fact that every negative integer can be expressed as negative one times a positive integer, the consideration of primes is often restricted to positive primes and positive prime factors. If this restriction is made, then any integer different from positive one, negative one, and zero can be expressed as positive or negative one times a product of positive primes. Further, since the non-negative integers are isomorphic to the set of cardinal numbers, the laws of exponents hold so that in such a factorization powers of positive primes may occur as well. Taking into account this condition, the Fundamental Theorem of Arithmetic for integers may be stated as follows.

Theorem 12-3 (Fundamental Theorem of Arithmetic): If n is a non-zero integer with $n \neq ^+1$ and $n \neq ^-1$, then n can be expressed as $^+1$ or $^-1$ times a product of positive primes. This expression is unique except for the order in which the prime factors occur.

Thus

$$^-24 = ^-1 \cdot 2 \cdot 2 \cdot 2 \cdot 3 = ^-1 \cdot 2 \cdot 2 \cdot 3 \cdot 2 = ^-1 \cdot 3 \cdot 2 \cdot 2 \cdot 2$$

$$^-98 = ^-1 \cdot 2 \cdot 7 \cdot 7 = ^-1 \cdot 7 \cdot 2 \cdot 7 = ^-1 \cdot 7 \cdot 7 \cdot 2, \text{ and}$$

$$154 = ^+1 \cdot 2 \cdot 7 \cdot 11 = ^+1 \cdot 7 \cdot 2 \cdot 11 = ^+1 \cdot 11 \cdot 7 \cdot 2$$

In each case the prime factors are positive as indicated by the Fundamental Theorem.

Once we have the prime factorization of integers and laws of exponents available, expanded notation may be used for the numerals which represent integers. This is again directly dependent upon the similarity of structure which the cardinals and non-negative integers exhibit. Using the expanded form of numerals, one may then justify the several algorithms for operations on the set of integers. These follow quite nicely the corresponding algorithms already discussed for the system of cardinal numbers. Thus it becomes more apparent that the concept of isomorphic systems is very useful.

As the reader may have suspected from the discussion of primeness, relatively prime pairs of integers may be defined in much the same way. The extension of the definition of relatively prime pairs of integers may be obvious to the reader, but we shall list a definition for convenient reference.

Definition 12-3: Two integers, a and b, are called **relatively prime** if

$$\text{G.C.F.}\,(a,b) = {}^{+}1$$

Thus 8 and $^-9$ are relatively prime, but 12 and 15 are not. Relative primeness will not be discussed further here, but we shall meet this concept again in the arithmetic of rational numbers.

EXERCISE SET 12-2

1. (a) Show that $2 \mid 0$.
   (b) Show that $7 \mid 0$.
   (c) Show in general that if n is a non-zero integer, then $n \mid 0$.
2. (a) Show that since $6 \mid 48$, it is also true that $6 \mid {}^-48$ and $^-6 \mid 48$.
   (b) Show that since $7 \mid 210$, it is also true that $7 \mid {}^-210$ and $^-7 \mid 210$.
   (c) Show in general that if $n \mid a$ then $n \mid {}^-a$ and $^-n \mid a$.
3. (a) Does divisibility exhibit the reflexive property?
   (b) If for integers a and b $a \mid b$, is it true that $b \mid a$? What can be said about divisibility with respect to the symmetric property?
   (c) Is the relation "is divisible by" an equivalence relation?
   (d) Does the relation "is divisible by" exhibit transitivity?
4. (a) Show in detail that if $7 \mid 42$ and $7 \mid 49$, then $7 \mid 91$.
   (b) Show that if $a \mid m$ and $a \mid n$ then $a \mid (m + n)$.
   (c) Show in detail that if $8 \mid 56$ and $8 \mid {}^-16$ then $8 \mid 72$.
   (d) Show that if $a \mid m$ and $a \mid n$ then $a \mid (m - n)$.
5. Determine the prime factorization of each of the following integers.
   (a) 180
   (b) $^-168$
   (c) $^-924$
   (d) 875
6. Show in detail that L.C.M. $(^-28,42)$ does not exist.
7. Determine the G.C.F. of
   (a) $\{^-42,98\}$
   (b) $\{54,^-48\}$
   (c) $\{32,72\}$
   (d) $\{^-27,^-72\}$
8. Try to find an alternative definition of prime integers which makes use of the *distinct* factors which are possible.
9. Show why the integer zero is composite.
10. If $^+1$ or $^-1$ were considered to be primes, would the Prime Factorization Theorem still hold? Give numerical examples to support your answer.
11. Write each of the following numerals in expanded notation.
    (a) 437685
    (b) $^-374251$
    (c) 89274
    (d) $^-76243$
12. (a) Use expanded notation to show that $378 + {}^-92 = 286$.
    (b) Use expanded notation to show that $^-423 - {}^-46 = {}^-377$.

13. Which of the following are pairs of relatively prime integers?
    (a) 16 and 17
    (b) 13 and 42
    (c) 4 and ⁻9
    (d) ⁻12 and 17
    (e) ⁻12 and ⁻21
    (f) ⁻8 and ⁻9

3. The Order Relation and Integers

The reader will recall that in Chapter Seven the relation $<$ was shown to be an order relation on the set of cardinal numbers. In particular it was agreed that $a < b$ if there is a non-zero cardinal number, k, such that $a + k = b$. Since $k \neq 0$, this means that $a + k = b > 0$ regardless of whether $a = 0$ or not. Equivalently, one could write that $b - a = k$, $k > 0$ or just $b - a > 0$. Since there is an isomorphism between the set of cardinal numbers and the non-negative integers, this same agreement would apparently yield useable results for the set of integers. That is, it might be useful to say with respect to integers that $a < b$ if $b - a$ is a positive integer. However, it remains to be seen whether such a definition would hold for the entire set of integers. Let us try, as a tentative definition, the following.

Definition 12-4: If a and b are integers, then $a < b$ if $b - a$ is a positive integer.

To gain an intuitive notion of the utility of this definition let us consider the number line in Figure 12-1 which makes use of Figure 9-6 and the isomorphism between cardinal numbers and the non-negative integers.

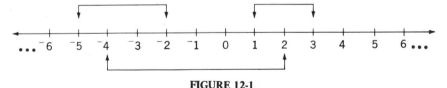

FIGURE 12-1

Examples: Refer to Figure 12-1.
    (a) ⁻5 is to the left of ⁻2 and ⁻2 − ⁻5 = ⁻2 + ⁺5 = ⁺3.
    (b) ⁻4 is to the left of 2 and 2 − ⁻4 = 2 + ⁺4 = ⁺6.
    (c) 1 is to the left of 3 and 3 − 1 = ⁺2.

In each case it makes sense to say that $a < b$ if $b - a$ is a positive integer, particularly if order is interpreted in terms of relative position along the number line. The consideration of Definition 12-4 in these terms may lead one to believe that the relation $<$ is indeed an order relation for the entire set of integers. The formal proof of this fact is the topic of the following theorem.

Theorem 12-4: The relation $<$ is an order relation on the set of integers.

Proof: We need to show that $<$ has neither the reflexive nor symmetric properties and that it does have the transitive property. Thus the proof has three parts.

(1) $<$ is not reflexive. In order to show this, consider any integer a. Is it true that $a < a$? Since $a - a = 0$ and 0 is not positive, the relation $<$ cannot be reflexive.

(2) $<$ is not symmetric. Suppose that $a < b$. Then $b - a = k$ where k is positive; however $a - b = {}^-k$ and ${}^-k$ is not positive. Consequently, the relation is not symmetric.

(3) $<$ is transitive. Let a, b, and c be any three integers such that $a < b$ and $b < c$. Then by Definition 12-4 we obtain $b - a = k$ and $c - b = m$ where k and m are both positive integers. Adding these equations we find that

$$(b - a) + (c - b) = k + m \qquad \text{Thm. 10-1}$$

$$(b + {}^-a) + (c + {}^-b) = k + m \qquad \text{Why?}$$

$$(b + {}^-b) + (c + {}^-a) = k + m \qquad \text{Why?}$$

$$0 + (c + {}^-a) = k + m \qquad \text{Why?}$$

$$c + {}^-a = k + m \qquad \text{Why?}$$

$$c - a = k + m \qquad \text{Why?}$$

Since $k + m$ is positive (i.e., the sum of two positive integers), Definition 12-4 assures us that $a < c$. Hence the relation $<$ has the transitive property.

Taking (1), (2), and (3) into account we conclude that the relation $<$ is an order relation on the set of integers. ∎

The fact that the relation $<$ is an order relation on the set of integers assures us that it is possible to arrange the integers in a linear order as illustrated in Figure 12-1. At the time Figure 12-1 was used, it was used at an intuitive level and we could not then guarantee the correctness of the linear order given to the integers. However once it is known that $<$ is an order relation, it is mathematically acceptable to use an interpretation such as that given in the figure.

As was the case in cardinal arithmetic it is possible to add the same integer to both sides of an inequality and obtain a true statement in which the sense of the inequality is unchanged. We might note that the following theorem is analogous to the results of both Theorems 7-2 and 7-3 for cardinals.

Theorem 12-5: If $a < b$ and c is any integer, then $a + c < b + c$.

Proof: If $a < b$, then $b - a = k$ where k is a positive integer. Then

$$(b - a) + (c - c) = k \qquad \text{Add. ident.}$$

$$(b + {}^-a) + (c + {}^-c) = k \qquad \text{Thm. 10-15}$$

$$(b + c) + (\bar{}a + \bar{}c) = k \qquad\qquad\text{Why?}$$
$$(b + c) + \bar{}(a + c) = k \qquad\qquad\text{Why?}$$
$$(b + c) - (a + c) = k \qquad\qquad\text{Why?}$$

Since k is positive, we have by Definition 12-4 that $a + c < b + c$. ∎

Theorem 12-5 is considerably stronger than the corresponding ones for cardinals. Since for integers, subtraction can always be restated in terms of addition, the theorem states that the same integer can be subtracted from both sides of an inequality and the resulting statement is true.

Example: Let us begin with $2 < 7$ and subtract 5 from each side.

Solution: $\qquad\qquad\qquad 2 + \bar{}5 < 7 + \bar{}5 \qquad\qquad$ By Theorem 12-5.

Since

$$2 + \bar{}5 = 2 - 5 \quad \text{and} \quad 7 + \bar{}5 = 7 - 5$$

we have that

$$2 - 5 < 7 - 5$$

That is,

$$\bar{}3 < 2$$

The other properties of inequalities for cardinals have exact analogues in the system of integers as well. However, there are two of these properties which are of some interest and which should be mentioned. These are listed below for reference and without proof.

Theorem 12-6: If $a < b$ and c is a positive integer, then $ac < bc$.

Proof: Left as an exercise. (Hint: Try to make use of the isomorphism between the cardinals and non-negative integers.)

Theorem 12-6 states that if both sides of the inequality are multiplied by the same positive integer, the sense of the inequality remains unchanged and the resulting inequality is a true statement. On the other hand, if both sides of the inequality are multiplied by the same negative integer, the result obtained is perhaps, an unexpected one. The following example illustrates the point.

Example: Determine the result of multiplying both sides of the inequality $\bar{}3 < 5$ by the integer $\bar{}2$.

Solution: $\bar{}3 \cdot \bar{}2 = 6$ and $\bar{}2 \cdot 5 = \bar{}10$, so it is clear that $6 \not< \bar{}10$. On the other hand,

$$\bar{}3 \cdot \bar{}2 > \bar{}2 \cdot 5$$

That is, $6 > {}^-10$ is a true statement.

On the basis of the above example and others similar to it, the following theorem may be formulated.

Theorem 12-7: If $a < b$ and c is a negative integer, then $ac > bc$.

Proof: Left as an exercise.

Related to these theorems are their converses. It is the latter which are of particular value in the determination of solution sets for inequalities. Though they are important, a discussion of these properties will be delayed until after the rational number system has been introduced. You are invited to give these consideration however.

We return now to reconsider the operation subtraction and its relation to order. As you will recall, the difference of any two integers always exists. That is, given any two integers $[a,b]$ and $[c,d]$, there is a unique integer $[e,f]$ such that $[a,b] \ominus [c,d] = [e,f]$. From Chapter 9 it may be noted that every integer $[e,f]$ is in one and only one of the following categories:

(1) $[e,f]$ is positive,

(2) $[e,f]$ is zero, or

(3) $[e,f]$ is negative.

From Definition 12-4, one can conclude that if $[a,b] \ominus [c,d] = [e,f]$ is positive, then $[c,d] < [a,b]$. If $[a,b] \ominus [c,d] = 0$, then $[a,b] = [c,d]$. In the third category, if $[a,b] \ominus [c,d]$ is a negative integer, then $[c,d] \ominus [a,b]$ is a positive integer and so by Definition 12-4 $[a,b] < [c,d]$. Thus given any two integers, there arise exactly three possibilities. Furthermore, one and only one of these possibilities holds for any pair of integers. These facts together comprise the Trichotomy Property for integers.

Trichotomy Property: If a and b are any two integers, then one and only one of the following holds:

(1) $a < b$,

(2) $a = b$, or

(3) $a > b$.

Considerable use will also be made of this property when the order of rational numbers is discussed.

EXERCISE SET 12-3

1. Use Definition 12-4 to determine if each of the following statements is valid.

(a) ${}^+2 < {}^+7$ (e) ${}^+5 < {}^-4$

(b) ${}^-2 < {}^-5$ (f) ${}^+3 < {}^+2$

(c) ${}^-6 < {}^+1$ (g) ${}^-8 < {}^-4$

(d) ${}^+3 < 0$ (h) ${}^-3 < {}^-3$

2. Give a definition analogous to Definition 12-4 for the relation
   (a) $>$
   (b) $\leqslant$
   (c) $\geqslant$
3. Use the definition formulated in problem 2 for $>$ to determine which of the
   following are valid.
   (a) $^+4 > {}^+1$ (d) $^-8 > {}^-7$
   (b) $^+5 > {}^-2$ (e) $^-6 > {}^+3$
   (c) $^-5 > {}^-6$ (f) $^-5 > {}^-5$
4. Use the definitions formulated in problem 2 for $\leqslant$ and $\geqslant$ to determine which
   of the following are valid.
   (a) $^-2 \leqslant {}^-1$ (e) $^+6 \geqslant {}^+5$
   (b) $^-2 \leqslant {}^-4$ (f) $^-5 \geqslant {}^-5$
   (c) $^+2 \geqslant {}^-2$ (g) $^-7 \leqslant {}^+3$
   (d) $^+3 \leqslant {}^+3$ (h) $^-1 \geqslant {}^-1$
5. Determine the solution set X for each of the following. [Hint: You may
   want to use the number line in some cases.]
   (a) $x + 5 < 3$ (e) $x - {}^-2 \geqslant 3$
   (b) $4x \geqslant 8$ (f) $2x - 2 \geqslant x + 7$
   (c) $6x + 4 < 3x + 7$ (g) $x - 5 > 1$
   (d) $4x - 6 \leqslant 8x + 10$

Chapter summary

Division of integers, if defined similarly to that for cardinals, yields a rather surprising result. That is, the quotient and remainder obtained by the process are not unique. This points out the fact that new number systems may have some disadvantages as well as advantages. We must admit that this apparent defect can be corrected by introducing the concept of *absolute value*, but since we view the integers primarily as a vehicle to be used to obtain rational numbers, we do not pursue the topic of division further.

As noted in Section 12-2, if one does pursue the idea of divisibility, other interesting results are obtained. First, the definition for prime cardinals can be adjusted to obtain a definition for prime integers. Secondly, we find that even though prime integers can be defined, their use in the discussion of L.C.M. is of no value since such a number does not even exist in the set of integers. This drawback needs to be avoided because of later work in rational numbers. In order to avoid the problem, we simply consider common multiples which are positive.

To conclude Chapter 12 we developed the concept of order for integers by making use of the information gained in the development of cardinals. In particular we were able to show how order is related to the operation subtraction. This led, in turn, to a statement of the Trichotomy Property for integers. Of the many interesting properties of the order relation for integers, we listed only a few, the intention being to complete the discussion in Chapter 16.

CHAPTER 13 Rational numbers

1. The Concept of Rational Number

The development of integers was undertaken in order to try to find a system of numbers which possessed two important characteristics. We wanted a system which could be used to

(1) give a better interpretation of physical phenomena than was possible with cardinals, and

(2) solve number sentences of the form $x + a = 0$.

At this stage it had already been determined that the system of cardinal numbers lacked these properties. The existence of unique additive inverses for integers gives assurance that the sentence $x + a = 0$ can be solved and properties of addition guarantee the uniqueness of the solution. However it is yet to be determined whether the system of integers can be used to give a satisfactory description of all physical phenomena or situations which we want to describe by use of this mathematical model.

It is a fairly easy matter to show that the system of integers does not satisfactorily describe all such physical situations. For example, suppose that 15 objects are distributed equally amongst five children, and then one of the children is asked what part of the total he received. The child cannot give an answer by using just one integer. From the child's point of view, however, it might be sufficient to say that he received 3 of the 15 objects. That is, perhaps a pair of integers can be used to give an acceptable description.

From a mathematical point of view, there is another problem to be considered, namely the solution of number sentences of the form $ax + b = 0$ where $a \neq 0$ and $b \neq 0$. It may be noted that such a sentence has no solution at all in the system of cardinals and has a solution in the integers only when b is divisible by a. Is it possible then to construct a number system which more adequately describes the physical world and in which the sentence $ax + b = 0$ has a solution?

We shall try to devise a system of numbers by means of which an affirmative answer can be given for the above question. It was noted above that pairs of integers might be useful in describing a given physical phenomenon. It should be clear from the situation involving children and objects as described above that we want to consider not just pairs of integers, but in fact ordered pairs. Also, in such cases it apparently makes no sense to have the integer zero as the second member of the ordered pair. Thus if

$$I = \{\ldots {}^-3, {}^-2, {}^-1, 0, 1, 2, 3, \ldots\}$$

and

$$I_0 = \{\ldots {}^-3, {}^-2, {}^-1, 1, 2, 3, \ldots\},$$

then we are really concerned with a study of members of the Cartesian product set $I \times I_0$. A portion of the graph of $I \times I_0$ would appear similar to that in Figure 13-1.

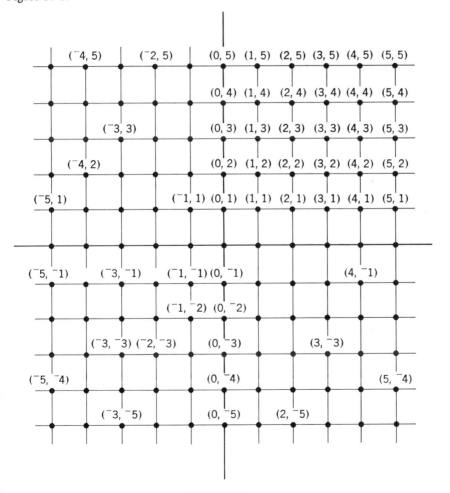

FIGURE 13-1

From situations similar to that involving the five children and 15 objects, a pattern begins to become evident.   Consider the following list of similar statements.

(1) 15 objects are distributed amongst 5 children.
(2) 30 objects are distributed amongst 10 children.
(3) 45 objects are distributed amongst 15 children.
(4) 60 objects are distributed amongst 20 children.

In each statement one may observe that each child, if asked how many objects he received, will answer "three." If such sentences are considered in this light, it becomes apparent that the ordered pairs (15,5), (30,10), (45,15), (60,20), and so forth, might somehow be related to the concept "three."   A further study reveals that from considering the integers within the ordered pairs one can observe a common pattern; for

$$(15,5) \quad \text{and} \quad (30,10), \qquad 15 \cdot 10 = 5 \cdot 30,$$

$$(45,15) \quad \text{and} \quad (60,20), \qquad 45 \cdot 20 = 15 \cdot 60,$$

$$(30,10) \quad \text{and} \quad (60,20), \qquad 30 \cdot 20 = 10 \cdot 60,$$

and so forth. For this reason, suppose we define a relation $\mathscr{R}$ on the set $I \times I_0$ as follows.

Definition 13-1: If (a,b) and (c,d) are any two members of $I \times I_0$, then (a,b) is **in the relation** $\mathscr{R}$ **with** (c,d) if and only if $ad = bc$. Symbolically, $(a,b)\mathscr{R}(c,d)$ if and only if $ad = bc$.

Examples: (a) $(^-1,3)\,\mathscr{R}(2,^-6)$ since $^-1 \cdot ^-6 = 3 \cdot 2$ in integers.
(b) $(1,^-3)\,\mathscr{R}(^-2,6)$ since $1 \cdot 6 = ^-3 \cdot ^-2$ in integers.
(c) $(1,4)\,\mathscr{R}(2,8)$ since $1 \cdot 8 = 4 \cdot 2$.
(d) $(2,^-5)\,\mathscr{R}(4,^-10)$ since $2 \cdot ^-10 = ^-5 \cdot 4$.

Thus we see that there are indeed pairs of ordered pairs which possess the relation $\mathscr{R}$. Note that if $\mathscr{R}$ is an equivalence relation, then $\mathscr{R}$ will partition this class of ordered pairs into mutually disjoint equivalence classes. Let us, then, try to determine if the reation $\mathscr{R}$ is an equivalence relation on $I \times I_0$.

Theorem 13-1: The relation $\mathscr{R}$ (as defined above) is an equivalence relation on the set $I \times I_0$.

Proof: We must show that $\mathscr{R}$ satisfies (1) the reflexive property, (2) the symmetric property, and (3) the transitive property.
(1): We need to show that $(a,b)\,\mathscr{R}(a,b)$ where (a,b) is any element of $I \times I_0$. According to the definition of $\mathscr{R}$, this is the case provided that $ab = ba$ for integers, but the latter is simply the commutative property of multiplication for integers. Therefore $(a,b)\mathscr{R}(a,b)$.
(2): We need to show that if $(a,b)\,\mathscr{R}(c,d)$, then $(c,d)\,\mathscr{R}(a,b)$. Since (a,b)

$\mathscr{R}$ (c,d), $ad = bc$ by Definition 13-1. Since $da = ad$ and $bc = cb$ for integers, we have $da = ad$ and $ad = bc$ so that $da = bc$. Now $da = bc$ and $bc = cb$ so that $da = cb$ by transitivity of equality. Since $da = cb$, Definition 13-1 yields (c,d) $\mathscr{R}(a,b)$ as desired.

(3): Here we must show that if (a,b) $\mathscr{R}(c,d)$ and (c,d) $\mathscr{R}(e,f)$, then (a,b) $\mathscr{R}(e,f)$. Since (a,b) $\mathscr{R}(c,d)$ and (c,d) $\mathscr{R}(e,f)$, we have that $ad = bc$ and $cf = de$ respectively by use of Definition 13-1. Using the uniqueness property of products for integers, we have

$$(ad)\,(cf) = (bc)\,(de)$$

The commutative and associative properties of integer multiplication assure us that

$$(af)\,(cd) = (be)\,(cd)$$

Since $d \neq 0$ (it is a second member of an ordered pair) the cancellation property of integer multiplication may be used to obtain

$$(af)c = (be)c$$

If we study this latter equation, we find that two cases arise, namely

(1) $c \neq 0$, or

(2) $c = 0$

Case (1): If $c \neq 0$, then by use of the cancellation property, $af = be$ and by Definition 13-1, $(a,b)\,\mathscr{R}(e,f)$.

Case (2): If $c = 0$, we can learn nothing from the statement $(af)c = (be)c$ since the equality would be true regardless of what integers af and be were used. However, if $c = 0$, then from $ad = bc$ one obtains

$$ad = b \cdot 0$$

$$= 0$$

Since d is a denominator, $d \neq 0$ and consequently $a = 0$. Further, from the equation $cf = de$ we obtain (with $c = 0$) that

$$0 \cdot f = de$$

$$0 = de$$

Again using the fact that d is a denominator, we find that since $d \neq 0$, it must be the case that $e = 0$.

Thus if $c = 0$, then $a = 0$ and $e = 0$, so that the statement $af = be$ is always true. That is, $0 \cdot f = b \cdot 0$ for all integers f and b. Therefore, regardless of whether $c \neq 0$ or $c = 0$, the statement $af = be$ is always true. Consequently, we obtain the fact that (a,b) $\mathscr{R}(e,f)$. Taking into account all three parts, we conclude that $\mathscr{R}$ is an equivalence relation on $I \times I_0$. ∎

Since $\mathscr{R}$ is an equivalence relation on $I \times I_0$, this class of ordered pairs is partitioned by $\mathscr{R}$ into mutually disjoint equivalence classes. Each of the classes formed by $\mathscr{R}$ will be referred to as a rational number. That is, each ordered pair in a given class represents the same number concept as any other ordered pair of that class.

Definition 13-2: An equivalence class as defined by the relation $\mathscr{R}$ is called a **rational number.**

Three rational numbers formed by $\mathscr{R}$ are illustrated by the equivalence classes below.

$$\left\{\begin{array}{c} \cdot \\ \cdot \\ \cdot \\ (^-8,4) \\ (^-6,3) \\ (^-4,2) \\ (^-2,1) \\ (2,^-1) \\ (4,^-2) \\ \cdot \\ \cdot \\ \cdot \end{array}\right\}, \quad \left\{\begin{array}{c} \cdot \\ \cdot \\ \cdot \\ (^-4,^-4) \\ (^-3,^-3) \\ (^-2,^-2) \\ (^-1,^-1) \\ (1,1) \\ (2,2) \\ \cdot \\ \cdot \\ \cdot \end{array}\right\}, \text{ and } \left\{\begin{array}{c} \cdot \\ \cdot \\ \cdot \\ (0,^-3) \\ (0,^-2) \\ (0,^-1) \\ (0,1) \\ (0,2) \\ (0,3) \\ \cdot \\ \cdot \\ \cdot \end{array}\right\}$$

are rational numbers.

An alternative method for illustrating these classes is to draw a graph (or grid) depicting the Cartesian product $I \times I_0$. Once the grid is constructed, diagonal lines can be drawn in such a way that every point belonging to the graph of $I \times I_0$ is on a diagonal, but no point is on more than one diagonal. All of the points on the graph of $I \times I_0$ which are on a given diagonal have ordered pair names which belong to the same equivalence class relative to the relation $\mathscr{R}$. This method is illustrated in Figure 13-2. It might be noted in conjunction with this figure that all of the diagonals pass through the point which, if we had taken $I \times I$ instead of $I \times I_0$, would have been labelled (0,0). However, if this had been done the ordered pair (0,0) would have belonged to each equivalence class. If this were the case, the classes would no longer have been disjoint and consequently $\mathscr{R}$ could not have been an equivalence relation. This fact also suggests that ordered pairs with second member zero should not be considered as belonging to any rational number.

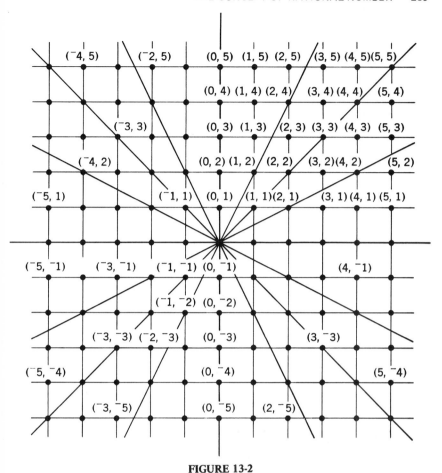

FIGURE 13-2

Now that we have a pictoral representation of rational numbers, we shall proceed to name them. Before doing so, it might be noted that the relation $\mathscr{R}$ has, in a sense, performed a certain kind of classification of the ordered pairs. To begin with, all ordered pairs which have zero as a first member are in one equivalence class. In addition to this, there appear to be two other types of classes. One type has as both members of each ordered pair either positive integers or negative integers. The second type has as members of each ordered pair one positive integer and one negative integer. Regarding the three classifications just mentioned, we shall make the following agreements:

(1) If in each ordered pair of a class the first integer is 0, we call this class the *rational number zero*.
(2) If in each ordered pair of a class both integers are positive or both are negative, we call this class a *positive rational number*.
(3) If in each ordered pair of a class one integer is positive and the other is negative, we call this class a *negative rational number*.

Definition 13-3: If $b \neq 0$, $\dfrac{a}{b}$ (read "*a* over *b*") names the class which contains the ordered pair (a,b). In the numeral $\frac{a}{b}$, a is called the **numerator** and b is called the **denominator**.

If one studies the equivalence classes illustrated above, he may observe that in each class there exist two ordered pairs in which the integers are relatively prime. This observation may be made for every possible class formed by the relation $\mathscr{R}$. Let us now state this formally and prove that the assertion we made is indeed true.

Theorem 13-2: Every rational number contains at least two ordered pairs of integers each having relatively prime members.

Proof: Let $(a,b) \in \frac{a}{b}$. The two possibilities which arise are that the G.C.F. $(a,b) = 1$ or G.C.F. $(a,b) \neq 1$. If the G.C.F. $(a,b) = 1$, then the only possibilities are for ordered pairs of the form $(^-m,n)$ or $(m, ^-n)$ where G.C.F. $(^-m,n) = $ G.C.F. $(m, ^-n) = 1$.

If G.C.F. $(a,b) \neq 1$, then there are common factors other than $^+1$ or $^-1$ so that the G.C.F. is some integer t greater than 1. That is,

$$a = t \cdot n \qquad \text{and} \qquad b = t \cdot m$$

where t is the largest common factor of a and b. This means that $(a,b) \, \mathscr{R}(n,m)$ where the only common factors of n and m are $^+1$ and $^-1$. In turn, this means that there exist ordered pairs $(n,^-m)$ and $(^-n,m)$ with G.C.F. $(n,^-m) = $ G.C.F. $(^-n,m) = 1$ which belong to the same class as (a,b). In either case there are two ordered pairs of integers belonging to each class such that the members of each ordered pair are relatively prime. ∎

We are now assured of the existence of two ordered pairs of relatively prime integers in each equivalence class. The next step is to show that there cannot be more than two such ordered pairs in a given class. Once this is done we will have established as fact that there are exactly two such ordered pairs in each class.

Theorem 13-3: No rational number contains more than two ordered pairs of integers each having relatively prime members.

Proof: From the preceding theorem it is known that there are at least two such pairs, which we denote $(^-n,m)$ and $(n, ^-m)$. Suppose that (a,b) is a third ordered pair in the same equivalence class and that a and b are relatively prime. Then

$$(a,b) \, \mathscr{R}(^-n,m) \qquad \text{and} \qquad (a,b) \, \mathscr{R}(n, ^-m)$$

By Definition 13-1,

$$am = b \, (^-n) \qquad \text{and} \qquad a(^-m) = bn$$

From these equations one can obtain the results that

$$m \mid b(^-n) \qquad \text{and} \qquad ^-m \mid bn$$

Therefore $m \mid b$ and $^-m \mid b$ since the pairs m and ^-n and ^-m and n are each relatively prime.

In a similar fashion one may write that

$$b \mid am \qquad \text{and} \qquad b \mid a(^-m)$$

Since it was assumed that a and b are relatively prime, it must be the case that $b \mid m$ and $b \mid ^-m$. The facts

$$(1) \quad m \mid b \qquad \text{and} \qquad ^-m \mid b, \qquad \text{and}$$

$$(2) \quad b \mid m \qquad \text{and} \qquad b \mid ^-m$$

together imply that $b = m$ or $b = ^-m$.

If $b = m$ then from the equation $am = b(^-n)$ we obtain

$$am = m(^-n)$$

and since m is a denominator (i.e., $m \neq 0$) it should be evident that $a = ^-n$. That is, $(a,b) = (^-n,m)$.

If $b = ^-m$ then from the equation $a(^-m) = bn$ we obtain

$$a(^-m) = (^-m)n$$

and since ^-m is a denominator it should be clear that $a = n$. Hence in this case $(a,b) = (n, ^-m)$.

We may now conclude that there are no more than two ordered pairs of relatively prime integers in any equivalence class formed by the relation $\mathscr{R}$. ▌

Theorems 13-2 and 13-3 together assure us that there are precisely two such ordered pairs of integers in each of the equivalence classes determined by the relation $\mathscr{R}$ on $I \times I_0$.

In order to make use of the results just obtained one needs to make note of the fact that all ordered pairs of a given class, other than the two pairs of relatively prime integers, are formed by taking the same non-zero multiples of both members of one of the two pairs of relatively prime integers.

Example: Select $(2, ^-3)$ and $(^-2,3)$ as the pairs of relatively prime integers. Consider the indicated non-zero multiples and associated pairs listed below if the pair $(2, ^-3)$ is used.

Multiples	Pairs	Multiples	Pairs
1 ⟶	$(2, ^-3)$	$^-1$ ⟶	$(^-2,3)$
2 ⟶	$(4, ^-6)$	$^-2$ ⟶	$(^-4,6)$
3 ⟶	$(6, ^-9)$	$^-3$ ⟶	$(^-6,9)$

4 $\longrightarrow$ (8, ⁻12)   ⁻4 $\longrightarrow$ (⁻8,12)

5 $\longrightarrow$ (10, ⁻15)   ⁻5 $\longrightarrow$ (⁻10,15)

. . . .

. . . .

. . . .

If the ordered pair (⁻2,3) is used, one finds that exactly the same collection of ordered pairs results when the non-zero multiples are formed. The equivalence class generated by this process is the class $\frac{-2}{3}$ or

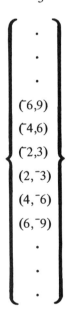

To show that such a process will always work requires the establishment of the following result. Once this is done the above procedure will be entirely justified.

Theorem 13-4: If (a,b) is any member of $I \times I_0$ and k is a non-zero integer then $(a,b)\,\mathscr{R}(ka, kb)$.

Proof: By Definition 13-1, $(a,b)\ \mathscr{R}(ka, kb)$ if and only if $a(kb) = b(ka)$. Since this can be established by the associative and commutative properties of integer multiplication, Definition 13-1 guarantees that $(a,b)\ \mathscr{R}\ (ka, kb)$ as claimed. ∎

From this we see that the procedure illustrated above for generating the equivalence classes is well founded. We therefore have a systematic method for constructing any particular class which we wish to consider.

Before proceeding to develop the arithmetic of rational numbers, we need to be able to determine when two numerals name the same rational number. In order to do this, let us reconsider Definition 13-3. It should be clear from Definition 13-3, for example, that if (4,3) and (ˉ4, ˉ3) are in the same class that $\frac{4}{3}$ and $\frac{ˉ4}{ˉ3}$ are two different names for that class. It should also be clear that (4,3) $\mathscr{R}$ (ˉ4, ˉ3), since $4 \cdot ˉ3 = ˉ4 \cdot 3$. Thus a convenient way to test for equality would apparently be to form products of integers as indicated in Definition 13-1. Consequently, we shall define equality for rational numbers as follows.

Definition 13-4: Two rationals $\frac{a}{b}$ and $\frac{c}{d}$ are **equal** if and only if $ad = bc$. Symbolically, $\frac{a}{b} = \frac{c}{d}$ if and only if $ad = bc$.

Thus we see that $\frac{2}{ˉ4} = \frac{ˉ4}{8}$, $\frac{ˉ1}{3} = \frac{6}{18}$, $\frac{1}{ˉ2} = \frac{ˉ1}{2}$, and so on.

Often times after a problem has been solved one finds that the answer obtained is not in reduced form. That is, numerator and denominator are not relatively prime. From the discussion thus far we find that two numerals exist in which numerator and denominator are relatively prime. For convenience and so that some standardization of results will be introduced we shall arbitrarily select the numeral which we shall call the reduced form.

Definition 13-5: The **reduced form (preferred form)** of the numeral $\frac{a}{b}$ is relatively prime pair $\frac{m}{n}$ such that $\frac{a}{b} = \frac{m}{n}$ and n is a positive integer.

In fact, let us agree that we shall always make use of numerals which have a positive denominator regardless of whether the numeral is in reduced form or not.

Throughout much of the succeeding discussion we shall need to be able to give equivalent names for certain rational numbers. One way to do this, of course, is to construct the classes of equivalent ordered pairs of integers and select from that class the pair desired for the particular instance. However, if we study the results of Theorem 13-4 and Definition 13-4 closely, we can prove the following result which gives a straight-forward method for selecting the required numerals.

Theorem 13-5: If $\frac{a}{b}$ is a rational number and k is any non-zero integer, then $\frac{a}{b} = \frac{ka}{kb}$.

Proof: From Theorem 13-4, we know that (a,b) $\mathscr{R}$ (ka, kb) for $k \neq 0$. Hence $a(kb) = b(ka)$. Then by Definition 13-4 we obtain the result that $\frac{a}{b} = \frac{ka}{kb}$. ∎

This theorem allows us to test for equality directly without going back to construct the equivalence classes. The theorem is used so often that for convenience we shall often refer to it as the *K-Theorem*.

Example: Does $\dfrac{15}{45} = \dfrac{1}{3}$?

Solution:
$$\frac{15}{45} = \frac{15 \cdot 1}{15 \cdot 3} \qquad \text{Def. } (\cdot)$$

$$= \frac{1}{3} \qquad \text{K-Thm.}$$

In this example we have chosen $a = 1$, $b = 3$, and $k = 15$.

Example: Select another numeral for $\dfrac{3}{7}$ whose denominator is 56.

Solution: Since $8 \cdot 7 = 56$, we use the *K*-Theorem with $k = 8$. Then $\dfrac{3}{7} = \dfrac{8 \cdot 3}{8 \cdot 7} = \dfrac{24}{56}$. Therefore $\dfrac{24}{56}$ is another numeral for the rational number named by $\dfrac{3}{7}$ and meets the requirement that it have 56 as a denominator.

The above examples illustrate two of the-more common uses of the *K*-Theorem, namely "reducing rationals to lowest form" or choosing new numerals to fit specified conditions. It should also be noted that many student readers confuse the *K*-Theorem with one of the cancellation properties. One way to avoid this problem is to note that in using cancellation we begin with a statement of equality and obtain an equivalent statement of equality, while the *K*-Theorem allows one to begin with a numeral for a rational number and select an equivalent name for that number. That is, using the *K*-Theorem we may begin with a numeral and form a statement of equality using that numeral and an equivalent numeral. Remember that these are not the same, so be sure you understand the difference between these two properties.

EXERCISE SET 13-1

1. Draw a graph like that in Figure 13-1 and fill in several ordered pair names.
2. Test each of the following pairs to see if they are in the relation $\mathscr{R}$ to each other.
   (a) $(2, {}^-3)$ and $({}^-6,9)$
   (b) $(3,5)$ and $({}^-9, {}^-15)$
   (c) $(2,3)$ and $(3,4)$
   (d) $(5,6)$ and $({}^-6,5)$
   (e) $(7, {}^-10)$ and $({}^-7,10)$
   (f) $({}^-4,7)$ and $(12,21)$
   (g) $(5, {}^-13)$ and $({}^-10, {}^-26)$
   (h) $({}^-4,5)$ and $(8, {}^-10)$
3. If possible, determine x or y so that each of the following statements is true.
   (a) $(2,x) \mathscr{R} ({}^-8,12)$
   (b) $(y,0) \mathscr{R} (3,0)$

(c) $(^-3,7) \mathscr{R} (9,y)$

(d) $(5,^-3) \mathscr{R} (x,6)$

4. Which of the following classes suggests the concept of rational number?

(a) $\{ \ (1,2), (2,3), (3,4), (4,5), \ldots \ \}$

(b) $\{ \ (1,13), (2,13), (3,13), (4,13), \ldots \ \}$

(c) $\{ \ (0,13), (1,13), (2,13), (3,13), \ldots \ \}$

(d) $\{ \ (1,13), (2,26), (3,39), (4,52), \ldots \ \}$

(e) $\{ \ (1,21), (2,42), (3,36), (4,82), \ldots \ \}$

(f) $\{ \ (1,6), (2,12), (4,24), (3,18), \ldots \ \}$

(g) $\{ \ (13,2), (26,4), (39,6), (65,10), \ldots \ \}$

5. Construct equivalence classes for each of the following.

(a) $\dfrac{^-2}{7}$

(c) $-\dfrac{3}{5}$

(b) $-\dfrac{3}{4}$

(d) $\dfrac{6}{2}$

6. By referring to the K-Theorem, determine k so that when k is removed, the numerator and denominator are relatively prime.

(a) $-\dfrac{16}{28}$

(d) $-\dfrac{^-20}{25}$

(b) $\dfrac{^-34}{68}$

(e) $-\dfrac{17}{51}$

(c) $\dfrac{8}{32}$

(f) $-\dfrac{8}{^-24}$

7. Write the reduced form of each of the following numerals.

(a) $\dfrac{^-4}{6}$

(d) $-\dfrac{16}{32}$

(b) $\dfrac{^-4}{2}$

(e) $-\dfrac{^-8}{^-24}$

(c) $\dfrac{5}{15}$

(f) $-\dfrac{9}{27}$

8. In each of the following find the integer k referred to in the K-Theorem.

(a) $\dfrac{3}{7} = \dfrac{18}{42}$

(d) $\dfrac{7}{15} = \dfrac{21}{45}$

(b) $\dfrac{0}{14} = \dfrac{0}{1}$

(e) $\dfrac{15}{30} = \dfrac{3}{6}$

(c) $\dfrac{4}{12} = \dfrac{12}{36}$

(f) $\dfrac{15}{30} = \dfrac{5}{10}$

(g) Referring to parts (e) and (f), could we say that $\dfrac{3}{6} = \dfrac{5}{10}$ without using the definition of equality of rationals? If so, how?

9. Determine x or y so that the relation of equality holds in each case.

(a) $\dfrac{2}{x} = \dfrac{10}{15}$

(d) $\dfrac{7}{8} = -\dfrac{x}{16}$

(b) $\dfrac{x}{3} = \dfrac{^-8}{6}$

(e) $\dfrac{^-5}{6} = -\dfrac{x}{18}$

(c) $\dfrac{2}{y} = \dfrac{^-10}{15}$

(f) $\dfrac{^-3}{4} = \dfrac{12}{y}$

10. Show that

(a) $\dfrac{0}{2} = \dfrac{0}{7}$.

(b) $\dfrac{0}{6} = \dfrac{0}{18}$.

(c) $\dfrac{0}{5} = \dfrac{0}{31}$.

(d) Show that if $\dfrac{0}{m}$ and $\dfrac{0}{n}$ are rationals, then $\dfrac{0}{m} = \dfrac{0}{n}$ for every n and m such that $n \neq 0$ and $m \neq 0$.

Chapter summary

During the course of constructing a system of numbers to adequately describe certain physical phenomena, we found that with the system of integers some advantages were realized. That is, number sentences of the form $x + a = b$ are always solvable. However, sentences of the form $ax + b = c$ do not always admit integer solutions and so the search for an adequate system of numbers must be continued. To this end, we defined in Chapter 13 what we referred to as a *rational* number and in doing so once again made use of the important concept of *equivalence* relation. As before, we used objects which were already familiar in order to define a new object.

By use of known properties of integers we showed that every rational number has a numeral which we called the reduced or preferred form. We also used the defining relation $\mathscr{R}$ and integer properties to decide when two numerals named the same rational number. Relative to the naming of rational numbers we stated what might be called the K-Theorem (Theorem 13-5). It should be stressed again that even though the K-Theorem may remind one of cancellation, it is in fact decidedly different. Perhaps one way to keep the two clearly in mind is that

1) the K-Theorem is simply one statement of equality while
2) cancellation involves the replacement of one statement of equality by an equivalent statement of equality.

CHAPTER 14 Addition and subtraction of rationals

---

1. Definition of Addition of Rationals

Again, as in our work with integers, we are faced with the prospect of developing an arithmetic for a set of numbers with which (for the purposes of this development) we have had no previous experience. This being the case, we are at liberty to try new ideas. It seems that a reasonable approach to the problem is to try to develop an arithmetic in such a way that if we set up a correspondence between a certain subset of the rationals and the set of integers, we obtain a correspondence between the resulting arithmetics. To this end, let us set up the following correspondences:

$$\textit{Integers} \qquad\qquad\qquad \textit{Rationals}$$

$$^{+}n \longleftrightarrow \frac{^{+}n}{1}$$

$$0 \longleftrightarrow \frac{0}{1}$$

$$^{-}n \longleftrightarrow \frac{^{-}n}{1}$$

Thus, if we have the correspondences

$$^{+}2 \longleftrightarrow \frac{^{+}2}{1}$$

and

$$^{-}5 \longleftrightarrow \frac{^{-}5}{1}$$

we want to obtain

$$^+2 + {}^-5 \longleftarrow \qquad \longrightarrow \frac{^+2}{1} + \frac{^-5}{1}$$

that is,

$$^-3 \longleftarrow \qquad \longrightarrow \frac{^-3}{1}$$

The problem, then, is to determine a procedure which will give the desired result that

$$\frac{^+2}{1} + \frac{^-5}{1} = \frac{^-3}{1}$$

However, there is an additional problem to consider, namely that the procedure must give the correct correspondence between integers and rationals even if we do not use the reduced form of the numerals involved. Obviously, one way in which this might be achieved is to take

$$\frac{^+2}{1} + \frac{^-5}{1} = \frac{^+2 + {}^-5}{1} = \frac{^-3}{1}$$

That is, in general we might add $\frac{a}{1}$ and $\frac{c}{1}$ by forming the sum

$$\frac{a}{1} + \frac{c}{1} = \frac{a+c}{1}$$

But what if the denominator is a positive integer different from one? For example, suppose we wish to add $\frac{a}{b} + \frac{c}{b}$ where $b \neq 1$. To illustrate this we consider the case $a = 2$, $b = 6$, and $c = 3$. In Figure 14-1(a) we observe that two of six parts of the region are shaded in the first diagram and three of six parts are shaded in the second diagram. Figure 14-1(b) shows the sum of the components of part (a).

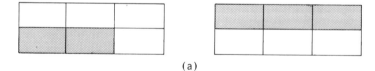

(a)

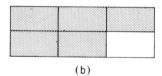

(b)

FIGURE 14-1

Thus we apparently have that $\frac{2}{6} + \frac{3}{6} = \frac{2+3}{6} = \frac{5}{6}$. Perhaps it is reasonable to say that in general

$$\frac{a}{b} + \frac{c}{b} = \frac{a+c}{b}$$

It is rather interesting to observe from Figure 14-1 the striking similarity to addition of cardinal numbers. It appears that the union of two disjoint sets was formed. If one trys other examples similar to that illustrated in Figure 14-1, he may decide upon the following as a tentative definition for addition of rational numbers.

Definition 14-1: If $\frac{a}{b}$ and $\frac{c}{b}$ are rational numbers, then their **sum** is the rational

number $\frac{a+c}{b}$. That is, $\frac{a}{b} + \frac{c}{b} = \frac{a+c}{b}^1$.

Since we are trying to construct a new system which preserves the desirable characteristics of the system of integers, we need to know that under Definition 14-1 sums do exist in the set of rational numbers. This is a relatively simple

matter, for in the sum $\frac{a+c}{b}$, b is a non-zero integer and the sum of integers a and

c is another integer. Thus $\frac{a+c}{b}$ does represent a rational number.

The next thing we must check is whether or not the sum of two rationals is unique regardless of which of their numerals is used to represent them. We do this in the following theorem.

Theorem 14-1: Addition of rational numbers yields unique sums.

Proof: We must show that if $\frac{a}{b}$ and $\frac{c}{b}$ are rationals and if $\frac{a}{b} = \frac{u}{v}$ and $\frac{c}{b} = \frac{w}{v}$, then

$\frac{a}{b} + \frac{c}{b} = \frac{u}{v} + \frac{w}{v}$. Now $\frac{a}{b} + \frac{c}{b} = \frac{u}{v} + \frac{w}{v}$ if and only if $\frac{a+c}{b} = \frac{u+w}{v}$. This can be in-

ferred by use of Definition 14-1 and the transitivity of equality. Thus if we can

show that $\frac{a+c}{b} = \frac{u+w}{v}$, we will be done. By Definition 13-4, $\frac{a+c}{b} = \frac{u+w}{v}$ if and

---

[1]We are using the symbol + in two different senses now, but this should not cause any consternation if we agree to the following interpretation.

Agreement: Whenever numerals in "fractional form" (i.e., $\frac{a}{b}$) are used, addition of rational

numbers is indicated. That is, $\frac{2}{3} + \frac{5}{3}$ means to add the rationals two thirds and

five thirds. On the other hand, $\frac{2+5}{3}$ indicates the addition of the integers two

and five.

only if $(a + c)v = b(u + w)$. Hence we need to show that the latter statement of equality holds for integers. Now since

$$
\begin{bmatrix}
\dfrac{a}{b} = \dfrac{u}{v} \\[1em]
\text{and} \\[1em]
\dfrac{c}{b} = \dfrac{w}{v}
\end{bmatrix}
\quad \text{we have} \quad
\begin{bmatrix}
av = bu \\[1em]
\text{and} \\[1em]
cv = bw
\end{bmatrix}
\quad \text{by Definition 13-4.}
$$

By uniqueness of sums of integers we obtain

$$av + cv = bu + bw$$

Then by use of distributivity of multiplication for integers, we obtain

$$(a + c)v = b(u + w)$$

We now conclude that addition gives unique sums. ▮

At this stage we still have not solved the problem of how to add rationals in the situation where their numerals have different denominators. For example, how do we add $\dfrac{2}{3} + \dfrac{3}{4}$? If we could obtain the same denominator for each rational numeral our problem would be solved. Suppose we use the K-Theorem and uniqueness to write

$$\frac{2}{3} + \frac{3}{4} = \frac{4 \cdot 2}{4 \cdot 3} + \frac{3 \cdot 3}{3 \cdot 4}$$

Then

$$\frac{2}{3} + \frac{3}{4} = \frac{8}{12} + \frac{9}{12} \qquad \text{Integer Mult.}$$

$$= \frac{8 + 9}{12} \qquad \text{Def. 14-1}$$

$$= \frac{17}{12} \qquad \text{Integer Add.}$$

In fact, we can make this general enough so that we need *not* go through all of these steps again.

Theorem 14-2: If $\dfrac{a}{b}$ and $\dfrac{c}{d}$ are rational numbers, then $\dfrac{a}{b} + \dfrac{c}{d} = \dfrac{ad + bc}{bd}$.

Proof: Using the K-Theorem and uniqueness we have

$$\frac{a}{b} + \frac{c}{d} = \frac{ad}{bd} + \frac{bc}{bd}$$

so that

$$\frac{a}{b} + \frac{c}{d} = \frac{ad + bc}{bd}. \blacksquare$$

The result of Theorem 14-2 is often taken as the definition of addition of rationals, but our procedure may be more meaningful to the beginning student since we are trying to develop the arithmetic directly from that of integers by using the integers as building blocks.

EXERCISE SET 14-1

1. Using Definition 14-1 add each of the following. (Write the numerals in preferred form first if necessary.)

   (a) $\frac{3}{2} + \frac{^-5}{2}$

   (c) $\frac{2}{3} + \frac{5}{^-3}$

   (b) $\frac{^-5}{6} + \frac{3}{6}$

   (d) $\frac{4}{^-5} + \frac{3}{^-5}$

2. Using Definition 14-1 add

   (a) $\frac{4}{7} + \frac{^-2}{7}$ and

   (b) $\frac{^-8}{^-14} + \frac{^-4}{14}$.

   (c) This illustrates what property of addition of rationals?

3. Add each of the following and in doing so use the K-Theorem.

   (a) $\frac{2}{3} + \frac{3}{4}$

   (b) $\frac{5}{6} + \frac{^-4}{3}$

   (c) $\frac{^-3}{5} + \frac{2}{6}$

   (d) $\frac{^-7}{8} + \frac{^-2}{3}$

   (e) Your working in determining the above four sums *illustrates* the proof of what theorem listed in the text?

4. Add $\frac{3}{5} + \frac{7}{8}$

   (a) by using the K-Theorem to determine a common denominator.

   (b) by using Theorem 14-2 directly.

   (c) Compare the methods used in parts (a) and (b) and explain how they are related.

2. Properties of Addition of Rationals

We have already studied the Associative and Commutative Properties in conjunction with cardinal numbers and integers and observed their usefulness there. Since we are trying to preserve these desirable characteristics, we need to check to see if they still hold under Definition 14-1.

Theorem 14-3 (Commutative): If $\frac{a}{b}$ and $\frac{c}{d}$ are rational numbers, then

$$\frac{a}{b} + \frac{c}{d} = \frac{c}{d} + \frac{a}{b}.$$

Proof: We leave this as an exercise. However, the student should illustrate the result with a numerical example and then attempt the proof.

As we have already observed, associativity and commutativity provide the basis for "checking" addition problems in both cardinal and integer arithmetic. Let us now show that addition of rationals is associative. Once this is done, we shall have established the analogous method of checking sums for rational numbers.

Theorem 14-4 (Associative): If $\frac{a}{b}$, $\frac{c}{d}$, and $\frac{e}{f}$ are rational numbers, then

$$\left(\frac{a}{b} + \frac{c}{d}\right) + \frac{e}{f} = \frac{a}{b} + \left(\frac{c}{d} + \frac{e}{f}\right).$$

Proof: Our proof here will be a direct one.

$$\left(\frac{a}{b} + \frac{c}{d}\right) + \frac{e}{f} = \frac{ad + bc}{bd} + \frac{e}{f} \qquad\qquad \text{Thm. 14-2}$$

$$= \frac{(ad + bc)f + (bd)e}{(bd)f} \qquad\qquad \text{Thm. 14-2}$$

$$= \frac{(adf + bcf) + bde}{bdf} \qquad\qquad \begin{array}{l}\text{Distr., Integers}\\ \text{Assoc. } (\cdot)\text{, Integers}\end{array}$$

$$= \frac{adf + (bcf + bde)}{bdf} \qquad\qquad \text{Assoc. }(+)\text{, Integers}$$

$$= \frac{adf}{bdf} + \frac{bcf + bde}{bdf} \qquad\qquad \text{Def. 14-1}$$

$$= \frac{a(df)}{b(df)} + \left(\frac{bcf}{bdf} + \frac{bde}{bdf}\right) \qquad\qquad \begin{array}{l}\text{Assoc. } (\cdot)\text{, Integers}\\ \text{Def. 14-1}\end{array}$$

$$= \frac{(df)a}{(df)b} + \left(\frac{(bf)c}{(bf)d} + \frac{(bd)e}{(bd)f}\right) \qquad\qquad \begin{array}{l}\text{Assoc. } (\cdot)\text{, Integers}\\ \text{Comm. } (\cdot)\text{, Integers}\end{array}$$

$$= \frac{a}{b} + \left(\frac{c}{d} + \frac{e}{f}\right) \qquad\qquad \text{K-Theorem, Uniq.}$$

Thus addition of rationals has the associative property. ∎

There is another way to prove associativity and this we leave to the student as an exercise (see exercise two at the end of this section).

Now that commutativity and associativity for addition of rational numbers has been established, you should show in detail how they can be used to check addition problems such as the following:

$$\frac{1}{4}$$

$$\frac{2}{3}$$

$$+\frac{5}{6}$$

If one uses Definition 14-1 or Theorem 14-2 to determine sums of rational numbers, he may observe that sums such as those below are sometimes obtained.

$$\frac{2}{3} + \frac{0}{1} = \frac{2}{3}$$

$$\frac{5}{8} + \frac{0}{1} = \frac{5}{8}$$

$$\frac{^-6}{7} + \frac{0}{1} = \frac{^-6}{7}$$

Such examples lead one to suspect that, in general, for any rational number $\frac{a}{b}$,

$$\frac{a}{b} + \frac{0}{1} = \frac{a}{b}$$

This fact, together with commutativity, implies that $\frac{0}{1}$ is an additive identity. It is not immediately clear however that $\frac{0}{1}$ is the only additive identity, even though from past experience you might guess that it is. Therefore let us prove that the additive identity is indeed unique in the system of rational numbers.

Theorem 14-5: $\frac{0}{1}$ is the unique additive identity for rationals.

Proof: Suppose that there is a second additive identity different from $\frac{0}{1}$, say $\frac{m}{n}$. Thus we have

$$\frac{a}{b} + \frac{0}{1} = \frac{0}{1} + \frac{a}{b} = \frac{a}{b} \qquad (1)$$

$$\frac{a}{b} + \frac{m}{n} = \frac{m}{n} + \frac{a}{b} = \frac{a}{b} \qquad (2)$$

Now in particular, equation (1) must hold for $\frac{a}{b} = \frac{m}{n}$; that is,

$$\frac{m}{n} + \frac{0}{1} = \frac{0}{1} + \frac{m}{n} = \frac{m}{n}$$

Also, Equation (2) must hold for $\frac{a}{b} = \frac{0}{1}$. Making this substitution, we obtain

$$\frac{0}{1} + \frac{m}{n} = \frac{m}{n} + \frac{0}{1} = \frac{0}{1}$$

Consequently, we have the two equations

$$\frac{m}{n} + \frac{0}{1} = \frac{m}{n}$$

and

$$\frac{m}{n} + \frac{0}{1} = \frac{0}{1}$$

both of which must hold.

Since sums are unique, it must be that $\frac{m}{n} = \frac{0}{1}$. This contradicts the assumption that $\frac{m}{n} \neq \frac{0}{1}$ and consequently there can be at most one identity element for addition. Since there is at least one identity and at most one identity, there is precisely one identity. Therefore the additive identity for rational numbers is unique. ∎

We shall show next that if

$$\frac{a}{b} + \frac{2}{3} = \frac{5}{6} + \frac{2}{3}$$

then

$$\frac{a}{b} = \frac{5}{6}$$

That is, just as for integers, there is a Cancellation Property for addition of rational numbers. It is probably easy to agree that this "makes sense" intuitively, but nevertheless, we really *do* need to show that it is always the case if we are to make use of it later as a method of solving problems.

Theorem 14-6 (Cancellation): If $\frac{a}{b}, \frac{c}{d}$, and $\frac{e}{f}$ are rational numbers and if $\frac{a}{b} + \frac{e}{f} = \frac{c}{d} + \frac{e}{f}$, then $\frac{a}{b} = \frac{c}{d}$.

Proof:

$$\frac{a}{b} + \frac{e}{f} = \frac{c}{d} + \frac{e}{f} \qquad \text{Assumption}$$

$$\frac{af + be}{bf} = \frac{cf + de}{df} \qquad \text{Thm. 14-2}$$

$$(af + be)df = bf(cf + de) \qquad \text{Def. 13-4}$$

$$(af + be)df = (cf + de)bf \qquad \text{Comm.}(\cdot) \text{ integers}$$

$$(af + be)d = (cf + de)b \qquad \text{Canc.}(\cdot) \text{ integers}$$

$$afd + bed = cfb + deb \qquad \text{Distr., integers}$$

$$adf + bed = bcf + bed \qquad \text{Assoc.}(\cdot), \text{Comm.}(\cdot)$$
$$\text{integers}$$

$$adf = bcf \qquad \text{Canc.(+) integers}$$

$$ad = bc \qquad \text{Canc.}(\cdot) \text{ integers}$$

Thus, by use of Definition 13-4, we find that

$$\frac{a}{b} = \frac{c}{d}$$

and the validity of the Cancellation Property is established. ▮

Using Theorem 14-6, we can solve problems of the following type even if nothing is known about subtraction.

Example: If $x + \dfrac{2}{3} = \dfrac{5}{6}$, determine the set X of rational numbers x which are solutions.

Solution:

$$x + \frac{2}{3} = \frac{1+4}{6} \qquad \text{Def.(+) integers}$$

$$x + \frac{2}{3} = \frac{1}{6} + \frac{4}{6} \qquad \text{Def. 14-1}$$

$$x = \frac{1}{6} \qquad \text{Thm. 14-6}$$

Therefore $X = \left\{ \dfrac{1}{6} \right\}$ is the set of solutions for the original equation.

The student should *not* draw the conclusion from the above example that all number sentences have a solution set consisting of a single number. Indeed, just as in the case of integers, number sentences may have none, one, several, or infinitely many solutions. The number of solutions depends entirely on the number sentence involved.

As in the work with cardinal numbers and integers there is a Converse of the Cancellation Property for addition of rationals. We shall state this theorem with a hint as to how it might be proved.

Theorem 14-7 (Converse of Cancellation): If $\dfrac{a}{b} = \dfrac{c}{d}$, then for every rational number $\dfrac{e}{f}$, $\dfrac{a}{b} + \dfrac{e}{f} = \dfrac{c}{d} + \dfrac{e}{f}$.

Proof: If the student will reverse the order of the steps of the proof of Theorem 14-6 this will provde a proof for this theorem.

If it turns out that every rational number has an additive inverse, Theorem 14-7 will be quite useful as a tool with which to solve certain types of number sentences. Since the additive inverse was so useful in the system of integers, let us investigate to try to determine if additive inverses exist in the system of rational numbers.

Theorem 14-8: Every rational number $\frac{a}{b}$ has an additive inverse.

Proof: We claim that if $\frac{a}{b}$ is any rational number whatever, then it has an additive inverse. Thus, to back up our claim, we must exhibit such a number. Our specific claim is that $\frac{^-a}{b}$ is such a number because of the fact that

$$\frac{a}{b} + \frac{^-a}{b} = \frac{a + ^-a}{b} = \frac{0}{b} = \frac{0}{1}$$

Therefore we have established the existence of such a number for every rational number $\frac{a}{b}$. ∎

Before Theorem 14-8 will be of any real value, we need to show that additive inverses are unique. We do this in the following theorem.

Theorem 14-9: Additive inverses for rational numbers are unique.

Proof: Suppose there is a rational number $\frac{c}{d}$ such that for any rational $\frac{a}{b}$,

$$\frac{a}{b} + \frac{c}{d} = \frac{0}{1} \quad \text{and} \quad \frac{c}{d} \neq \frac{^-a}{b}$$

We already know from Theorem 14-8 that

$$\frac{a}{b} + \frac{^-a}{b} = \frac{0}{1}$$

Hence by symmetry and transitivity of equality we obtain

$$\frac{a}{b} + \frac{c}{d} = \frac{a}{b} + \frac{^-a}{b}$$

Then by use of the Cancellation Property of addition we obtain the result

$$\frac{c}{d} = \frac{^-a}{b}$$

Thus our supposition that $\frac{c}{d} \neq \frac{^-a}{b}$ is false and consequently there is no such

number $\frac{c}{d}$ different from $\frac{^-a}{b}$ which is an additive inverse of $\frac{a}{b}$. Therefore additive

inverses for rational numbers are unique.∎

To see how Theorems 14-7, 14-8, and 14-9 can be used, consider the following number sentence in which we are to determine the number $\frac{x}{y}$:

Example: If $\frac{x}{y} + \frac{2}{3} = \frac{^-3}{4}$, determine $\frac{x}{y}$.

Solution:

$\left(\frac{x}{y} + \frac{2}{3}\right) + \frac{^-2}{3} = \frac{^-3}{4} + \frac{^-2}{3}$	Thm. 14-7 or Uniq. (+)
$\frac{x}{y} + \left(\frac{2}{3} + \frac{^-2}{3}\right) = \frac{^-3}{4} + \frac{^-2}{3}$	Thm. 14-4
$\frac{x}{y} + \frac{0}{1} = \frac{^-3}{4} + \frac{^-2}{3}$	Thms. 14-8, 14-9
$\frac{x}{y} = \frac{^-3}{4} + \frac{^-2}{3}$	Thm. 14-5
$\frac{x}{y} = \frac{^-3 \cdot 3 + 4 \cdot {^-2}}{4 \cdot 3}$	Thm. 14-2
$\frac{x}{y} = \frac{^-17}{12}$	Def.(+),(·) integers

As you may recall, some rules for adding "signed" numbers were discussed in Section 10-2a. Using these properties of integers and the properties of addition of rationals developed thus far, we are in a position to investigate these so-called "rules of signs" as applied to addition of rational numbers. In each of the following cases let us assume for convenience that a, b, c, and d are positive integers.

Theorem 14-10: The sum of two positive rational numbers is a positive rational number.

Proof: Let $\frac{a}{b}$ and $\frac{c}{d}$ be positive rationals. Then by Theorem 14-2

$$\frac{a}{b} + \frac{c}{d} = \frac{ad + bc}{bd}$$

Since a, b, c, and d are positive integers, ad, bc, and bd are each positive integers.

Consequently, $ad + bc$ is a positive integer and $\dfrac{ad + bc}{bd}$ is a positive rational number. ∎

Theorem 14-11: The sum of two negative rational numbers is a negative rational number.

Proof: Let $\dfrac{^-a}{b}$ and $\dfrac{^-c}{d}$ be two negative rational numbers. Then using Theorem 14-2 we obtain

$$\frac{^-a}{b} + \frac{^-c}{d} = \frac{^-a \cdot d + b \cdot ^-c}{bd} = \frac{^-ad + ^-bc}{bd}$$

Using the rules of signs for integers we find that ^-ad and ^-bc are negative while bd is a positive integer. Thus $^-ad + ^-bc$ is a negative integer and $\dfrac{^-ad + ^-bc}{bd}$ is a negative rational number. ∎

Theorem 14-12: If $\dfrac{a}{b}$ is a positive rational number and $\dfrac{^-c}{d}$ is a negative rational number, then $\dfrac{a}{b} + \dfrac{^-c}{d}$ is positive if $\dfrac{a}{b} > \dfrac{c}{d}$ is negative if $\dfrac{a}{b} < \dfrac{c}{d}$.

Proof: $\dfrac{a}{b} + \dfrac{^-c}{d} = \dfrac{ad + ^-bc}{bd}$ by Theorem 14-2 and integer arithmetic.

Now if $ad > bc$, then $\dfrac{ad + ^-bc}{bd}$ is positive and if $ad < bc$ then $\dfrac{ad + ^-bc}{bd}$ is negative. [We shall see later that these inequalities are precisely the conditions for $\dfrac{a}{b} > \dfrac{c}{d}$ and $\dfrac{a}{b} < \dfrac{c}{d}$.] ∎

Even though order for rational numbers has not been discussed, Theorem 14-12 is included here for completeness. If you do not find the proof of the theorem entirely satisfactory, perhaps the following two examples will help make it more acceptable to you.

Examples: $\dfrac{2}{3} + \dfrac{^-1}{2} = \dfrac{2 \cdot 2 + ^-3 \cdot 1}{3 \cdot 2} = \dfrac{4 + ^-3}{6} = \dfrac{1}{6}$.

Note that $2 \cdot 2 > 3 \cdot 1$ and the sum is indeed a positive rational number.

$$\frac{1}{2} + \frac{^-2}{3} = \frac{1 \cdot 3 + ^-2 \cdot 2}{2 \cdot 3} = \frac{3 + ^-4}{6} = \frac{^-1}{6}$$

Note that in this case $1 \cdot 3 < 2 \cdot 2$ and the sum is a negative rational number.

The results illustrated in the two preceding examples are exactly those predicted in Theorem 14-12. We encourage you to try other numerical examples to convince yourself of the validity of the theorem.

Suppose now that we consider an addition problem such as the following:

$$2\frac{3}{5}$$

$$+\ {}^{-}1\frac{4}{5}$$

Here a problem of interpretation presents itself. First of all, most of us read $2\frac{3}{5}$ as "two and three fifths" and it is probably safe to assume that what most of us really mean is $2\frac{3}{5} = 2 + \frac{3}{5}$. This is, the two numbers represented in each addend are actually added. A second problem of interpretation arises here. What kind of number is represented by the numeral 2? If the number is two, then what kind of two: cardinal, integer, or rational? Based on the development of number systems thus far discussed, we cannot interpret the 2 as either a cardinal or integer, for then we are adding numbers from two different number systems. This type of addition has not been discussed at all. In fact, we have gone to great lengths to avoid such a situation. If we are to continue our development along these lines we must of necessity require that the two be a rational number so that 2 represents rational two. It should be pointed out that at the beginning of Section 14-1 we set up a correspondence between the set of integers and the rational numbers having denominator one. If it happens that the system of integers is isomorphic to this subsystem of rationals having denominator one, then it might be useful to be able to replace a rational numeral $\frac{a}{1}$ with an integer numeral a provided that it is understood that the numeral a now *represents a rational number*. Such a replacement of numerals might not always be made, but where some simplification might result it would prove most useful. We shall feel free to make such replacements of numerals from this point onward, since it will be shown later that the isomorphism mentioned does in fact exist.

It is of particular interest to note that the interpretation of the addition problem mentioned above centers around the use of the numerals involved. For this reason, such problems are more properly referred to as problems involving *mixed numerals* rather than mixed numbers. It is the isomorphism between the integers and rationals with denominator one which allows this convenient "mixing" of numerals.

Of course, one way to work the above problem is to write

$$2\frac{3}{5} + {}^{-}1\frac{4}{5} = \left(\frac{10}{5} + \frac{3}{5}\right) + \left(\frac{{}^{-}5}{5} + \frac{{}^{-}4}{5}\right)$$

$$= \frac{13}{5} + \frac{{}^{-}9}{5}$$

$$= \frac{13 + {}^-9}{5}$$

$$= \frac{4}{5}.$$

However, since the original numerals were *mixed numerals,* it may be possible to work it by splitting it up into two parts, one involving just integer numerals and one which involves only rational numerals. If such a problem is split up in this way, it should be borne in mind that these numerals (all of them) represent rational numbers and only rational numbers. For example, perhaps the problem could be worked as follows.

$$2\frac{3}{5} + {}^-1\frac{4}{5} = \left(2 + \frac{3}{5} \right) + \left({}^-1 + \frac{{}^-4}{5} \right)$$

$$= \left(2 + {}^-1 \right) + \left(\frac{3}{5} + \frac{{}^-4}{5} \right)$$

$$= 1 + \frac{{}^-1}{5}$$

$$= \frac{5}{5} + \frac{{}^-1}{5}$$

$$= \frac{4}{5}.$$

This method of solution may be stated formally as follows.

Theorem 14-13: If $\frac{a}{b}, \frac{c}{d}, \frac{e}{f}$ and $\frac{g}{h}$ are any four rational numbers, then

$$\left(\frac{a}{b} + \frac{c}{d} \right) + \left(\frac{e}{f} + \frac{g}{h} \right) = \left(\frac{a}{b} + \frac{e}{f} \right) + \left(\frac{c}{d} + \frac{g}{h} \right).$$

Proof: $\quad \left(\frac{a}{b} + \frac{c}{d} \right) + \left(\frac{e}{f} + \frac{g}{h} \right) = \frac{a}{b} + \left[\frac{c}{d} + \left(\frac{e}{f} + \frac{g}{h} \right) \right] \qquad$ Thm. 14-4

$$= \frac{a}{b} + \left[\left(\frac{c}{d} + \frac{e}{f} \right) + \frac{g}{h} \right] \qquad \text{Thm. 14-4}$$

$$= \frac{a}{b} + \left[\left(\frac{e}{f} + \frac{c}{d} \right) + \frac{g}{h} \right] \qquad \text{Why?}$$

$$= \left(\frac{a}{b} + \frac{e}{f} \right) + \left(\frac{c}{d} + \frac{g}{h} \right) \qquad \text{Why?} \blacksquare$$

With the agreement made above regarding interpretation of numerals and Theorem 14-13, we can now work problems involving mixed numerals rather easily since there is no need to change to the fractional form of the numeral. On the other hand, as indicated in the proof, this theorem is not restricted just to problems which involve mixed numerals. It is valid for rational numbers irrespective of the numerals used to represent them.

EXERCISE SET 14-2

1. Determine (a) $\frac{2}{3} + \frac{3}{4}$ and (b) $\frac{3}{4} + \frac{2}{3}$. What property of addition do parts (a) and (b) illustrate?

2. (a) Choose three rational numbers and use them to illustrate the associativity of addition of rational numbers.
   (b) Find a second proof, different from that in the text, for associativity of addition of rationals.

3. (a) Show directly by adding $\frac{2}{5} + \frac{6}{7}$ that $\frac{6}{7}$ cannot be an additive identity for rational numbers.
   (b) Prove that $\frac{a}{b} + \frac{0}{1} = \frac{a}{b}$ for every rational number $\frac{a}{b}$.
   (c) Is part (b) sufficient to guarantee the existence of the additive identity?

4. Solve each of the following by somewhere making use of cancellation of addition.

   (a) $\frac{x}{y} + \frac{2}{5} = \frac{7}{5}$

   (b) $\frac{x \cdot 3 + y \cdot 2}{y \cdot 3} = \frac{3}{2}$

   (c) $\frac{x}{y} + \left(\frac{2}{3} + \frac{1}{4} \right) = \frac{3}{2}$

   (d) $\frac{x}{y} + \frac{^-2}{3} = \frac{^-4 \cdot 5 + 6 \cdot 3}{6 \cdot 5}$

   (e) $\frac{25}{60} + \frac{x}{12} = \frac{1}{2}$

   (f) $\frac{2}{3} + \frac{x}{6} = \frac{4}{6} + \frac{1}{2}$

   (g) $\frac{2x}{y} = \frac{x}{y} + \frac{2}{3}$

   (h) $\frac{x}{y} + \frac{1}{5} = \frac{2}{4}$

   (i) $\frac{1}{7} + \frac{3}{4} = \frac{x}{y} + \frac{3}{14}$

   (j) $\frac{x \cdot 5 + y \cdot 2}{y \cdot 5} = \frac{4}{7}$

5. List the additive inverse of each of the following rationals.

   (a) $\frac{^-2}{3}$

   (b) $\frac{3}{7}$

   (c) $\frac{3}{^-13}$

   (d) $\frac{^-4}{^-5}$

6. By making use of the converse of cancellation and additive inverse, find the solution to each of the following number sentences.

   (a) $\frac{x}{y} + \frac{^-3}{4} = \frac{^-5}{6}$

   (b) $\frac{2}{5} + \frac{^-x}{y} = \frac{^-1}{6}$

   (c) $\frac{1 \cdot y + 4 \cdot x}{4 \cdot y} = \frac{^-2}{3}$

   (d) $\frac{xy + yx}{yy} = \frac{x}{y} + \frac{2}{7}$

7. Use Theorem 14-13 to work the following problems involving mixed numerals.

(a) $2\dfrac{3}{5}$

$+\,1\dfrac{4}{5}$

(b) $^-3\dfrac{4}{7}$

$+\,^-2\dfrac{1}{5}$

(c) $4\dfrac{7}{8}$

$+\,^-2\dfrac{1}{4}$

(d) $^-1\dfrac{2}{3}$

$+\,^-2\dfrac{1}{4}$

8. For what set of rational numbers is the statement $\dfrac{1\cdot y + 3\cdot x}{3\cdot y} = \dfrac{2\cdot y + 6\cdot x}{6\cdot y}$

true? Be able to support your answer with mathematical arguments.

[For problems 9 through 11 give the reason or reasons which justify each step of the solution.]

Step

9. $\dfrac{3}{7}+\dfrac{8}{3}=\dfrac{3\cdot 3}{3\cdot 7}+\dfrac{7\cdot 8}{7\cdot 3}$

(a)

$=\dfrac{3\cdot 3}{3\cdot 7}+\dfrac{7\cdot 8}{3\cdot 7}$

(b)

$=\dfrac{9}{21}+\dfrac{56}{21}$

(c)

$=\dfrac{9+56}{21}$

(d)

$=\dfrac{65}{21}$

(e)

Step

10. $\left(\dfrac{1}{3}+\dfrac{1}{2}\right)+\left(\dfrac{4}{6}+\dfrac{5}{10}\right)=\dfrac{1}{3}+\left[\left(\dfrac{1}{2}+\dfrac{4}{6}\right)+\dfrac{5}{10}\right]$

(a)

$=\dfrac{1}{3}+\left[\left(\dfrac{4}{6}+\dfrac{1}{2}\right)+\dfrac{5}{10}\right]$

(b)

$=\dfrac{1}{3}+\left[\dfrac{4}{6}+\left(\dfrac{1}{2}+\dfrac{5}{10}\right)\right]$

(c)

$=\left(\dfrac{1}{3}+\dfrac{4}{6}\right)+\left(\dfrac{1}{2}+\dfrac{5}{10}\right)$

(d)

$=\left(\dfrac{1}{3}+\dfrac{2}{3}\right)+\left(\dfrac{1}{2}+\dfrac{1}{2}\right)$

(e)

$=\dfrac{1+2}{3}+\dfrac{1+1}{2}$

(f)

$=\dfrac{3}{3}+\dfrac{2}{2}$

(g)

$=\dfrac{1}{1}+\dfrac{1}{1}$

(h)

$=\dfrac{1+1}{1}$

(i)

$=\dfrac{2}{1}$

(j)

Step

11. $\left(\dfrac{3}{1}+\dfrac{4}{6}\right)+\left(\dfrac{1}{2}+\dfrac{1}{3}\right)=\left(\dfrac{3}{1}+\dfrac{2\cdot2}{2\cdot3}\right)+\dfrac{1}{2}+\dfrac{1}{3}$ (a)

$=\left(\dfrac{3}{1}+\dfrac{2}{3}\right)+\left(\dfrac{1}{2}+\dfrac{1}{3}\right)$ (b)

$=\left[\dfrac{3}{1}+\left(\dfrac{2}{3}+\dfrac{1}{2}\right)\right]+\dfrac{1}{3}$ (c)

$=\left[\dfrac{3}{1}+\left(\dfrac{1}{2}+\dfrac{2}{3}\right)\right]+\dfrac{1}{3}$ (d)

$=\left(\dfrac{3}{1}+\dfrac{1}{2}\right)+\left(\dfrac{2}{3}+\dfrac{1}{3}\right)$ (e)

$=\left(\dfrac{3}{1}+\dfrac{1}{2}\right)+\dfrac{2+1}{3}$ (f)

$=\left(\dfrac{3}{1}+\dfrac{1}{2}\right)+\dfrac{3}{3}$ (g)

$=\left(\dfrac{3}{1}+\dfrac{1}{2}\right)+\dfrac{1}{1}$ (h)

$=\dfrac{3}{1}+\left(\dfrac{1}{2}+\dfrac{1}{1}\right)$ (i)

$=\dfrac{3}{1}+\left(\dfrac{1}{1}+\dfrac{1}{2}\right)$ (j)

$=\left(\dfrac{3}{1}+\dfrac{1}{1}\right)+\dfrac{1}{2}$ (k)

$=\dfrac{3+1}{1}+\dfrac{1}{2}$ (l)

$=\dfrac{4}{1}+\dfrac{1}{2}$ (m)

$=\dfrac{2\cdot4}{2\cdot1}+\dfrac{1}{2}$ (n)

$=\dfrac{8}{2}+\dfrac{1}{2}$ (o)

$=\dfrac{8+1}{2}$ (p)

$=\dfrac{9}{2}$ (q)

12. Clementine Crabgrass teaches her brother, Kinky, to add rational numbers in the following way:

$\dfrac{1}{2}+\dfrac{2}{3}=\dfrac{3}{5}$, $\dfrac{3}{7}+\dfrac{2}{3}=\dfrac{1}{2}$, $\dfrac{2}{9}+\dfrac{4}{7}=\dfrac{3}{8}$, and so on.

(a) Give the general definition which Clemmie has used for addition.

(b) Will Kinky have any trouble in getting his addition to work properly?

In order to answer this question, you must provide examples which illustrate some trouble or else prove that all is well.

13. Suppose we define a process Δ (read "delta") on the set of rational numbers as follows: $\dfrac{a}{b} \Delta \dfrac{c}{d} = \dfrac{a}{b} + \dfrac{d}{c} = \dfrac{ac + bd}{bc}$.

(a) Does an answer always exist in the set of rationals under Δ?

(b) If answers exist under Δ, are they unique?

(c) Does $\dfrac{a}{b} \Delta \dfrac{c}{d} = \dfrac{c}{d} \Delta \dfrac{a}{b}$? [Hint: Try some numbers first.]

(d) Does $\left(\dfrac{a}{b} \Delta \dfrac{c}{d} \right) \Delta \dfrac{e}{f} = \dfrac{a}{b} \Delta \left(\dfrac{c}{d} \Delta \dfrac{e}{f} \right)$?

(e) Is there an identity element for Δ?

(f) Is there a cancellation property which holds for Δ?

3. Definition of Subtraction for Rational Numbers

Now that a useful definition for addition has been developed, let us try to develop a workable definition for subtraction of rational numbers. In doing this we shall again require that our definition preserve the same type of correspondence between the integers and rational numbers as did the definition of addition. Thus if we have the correspondences

Integers		*Rationals*
^{+}n	$\longleftrightarrow$	$\dfrac{^{+}n}{1}$
0	$\longleftrightarrow$	$\dfrac{0}{1}$
^{-}m	$\longleftrightarrow$	$\dfrac{^{-}m}{1}$

we shall require the correspondence

$$^{+}n - {}^{-}m \longleftrightarrow \dfrac{^{+}n}{1} - \dfrac{^{-}m}{1} = \dfrac{^{+}n - {}^{-}m}{1}.$$

More specifically, if

$$^{+}3 \longleftrightarrow \dfrac{^{+}3}{1}$$

and

$$^{-}2 \longleftrightarrow \dfrac{^{-}2}{1},$$

then we want

$$^{+}5 = {}^{+}3 - {}^{-}2 \longleftrightarrow \dfrac{^{+}3}{1} - \dfrac{^{-}2}{1} = \dfrac{^{+}3 - {}^{-}2}{1} = \dfrac{^{+}5}{1}.$$

By now the student should suspect that we shall require that

$$\frac{a}{1} - \frac{b}{1} = \frac{a-b}{1}$$

and this is indeed the case. Paralleling the development in Section 14-1, we shall take as a tentative definition for subtraction the following.

Definition 14-2: The **difference**, $\frac{a}{b}$ minus $\frac{c}{b}$, is the rational number $\frac{a-c}{b}$.

Symbolically, $\frac{a}{b} - \frac{c}{b} = \frac{a-c}{b}$.

Similar to the agreement made regarding addition of rationals, the symbol $-$ plays two distinct roles. If fractional numerals are used, $\frac{a}{b} - \frac{c}{b}$, then $-$ means subtraction of rational numbers. If $-$ appears in a numerator, then it means integer subtraction. It should be clear from the context in which it is used which type of subtraction $-$ indicates.

We note that using Definition 14-2 differences always exist and those differences are rational numbers. Since the uniqueness argument is very similar to that for addition, we shall not discuss it here. Rather, we shall simply assume that subtraction of rationals does give unique differences. It would be instructive for the student to attempt this uniqueness proof however.

Theorem 14-14: Subtraction of rational numbers yields unique differences.

Proof: Left as an exercise.

At this point, we have yet to consider the problem of how to subtract rationals which have different denominators, but we shall do this now.

Theorem 14-15: If $\frac{a}{b}$ and $\frac{c}{d}$ are rational numbers, then $\frac{a}{b} - \frac{c}{d} = \frac{ad-bc}{bd}$.

Proof: By the K-Theorem, we have $\frac{a}{b} = \frac{ad}{bd}$ and $\frac{c}{d} = \frac{bc}{bd}$. Then

$$\frac{a}{b} - \frac{c}{d} = \frac{ad}{bd} - \frac{bc}{bd} \qquad \text{Why?}$$

$$= \frac{ad-bc}{bd} \qquad \text{Def. 14-2.} \blacksquare$$

You will recall that in integer subtraction the concept of additive inverse played a prime role in showing the close relationship between subtraction and addition. We can now show that subtraction and addition of rational numbers are related in the same way that these operations are in integer arithmetic. That is, if we wish to determine $\frac{a}{b} - \frac{c}{d}$ we may instead add the additive inverse of $\frac{c}{d}$ to $\frac{a}{b}$. A formal statement of this fact is found in the following theorem.

Theorem 14-16: If $\frac{a}{b}$ and $\frac{c}{d}$ are rational numbers, then $\frac{a}{b} - \frac{c}{d} = \frac{a}{b} + \frac{^-c}{d}$.

Proof:	$\dfrac{a}{b} - \dfrac{c}{d} = \dfrac{ad - bc}{bd}$	Thm. 14-15
	$= \dfrac{ad + ^-(bc)}{bd}$	Thm. 10-15
	$= \dfrac{ad + b \cdot ^-c}{bd}$	Thm. 11-15
	$= \dfrac{ad}{bd} + \dfrac{b \cdot ^-c}{bd}$	Def. 14-1
	$= \dfrac{a}{b} + \dfrac{^-c}{d}$	K-Thm. ▮

We have already seen how the additive inverses of rational numbers can be used to exhibit a relationship between the operations of addition and subtraction. As was the case for integers, we can exhibit an even stronger relationship which will result in an inverse definition for subtraction of rational numbers. We shall now prove a theorem which will justify such an alternative definition and its use in subtraction of rationals.

Theorem 14-17: $\frac{a}{b} - \frac{c}{d} = \frac{x}{y}$ if and only if $\frac{c}{d} + \frac{x}{y} = \frac{a}{b}$.

Proof: There are two statements to be proved in order to establish the validity of this theorem:

> (1) If $\dfrac{a}{b} - \dfrac{c}{d} = \dfrac{x}{y}$, then $\dfrac{c}{d} + \dfrac{x}{y} = \dfrac{a}{b}$ and
>
> (2) If $\dfrac{c}{d} + \dfrac{x}{y} = \dfrac{a}{b}$, then $\dfrac{a}{b} - \dfrac{c}{d} = \dfrac{x}{y}$.

We shall prove these statements in the order listed.

> (1) To show: If $\dfrac{a}{b} - \dfrac{c}{d} = \dfrac{x}{y}$, then $\dfrac{c}{d} + \dfrac{x}{y} = \dfrac{a}{b}$.

Now	$\dfrac{x}{y} = \dfrac{a}{b} - \dfrac{c}{d}$	Assumption

$$\frac{x}{y} = \frac{ad - bc}{bd}$$ Thm. 14-15

$$\frac{c}{d} + \frac{x}{y} = \frac{c}{d} + \frac{ad - bc}{bd}$$ Thm. 14-7

$$= \frac{c(bd) + d(ad - bc)}{d(bd)}$$ Thm. 14-2

$$= \frac{cbd + d(ad + {}^-bc)}{dbd}$$ Thm. 10-15

$$= \frac{bd + (dad + {}^-dbc)}{dbd}$$ Thms. 11-4, 11-5

$$= \frac{dbc + (dda + {}^-dbc)}{ddb}$$ Thms. 11-2, 11-3

$$= \frac{dbc + ({}^-dbc + dda)}{ddb}$$ Thm. 11-2

$$= \frac{(dbc + {}^-dbc) + dda}{ddb}$$ Thm. 10-3

$$= \frac{0 + dda}{ddb}$$ Def. 10-2

$$= \frac{dda}{ddb}$$ Thm. 10-4

$$= \frac{a}{b}$$ K-Thm.

Therefore there is a rational number which added to the indicated difference gives $\frac{a}{b}$.

(2) To show: If $\frac{c}{d} + \frac{x}{y} = \frac{a}{b}$,   then $\frac{a}{b} - \frac{c}{d} = \frac{x}{y}$.

Now $$\frac{c}{d} + \frac{x}{y} = \frac{a}{b}$$ Assumption

$$\left(\frac{c}{d} + \frac{x}{y}\right) + \frac{{}^-c}{d} = \frac{a}{b} + \frac{{}^-c}{d}$$ Thm. 14-7

$$\left(\frac{x}{y} + \frac{c}{d}\right) + \frac{{}^-c}{d} = \frac{a}{b} + \frac{{}^-c}{d}$$ Thm. 10-3

$$\frac{x}{y} + \left(\frac{c}{d} + \frac{{}^-c}{d}\right) = \frac{a}{b} + \frac{{}^-c}{d}$$ Thm. 10-4

$$\frac{x}{y} + \frac{0}{1} = \frac{a}{b} + \frac{^-c}{d} \qquad\qquad \text{Thm. 14-8}$$

$$\frac{x}{y} = \frac{a}{b} + \frac{^-c}{d} \qquad\qquad \text{Thm. 14-5}$$

$$\frac{x}{y} = \frac{a}{b} - \frac{c}{d} \qquad\qquad \text{Thm. 14-16}\ \blacksquare$$

Furthermore, from Theorem 14-14, $\frac{x}{y}$ is unique. Hence it is the only rational number such that if added to $\frac{c}{d}$ yields $\frac{a}{b}$. Consequently, we are justified in making the following inverse definition for subtraction of rational numbers.

Definition 14-3: The **difference** $\frac{a}{b} - \frac{c}{d}$ is the unique rational number $\frac{x}{y}$ such that $\frac{c}{d} + \frac{x}{y} = \frac{a}{b}$.

There are other interesting results concerning subtraction which may now be established by using the inverse definition just stated. We shall list two of these and leave it to the student to complete their proofs.

Theorem 14-18: $\frac{a}{b} - \frac{0}{1} = \frac{a}{b}$ for every rational number $\frac{a}{b}$.

Proof: Left as an exercise.

Theorem 14-19: $\frac{a}{b} - \frac{a}{b} = \frac{0}{1}$ for every rational number $\frac{a}{b}$.

Proof: Left as an exercise.

It was determined in the cardinal number system and the system of integers that subtraction did not satisfy the commutative and associative properties. This was done by actually choosing numbers in those representative systems and showing that the same differences were not obtained. This same technique of providing a numerical counterexample can be used to show that neither the commutative nor associative properties holds for subtraction of rational numbers. These we leave as exercises for the student.

We note in passing that we need not concern ourselves with the rules of signs for subtraction since each problem in subtraction can be rephrased as an equivalent addition problem and rules of signs for addition have already been discussed.

EXERCISE SET 14-3

1. Use Definition 14-2 to determine each of the following differences.

   (a) $\dfrac{7}{16} - \dfrac{4}{16}$ (b) $\dfrac{^-8}{9} - \dfrac{^-2}{9}$ (c) $\dfrac{^-5}{7} - \dfrac{3}{7}$ (d) $\dfrac{13}{4} - \dfrac{^-9}{4}$

2. Use Theorem 14-15 to determine the following differences.

   (a) $\dfrac{3}{8} - \dfrac{4}{5}$ (e) $\dfrac{9}{16} - \dfrac{2}{5}$

   (b) $\dfrac{^-4}{7} - \dfrac{^-8}{12}$ (f) $\dfrac{^-5}{2} - \dfrac{^-2}{3}$

   (c) $\dfrac{^-7}{8} - \dfrac{2}{3}$ (g) $\dfrac{2}{5} - \dfrac{^-3}{4}$

   (d) $\dfrac{5}{6} - \dfrac{^-3}{4}$ (h) $\dfrac{^-5}{9} - \dfrac{5}{2}$

3. Use Theorem 14-16 to "rephrase" each of the following subtraction problems.

   (a) $\dfrac{2}{3} - \dfrac{3}{4}$ (b) $\dfrac{^-7}{8} + \dfrac{3}{5}$ (c) $\dfrac{7}{6} - \dfrac{^-2}{3}$ (d) $\dfrac{^-3}{5} + \dfrac{^-2}{3}$

4. In problem *three* work each part twice, once using + and once using − and see if your answers agree.

5. Prove Theorem 14-18 by using Theorem 14-15, then by using Definition 14-3.

6. Prove Theorem 14-19 by using Theorem 14-15, then by using Definition 14-3.

7. Show by numerical example that subtraction is not commutative. That is, show that $\dfrac{a}{b} - \dfrac{c}{d} \ne \dfrac{c}{d} - \dfrac{a}{b}$.

8. Show by example that subtraction is not associative. That is, show that $\left(\dfrac{a}{b} - \dfrac{c}{d}\right) - \dfrac{e}{f} \ne \dfrac{a}{b} - \left(\dfrac{c}{d} - \dfrac{e}{f}\right)$.

9. Find a common denominator for each of the following pairs of rational numerals.

   (a) $\dfrac{6}{7}$ and $\dfrac{4}{3}$ (d) $\dfrac{5}{42}$ and $\dfrac{11}{70}$

   (b) $\dfrac{4}{9}$ and $\dfrac{6}{15}$ (e) $\dfrac{4}{35}$ and $\dfrac{7}{65}$

   (c) $\dfrac{3}{169}$ and $\dfrac{4}{39}$ (f) $\dfrac{13}{72}$ and $\dfrac{15}{36}$

10. What is the relationship between a common denominator and the least common denominator? Make up an example to illustrate this relationship and be very explicit. [Hint: Review *common multiple* and *least common multiple*.]

11. Find the L.C.D. for each of the pairs of rational numbers listed in Prob. 3.

12. By determining the L.C.D. and then using the definition of subtraction find $\dfrac{7}{8} - \dfrac{5}{6}$. Write out each step of the subtraction.

13. Using any preceding material you wish, determine the value of x and/or y (if they exist) for each of the following.

(a) $\dfrac{^-2}{3}+\dfrac{x}{y}=\dfrac{3}{4}$

(h) $\dfrac{x}{4}-\dfrac{^-7}{8}=\dfrac{3}{2}$

(b) $\dfrac{2}{3}+\dfrac{^-3}{4}=\dfrac{x}{y}$

(i) $\dfrac{x}{4}-\dfrac{7}{8}=\dfrac{^-3}{2}$

(c) $\dfrac{x}{4}-\dfrac{7}{8}=\dfrac{3}{2}$

(j) $\dfrac{x}{3}-\dfrac{y}{6}=\dfrac{3}{9}$

(d) $\dfrac{x}{3}+\dfrac{y}{6}=\dfrac{3}{9}$

(k) $\dfrac{4}{7}-\dfrac{x}{5}=\dfrac{y}{35}$

(e) $\dfrac{^-4}{7}+\dfrac{x}{5}=\dfrac{y}{35}$

(l) $\dfrac{5}{3}-\dfrac{3}{x}=\dfrac{11}{12}$

(f) $\dfrac{^-5}{3}-\dfrac{3}{x}=\dfrac{^-11}{12}$

(m) $\dfrac{13}{5}+\dfrac{x}{y}=\dfrac{^-3}{4}$

(g) $\dfrac{13}{5}+\dfrac{x}{y}=\dfrac{3}{4}$

(n) $\dfrac{^-13}{5}+\dfrac{x}{y}=\dfrac{^-3}{4}$

14. When we subtract $\dfrac{1}{3}$ from 1, we can make use of subtraction of rationals and we might think as follows: 1 is the same as $\dfrac{3}{3}$ and $\dfrac{3}{3}$ minus $\dfrac{1}{3}$ equals $\dfrac{2}{3}$. Written out the problem might well appear as follows.

$$\left(\frac{2}{3}+\frac{1}{3}\right)-\frac{1}{3}=\frac{2}{3}+\left(\frac{1}{3}-\frac{1}{3}\right)$$

$$=\frac{2}{3}+\frac{0}{1}$$

$$=\frac{2}{3}$$

What theorems and definitions justify the reasoning used?

15. Consider the following statement for rational numbers:

$$\left(\frac{a}{b}+\frac{c}{d}\right)-\left(\frac{e}{f}+\frac{g}{h}\right)=\left(\frac{a}{b}-\frac{e}{f}\right)+\left(\frac{c}{d}-\frac{g}{h}\right)$$

Either prove it or disprove it.

16. If the result in problem 15 is true, use it to work each of the following.

(a) $\begin{array}{r} 2\dfrac{1}{4} \\ -\dfrac{1}{4} \\ \hline \end{array}$

(b) $\begin{array}{r} 3\dfrac{2}{5} \\ -\dfrac{2}{5} \\ \hline \end{array}$

(c) $\begin{array}{r} 5\dfrac{3}{7} \\ -\dfrac{3}{7} \\ \hline \end{array}$

(d) $\begin{array}{r} 3\dfrac{4}{5} \\ -2\dfrac{1}{5} \\ \hline \end{array}$

(e) $\begin{array}{r} 2\dfrac{9}{11} \\ -1\dfrac{3}{4} \\ \hline \end{array}$

(f) $\begin{array}{r} 7\dfrac{3}{8} \\ -5\dfrac{1}{4} \\ \hline \end{array}$

17. Write the reason which justifies each step in each of the following problems.

Step

(a) $\left(\dfrac{1}{3}+\dfrac{2}{5}\right)-\dfrac{2}{3}=\left(\dfrac{5\cdot1}{5\cdot3}+\dfrac{3\cdot2}{3\cdot5}\right)-\dfrac{2}{3}$ (a)

$=\left(\dfrac{5}{15}+\dfrac{6}{15}\right)-\dfrac{2}{3}$ (b)

$=\dfrac{5+6}{15}-\dfrac{2}{3}$ (c)

$=\dfrac{11}{15}-\dfrac{2}{3}$ (d)

$=\dfrac{1+10}{15}-\dfrac{2}{3}$ (e)

$=\left(\dfrac{1}{15}+\dfrac{10}{15}\right)-\dfrac{2}{3}$ (f)

$=\dfrac{1}{15}+\left(\dfrac{10}{15}-\dfrac{2}{3}\right)$ (g)

$=\dfrac{1}{15}+\left(\dfrac{5\cdot2}{5\cdot3}-\dfrac{2}{3}\right)$ (h)

$=\dfrac{1}{15}+\left(\dfrac{2}{3}-\dfrac{2}{3}\right)$ (i)

$=\dfrac{1}{15}+\dfrac{0}{1}$ (j)

$=\dfrac{1}{15}+\dfrac{0}{15}$ (k)

$=\dfrac{1+0}{15}$ (l)

$=\dfrac{1}{15}$ (m)

Step

(b) $\left(\dfrac{4}{7}-\dfrac{1}{3}\right)+\left(\dfrac{3}{2}-\dfrac{4}{3}\right)=\left(\dfrac{4}{7}+\dfrac{3}{2}\right)-\left(\dfrac{1}{3}+\dfrac{4}{3}\right)$ (a)

$=\left(\dfrac{4}{7}+\dfrac{3}{2}\right)-\dfrac{1+4}{3}$ (b)

$=\left(\dfrac{4}{7}+\dfrac{3}{2}\right)-\dfrac{5}{3}$ (c)

$=\left(\dfrac{2\cdot4}{2\cdot7}+\dfrac{7\cdot3}{7\cdot2}\right)-\dfrac{5}{3}$ (d)

$=\left(\dfrac{8}{14}+\dfrac{21}{14}\right)-\dfrac{5}{3}$ (e)

$$= \frac{8 + 21}{14} - \frac{5}{3} \qquad \text{(f)}$$

$$= \frac{29}{14} - \frac{5}{3} \qquad \text{(g)}$$

$$= \frac{29 \cdot 3}{14 \cdot 3} - \frac{14 \cdot 5}{14 \cdot 3} \qquad \text{(h)}$$

$$= \frac{87}{42} - \frac{70}{42} \qquad \text{(i)}$$

$$= \frac{87 - 70}{42} \qquad \text{(j)}$$

$$= \frac{(17 + 70) - 70}{42} \qquad \text{(k)}$$

$$= \frac{17 + (70 - 70)}{42} \qquad \text{(l)}$$

$$= \frac{17 + 0}{42} \qquad \text{(m)}$$

$$= \frac{17}{42} \qquad \text{(n)}$$

18. Stacey Crinkle and Garble Gumshoe, who study arithmetic together, decide to pose the following question to their teacher, Miss Greta Snakfast: Why don't we define subtraction as

$$\frac{a}{b} - \frac{c}{b} = \frac{ab - cb}{b} \ ?$$

Assume that you are Miss Snakfast and answer the question in detail.

19. Let us define a process, $\star$, (read star) by

$$\frac{a}{b} \star \frac{c}{d} = \frac{(a + d) - (b + c)}{bd}.$$

Then for example, $\dfrac{1}{2} \star \dfrac{2}{3} = \dfrac{(1 + 3) - (2 + 2)}{2 \cdot 3} = \dfrac{4 - 4}{6} = \dfrac{0}{1}$.

(a) Does an answer always exist in the set of rationals?
(b) Are answers unique under the process $\star$?
(c) Is $\star$ an operation on the set of rationals?
(d) Is $\star$ commutative?
(e) Is $\star$ associative?

Chapter summary

In this chapter we continued our development of arithmetic by imposing the requirement that, if at all possible, sums of rationals should correspond to sums of integers. We found that this could be done without difficulty provided the denominators of the rationals being added were the same. Using this result along with the K-Theorem, we found that the usual method for adding rationals having unlike denominators could be derived. Once this was done we were able to show that the system of rationals has all of the addition properties possessed by the integers including additive inverses.

By making similar requirements for subtraction, we showed that subtraction of rationals is related to addition of rationals in the same way as the two operations are related in the system of integers. That is, addition and subtraction are *inverse operations.*

No new properties for rational numbers were discovered which were not already known to exist for the system of integers. This might have been expected because of the fact that number sentences of the form $ax + b = c$ can always be changed to the form $ax = d$ where $d = c - b$ by use of addition and subtraction. Thus if there is to be some new property appearing for rationals it seems reasonable that it appear as a result of some multiplication property.

CHAPTER 15 Multiplication and division of rational numbers

1. Definition of Multiplication for Rationals

Continuing with our development, we shall now try to define multiplication for rational numbers so that the correspondence which we decided upon earlier can be maintained. This means that if we have the correspondences

Integers	Rationals
$^+n \longleftrightarrow$	$\dfrac{^+n}{1}$
$^-m \longleftrightarrow$	$\dfrac{^-m}{1}$

we shall require that

$$^-nm = {}^+n \cdot {}^-m \longleftrightarrow \frac{^+n}{1} \cdot \frac{^-m}{1} = \frac{^-nm}{1}$$

For example, we want

$$^-6 = {}^+3 \cdot {}^-2 \longleftrightarrow \frac{^-6}{1}$$

This could be accomplished if we require that for rationals with denominator one

$$\frac{n}{1} \cdot \frac{^-m}{1} = \frac{n \cdot {}^-m}{1} = \frac{^-nm}{1}$$

Note that above we have taken the product of numerators. It should be clear that sums and differences will not work in the denominator since then the desired correspondence is lost. Therefore the question is whether to use products or quotients in the denominator. In order to decide which of the two possibilities to select, let us consider a case in which the denominators involved are not the integer *one*. For whatever definition is eventually selected for multiplication, this definition is supposed to "work" for *all* rational numbers independent of their representation. Let us consider what happens then if we take as a definition

$$\frac{n}{b} \cdot \frac{^-m}{b} = \text{SOMETHING (to be determined)}.$$

In order to maintain the desired correspondence, agreed to above, we must have $n \cdot {}^-m$ in the numerator.

Example:
$$\frac{2}{3} \cdot \frac{^-4}{3} = \text{SOMETHING}$$

We could write that

$$\frac{2}{3} \cdot \frac{^-4}{3} = \frac{2 \cdot {}^-4}{3 \cdot 3}$$

or

$$\frac{2}{3} \cdot \frac{^-4}{3} = \frac{2 \cdot {}^-4}{3 \div 3}$$

This example does not yield a solution to our problem, since in this case one denominator is divisible by the other. Therefore we shall try a second example where one denominator is not divisible by the other, say

$$\frac{2}{3} \cdot \frac{^-4}{5}.$$

It is clear from this example that we cannot use division in denominators and obtain a denominator which is an integer. Therefore we shall select as a tentative definition for multiplication the following.

Definition 15-1: The **product** of two rational numbers, $\frac{a}{b}$ and $\frac{c}{d}$, is the rational number $\frac{ac}{bd}$. Symbolically, $\frac{a}{b} \cdot \frac{c}{d} = \frac{ac}{bd}$.

Next we must check to see that products obtained by the use of Definition 15-1 always exist and are unique. For existence, we note that ac is an integer and bd is an integer. Further, $bd \neq 0$, since neither b nor d is zero. Hence by definition of rational numbers, $\frac{ac}{bd}$ is a rational number. Uniqueness is considered in the following theorem.

Theorem 15-1: Products of rational numbers are unique.

Proof: What we want to show is that if we form $\frac{a}{b} \cdot \frac{c}{d}$ and $\frac{u}{v} \cdot \frac{x}{y}$ where $\frac{a}{b} = \frac{u}{v}$ and

$\dfrac{c}{d} = \dfrac{x}{y}$, then $\dfrac{a}{b} \cdot \dfrac{c}{d} = \dfrac{u}{v} \cdot \dfrac{x}{y}$. That is, we want to show that $\dfrac{ac}{bd}$ and $\dfrac{ux}{vy}$ name the same rational number. Now since

$$\left[\begin{array}{c} \dfrac{a}{b} = \dfrac{u}{v} \\[2mm] \text{and} \\[2mm] \dfrac{c}{d} = \dfrac{x}{y} \end{array}\right]$$, we have by definition of equality that $$\left[\begin{array}{c} av = bu \\[2mm] \text{and} \\[2mm] cy = dx \end{array}\right]$$

for integers. Multiplying the integers we obtain

$$(av)(cy) = (bu)(dx)$$ \qquad Uniq. $(\cdot)$ integers

$$(ac)(vy) = (bd)(ux)$$ \qquad Assoc., Comm. $(\cdot)$ integers

$$\frac{ac}{bd} = \frac{ux}{vy}$$ \qquad Def. 13-4

$$\frac{a}{b} \cdot \frac{c}{d} = \frac{u}{v} \cdot \frac{x}{y}$$ \qquad Def. 15-1.

Therefore the theorem is proved and products of rationals are unique.∎

Theorem 15-1 states that, if we care to do so, we can compute instead of the product $\dfrac{4}{6} \cdot \dfrac{8}{10}, \dfrac{2}{3} \cdot \dfrac{4}{5}$ and be assured that the same rational number is named in both cases.

EXERCISE SET 15-1

1. Use Definition 15-1 and the K-Theorem to determine each of the following products.

(a) $\dfrac{1}{3} \cdot \dfrac{15}{5}$

(b) $\dfrac{2}{7} \cdot \dfrac{^-42}{12}$

(c) $\dfrac{^-3}{11} \cdot \dfrac{77}{12}$

(d) $\dfrac{^-8}{26} \cdot \dfrac{^-101}{54}$

(e) $\dfrac{5}{16} \cdot \dfrac{12}{15}$

(f) $\dfrac{14}{16} \cdot \dfrac{^-56}{56}$

2. (a) By working first the left and then the right side, show that

$$\frac{3}{5} \cdot \frac{^-4}{9} = \frac{9}{15} \cdot \frac{^-20}{45} .$$

(b) What property of multiplication is illustrated?

(c) Does $\dfrac{6}{10} \cdot \dfrac{^-28}{63}$ name the same rational as do the numerals in part (a)?

2. Properties of Multiplication of Rationals

Next we shall show that products of rational numbers satisfy the commutative property.

As can be observed in the proof of Theorem 15-2, the commutativity of multiplication of integers is essential in order to prove that products of rationals are commutative. This is an exact analog to the relationship between cardinal and integer multiplication, which you may have observed earlier.

Theorem 15-2 (Commutative): If $\dfrac{a}{b}$ and $\dfrac{c}{d}$ are any two rational numbers, then

$$\frac{a}{b} \cdot \frac{c}{d} = \frac{c}{d} \cdot \frac{a}{b}.$$

Proof:

$$\frac{a}{b} \cdot \frac{c}{d} = \frac{ac}{bd} \qquad\qquad \text{Def. 15-1}$$

$$= \frac{ca}{db} \qquad\qquad \text{Why?}$$

$$= \frac{c}{d} \cdot \frac{a}{b} \qquad\qquad \text{Why?} \quad\blacksquare$$

Thus, according to Theorem 15-2, $\dfrac{2}{3} \cdot \dfrac{^-4}{5} = \dfrac{^-4}{5} \cdot \dfrac{2}{3}$. Sure enough, if each of the indicated products is determined, we find that

$$\frac{2}{3} \cdot \frac{^-4}{5} = \frac{2 \cdot {}^-4}{3 \cdot 5} = \frac{^-8}{15}$$

and

$$\frac{^-4}{5} \cdot \frac{2}{3} = \frac{^-4 \cdot 2}{5 \cdot 3} = \frac{^-8}{15}$$

The commutative property saves us from doing this unnecessary work with the assurance that the products are equal.

As in integer arithmetic, the associative property also holds for products of rational numbers. Thus, for example,

$$\left(\frac{3}{4} \cdot \frac{2}{3}\right) \cdot \frac{4}{5} = \frac{3}{4} \cdot \left(\frac{2}{3} \cdot \frac{4}{5}\right)$$

The way in which factors are grouped has no effect on the product obtained. It may be further noted that the proof of Theorem 15-3 below depends on the fact that integer multiplication is associative.

Theorem 15-3 (Associative): If $\dfrac{a}{b}, \dfrac{c}{d}$, and $\dfrac{e}{f}$ are any three rational numbers, then

$$\left(\frac{a}{b} \cdot \frac{c}{d}\right) \cdot \frac{e}{f} = \frac{a}{b} \cdot \left(\frac{c}{d} \cdot \frac{e}{f}\right).$$

Proof: Left as an exercise. [Hint: Work with both sides of the result stated in the theorem and show that you obtain the same expression.]

In this arithmetic too there is a multiplicative identity and as you should have suspected, it is the rational number one.

Theorem 15-4: $\frac{1}{1}$ is a multiplicative identity for rational numbers.

Proof: We already know what a multiplicative identity is, hence all that must be checked is whether $\frac{a}{b} \cdot \frac{1}{1} = \frac{a}{b}$ and $\frac{a}{b} \cdot \frac{1}{1} = \frac{1}{1} \cdot \frac{a}{b}$ for every rational number $\frac{a}{b}$. Now

$$\frac{a}{b} \cdot \frac{1}{1} = \frac{a \cdot 1}{b \cdot 1} \qquad\qquad \text{Why?}$$

$$= \frac{a}{b} \qquad\qquad \text{Ident. } (\cdot) \text{ integers}$$

Further, by Theorem 15-2, we have that

$$\frac{1}{1} \cdot \frac{a}{b} = \frac{a}{b} \cdot \frac{1}{1}$$

and consequently $\frac{1}{1}$ is a multiplicative identity. ∎

Not only is $\frac{1}{1}$ *an* identity for multiplication of rationals, it is the unique multiplicative identity. This fact could be proved in much the same way the corresponding result was proved when the system of integers was being discussed. If the multiplicative identity were not unique, the resulting arithmetic would be of no value to us as is illustrated by the following example.

Example: Suppose that $\frac{1}{1}$ and $\frac{2}{3}$ are both multiplicative identities. Then

$$\frac{3}{4} \cdot \frac{1}{1} = \frac{3}{4} \cdot \frac{2}{3}$$

so that

$$\frac{3 \cdot 1}{4 \cdot 1} = \frac{3 \cdot 2}{4 \cdot 3}$$

or

$$\frac{3}{4} = \frac{6}{12}$$

or

$$\frac{3}{4} = \frac{1}{2}$$

But this is utterly ridiculous, since it would mean that disjoint equivalence classes contain precisely the same ordered pairs of integers!! It also means that uniqueness properties are lost, and consequently commutativity or associativity may not hold. Thus it is easy to see that the arithmetic would be virtually useless.

As we have noted previously, while discussing integers, the cancellation property may be used to establish the uniqueness of the multiplicative identity. It was also determined that such a property is of considerable value for use in the determination of solution sets for number sentences or equations. Even though we are assuming the uniqueness of the multiplicative identity we may still want to use cancellation in connection with number sentences and their solutions.

Theorem 15-5 (Cancellation): If $\frac{a}{b}, \frac{c}{d}$, and $\frac{e}{f}$ are rational numbers such that $\frac{e}{f} \neq \frac{0}{1}$ and $\frac{a}{b} \cdot \frac{e}{f} = \frac{c}{d} \cdot \frac{e}{f}$, then $\frac{a}{b} = \frac{c}{d}$.

Proof: Suppose that $\frac{a}{b} \cdot \frac{e}{f} = \frac{c}{d} \cdot \frac{e}{f}$ as suggested. Then

$\frac{ae}{bf} = \frac{ce}{df}$	Def. 15-1
$(ae)(df) = (bf)(ce)$	Def. 13-4
$(ad)(ef) = (bc)(ef)$	Assoc. ($\cdot$), Comm. ($\cdot$) integers
$ad = bc$	Why?

Therefore

$$\frac{a}{b} = \frac{c}{d} \qquad \text{Def. 13-4}$$

and the theorem is proved. ∎

Example: Determine the rational number $\frac{x}{y}$ such that $\frac{x}{y} \cdot \frac{2}{3} = \frac{10}{21}$.

Solution: $\frac{x}{y} \cdot \frac{2}{3} = \frac{2 \cdot 5}{3 \cdot 7}$ Def. ($\cdot$) integers

$$= \frac{5}{7} \cdot \frac{2}{3} \qquad \text{Def. 15-1}$$

$$\frac{x}{y} = \frac{5}{7} \qquad \text{Thm. 15-5}$$

It is also true that the converse of the cancellation property holds for multiplication of rationals. This is illustrated in the following example.

Example: Determine the rational number $\frac{x}{y}$ such that $\frac{2}{3} \cdot \frac{x}{y} = \frac{^-7}{8}$.

Solution: If there is a converse of the cancellation property, the problem may be solved as follows:

$$\frac{2}{3} \cdot \frac{x}{y} = \frac{^-7}{8} \qquad \text{Given}$$

$$\frac{3}{2} \cdot \left(\frac{2}{3} \cdot \frac{x}{y} \right) = \frac{3}{2} \cdot \frac{^-7}{8} \qquad \text{Conv. Canc. } (\cdot)$$

$$\left(\frac{3}{2} \cdot \frac{2}{3} \right) \cdot \frac{x}{y} = \frac{3}{2} \cdot \frac{^-7}{8} \qquad \text{Thm. 15-3}$$

$$\frac{3 \cdot 2}{2 \cdot 3} \cdot \frac{x}{y} = \frac{3 \cdot {}^-7}{2 \cdot 8} \qquad \text{Def. 15-1}$$

$$\frac{6}{6} \cdot \frac{x}{y} = \frac{^-21}{16} \qquad \text{Def.} (\cdot) \text{ integers}$$

$$\frac{x}{y} = \frac{^-21}{16} \qquad \text{Thm. 15-4}$$

As can be observed the solution in the preceding example depends on the existence of a valid converse of the cancellation property for multiplication. This property does indeed exist and is valid. Its formal statement follows and its proof is left to the student.

Theorem 15-6 (Converse of Cancellation): If $\frac{a}{b}$, $\frac{c}{d}$, and $\frac{e}{f}$ are rational numbers and $\frac{a}{b} = \frac{c}{d}$, then $\frac{a}{b} \cdot \frac{e}{f} = \frac{c}{d} \cdot \frac{e}{f}$.

Proof: An easy way to prove this theorem is to reverse the order of the steps of the proof of Theorem 15-5. We shall leave this proof to the student.

The student may have noticed something familiar in the example problem which precedes Theorem 15-6. The number selected to multiply both sides of the equation happened to give $\frac{1}{1} \cdot \frac{x}{y}$ on the left-hand side of the equals sign. That is, we selected $\frac{3}{2}$ purposely so that

$$\frac{3}{2} \cdot \frac{2}{3} \text{ gave the result } \frac{1}{1}.$$

This may remind one very much of the additive inverse in integers and rationals, since once again it was possible to obtain an identity element. Thus perhaps it is possible that each rational number has a *multiplicative inverse* as well as an additive inverse. With this in mind, suppose we try to determine a rational number $\frac{x}{y}$ such that

$$\frac{0}{1} \cdot \frac{x}{y} = \frac{1}{1}.$$

Using the definition of multiplication, we find that

$$\frac{0}{1} \cdot \frac{x}{y} = \frac{0 \cdot x}{1 \cdot y} = \frac{0}{y} = \frac{0}{1}.$$

That is, $\frac{0}{1}$ multiplied by any other rational number is the rational number $\frac{0}{1}$.

Consequently, it is apparent that $\frac{0}{1}$ has no multiplicative inverse because of the fact that there is no rational number $\frac{x}{y}$ such that

$$\frac{0}{1} \cdot \frac{x}{y} = \frac{1}{1}.$$

This being the case, suppose we try to determine whether all non-zero rational numbers have multiplicative inverses for the concept does have some apparent usefulness in solving number sentences.

Theorem 15-7: If $\frac{a}{b} \neq \frac{0}{1}$, then a multiplicative inverse of $\frac{a}{b}$ is the rational number $\frac{b}{a}$.

Proof:

$$\frac{a}{b} \cdot \frac{b}{a} = \frac{a \cdot b}{b \cdot a} \qquad\qquad \text{Def. 15-1}$$

$$= \frac{a \cdot b}{a \cdot b} \qquad\qquad \text{Comm. } (\cdot) \text{ integers}$$

$$= \frac{(a \cdot b) \cdot 1}{(a \cdot b) \cdot 1} \qquad\qquad \text{Ident. } (\cdot) \text{ integers}$$

$$= \frac{1}{1} \qquad\qquad K\text{-Thm.}$$

Therefore, every *non-zero* rational number has a multiplicative inverse. ∎

Examples: (a) $\frac{2}{7}$ is the multiplicative inverse of $\frac{7}{2}$ since

$$\frac{2}{7} \cdot \frac{7}{2} = \frac{1}{1}$$

(b) $\frac{^-3}{4}$ is the multiplicative inverse of $\frac{^-4}{3}$ since

$$\frac{^-3}{4} \cdot \frac{^-4}{3} = \frac{1}{1}$$

Now that it is known that non-zero rationals have multiplicative inverses, it must be shown that these inverses are unique. Even though you may think you are sure of the uniqueness of these inverses, it must still be proved. We shall do this in Theorem 15-8 which follows.

Theorem 15-8: Multiplicative inverses for non-zero rational numbers are unique.

Proof: Let $\frac{a}{b}$ be a non-zero rational number and suppose that multiplicative in-

verses are not unique. That is, suppose that $\frac{a}{b} \cdot \frac{b}{a} = \frac{1}{1}$ and $\frac{a}{b} \cdot \frac{p}{q} = \frac{1}{1}$ where $\frac{p}{q}$ is a

second inverse element with $\frac{a}{b} \neq \frac{p}{q}$. By transitivity of equality, we have that

$$\frac{a}{b} \cdot \frac{b}{a} = \frac{a}{b} \cdot \frac{p}{q}$$

Since $\frac{a}{b} \neq \frac{0}{1}$, we obtain by use of the cancellation property for multiplication

that $\frac{b}{a} = \frac{p}{q}$. Since this contradicts the assumption that $\frac{a}{b} \neq \frac{p}{q}$, the proof is com-

plete. ∎

The fact that each non-zero rational number has a multiplicative inverse is very important. As we shall see in Section 15-3, this concept plays a fundamental role in the division of rational numbers. It is also important from the point of view that we now have another property which did not exist in either the system of cardinal numbers or integers.

We have yet to discuss the distributivity of multiplication with respect to addition and subtraction of rationals. These properties hold just as they did in the system of integers and we shall prove this in Theorems 15-9 and 15-12 below.

Theorem 15-9 (Distributive ·/+): If $\frac{a}{b}$, $\frac{c}{d}$, and $\frac{e}{f}$ are rational numbers, then

$$\frac{a}{b} \cdot \left(\frac{c}{d}+\frac{e}{f}\right) = \left(\frac{a}{b} \cdot \frac{c}{d}\right) + \left(\frac{a}{b} \cdot \frac{e}{f}\right).$$

Proof: There are two proofs which are readily available. We shall do the more difficult proof and leave the relatively easy proof for the student to complete.

$$\frac{a}{b} \cdot \left(\frac{c}{d}+\frac{e}{f}\right) = \frac{a}{b} \cdot \frac{cf+de}{df} \qquad\qquad \text{Thm. 14-2}$$

$$= \frac{a(cf+de)}{b(df)} \qquad\qquad \text{Def. 15-1}$$

$$= \frac{a(cf)+a(de)}{b(df)} \qquad\qquad \text{Why?}$$

$$= \frac{a(cf)}{b(df)} + \frac{a(de)}{b(df)} \qquad\qquad \text{Def. 14-1}$$

$$= \frac{f(ac)}{f(bd)} + \frac{d(ae)}{d(bf)} \qquad\qquad \text{Why?}$$

$$= \frac{ac}{bd} + \frac{ae}{bf} \qquad\qquad \text{Why?}$$

$$= \left(\frac{a}{b} \cdot \frac{c}{d}\right) + \left(\frac{a}{b} \cdot \frac{e}{f}\right) \qquad\qquad \text{Def. 15-1}$$

Hence multiplication is distributive with respect to addition of rationals. ∎

Before showing that the distributive property holds over subtraction of rationals, we shall make a definition similar to one we made in integer arithmetic regarding the relation between the additive inverse of an integer and negative one.

Definition 15-2: If $\frac{a}{b}$ is any rational number, then $\frac{^-a}{b} = \frac{^-1}{1} \cdot \frac{a}{b}$.

Using Definition 15-2, two theorems can be proved regarding rational numbers which parallel theorems for integers. The latter of these will be quite useful in proving that distributivity of multiplication over subtraction holds for rational numbers.

Theorem 15-10: If $\frac{a}{b}$ and $\frac{c}{d}$ are rational numbers, then

$$^-\left(\frac{a}{b}+\frac{c}{d}\right) = \frac{^-a}{b} + \frac{^-c}{d}$$

Proof:
$$^-\left(\frac{a}{b}+\frac{c}{d}\right) = \frac{^-1}{1} \cdot \left(\frac{a}{b}+\frac{c}{d}\right) \qquad\qquad \text{Def. 15-2}$$

$$= \left(\frac{^-1}{1} \cdot \frac{a}{b} \right) + \left(\frac{^-1}{1} \cdot \frac{c}{d} \right) \qquad \text{Thm. 15-9}$$

$$= \frac{^-a}{b} + \frac{^-c}{d} \qquad \text{Def. 15-2}$$

That is, the negative of the sum of two rationals is the same as the sum of the negatives of the two rationals. Alternatively, the additive inverse of the sum of two rationals is the same as the sum of the additive inverses of the two. ■

Theorem 15-11: If $\frac{a}{b}$ and $\frac{c}{d}$ are rationals, then

$$\frac{^-a}{b} \cdot \frac{c}{d} = \frac{a}{b} \cdot \frac{^-c}{d} = {}^-\left(\frac{a}{b} \cdot \frac{c}{d} \right)$$

Proof: We shall prove two of the three cases and then use transitivity of equality to obtain the third case.

(1) To show: $\frac{^-a}{b} \cdot \frac{c}{d} = \frac{a}{b} \cdot \frac{^-c}{d}$

$$\frac{^-a}{b} \cdot \frac{c}{d} = \left(\frac{^-1}{1} \cdot \frac{a}{b} \right) \cdot \frac{c}{d} \qquad \text{Def. 15-2}$$

$$= \left(\frac{a}{b} \cdot \frac{^-1}{1} \right) \cdot \frac{c}{d} \qquad \text{Thm. 15-2}$$

$$= \frac{a}{b} \cdot \left(\frac{^-1}{1} \cdot \frac{c}{d} \right) \qquad \text{Thm. 15-3}$$

$$= \frac{a}{b} \cdot \frac{^-c}{d} \qquad \text{Def. 15-2}$$

(2) To show: $\frac{a}{b} \cdot \frac{^-c}{d} = {}^-\left(\frac{a}{b} \cdot \frac{c}{d} \right)$

$$\frac{a}{b} \cdot \frac{^-c}{d} = \frac{a}{b} \cdot \left(\frac{^-1}{1} \cdot \frac{c}{d} \right) \qquad \text{Def. 15-2}$$

$$= \left(\frac{a}{b} \cdot \frac{^-1}{1} \right) \cdot \frac{c}{d} \qquad \text{Thm. 15-3}$$

$$= \left(\frac{^-1}{1} \cdot \frac{a}{b} \right) \cdot \frac{c}{d} \qquad \text{Thm. 15-2}$$

$$= \frac{^-1}{1} \cdot \left(\frac{a}{b} \cdot \frac{c}{d} \right) \qquad \text{Thm. 15-3}$$

$$= {}^-\left(\frac{a}{b} \cdot \frac{c}{d} \right) \qquad \text{Def. 15-2}$$

(3) Now $\dfrac{^-a}{b} \cdot \dfrac{c}{d} = \dfrac{a}{b} \cdot \dfrac{^-c}{d}$ and $\dfrac{a}{b} \cdot \dfrac{^-c}{d} = ^-\left(\dfrac{a}{b} \cdot \dfrac{c}{d}\right)$, so that the transitive property of equality yields $\dfrac{^-a}{b} \cdot \dfrac{c}{d} = ^-\left(\dfrac{a}{b} \cdot \dfrac{c}{d}\right)$. These arguments allow the continued equality given in the statement of this theorem. ∎

Now let us show that distributivity of multiplication over subtraction holds in the rational number system by using the results of Theorem 15-11.

Theorem 15-12 (Distributive $\cdot/-$): If $\dfrac{a}{b}, \dfrac{c}{d}$, and $\dfrac{e}{f}$ are rational numbers, then

$$\frac{a}{b} \cdot \left(\frac{c}{d} - \frac{e}{f}\right) = \left(\frac{a}{b} \cdot \frac{c}{d}\right) - \left(\frac{a}{b} \cdot \frac{e}{f}\right).$$

Proof: In this proof, we shall make use of some of the facts just obtained as well as some of our earlier results.

$$\frac{a}{b} \cdot \left(\frac{c}{d} - \frac{e}{f}\right) = \frac{a}{b} \cdot \left(\frac{c}{d} + \frac{^-e}{f}\right) \qquad \text{Thm. 14-16}$$

$$= \left(\frac{a}{b} \cdot \frac{c}{d}\right) + \left(\frac{a}{b} \cdot \frac{^-e}{f}\right) \qquad \text{Thm. 15-9}$$

$$= \left(\frac{a}{b} \cdot \frac{c}{d}\right) + ^-\left(\frac{a}{b} \cdot \frac{e}{f}\right) \qquad \text{Thm. 15-11}$$

$$= \left(\frac{a}{b} \cdot \frac{c}{d}\right) - \left(\frac{a}{b} \cdot \frac{e}{f}\right) \qquad \text{Thm. 14-16.} ∎$$

We note that the above is not the usual proof given for Theorem 15-12, and so we invite the student to try to find a second proof of the theorem.

You will recall that for integers it was possible to actually formulate and prove the validity of the so-called rules of signs for addition and multiplication. Similarly, we have been able to prove the validity of some "rules of signs" for addition of rational numbers. It is possible to do this for multiplication of rationals as well. However, since the proofs of these are relatively straight forward, we shall simply list them for reference and leave their proofs for you to construct.

Theorem 15-13: The product of two positive rational numbers is a positive rational number.

Proof: Left as an exercise.

Theorem 15-14: The product of a negative rational number and a positive rational number is a negative rational number.

Proof: Left as an exercise.

Theorem 15-15: The product of two negative rational numbers is a positive rational number.

Proof: Left as an exercise.

To illustrate the above three theorems, consider the following examples.

Examples:

(a) $\dfrac{2}{3} \cdot \dfrac{7}{5} = \dfrac{2 \cdot 7}{3 \cdot 5} = \dfrac{14}{15}$ which is a positive rational number.

(b) $\dfrac{^-3}{5} \cdot \dfrac{4}{13} = \dfrac{^-3 \cdot 4}{5 \cdot 13} = \dfrac{^-12}{65}$ which is a negative rational number.

(c) $\dfrac{^-5}{6} \cdot \dfrac{^-3}{7} = \dfrac{^-5 \cdot ^-3}{6 \cdot 7} = \dfrac{15}{42} = \dfrac{5}{14}$ which is a positive rational number.

The foregoing discussion establishes most of the properties of multiplication. However, we shall see when decimal numerals for rationals are discussed that the concept of multiplication plays a primary role. There we will find that it is possible to construct new numerals for rational numbers which are extensions of the expanded form of numerals previously used in the systems of cardinal numbers and integers.

EXERCISE SET 15-2

1. Illustrate the commutative property of multiplication by first calculating $\dfrac{3}{5} \cdot \dfrac{4}{7}$, then $\dfrac{4}{7} \cdot \dfrac{3}{5}$. These two results should be the same. Using this procedure, what justifies writing the statement $\dfrac{3}{5} \cdot \dfrac{4}{7} = \dfrac{4}{7} \cdot \dfrac{3}{5}$?

2. (a) Using the same technique as in problem one, show that

$$\frac{2}{3} \cdot \left(\frac{^-4}{5} \cdot \frac{6}{7} \right) = \left(\frac{2}{3} \cdot \frac{^-4}{5} \right) \cdot \frac{6}{7}.$$

   (b) Prove Theorem 15-3.

3. (a) Show that $\dfrac{^-1}{1}$ is *not* a multiplicative identity by working out a numerical example.

   (b) Show that the multiplicative identity is unique by use of a uniqueness argument.

4. Phoebe Drachma is given the problem $\dfrac{3}{7} \cdot \left(\dfrac{5}{3} + \dfrac{2}{3} \right)$ by her teacher, Zacharius Zott. Phoebe, being a bright child, decides that the easy way to do the problem is to write $\dfrac{3}{7} \cdot \left(\dfrac{5}{3} + \dfrac{2}{3} \right) = \dfrac{3}{7} \cdot \dfrac{7}{3} = \dfrac{1}{1}$. What concepts has Phoebe made particular use of?

5. Determine the answer to each of the following problems and also find a "key" which if used saves considerable effort for the problem solver.

(a) $\dfrac{4}{9} \cdot \dfrac{18}{12} =$

(d) $\dfrac{6}{5} \cdot \left(\dfrac{1}{2} + \dfrac{1}{3} \right) =$

(b) $\dfrac{3}{13} \cdot \left(\dfrac{26}{6} \cdot \dfrac{2}{2} \right) =$

(e) $\left(\dfrac{5}{8} \cdot \dfrac{8}{3} \right) \cdot \dfrac{3}{5} =$

(c) $\dfrac{5}{6} \cdot \left(\dfrac{13}{39} \cdot \dfrac{9}{3} \right) =$

6. Determine a solution (if it exists) to each of the following problems by making use of the cancellation property or converse of the cancellation property.

(a) $\dfrac{x}{y} \cdot \dfrac{3}{2} = \dfrac{^-15}{8}$

(f) $\dfrac{3}{7} \cdot \dfrac{4}{5} = \dfrac{4}{7} \cdot \dfrac{x}{y}$

(b) $\dfrac{^-2}{5} \cdot \dfrac{x}{y} = \dfrac{14}{25}$

(g) $\dfrac{18}{11} = \dfrac{x}{y} \cdot \dfrac{2}{11}$

(c) $\dfrac{^-4}{3} \cdot \dfrac{x}{y} = \dfrac{^-24}{9}$

(h) $\dfrac{15}{14} = \dfrac{x}{14} \cdot \dfrac{5}{y}$

(d) $\dfrac{^-3x}{5y} = \dfrac{27}{50}$

(i) $\left(\dfrac{2}{3} + \dfrac{5}{6} \right) \cdot \dfrac{x}{y} = \dfrac{1}{1}$

(e) $\dfrac{5x}{32} = \dfrac{25}{16}$

(j) $\left(\dfrac{3}{4} - \dfrac{4}{7} \right) \cdot \dfrac{x}{5} = \dfrac{1}{1}$

(k) $\dfrac{3}{7} \cdot \left(\dfrac{3}{8} + \dfrac{x}{4} \right) = \dfrac{27}{56}$

7. Determine the product $\left(\dfrac{1}{2} + \dfrac{3}{5} \right) \cdot \left(\dfrac{1}{3} + \dfrac{2}{5} \right)$ in two different ways.

8. Carpella Crutch works problem seven as follows.

$$\left(\dfrac{1}{2} + \dfrac{3}{5} \right) \cdot \left(\dfrac{1}{3} + \dfrac{2}{5} \right) = \left(\dfrac{1}{2} + \dfrac{1}{3} \right) \cdot \left(\dfrac{3}{5} + \dfrac{2}{5} \right) = \dfrac{5}{6} \cdot \dfrac{1}{1} = \dfrac{5}{6}$$

Has Carpella done anything incorrectly? If so, what?

For each of the following ledger problems, write the name of the property or definition used to justify each step. If a theorem is used which has no name, write it symbolically.

Step

9. $\dfrac{3}{4} \cdot \left(\dfrac{3}{7} \cdot \dfrac{7}{4} \right) = \dfrac{3}{4} \cdot \left[\left(\dfrac{3}{1} \cdot \dfrac{1}{7} \right) \cdot \left(\dfrac{7}{1} \cdot \dfrac{1}{4} \right) \right]$ (a)

$= \dfrac{3}{4} \cdot \left(\left[\dfrac{3}{1} \cdot \left(\dfrac{1}{7} \cdot \dfrac{7}{1} \right) \right] \cdot \dfrac{1}{4} \right)$ (b)

$= \dfrac{3}{4} \cdot \left[\left(\dfrac{3}{1} \cdot \dfrac{1 \cdot 7}{7 \cdot 1} \right) \cdot \dfrac{1}{4} \right]$ (c)

$= \dfrac{3}{4} \cdot \left[\left(\dfrac{3}{1} \cdot \dfrac{7}{7} \right) \cdot \dfrac{1}{4} \right]$ (d)

$$= \frac{3}{4} \cdot \left[\left(\frac{3}{1} \cdot \frac{1}{1} \right) \cdot \frac{1}{4} \right] \qquad \text{(e)}$$

$$= \frac{3}{4} \cdot \left(\frac{3}{1} \cdot \frac{1}{4} \right) \qquad \text{(f)}$$

$$= \frac{3}{4} \cdot \frac{3 \cdot 1}{1 \cdot 4} \qquad \text{(g)}$$

$$= \frac{3}{4} \cdot \frac{3}{4} \qquad \text{(h)}$$

$$= \frac{3 \cdot 3}{4 \cdot 4} \qquad \text{(i)}$$

$$= \frac{9}{16} \qquad \text{(j)}$$

Step

$$10. \quad \frac{2}{5} \cdot \left(\frac{5}{3} + \frac{3}{5} \right) = \frac{2}{5} \cdot \left(\frac{5 \cdot 5}{5 \cdot 3} + \frac{3 \cdot 3}{3 \cdot 5} \right) \qquad \text{(a)}$$

$$= \frac{2}{5} \cdot \left(\frac{25}{15} + \frac{9}{15} \right) \qquad \text{(b)}$$

$$= \frac{2}{5} \cdot \frac{25 + 9}{15} \qquad \text{(c)}$$

$$= \frac{2}{5} \cdot \frac{34}{15} \qquad \text{(d)}$$

$$= \frac{2 \cdot 34}{5 \cdot 15} \qquad \text{(e)}$$

$$= \frac{68}{75} \qquad \text{(f)}$$

Step

$$11. \quad \frac{2}{5} \cdot \left(\frac{5}{3} - \frac{3}{5} \right) = \frac{2}{5} \cdot \frac{5 \cdot 5 - 3 \cdot 3}{3 \cdot 5} \qquad \text{(a)}$$

$$= \frac{2}{5} \cdot \frac{25 - 9}{15} \qquad \text{(b)}$$

$$= \frac{2}{5} \cdot \frac{16}{15} \qquad \text{(c)}$$

$$= \frac{2 \cdot 16}{5 \cdot 15} \qquad \text{(d)}$$

$$= \frac{32}{75} \qquad \text{(e)}$$

Step

$$12. \quad \frac{2}{5} \cdot \left[\frac{5}{3} - \left(\frac{2}{7} \cdot \frac{21}{6} \right) \right] = \frac{2}{5} \cdot \left[\frac{5}{3} - \left(\frac{2}{7} \cdot \frac{3 \cdot 7}{3 \cdot 2} \right) \right] \qquad \text{(a)}$$

$$= \frac{2}{5} \cdot \left[\frac{5}{3} - \left(\frac{2}{7} \cdot \frac{7}{2} \right) \right] \qquad \text{(b)}$$

$$= \frac{2}{5} \cdot \left(\frac{5}{3} - \frac{1}{1} \right) \qquad \text{(c)}$$

$$= \frac{2}{5} \cdot \left(\frac{5}{3} - \frac{3}{3} \right) \qquad \text{(d)}$$

$$= \frac{2}{5} \cdot \frac{5-3}{3} \qquad \text{(e)}$$

$$= \frac{2}{5} \cdot \frac{2}{3} \qquad \text{(f)}$$

$$= \frac{2 \cdot 2}{5 \cdot 3} \qquad \text{(g)}$$

$$= \frac{4}{15} \qquad \text{(h)}$$

Step

13. $\left(\dfrac{5}{2} - \dfrac{2}{5} \right) \cdot \left(\dfrac{5}{2} + \dfrac{2}{5} \right) = \left(\dfrac{5 \cdot 5}{5 \cdot 2} - \dfrac{2 \cdot 2}{2 \cdot 5} \right) \cdot \left(\dfrac{5 \cdot 5}{5 \cdot 2} + \dfrac{2 \cdot 2}{2 \cdot 5} \right)$ (a)

$$= \left(\frac{25}{10} - \frac{4}{10} \right) \cdot \left(\frac{25}{10} + \frac{4}{10} \right) \qquad \text{(b)}$$

$$= \frac{25 - 4}{10} \cdot \frac{25 + 4}{10} \qquad \text{(c)}$$

$$= \frac{21}{10} \cdot \frac{29}{10} \qquad \text{(d)}$$

$$= \frac{21 \cdot 29}{10 \cdot 10} \qquad \text{(e)}$$

$$= \frac{609}{100} \qquad \text{(f)}$$

14. Does $\left(\dfrac{5}{2} \cdot \dfrac{5}{2} \right) - \left(\dfrac{2}{5} \cdot \dfrac{2}{5} \right) = \dfrac{609}{100}$?

15. Try the technique of problems 13 or 14 on each of the following.

(a) $\left(\dfrac{3}{4} - \dfrac{1}{4} \right) \cdot \left(\dfrac{3}{4} + \dfrac{1}{4} \right)$

(b) $\left(\dfrac{3}{5} - \dfrac{1}{2} \right) \cdot \left(\dfrac{3}{5} + \dfrac{1}{2} \right)$

(c) $\left(\dfrac{7}{8} - \dfrac{1}{4} \right) \cdot \left(\dfrac{7}{8} + \dfrac{1}{4} \right)$

16. Is it true in general that $\left(\dfrac{a}{b} - \dfrac{c}{d} \right) \cdot \left(\dfrac{a}{b} + \dfrac{c}{d} \right) = \left(\dfrac{a}{b} \cdot \dfrac{a}{b} \right) - \left(\dfrac{c}{d} \cdot \dfrac{c}{d} \right)$?

17. Suppose we define multiplication as $\frac{a}{b} \cdot \frac{c}{d} = \frac{ad}{bc}$. Would this definition lead to any complications in the resulting arithmetic? If so, illustrate (with numbers) at least three of these complications.

18. Let us define a process \ (read "slash") as follows:

$$\frac{a}{b} \backslash \frac{c}{d} = \frac{(a+d)(b+c)}{bd}.$$

Investigate to see if any undesirable properties result from this definition.

19. Find an alternate proof for (a) Theorem 15-9, (b) Theorem 15-12.

20. Prove that the product of two negative rational numbers is a positive rational number.

21. Show that if $\frac{a}{b}$ and $\frac{c}{d}$ are rational numbers, then $\frac{a}{b} - \frac{c}{d} = \frac{a}{b} + \left(\frac{^-1}{1} \cdot \frac{c}{d} \right)$.

22. Show that $\frac{a}{b} \cdot \left(\frac{c}{d} + \frac{e}{f} + \frac{g}{h} \right) = \left(\frac{a}{b} \cdot \frac{c}{d} \right) + \left(\frac{a}{b} \cdot \frac{e}{f} \right) + \left(\frac{a}{b} \cdot \frac{g}{h} \right)$. Could this result be extended to cover the sum of four rational numbers? Five rational numbers? n rational numbers?

23. Show that $\left(\frac{a}{b} + \frac{c}{d} \right) \cdot \left(\frac{e}{f} + \frac{g}{h} \right) = \left(\frac{a}{b} \cdot \frac{e}{f} \right) + \left(\frac{a}{b} \cdot \frac{g}{h} \right) + \left(\frac{c}{d} \cdot \frac{e}{f} \right) + \left(\frac{c}{d} \cdot \frac{g}{h} \right)$
Could this result be extended similar to that of problem 22?

24. Show that if $\frac{a}{b} \cdot \frac{c}{d} = \frac{0}{1}$, then $\frac{a}{b} = \frac{0}{1}$, or $\frac{c}{d} = \frac{0}{1}$.

25. Use the result of problem 24 to solve each of the following.

(a) $\left(\frac{x}{y} + \frac{^-3}{2} \right) \cdot \left(\frac{x}{y} - \frac{3}{5} \right) = \frac{0}{1}$

(b) $\left(\frac{u}{v} - \frac{^-2}{3} \right) \cdot \frac{u}{v} = \frac{0}{1}$

(c) $\frac{x^2}{y^2} - \frac{1}{4} = \frac{0}{1}$

(d) $\left(\frac{x}{y} + \frac{1}{1} \right) \cdot \left(\frac{x}{y} - \frac{2}{5} \right) = \frac{0}{1}$

3. Definition of Division of Rationals

We shall investigate *two* ways in which division of rational numbers may be defined. The second method is more mathematical in nature than the first. However, the first method is not only more meaningful to the elementary student, but it also gives some intuitive insight for using the second method. In both methods we shall use the symbol ÷ to mean division of rationals, and if ÷ is part of the numeral used in numerator or denominator it is to be interpreted as divisibility for integers.

Method 1:

Let us consider for a moment some problems in division of rationals.

(1) $\dfrac{9}{16} \div \dfrac{3}{4}$

(5) $\dfrac{^-1}{10} \div \dfrac{1}{5}$

(2) $\dfrac{^-8}{27} \div \dfrac{^-4}{9}$

(6) $\dfrac{18}{1} \div \dfrac{^-9}{1}$

(3) $\dfrac{^-6}{26} \div \dfrac{^-3}{13}$

(7) $\dfrac{24}{1} \div \dfrac{12}{1}$

(4) $\dfrac{1}{4} \div \dfrac{1}{2}$

(8) $\dfrac{5}{8} \div \dfrac{4}{3}$

In each of the problems just listed we shall try to determine the quotient by means of divisibility of integers. For example, we shall write

$$\frac{9}{16} \div \frac{3}{4} = \frac{9 \div 3}{16 \div 4}$$

$$= \frac{3}{4}$$

To the student who insists on "inverting" and then multiplying, does the above method appear to yield the same results as yours?

Try each of the other examples listed above by the method which was just illustrated. Now that you have tried the examples, you find that example (8) cannot be worked directly by the method suggested since neither 4 divides 5 nor 3 divides 8. Hence let us now try to work example (8) by using a slightly different approach. We want to determine the answer to the problem

$$\frac{5}{8} \div \frac{4}{3}.$$

In order to do this we must determine a rational number $\dfrac{5a}{8b}$ such that $\dfrac{5a}{8b} = \dfrac{5}{8}$, $5a$ is a multiple of 4, and $8b$ is a multiple of 3. Perhaps an obvious choice would be to select $a = 4$ and $b = 3$, but then

$$\frac{5 \cdot 4}{8 \cdot 3} \neq \frac{5}{8}$$

Hence we select $a = 4 \cdot 3$ and $b = 3 \cdot 4$ so that we obtain

$$\frac{5 \cdot 4 \cdot 3}{8 \cdot 3 \cdot 4} = \frac{5}{8}$$

by the K-Theorem. Further we note that now $(4 \cdot 3)$ and $(3 \cdot 4)$ are multiples of 4 and 3 respectively. Therefore,

$$\frac{5 \cdot 4 \cdot 3}{8 \cdot 3 \cdot 4} \div \frac{4}{3} = \frac{(5 \cdot 4 \cdot 3) \div 4}{(8 \cdot 3 \cdot 4) \div 3}$$

$$= \frac{5 \cdot 3}{8 \cdot 4}$$

$$= \frac{15}{32}$$

In general then if we wish to divide $\frac{a}{b}$ by $\frac{c}{d}$ where $\frac{c}{d} \neq \frac{0}{1}$, we would write

$$\frac{a}{b} \div \frac{c}{d} = \frac{acd}{bcd} \div \frac{c}{d}$$

$$= \frac{acd \div c}{bcd \div d}$$

$$= \frac{ad}{bc}$$

$$= \frac{a}{b} \cdot \frac{d}{c}$$

which is the same result we are already familiar with. This method should have a considerable advantage for the beginning student because of the fact that the method is derived from previously learned division facts concerning the system of integers, and also because this technique seems natural once multiplication has been defined.

Method 2:

Our second method will be to define what we shall mean by division of rational numbers, and then show that the same results are obtained as in method one.

Definition 15-3: If $\frac{a}{b}$ and $\frac{c}{d}$ are rational numbers and $\frac{c}{d} \neq \frac{0}{1}$, then $\frac{a}{b}$ **divided by** $\frac{c}{d}$ is the rational number $\frac{x}{y}$ such that $\frac{a}{b} = \frac{c}{d} \cdot \frac{x}{y}$. Symbolically, $\frac{a}{b} \div \frac{c}{d} = \frac{x}{y}$ if and only if $\frac{a}{b} = \frac{c}{d} \cdot \frac{x}{y}$.

In Definition 15-3 let us try to determine what rational number $\frac{x}{y}$ must be. In order to do this consider the product $\frac{a}{b} = \frac{c}{d} \cdot \frac{x}{y}$.   Then

$$\frac{a}{b} = \frac{cx}{dy} \qquad \text{Definition 15-1}$$

$$a(dy) = b(cx) \qquad \text{Definition 13-4}$$

$$(ad)y = (bc)x \qquad \text{Assoc. } (\cdot) \text{ integers}$$

Thus, all that must be done is to select integers y and x in such a way that the indicated equality holds. This can be done rather easily if the choices made are

$$y = bc \text{ and } x = ad$$

Then according to Definition 15-3, $\dfrac{a}{b} \div \dfrac{c}{d} = \dfrac{x}{y}$

$$= \dfrac{ad}{bc}$$

$$= \dfrac{a}{b} \cdot \dfrac{d}{c}$$

which is precisely the same result as obtained in terms of multiplication, and products of rational numbers exist and are unique.

If one does not wish to determine $\dfrac{x}{y}$ as illustrated above, he could make use of the multiplicative inverse of $\dfrac{c}{d}$ and the equation $\dfrac{a}{b} = \dfrac{c}{d} \cdot \dfrac{x}{y}$ to obtain the same result. This would be a valid approach since $\dfrac{c}{d} \neq \dfrac{0}{1}$ implies the existence of the multiplicative inverse of $\dfrac{c}{d}$ and since the converse of cancellation for rational multiplication holds.

EXERCISE SET 15-3

1. Show that if we take $\dfrac{x}{y} = \dfrac{ad}{bc}$ in Definition 15-3, then $\dfrac{c}{d} \cdot \dfrac{x}{y}$ is indeed $\dfrac{a}{b}$.
2. If one of the following problems is stated in terms of division, restate it in terms of an equivalent multiplication problem, and conversely, if stated in terms of multiplication, state it in terms of a division problem.

   (a) $\dfrac{2}{7} \cdot \dfrac{4}{6} =$ (b) $\dfrac{3}{4} \cdot \dfrac{4}{3} =$ (c) $\dfrac{3}{5} \div \dfrac{5}{3} =$

   (d) $\left(\dfrac{3}{7} \cdot \dfrac{4}{3} \right) \div \dfrac{7}{4} =$ (e) $\left(\dfrac{3}{8} \div \dfrac{4}{6} \right) \div \dfrac{9}{16} =$

3. What are the answers to parts (b), (c), and (d) of problem 2?
4. Determine the answers to each of the following problems by making use of method one for division of rationals.

   (a) $\dfrac{3}{5} \div \dfrac{7}{3} =$ (b) $\dfrac{^-7}{3} \div \dfrac{3}{5} =$ (c) $\dfrac{4}{5} \div \dfrac{^-3}{8} =$ (d) $\dfrac{3}{8} \div \dfrac{4}{5} =$

5. Discuss why division of rationals is or is not an operation.

4. Properties of Division of Rationals

One might suspect that since division is defined in terms of multiplication and since multiplication is commutative, division is commutative. Surprisingly however, this is not the case. It is also true that division of rationals does not satisfy the associative property. We have already seen similar results in subtraction of integers and rational numbers. We leave the proofs of these facts to the student as exercises.

Even though division does not satisfy the commutative and associative properties, it does satisfy the right distributive property both with respect to addition and subtraction.

Example: $\left(\dfrac{2}{3}+\dfrac{4}{5}\right) \div \dfrac{7}{8} = \left(\dfrac{2}{3} \div \dfrac{7}{8}\right) + \left(\dfrac{4}{5} \div \dfrac{7}{8}\right)$.

Solution:

$$\left(\frac{2}{3}+\frac{4}{5}\right) \div \frac{7}{8} = \frac{2 \cdot 5 + 3 \cdot 4}{3 \cdot 5} \div \frac{7}{8} \qquad \text{Thm. 14-2}$$

$$= \frac{2 \cdot 5 + 3 \cdot 4}{3 \cdot 5} \cdot \frac{8}{7} \qquad \text{Def. 15-3}$$

$$= \frac{(2 \cdot 5 + 3 \cdot 4) \cdot 8}{(3 \cdot 5) \cdot 7} \qquad \text{Def. 15-1}$$

$$= \frac{(2 \cdot 5) \cdot 8 + (3 \cdot 4) \cdot 8}{(3 \cdot 5) \cdot 7} \qquad \text{Why?}$$

$$= \frac{(2 \cdot 5) \cdot 8}{(3 \cdot 5) \cdot 7} + \frac{(3 \cdot 4) \cdot 8}{(3 \cdot 5) \cdot 7} \qquad \text{Def. 14-1}$$

$$= \frac{2 \cdot 8}{3 \cdot 7} + \frac{4 \cdot 8}{5 \cdot 7} \qquad \text{Why?}$$

$$= \left(\frac{2}{3} \cdot \frac{8}{7}\right) + \left(\frac{4}{5} \cdot \frac{8}{7}\right) \qquad \text{Why?}$$

$$= \left(\frac{2}{3} \div \frac{7}{8}\right) + \left(\frac{4}{5} \div \frac{7}{8}\right) \qquad \text{Def. 15-3}$$

The theorem which justifies the result of the preceding example is listed below. As you will notice, the steps of its proof are nearly identical to those in the example problem.

Theorem 15-16: If $\dfrac{a}{b}, \dfrac{c}{d}$, and $\dfrac{e}{f}$ are rational numbers with $\dfrac{e}{f} = \dfrac{0}{1}$, then

$$\left(\frac{a}{b}+\frac{c}{d}\right) \div \frac{e}{f} = \left(\frac{a}{b} \div \frac{e}{f}\right) + \left(\frac{c}{d} \div \frac{e}{f}\right)$$

Proof: $\left(\dfrac{a}{b}+\dfrac{c}{d}\right) \div \dfrac{e}{f} = \dfrac{ad+bc}{bd} \div \dfrac{e}{f}$ \qquad Thm. 14-2

$$= \frac{ad + bc}{bd} \cdot \frac{f}{e} \qquad \qquad \text{Def. 15-3}$$

$$= \frac{(ad + bc)f}{(bd)e} \qquad \qquad \text{Def. 15-1}$$

$$= \frac{(ad)f + (bc)f}{(bd)e} \qquad \qquad \text{Dist. } (\cdot/+) \text{ integers}$$

$$= \frac{(ad)f}{(bd)e} + \frac{(bc)f}{(bd)e} \qquad \qquad \text{Def. 14-1}$$

$$= \frac{d(af)}{d(be)} + \frac{b(cf)}{b(de)} \qquad \qquad \text{Assoc., Comm. } (\cdot) \text{ integers}$$

$$= \frac{af}{be} + \frac{cf}{de} \qquad \qquad K\text{-Theorem}$$

$$= \left(\frac{a}{b} \cdot \frac{f}{e} \right) + \left(\frac{c}{d} \cdot \frac{f}{e} \right) \qquad \text{Def. 15-1}$$

$$= \left(\frac{a}{b} \div \frac{e}{f} \right) + \left(\frac{c}{d} \div \frac{e}{f} \right) \qquad \text{Def. 15-3}$$

Thus we see that division is right distributive with respect to addition of rational numbers. ∎

Because of the relationship between the additive inverse and the operation subtraction, we are assured that division is also right distributive with respect to subtraction of rationals. If + is replaced by − in the example preceding Theorem 15-16 it is easy to show that the correct answer is obtained. The formal statement of the theorem which justifies distributivity on the right of division over subtraction of rationals is given below without proof.

Theorem 15-17: If $\frac{a}{b}$, $\frac{c}{d}$, and $\frac{e}{f}$ are rational numbers with $\frac{e}{f} \neq \frac{0}{1}$, then

$$\left(\frac{a}{b} - \frac{c}{d} \right) \div \frac{e}{f} = \left(\frac{a}{b} \div \frac{e}{f} \right) - \left(\frac{c}{d} \div \frac{e}{f} \right).$$

It is interesting to note that division is *not* distributive with respect to addition (or subtraction) on the left. To show this, all that is required is to construct a numerical example in which the expressions on each side of the "equals" sign yield names for different rational numbers.

Example: Show that $\frac{2}{3} \div \left(\frac{3}{4} + \frac{4}{5} \right) \neq \left(\frac{2}{3} \div \frac{3}{4} \right) + \left(\frac{2}{3} \div \frac{4}{5} \right).$

Solution: We shall work the left- and right-hand expressions and show that different rational numbers are named in each instance. For the left-hand expression

(a)
$$\frac{2}{3} \div \left(\frac{3}{4} + \frac{4}{5} \right) = \frac{2}{3} \div \left(\frac{3 \cdot 5 + 4 \cdot 4}{4 \cdot 5} \right)$$

$$= \frac{2}{3} \div \frac{15 + 16}{20}$$

$$= \frac{2}{3} \div \frac{31}{20}$$

$$= \frac{2}{3} \cdot \frac{20}{31}$$

$$= \frac{2 \cdot 20}{3 \cdot 31}$$

$$= \frac{40}{93}$$

(b) For the right-hand expression

$$\left(\frac{2}{3} \div \frac{3}{4} \right) + \left(\frac{2}{3} \div \frac{4}{5} \right) = \left(\frac{2}{3} \cdot \frac{4}{3} \right) + \left(\frac{2}{3} \cdot \frac{5}{4} \right)$$

$$= \frac{2 \cdot 4}{3 \cdot 3} + \frac{2 \cdot 5}{3 \cdot 4}$$

$$= \frac{8}{9} + \frac{10}{12}$$

$$= \frac{8}{9} + \frac{5}{6}$$

$$= \frac{8 \cdot 6 + 9 \cdot 5}{9 \cdot 6}$$

$$= \frac{48 + 45}{54}$$

$$= \frac{93}{54}$$

$$= \frac{31}{18} .$$

Since $\frac{40}{93} \neq \frac{31}{18}$, we can conclude that

$$\frac{2}{3} \div \left(\frac{3}{4} + \frac{4}{5} \right) \neq \left(\frac{2}{3} \div \frac{3}{4} \right) + \left(\frac{2}{3} \div \frac{4}{5} \right)$$

and hence in general that

$$\frac{a}{b} \div \left(\frac{c}{d} + \frac{e}{f}\right) \neq \left(\frac{a}{b} \div \frac{c}{d}\right) + \left(\frac{a}{b} \div \frac{e}{f}\right)$$

A similar example can be constructed to show that in general

$$\frac{a}{b} \div \left(\frac{c}{d} - \frac{e}{f}\right) \neq \left(\frac{a}{b} \div \frac{c}{d}\right) - \left(\frac{a}{b} \div \frac{e}{f}\right)$$

We leave this for the student to show. Another approach for the latter would be to appeal to the relationship between addition and subtraction of rationals.

There will be, in the material which follows, problems in which we will want to multiply and divide by the same rational number in order to effect a solution. We shall prove this desirable result now and then when we need it, we shall have it. We shall be in particular need of this result when we discuss the division of decimal rationals.

Theorem 15-18:   If $\frac{a}{b} \div \frac{c}{d} = \frac{e}{f}$ and if $\frac{m}{n} \neq \frac{0}{1}$, then $\left(\frac{a}{b} \cdot \frac{m}{n}\right) \div \left(\frac{c}{d} \cdot \frac{m}{n}\right) = \frac{e}{f}$.

Proof:

$$\left(\frac{a}{b} \cdot \frac{m}{n}\right) \div \left(\frac{c}{d} \cdot \frac{m}{n}\right) = \frac{am}{bn} \div \frac{cm}{dn} \qquad \qquad \text{Def. 15-1}$$

$$= \frac{am}{bn} \cdot \frac{dn}{cm} \qquad \qquad \text{Def. 15-3}$$

$$= \frac{(am)(dn)}{(bn)(cm)} \qquad \qquad \text{Def. 15-1}$$

$$= \frac{(mn)(ad)}{(mn)(bc)} \qquad \text{Assoc., Comm. } (\cdot) \text{ for integers}$$

$$= \frac{ad}{bc} \qquad \qquad K\text{-Theorem}$$

$$= \frac{a}{b} \cdot \frac{d}{c} \qquad \qquad \text{Def. 15-1}$$

$$= \frac{a}{b} \div \frac{c}{d} \qquad \qquad \text{Def. 15-3}$$

$$= \frac{e}{f} \qquad \qquad \text{Given.} \blacksquare$$

This concludes our discussion of division of rationals for the present. However, once we start to work with decimal rationals, we shall again discuss addition, subtraction, multiplication, and division. When this is done we shall be able to observe some characteristics of rational numbers which appear only through the use of decimal numerals.

EXERCISE SET 15-4

1. Is it true in general that $\dfrac{a}{b} \div \dfrac{c}{d} \neq \dfrac{c}{d} \div \dfrac{a}{b}$? Illustrate with a numerical example.

2. Show that $\dfrac{a}{b} \div \left(\dfrac{c}{d} \div \dfrac{e}{f} \right) \neq \left(\dfrac{a}{b} \div \dfrac{c}{d} \right) \div \dfrac{e}{f}$ by choosing a numerical example which yields different numbers.

3. (a) Is it true that $\dfrac{1}{4} \div \left(\dfrac{1}{2} + \dfrac{3}{4} \right) = \left(\dfrac{1}{2} + \dfrac{3}{4} \right) \div \dfrac{1}{4}$?

   (b) Is it true that $\dfrac{1}{4} \div \left(\dfrac{3}{4} - \dfrac{1}{2} \right) = \left(\dfrac{3}{4} - \dfrac{1}{2} \right) \div \dfrac{1}{4}$?

4. Calculate

   (a) $\left(\dfrac{1}{2} + \dfrac{3}{4} \right) \div \dfrac{1}{4}$ and   (b) $\left(\dfrac{1}{2} \div \dfrac{1}{4} \right) + \left(\dfrac{3}{4} \div \dfrac{1}{4} \right)$.

   (c) Are the answers to parts (a) and (b) the same?

   (d) What theorem is illustrated?

5. Show that $\left(\dfrac{2}{3} - \dfrac{4}{5} \right) \div \dfrac{7}{8} = \left(\dfrac{2}{3} \div \dfrac{7}{8} \right) - \left(\dfrac{4}{5} \div \dfrac{7}{8} \right)$.

6. Determine

   (a) $\dfrac{5}{6} \div \dfrac{7}{8}$ and   (b) $\left(\dfrac{5}{6} \cdot \dfrac{3}{4} \right) \div \left(\dfrac{7}{8} \cdot \dfrac{3}{4} \right)$.

   (c) Are the answers to parts (a) and (b) the same?

   (d) What theorem is illustrated?

7. Determine x and/or y if they exist for each of the following problems.

   (a) $\left(\dfrac{3}{8} \cdot \dfrac{4}{7} \right) \div \dfrac{x}{y} = \dfrac{1}{1}$

   (b) $\left(\dfrac{3}{8} \div \dfrac{x}{y} \right) \cdot \dfrac{4}{7} = \dfrac{1}{1}$

   (c) $\dfrac{9}{20} \div \dfrac{6}{12} = \dfrac{x}{y}$

   (d) $\left(\dfrac{4}{5} - \dfrac{3}{7} \right) \div \dfrac{26}{70} = \dfrac{x}{y}$

   (e) $\left(\dfrac{3}{4} + \dfrac{3}{2} \right) \div \dfrac{3}{x} = \dfrac{y}{2}$

   (f) $\left(\dfrac{^-2}{3} \cdot \dfrac{^-3}{5} \right) \div \dfrac{x}{y} = \dfrac{^-1}{1}$

   (g) $\left(\dfrac{^-4}{3} \div \dfrac{x}{y} \right) \cdot \dfrac{5}{6} = \dfrac{1}{1}$

   (h) $\dfrac{^-15}{11} \div \dfrac{40}{110} = \dfrac{^-x}{y}$

   (i) $\left(\dfrac{3}{7} - \dfrac{^-4}{5} \right) \div \dfrac{x}{y} = \dfrac{^-3}{2}$

   (j) $\left(\dfrac{^-3}{4} + \dfrac{3}{2} \right) \div \dfrac{^-3}{x} = \dfrac{y}{2}$

8. Show that

   (a) $\left(\dfrac{1}{2} \cdot \dfrac{3}{5} \right) \div \dfrac{2}{3} = \dfrac{1}{2} \left(\dfrac{3}{5} \div \dfrac{2}{3} \right)$

   (b) $\left(\dfrac{1}{2} \cdot \dfrac{3}{5} \right) \div \dfrac{2}{3} = \dfrac{3}{5} \left(\dfrac{1}{2} \div \dfrac{2}{3} \right)$

9. Prove that if $\dfrac{e}{f} \neq \dfrac{0}{1}$, then

   (a) $\left(\dfrac{a}{b} \cdot \dfrac{c}{d} \right) \div \dfrac{e}{f} = \dfrac{a}{b} \cdot \left(\dfrac{c}{d} \div \dfrac{e}{f} \right)$.

   (b) $\left(\dfrac{a}{b} \cdot \dfrac{c}{d} \right) \div \dfrac{e}{f} = \dfrac{c}{d} \cdot \left(\dfrac{a}{b} \div \dfrac{e}{f} \right)$.

10. In integer arithmetic we know that if $b \neq 0$, then $(a \div b) \cdot b = a$. Does an analogous statement hold for rational numbers? That is, if $\dfrac{c}{d} \neq \dfrac{0}{1}$, is it true

that $\left(\dfrac{a}{b} \div \dfrac{c}{d}\right) \cdot \dfrac{c}{d} = \dfrac{a}{b}$? To answer *No* requires a supporting numerical example. To answer *Yes* requires a proof.

11. Is it true that if $\dfrac{c}{d} \neq \dfrac{0}{1}$, then $\left(\dfrac{a}{b} \cdot \dfrac{c}{d}\right) \div \dfrac{c}{d} = \dfrac{a}{b}$? Why or why not? Be able to support your answer with a mathematical argument.

12. What do your results for problems 14 and 15 tell you about the relationship between multiplication and division?

13. Work each of the following as follows: If given $\dfrac{a}{b} \div \dfrac{c}{b}, \dfrac{c}{b} \neq \dfrac{0}{1}$, write $\dfrac{a}{c}$ as the

answer, then write the reduced form of $\dfrac{a}{c}$.

(a) $\dfrac{7}{6} \div \dfrac{9}{6}$

(b) $\dfrac{8}{13} \div \dfrac{5}{13}$

(c) $\dfrac{^-5}{7} \div \dfrac{8}{7}$

(d) $\dfrac{5}{14} \div \dfrac{^-11}{14}$

(e) $\dfrac{^-4}{33} \div \dfrac{^-19}{33}$

(f) $\dfrac{^-10}{21} \div \dfrac{^-13}{21}$

(g) Does this method of division appear similar to any previous definitions used for operations on rationals? If so, which ones?

(h) Show that the definition stated above is a valid way to divide rational numbers.

(i) Using this definition how would one work division problems in which denominators are different? Give a numerical example to illustrate your suggestion.

14. Instead of defining division as in Section 15-3 suppose it is defined as follows.

$$\dfrac{a}{b} \div \dfrac{c}{d} = \dfrac{b}{a} \cdot \dfrac{c}{d} = \dfrac{bc}{ad}$$

(a) Does an answer always exist in the set of rationals?

(b) Does the theorem $\dfrac{0}{1} \div \dfrac{c}{d} = \dfrac{0}{1}$ still hold?

(c) When an answer exists, is it unique?

15. Could one say that $\dfrac{a}{b} \div \dfrac{c}{d}$ is the same as the multiplicative inverse of $\dfrac{c}{d} \div \dfrac{a}{b}$?

16. Prove that if $\dfrac{c}{d} \neq \dfrac{0}{1}$ and $\dfrac{a}{b} \neq \dfrac{0}{1}$, then

$$\dfrac{a}{b} \div \dfrac{c}{d} = \dfrac{1}{1} \div \left(\dfrac{c}{d} \div \dfrac{a}{b}\right)$$

For each of the following problems write the name of the property or definition used to justify each step. If a theorem is used which has no name, write it symbolically.

17. $\left[\dfrac{1}{2} + \left(\dfrac{3}{5} \cdot \dfrac{4}{3}\right)\right] \div \dfrac{4}{5} = \left(\dfrac{1}{2} \div \dfrac{4}{5}\right) + \left[\left(\dfrac{3}{5} \cdot \dfrac{4}{3}\right) \div \dfrac{4}{5}\right]$ Step (a)

$= \left(\dfrac{1}{2} \div \dfrac{4}{5}\right) + \left(\dfrac{3 \cdot 4}{5 \cdot 3} \div \dfrac{4}{5}\right)$ (b)

$$= \left(\frac{1}{2} \div \frac{4}{5} \right) + \left(\frac{3 \cdot 4}{3 \cdot 5} \div \frac{4}{5} \right) \qquad \text{(c)}$$

$$= \left(\frac{1}{2} \div \frac{4}{5} \right) + \left(\frac{4}{5} \div \frac{4}{5} \right) \qquad \text{(d)}$$

$$= \left(\frac{1}{2} \div \frac{4}{5} \right) + \frac{1}{1} \qquad \text{(e)}$$

$$= \left(\frac{1}{2} \cdot \frac{5}{4} \right) + \frac{1}{1} \qquad \text{(f)}$$

$$= \frac{1 \cdot 5}{2 \cdot 4} + \frac{1}{1} \qquad \text{(g)}$$

$$= \frac{5}{8} + \frac{1}{1} \qquad \text{(h)}$$

$$= \frac{5}{8} + \frac{8 \cdot 1}{8 \cdot 1} \qquad \text{(i)}$$

$$= \frac{5}{8} + \frac{8}{8} \qquad \text{(j)}$$

$$= \frac{5 + 8}{8} \qquad \text{(k)}$$

$$= \frac{13}{8} \qquad \text{(l)}$$

18.
$$\left(\frac{3}{4} + \frac{5}{8} \right) \div \frac{1}{2} = \left(\frac{3 \cdot 1}{2 \cdot 2} + \frac{5 \cdot 1}{4 \cdot 2} \right) \div \frac{1}{2} \qquad \begin{array}{c} \textit{Step} \\ \text{(a)} \end{array}$$

$$= \left[\left(\frac{3}{2} \cdot \frac{1}{2} \right) + \left(\frac{5}{4} \cdot \frac{1}{2} \right) \right] \div \frac{1}{2} \qquad \text{(b)}$$

$$= \left[\left(\frac{3}{2} + \frac{5}{4} \right) \cdot \frac{1}{2} \right] \div \frac{1}{2} \qquad \text{(c)}$$

$$= \left(\frac{3}{2} + \frac{5}{4} \right) \cdot \left(\frac{1}{2} \div \frac{1}{2} \right) \qquad \text{(d)}$$

$$= \left(\frac{3}{2} + \frac{5}{4} \right) \cdot \frac{1}{1} \qquad \text{(e)}$$

$$= \frac{3}{2} + \frac{5}{4} \qquad \text{(f)}$$

$$= \frac{3 \cdot 2}{2 \cdot 2} + \frac{5}{4} \qquad \text{(g)}$$

$$= \frac{6}{4} + \frac{5}{4} \qquad \text{(h)}$$

$$= \frac{6 + 5}{4} \tag{i}$$

$$= \frac{11}{4} \tag{j}$$

5. Similarity of Integers and Rational Numbers

Throughout the development thus far, we have consistently made a requirement that results of operations from integer arithmetic carryover to those of rational arithmetic. By making this requirement, we have found that the properties which hold in the two systems parallel each other *very* closely. In addition to this, we have established that the rational number system has two useful properties which do not exist in either the system of cardinals or in the system of integers. They are that

(1) if the divisor is non-zero, the set of rational numbers is closed with respect to division, and

(2) in the system of rationals each non-zero element possesses a multiplicative inverse.

Further, note that the set of integers is equivalent to the set of rational numbers which have denominator *one*.

$$I = \left\{ \ldots, {}^-n, \ldots, {}^-4, {}^-3, {}^-2, {}^-1, 0, 1, 2, 3, 4, \ldots, k, \ldots \right\}$$

$$R_1 = \left\{ \ldots, \frac{{}^-n}{1}, \ldots, \frac{{}^-4}{1}, \frac{{}^-3}{1}, \frac{{}^-2}{1}, \frac{{}^-1}{1}, \frac{0}{1}, \frac{1}{1}, \frac{2}{1}, \frac{3}{1}, \frac{4}{1}, \ldots, \frac{k}{1}, \ldots \right\}$$

Thus we have successfully constructed an arithmetic for rational numbers in such a way that if we select the correspondences

Integers		*Rationals*
a	$\longleftrightarrow$	$\dfrac{a}{1}$
b	$\longleftrightarrow$	$\dfrac{b}{1}$

then we obtain the correspondences

$a + b$	$\longleftrightarrow$	$\dfrac{a}{1} + \dfrac{b}{1} = \dfrac{a + b}{1}$
ab	$\longleftrightarrow$	$\dfrac{a}{1} \cdot \dfrac{b}{1} = \dfrac{a \cdot b}{1}.$

As in Section 11-3, we have two mathematical systems which exhibit three very important characteristics:

(1) a one-to-one onto mapping exists between the integers and the rationals with denominator one,

(2) sums of integers correspond to sums of rationals having denominator one, and

(3) products of integers correspond to products of rationals having denominator one.

As in the case of cardinals and non-negative integers we may say that the system of integers is *isomorphic* to the system of rationals with denominator one.

The existence of this isomorphism means that the systems of integers and rational numbers are similarly structured and that any integer problem which can be stated in terms of addition or multiplication can, in essence, be solved by using rational numbers which have a denominator of one. Since the system of rationals has the additional advantages listed above, we can use the system of rationals for problem solving and no disadvantages in computation will arise. Hence we are now free to use our newly constructed system which is more general in nature and therefore much less restrictive.

As a final item to be mentioned which is related to the concept of isomorphism, let us reconsider the meaning associated with the numeral $\frac{a}{b}$. Some of us are used to interpreting $\frac{a}{b}$ not simply as rational $\frac{a}{b}$, but as "a divided by b." As you will note, we have thus far been very careful not to interpret the *bar* between the integers a and b as a symbol for division. However, there is definitely a case for such an interpretation as we shall now show. To do this, we consider the rational number $\frac{4}{5}$.

$$\frac{4}{5} = \frac{4 \cdot 1}{1 \cdot 5}$$

$$= \frac{4}{1} \cdot \frac{1}{5}$$

$$= \frac{4}{1} \div \frac{5}{1}$$

$$= 4 \div 5$$

This latter statement can be made because we have previously agreed that we could write a for the rational number $\frac{a}{1}$. The reason for this agreement in the first place was because of the isomorphism between the integers and the subset of rationals expressible with denominator one. Using this interpretation, it is indeed reasonable to say "four divided by five" for $\frac{4}{5}$. We shall free to use this interpretation from this point onward wherever it happens to be convenient to do so.

EXERCISE SET 15-5

1. Under what conditions are differences of integers isomorphic to differences of rational numbers?

2. For each of the following determine the sum of the number and its reciprocal (multiplicative inverse).

(a) $\dfrac{2}{1} + \dfrac{1}{2}$ (c) $\dfrac{4}{1} + \dfrac{1}{4}$

(b) $\dfrac{3}{1} + \dfrac{1}{3}$ (d) $\dfrac{5}{1} + \dfrac{1}{5}$

(e) $\dfrac{n}{1} + \dfrac{1}{n}$ where n is a non-zero integer

(f) Do any of the sums of part (e) have a counterpart in the system of integers?

3. If two mathematical systems are formed using sets A and B and it is known that (1) $A \sim \overline{B} \subset B$ and (2) system A is isomorphic to system $\overline{B}$, we say that system A is embedded in system B.

(a) Give two examples of such systems in arithmetic.
(b) Draw Venn diagrams to illustrate your choices in part (a).
(c) Can you find a third different example of two systems such that one is embedded in the other?

Chapter summary

By imposing the requirement that products of rationals correspond to products of integers, insofar as possible, a workable definition for multiplication of rationals was developed. Using this definition we were able to establish all of the properties previously established for the system of integers. In addition to these properties we observed that for each non-zero rational number there is a rational number called the *multiplicative inverse* such that the product of the two is the multiplicative identity.

Once the discussion of multiplication properties was completed, we used divisibility of integers to help define division of rationals. Later, when the results of division for rationals were scrutinized, we were able to show that the multiplicative inverse can be used to express division problems in terms of equivalent multiplication problems. Thus we were able to conclude that even though division is not an operation on the set of rationals, the set of rationals is closed under division by non-zero divisors.

By making the restrictions concerning the correspondence between integers and rationals having denominator one, and observing the resulting correspondences of sums to sums and products to products, we have once more established an isomorphism between number systems. That is, the system of integers is similar in structure to the system of rationals expressible with denominator one. Because of this we may say intuitively that the integers are a subset of the set of rationals. Further, on the basis of this isomorphism we are able to give some justification for the interpretation of the "bar" in $\dfrac{a}{b}$ as representing division.

CHAPTER 16 The order relation and absolute value

---

1. Definition of Order for Rationals

In Chapter Seven we gave a definition of what constitutes an order relation on a set and in particular we were able to show that the set of cardinal numbers is ordered under the relation "is less than." In Chapter 12 we found that it was possible to adapt the order relation for cardinal numbers to the system of integers. This extension was accomplished in such a way that the essential features of order for cardinals were retained. Since the relation $<$ as defined for cardinal numbers gives rise to the corresponding order relation for integers, let us try a similar approach for defining an order relation on the set of rational numbers. This approach appears especially promising in view of the fact that the integers are isomorphic to the rationals which have denominator one. Therefore, let us try the following as a tentative definition of order for rational numbers.

Definition 16-1: If $\dfrac{a}{b}$ and $\dfrac{c}{d}$ are rational numbers, then $\dfrac{a}{b}$ **"is less than"** $\dfrac{c}{d}$ if and only if $\dfrac{c}{d} - \dfrac{a}{b}$ is a positive rational number. Symbolically this is denoted by $\dfrac{a}{b} < \dfrac{c}{d}$.

Examples: (a) $\dfrac{2}{3} < \dfrac{3}{4}$ since $\dfrac{3}{4} - \dfrac{2}{3} = \dfrac{9-8}{12} = \dfrac{1}{12}$.

(b) $\dfrac{^{-}1}{5} < \dfrac{0}{1}$ since $\dfrac{0}{1} - \dfrac{^{-}1}{5} = \dfrac{0-^{-}1}{5} = \dfrac{1}{5}$.

(c) $\dfrac{^{-}7}{8} < \dfrac{^{-}2}{3}$ since $\dfrac{^{-}2}{3} - \dfrac{^{-}7}{8} = \dfrac{^{-}16-^{-}21}{24} = \dfrac{5}{24}$.

In each of the three examples above, one may observe that the difference which was calculated in a positive rational number. The examples used also make sense

304

intuitively if one considers the points of a number line which are associated with them and recalls the corresponding results which were obtained for integers. There, we found that the smaller of two integers was to the left of the larger on the number line. Figure 16-1 illustrates the corresponding results for the examples from the rational number system just discussed.

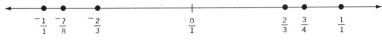

FIGURE 16-1

In each case we observe that the smaller of the pair is located to the left of the larger of the pair. However it must again be noted that at this stage only an "intuitive" discussion has been given. The only way to show that number line diagrams such as that of Figure 16-1 can legitimately be used is to establish as fact that the relation $<$, as defined in Definition 16-1, is an order relation on the set of rational numbers. It is a relatively easy matter to show that the relation $<$ does not have the reflexive and symmetric properties, hence we shall leave this to the student. That the relation has the transitive property is somewhat more involved.

Theorem 16-1: The relation $<$ is a transitive relation.

Proof: We need to establish that if $\frac{a}{b}$, $\frac{c}{d}$, and $\frac{e}{f}$ are any three rational numbers and if $\frac{a}{b} < \frac{c}{d}$ and $\frac{c}{d} < \frac{e}{f}$, then $\frac{a}{b} < \frac{e}{f}$. From

$$\begin{bmatrix} \frac{a}{b} < \frac{c}{d} \\[2mm] \text{and} \\[2mm] \frac{c}{d} < \frac{e}{f} \end{bmatrix} \quad \text{we have by Definition 16-1 that} \quad \begin{bmatrix} \frac{c}{d} - \frac{a}{b} = \frac{m}{n} \\[2mm] \text{and} \\[2mm] \frac{e}{f} - \frac{c}{d} = \frac{p}{q} \end{bmatrix}$$

where $\frac{m}{n}$ and $\frac{p}{q}$ are positive rationals. Then since $\frac{c}{d} - \frac{a}{b} = \frac{m}{n}$, $\frac{c}{d} = \frac{a}{b} + \frac{m}{n}$ by the inverse definition of subtraction. Using this fact we have that

$$\frac{e}{f} - \left(\frac{a}{b} + \frac{m}{n} \right) = \frac{p}{q} \qquad\qquad \text{Prin. Subst., Thm. 14-14}$$

$$\frac{e}{f} + {}^{-}\!\left(\frac{a}{b} + \frac{m}{n} \right) = \frac{p}{q} \qquad\qquad \text{Thm. 14-16}$$

$$\frac{e}{f} + \left(\frac{{}^{-}a}{b} + \frac{{}^{-}m}{n} \right) = \frac{p}{q} \qquad\qquad \text{Thm. 15-10}$$

$$\left(\frac{e}{f} + \frac{{}^{-}a}{b} \right) + \frac{{}^{-}m}{n} = \frac{p}{q} \qquad\qquad \text{Thm. 14-4}$$

$$\frac{e}{f} + \frac{^-a}{b} = \frac{p}{q} + \frac{m}{n} \qquad \text{Def. 14-3}$$

$$\frac{e}{f} - \frac{a}{b} = \frac{p}{q} + \frac{m}{n} \qquad \text{Thm. 14-16}$$

Since $\frac{p}{q} + \frac{m}{n}$ is positive, we have by Definition 16-1 that $\frac{a}{b} < \frac{e}{f}$ as desired. Thus the relation $<$ has the transitive property. ∎

Taking into account the facts that the relation $<$ has neither the reflexive nor symmetric properties and the result of Theorem 16-1, the relation $<$ as defined in Definition 16-1 is established as an order relation on the set of rational numbers. Because of this, the use of number line interpretations such as that in Figure 16-1 is justified.

The relation "is greater than" can be defined much as it was in the systems of cardinal numbers and integers. It is just as useful as the relation $<$, but the latter is often used simply as a matter of convenience and by mutual agreement.

Definition 16-2: If $\frac{a}{b}$ and $\frac{c}{d}$ are rational numbers, then $\frac{a}{b}$ **"is greater than"** $\frac{c}{d}$ if and only if $\frac{c}{d}$ "is less than" $\frac{a}{b}$. Symbolically, "$\frac{a}{b}$ is greater than $\frac{c}{d}$" is denoted by $\frac{a}{b} > \frac{c}{d}$.

To observe how Definition 16-2 can be used consider the following example.

Example: Show that $\frac{^-1}{2} > \frac{^-5}{3}$.

Solution: By Definition 16-2, $\frac{^-1}{2} > \frac{^-5}{3}$ if and only if $\frac{^-5}{3} < \frac{^-1}{2}$. The latter can be checked by using Definition 16-1.

$$\frac{^-5}{3} < \frac{^-1}{2} \quad \text{since} \quad \frac{^-1}{2} - \frac{^-5}{3} = \frac{^-3 - ^-10}{6} = \frac{7}{6} \text{ which is positive.}$$

Therefore, $\frac{^-5}{3} < \frac{^-1}{2}$ and so by Definition 16-2 we obtain $\frac{^-1}{2} > \frac{^-5}{3}$ as desired.

As most of us are aware there are certain variations in the manufacture of most products. That is, there are certain acceptable tolerances for these articles. These tolerances may be given to people in charge of quality control in terms of inequalities. For example if the optimum thickness of a steel plate is to be $\frac{5}{8}$ of an inch and the maximum allowable error is $\frac{1}{32}$ of an inch then the thickness may vary between $\frac{5}{8} + \frac{1}{32} = \frac{21}{32}$ inches and $\frac{5}{8} - \frac{1}{32} = \frac{19}{32}$ inches. For those in qual-

ity control these tolerances might be expressed as $\frac{19}{32} \leqslant x \leqslant \frac{21}{32}$ where x repre-

sents the thickness of the plate. The equality indicated in $\leqslant$ indicates that $\frac{19}{32}$ is

the minimum and $\frac{21}{32}$ is the maximum acceptable thickness. These values and all

others between would be acceptable.

Such inequalities are also desirable in theoretical investigations in mathematics and are in fact often used there. Because of these needs, we shall now define the relations $\leqslant$ and $\geqslant$ for rational numbers.

Definition 16-3: If $\frac{a}{b}$ and $\frac{c}{d}$ are rational numbers, then $\frac{a}{b}$ "**is less than or equal to**"

$\frac{c}{d}$ if and only if $\frac{a}{b} < \frac{c}{d}$ or $\frac{a}{b} = \frac{c}{d}$. Symbolically this is denoted $\frac{a}{b} \leqslant \frac{c}{d}$.

This definition states then that "or $\frac{a}{b} = \frac{c}{d}$" is required in order to include the maximum allowable error in the case of the steel plate above. If we refer to Definition 16-1 and compare it with Definition 16-3, we observe that in the lat-

ter definition $\frac{c}{d} - \frac{a}{b}$ may be either a positive rational number or zero. Because of this fact, an alternate definition for $\leqslant$ may be given.

Definition 16-3a: If $\frac{a}{b}$ and $\frac{c}{d}$ are rational numbers, then $\frac{a}{b}$ "**is less than or equal**

to" $\frac{c}{d}$ if and only if $\frac{c}{d} - \frac{a}{b}$ is a non-negative rational number.

As with $<$ and $>$, we may define the relation $\geqslant$ as follows.

Definition 16-4: If $\frac{a}{b}$ and $\frac{c}{d}$ are rational numbers, then $\frac{a}{b}$ "**is greater than or equal**

to" $\frac{c}{d}$ if and only if $\frac{c}{d}$ "is less than or equal to" $\frac{a}{b}$. Symbolically this is denoted

$\frac{a}{b} \geqslant \frac{c}{d}$.

EXERCISE SET 16-1

1. Use definitions 16-1 and 16-2 to decide the truth or falsity of each of the following inequalities.

(a) $\frac{2}{5} < \frac{4}{7}$ (e) $\frac{^-2}{7} > \frac{1}{3}$

(b) $\frac{^-3}{7} < \frac{^-2}{5}$ (f) $\frac{5}{6} < \frac{6}{5}$

(c) $\dfrac{^-4}{3} > \dfrac{^-3}{4}$

(g) $\dfrac{4}{3} > \dfrac{^-5}{4}$

(d) $\dfrac{3}{7} < \dfrac{^-1}{6}$

(h) $\dfrac{1}{2} > \dfrac{4}{8}$

2. (a) Show that $\dfrac{7}{16} > \dfrac{3}{7}$ and calculate $\dfrac{7}{16} - \dfrac{3}{7}$.

   (b) Show that $\dfrac{^-2}{3} > \dfrac{^-5}{4}$ and calculate $\dfrac{^-2}{3} - \dfrac{^-5}{4}$.

   (c) Show that $\dfrac{4}{5} > \dfrac{^-3}{8}$ and calculate $\dfrac{4}{5} - \dfrac{^-3}{8}$.

   (d) On the basis of parts (a), (b), and (c) try to formulate a definition for $>$ in terms of subtraction.

   (e) Does your definition formulated in part (d) state the same thing as Definition 16-2?

3. Use Definitions 16-3 and 16-4 to determine which of the following inequalities are true statements.

   (a) $\dfrac{3}{7} < \dfrac{4}{8}$

   (e) $\dfrac{1}{3} > \dfrac{2}{6}$

   (i) $\dfrac{^-4}{5} \leqslant \dfrac{^-3}{4}$

   (b) $\dfrac{5}{9} \leqslant \dfrac{6}{10}$

   (f) $\dfrac{3}{32} \geqslant \dfrac{5}{64}$

   (j) $\dfrac{^-6}{7} \geqslant \dfrac{^-5}{6}$

   (c) $\dfrac{5}{8} \leqslant \dfrac{11}{18}$

   (g) $\dfrac{^-7}{8} \leqslant \dfrac{3}{7}$

   (k) $\dfrac{^-7}{16} \geqslant \dfrac{^-5}{9}$

   (d) $\dfrac{5}{7} \geqslant \dfrac{3}{4}$

   (h) $\dfrac{^-3}{4} \leqslant \dfrac{^-2}{3}$

   (l) $\dfrac{^-4}{3} \geqslant \dfrac{^-5}{2}$

4. If there is a rational number $\dfrac{x}{y}$ such that $\dfrac{x}{y} \geqslant \dfrac{0}{1}$ and $\dfrac{x}{y} \leqslant \dfrac{0}{1}$, what is this rational number?

5. (a) Show by comparison of appropriate definitions that if $\dfrac{2}{3} < \dfrac{4}{5}$, then $\dfrac{2}{3} \leqslant \dfrac{4}{5}$.

   (b) As in part (a), show that if $\dfrac{6}{5} > \dfrac{3}{4}$, then $\dfrac{6}{5} \geqslant \dfrac{3}{4}$.

   (c) Generalize the results of parts (a) and (b).

6. For each of the following, decide whether the statement is *true* or *false,* and give a numerical example to support your answer.

   (a) If $\dfrac{a}{b} < \dfrac{c}{d}$, then $\dfrac{a}{b} \leqslant \dfrac{c}{d}$.

   (b) If $\dfrac{a}{b} > \dfrac{c}{d}$, then $\dfrac{a}{b} \geqslant \dfrac{c}{d}$.

   (c) If $\dfrac{a}{b} \leqslant \dfrac{c}{d}$, then $\dfrac{a}{b} < \dfrac{c}{d}$.

   (d) If $\dfrac{a}{b} \geqslant \dfrac{c}{d}$, then $\dfrac{a}{b} > \dfrac{c}{d}$.

(e) If $\dfrac{a}{b} \leqslant \dfrac{c}{d}$, then $\dfrac{c}{d} \geqslant \dfrac{a}{b}$.

(f) If $\dfrac{a}{b} \geqslant \dfrac{c}{d}$, then $\dfrac{c}{d} \leqslant \dfrac{a}{b}$.

7. By use of the isomorphism between the integers and rational numbers with denominator one, show how the relations $<, >, \leqslant, \geqslant$ for rational numbers give rise to the corresponding definitions of these relations on the set of integers.

2. Properties of Order

We have mentioned in Section 16-1 that some order relations are useful in solving physical problems as well as theoretical ones. To utilize these relations effectively, some of their properties must be known and readily available. In this section we shall state and prove some of those properties which will be of interest to us.

To begin with, we have noted that if given two different rational numbers, a number line can be used to determine which is the smaller. However, the only way this can be done is to use the definition of the order relation and in so doing we find that the number line is no longer needed. In order to avoid this problem let us try to construct tests for order which will make such comparisons a relatively easy matter.

Example: Determine the condition for which $\dfrac{2}{3} < \dfrac{4}{5}$.

Solution: $\dfrac{2}{3} < \dfrac{4}{5}$ provided that $\dfrac{4}{5} - \dfrac{2}{3}$ is positive by Definition 16-1. Now

$$\frac{4}{5} - \frac{2}{3} = \frac{4 \cdot 3}{5 \cdot 3} - \frac{2 \cdot 5}{3 \cdot 5}$$

$$= \frac{4 \cdot 3}{5 \cdot 3} - \frac{2 \cdot 5}{5 \cdot 3}.$$

Since the denominators are the same, we need only consider the difference of the numerators, $4 \cdot 3 - 2 \cdot 5$. Because of the fact that $4 \cdot 3 - 2 \cdot 5 = 2$ and 2 is positive, we have by Definition 12-4 that $2 \cdot 5 < 4 \cdot 3$. The fact that the products $2 \cdot 5$ and $4 \cdot 3$ appear is a direct result of determining a common denominator so that numerators alone could be considered. Even though it might appear that "cross" products were formed, this is simply a by-product of the method of comparison of the numerators.

If the result of the above example is generalized, the following theorem is obtained.

Theorem 16-2: If $\frac{a}{b}$ and $\frac{c}{d}$ are rational numbers, then $\frac{a}{b} < \frac{c}{d}$ if and only if $ad < bc$.

Proof: The method of proof is much like the method used in the preceding example. From Definition 16-1, it is known that $\frac{a}{b} < \frac{c}{d}$ if and only if $\frac{c}{d} - \frac{a}{b}$ is a positive rational number. We must therefore prove that (1) if $\frac{c}{d} - \frac{a}{b}$ is a positive rational number then $ad < bc$ and (2) if $ad < bc$, $b \neq 0$, $d \neq 0$, then $\frac{c}{d} - \frac{a}{b}$ is a positive rational number.

(1) Since $\frac{c}{d} - \frac{a}{b}$ is positive, suppose that

$$\frac{c}{d} - \frac{a}{b} = \frac{m}{n} \quad \text{where} \quad \frac{m}{n} \text{ is positive.}$$

Since $\frac{c}{d} - \frac{a}{b} = \frac{cb - da}{db} = \frac{bc - ad}{db}$, and since we have agreed previously that denominators are to be positive, we must conclude that the numerator $bc - ad$ is positive. However, if $bc - ad$ is positive, we obtain the fact that $ad < bc$ by Definition 12-4. Therefore, if $\frac{c}{d} - \frac{a}{b}$ is a positive rational number, then $ad < bc$.

(2) Next, we suppose that $ad < bc$. If this is the case, then $bc - ad$ is positive, say $bc - ad = m$. If $n = bd$ is a positive integer, then the rational number

$$\frac{bc - ad}{bd} = \frac{m}{n}$$

is positive. Consequently, since $\frac{cb - da}{db} = \frac{bc - ad}{bd}$,

$$\frac{cb - da}{db} = \frac{m}{n}$$

is a positive rational number and so is $\frac{c}{d} - \frac{a}{b}$. By Definition 16-1, we obtain the result that $\frac{a}{b} < \frac{c}{d}$. ∎

In a similar fashion, one may establish the following result which concerns the relation $>$.

Theorem 16-3: If $\frac{a}{b}$ and $\frac{c}{d}$ are rational numbers, then $\frac{a}{b} > \frac{c}{d}$ if and only if $ad > bc$.

Proof: Left as an exercise.

Example: Show that $\frac{^-3}{4} > \frac{^-5}{2}$.

Solution: Using Theorem 16-3, we note that $^-3 \cdot 2 = {}^-6$ and $4 \cdot {}^-5 = {}^-20$ since $^-6 > {}^-20, {}^-3 \cdot 2 > 4 \cdot {}^-5$. Therefore $\frac{^-3}{4} > \frac{^-5}{2}$.

The results of Theorems 16-2, 16-3, and the definition of equality may be collected and used as a handy reference for testing order as follows.

Order Tests for Rational Numbers: If $\frac{a}{b}$ and $\frac{c}{d}$ are rational numbers, then

$$(1) \quad \frac{a}{b} < \frac{c}{d} \quad \text{iff} \quad ad < bc$$

$$(2) \quad \frac{a}{b} = \frac{c}{d} \quad \text{iff} \quad ad = bc$$

$$(3) \quad \frac{a}{b} > \frac{c}{d} \quad \text{iff} \quad ad > bc$$

It should be noted that given any two rational numbers, they exhibit one and only one of the relations. This fact can be established by considering the difference of the two. Consider two rationals $\frac{a}{b}$ and $\frac{c}{d}$ and let

$$\frac{a}{b} - \frac{c}{d} = \frac{e}{f}$$

Since there are just three types of rational numbers, $\frac{e}{f}$ is either zero, positive, or negative. If $\frac{e}{f} = \frac{0}{1}$, then $\frac{a}{b}$ and $\frac{c}{d}$ are additive inverses so that $\frac{a}{b} = \frac{c}{d}$ as in case (2) above. If $\frac{e}{f}$ is positive, then by Definition 16-1 $\frac{c}{d} < \frac{a}{b}$ or equivalently, $\frac{a}{b} > \frac{c}{d}$ as in case (3) by Definition 16-2. If $\frac{a}{b} - \frac{c}{d}$ is negative, then $\frac{^-1}{1} \cdot \left(\frac{a}{b} - \frac{c}{d} \right) = \frac{c}{d} - \frac{a}{b}$ is positive so that $\frac{a}{b} < \frac{c}{d}$ by Definition 16-1 and we obtain case (1). These are the only possibilities and these are usually stated as the Trichotomy Property for rational numbers.

Trichotomy Property: If $\frac{a}{b}$ and $\frac{c}{d}$ are rational numbers, then one and only one of the following holds:

$$(1) \quad \frac{a}{b} < \frac{c}{d}$$

$$(2) \ \frac{a}{b} = \frac{c}{d}, \text{ or}$$

$$(3) \ \frac{a}{b} > \frac{c}{d}$$

It is of more than just passing interest to observe that between any two different rational numbers one may always determine a third rational number which is unequal to either of the original ones.

Examples: (a) A rational number between $\frac{5}{6}$ and $\frac{7}{8}$ can be determined as follows: $\frac{5}{6} = \frac{40}{48}$ and $\frac{7}{8} = \frac{42}{48}$ so that

$$\frac{40}{48} < \frac{41}{48} < \frac{42}{48}$$

That is,

$$\frac{5}{6} < \frac{41}{48} < \frac{7}{8}$$

(b) A rational number between $\frac{^-3}{4}$ and $\frac{^-13}{32}$ can be determined as follows:

$$\frac{^-3}{4} = \frac{^-24}{32} \text{ so that } \frac{^-24}{32} < \frac{^-17}{32} < \frac{^-13}{32} \text{ or } \frac{^-3}{4} < \frac{^-17}{32} < \frac{^-13}{32}.$$

In this example any numerator n could have been chosen for which $^-24 < n < ^-13$. This method, commonly referred to as the common denominator method, is a nice systematic method which would have considerable appeal to the beginning student. One drawback which might occur however is that the K-Theorem may have to be used to select other numerals so that there is enough difference between numerators to enable one to select a third rational.

Because of the complication which may result by use of the above method we shall consider a second systematic method which is based on the idea of averaging. For this method, all that need be done is to add the given rationals and then multiply the sum by one-half.

Example: Determine a rational number between $\frac{3}{7}$ and $\frac{5}{8}$.

Solution: Adding, we obtain

$$\frac{3}{7} + \frac{5}{8} = \frac{24 + 35}{56} = \frac{59}{56}$$

Then supposedly $\frac{1}{2} \cdot \frac{59}{56}$ is between the original two. That is $\frac{3}{7} < \frac{59}{112} < \frac{5}{8}$ is sup-

posed to be a true statement. This can easily be verified by use of the order test.
$\frac{3}{7} < \frac{59}{112}$ since $3 \cdot 112 < 7 \cdot 59$ and $\frac{59}{112} < \frac{5}{8}$ since $59 \cdot 8 < 112 \cdot 5$. If this
technique is generalized, it culminates in the following theorem.

Theorem 16-4: Between any two distinct rational numbers there is another rational number.

Proof: Let $\frac{a}{b} \neq \frac{c}{d}$ and suppose that $\frac{a}{b} < \frac{c}{d}$. Our claim is that $\frac{ad + bc}{2bd}$ is larger than

$\frac{a}{b}$ but smaller than $\frac{c}{d}$. That is, we contend that

$$\frac{a}{b} < \frac{ad + bc}{2bd} < \frac{c}{d}$$

(1) We shall first establish that $\frac{a}{b} < \frac{ad + bc}{2bd}$. To do this requires that we show

that $\frac{ad + bc}{2bd} - \frac{a}{b}$ is a positive rational number. This can be done as follows:

$$\frac{ad + bc}{2bd} - \frac{a}{b} = \frac{ad + bc}{2bd} + \frac{^-a}{b} \qquad \text{Thm. 14-16}$$

$$= \frac{ad + bc}{2bd} + \frac{^-2ad}{2bd} \qquad \text{K-Thm.}$$

$$= \frac{(ad + bc) + {}^-2ad}{2bd} \qquad \text{Def. 14-1}$$

$$= \frac{(bc + ad) + {}^-2ad}{2bd} \qquad \text{Thm. 10-2}$$

$$= \frac{bc + (ad + {}^-2ad)}{2bd} \qquad \text{Thm. 10-3}$$

$$= \frac{bc + {}^-ad}{2bd} \qquad \text{Def. 10-1}$$

$$= \frac{bc - ad}{2bd} \qquad \text{Thm. 10-15}$$

$$= \frac{bc}{2bd} - \frac{ad}{2bd} \qquad \text{Def. 14-2}$$

$$= \frac{c}{2d} - \frac{a}{2b} \qquad \text{K-Thm.}$$

$$= \frac{1}{2} \cdot \left(\frac{c}{d} - \frac{a}{b} \right) \qquad \begin{array}{l} \text{Thm. 11-5} \\ \text{Distr.} \cdot / - \text{(integers).} \end{array}$$

But by assumption, $\frac{a}{b} < \frac{c}{d}$ so that $\frac{c}{d} - \frac{a}{b}$ is positive and consequently so is

$\frac{1}{2}\left(\frac{c}{d} - \frac{a}{b}\right)$. Thus by Definition 16-1, $\frac{a}{b} < \frac{ad + bc}{2bd}$.

(2) The argument for showing that $\frac{ad + bc}{2bd} < \frac{c}{d}$ is much like that used in part (1). For this reason, we leave this part of the proof for the student to complete.

Once the proofs of parts (1) and (2) are complete, we may conclude that $\frac{a}{b} < \frac{ad + bc}{2bd} < \frac{c}{d}$ as claimed. ∎

Theorem 16-4 establishes a result which does not hold in either the systems of integers or cardinal numbers. For instance there is no integer between $^+3$ and $^+4$ and no cardinal number between 1 and 2. This result is of considerable importance and is usually described as follows.

Definition 16-5: If between every two distinct elements of a set there is another element of the set, the set is said to be **dense.**

Thus according to Theorem 16-4, the set of rational numbers is a dense set. It may also be noted that neither the set of cardinal numbers nor the set of integers is dense. The student will find further consideration of dense sets in Exercise Set 16-2 and later in Chapter 18 when real numbers and decimal approximations are discussed.

Some other interesting properties of the order relation $<$ are those which parallel Theorems 12-5, 12-6, and 12-7.

Example: Determine the solution set for the number sentence

$$\frac{x}{y} + \frac{^-3}{5} < \frac{4}{3} \ .$$

Solution: If it is legitimate to add the same rational number to both sides of an inequality, then we would have

$$\left(\frac{x}{y} + \frac{^-3}{5}\right) + \frac{3}{5} < \frac{4}{3} + \frac{3}{5}$$

$$\frac{x}{y} + \left(\frac{^-3}{5} + \frac{3}{5}\right) < \frac{4}{3} + \frac{3}{5}$$

$$\frac{x}{y} + \frac{0}{1} < \frac{4}{3} + \frac{3}{5}$$

$$\frac{x}{y} < \frac{4}{3} + \frac{3}{5}$$

$$\frac{x}{y} < \frac{4 \cdot 5 + 3 \cdot 3}{3 \cdot 5}$$

$$\frac{x}{y} < \frac{29}{15}$$

Hence the solution set would be denoted $\left\{ \dfrac{x}{y} \;\middle|\; \dfrac{x}{y} < \dfrac{29}{15} \right\}$.

That the same rational number can be added to both sides of an inequality without changing the sense of the inequality is the purpose of Theorem 16-5 below. The proof of the theorem is so similar to that of Theorem 12-5 that we shall omit it.

Theorem 16-5: If $\dfrac{a}{b}, \dfrac{c}{d}$, and $\dfrac{e}{f}$ are rational numbers and $\dfrac{a}{b} < \dfrac{c}{d}$, then $\dfrac{a}{b} + \dfrac{e}{f} < \dfrac{c}{d} + \dfrac{e}{f}$.

Proof: Left as an exercise.

Corresponding to Theorem 12-6 is Theorem 16-6 below. This theorem states that if $\dfrac{a}{b} < \dfrac{c}{d}$ then both sides may be multiplied by the same positive rational number and the resulting inequality holds with the sense of the inequality unchanged. Do not expect to obtain the same inequality by these methods however. Even though the results remind one of the converse of a cancellation property, equality does not hold. In fact, even for equality, the resulting statement is not equal to the original but rather is an equivalent statement of equality. The same remark may be made regarding inequalities such as we are discussing here.

Theorem 16-6: If $\dfrac{a}{b}, \dfrac{c}{d}$, and $\dfrac{e}{f}$ are rational numbers with $\dfrac{a}{b} < \dfrac{c}{d}$ and $\dfrac{e}{f} > \dfrac{0}{1}$, then $\dfrac{a}{b} \cdot \dfrac{e}{f} < \dfrac{c}{d} \cdot \dfrac{e}{f}$.

Proof: Since $\dfrac{a}{b} < \dfrac{c}{d}, \dfrac{c}{d} - \dfrac{a}{b} = \dfrac{m}{n}$ where $\dfrac{m}{n}$ is a positive rational number. Because of the facts that $\dfrac{e}{f}$ is positive and the product of positive rationals is positive, we have that

$$\left(\dfrac{c}{d} - \dfrac{a}{b} \right) \cdot \dfrac{e}{f} = \dfrac{m}{n} \cdot \dfrac{e}{f}$$

is positive. That is,

$$\left(\dfrac{c}{d} \cdot \dfrac{e}{f} \right) - \left(\dfrac{a}{b} \cdot \dfrac{e}{f} \right)$$

is a positive rational number. By use of Definition 16-1, we obtain as a consequence that $\dfrac{a}{b} \cdot \dfrac{e}{f} < \dfrac{c}{d} \cdot \dfrac{e}{f}$. This completes the proof. ∎

It was noted following Theorem 12-6 that the converse of that theorem was really the more useful for problem solving, but it was not discussed there. The reason for this is that the converse could intuitively be thought of in terms of divisibility and we could not guarantee that divisibility would always work. For example the inequality $3x < 5$ cannot be solved in the system of integers through use of the concept of divisibility even though the inequality $2x < 8$ does have a solution in integers which can be determined by this means. However, if the isomorphism between the integers and rationals is used, these two problems and others similar to them are always solvable in the system of rational numbers. By waiting until the isomorphism is available, it is possible to avoid obtaining only partial solutions, but at the same time one can use the isomorphism to obtain the result of Theorem 12-6 in integers. To illustrate this consider the following example.

Example: Determine the solution of $\frac{2}{1} \cdot \frac{x}{y} < \frac{4}{1}$.

Solution: According to Theorem 16-6, we have

$$\frac{1}{2}\left(\frac{2}{1} \cdot \frac{x}{y}\right) < \frac{1}{2} \cdot \frac{4}{1}$$

$$\left(\frac{1}{2} \cdot \frac{2}{1}\right) \cdot \frac{x}{y} < \frac{4}{2}$$

$$\frac{1}{1} \cdot \frac{x}{y} < \frac{2}{1}$$

$$\frac{x}{y} < \frac{2}{1}$$

Corresponding to this in the system of integers we have the inequality $2n < 4$ so that apparently $n < 2$. It should be noted that although the solution sets are not identical, there is still a correspondence between the given inequalities and their solution sets even though in the steps involved in the solution the correspondence breaks down. That is, there is no integer corresponding to $\frac{1}{2}$.

In Theorem 12-7 we claimed that if one multiplies both sides of an inequality by the same negative integer, the sense of the inequality is reversed in the resulting inequality. We shall now make the same claim for inequalities which involve rational numbers except that now we shall establish its validity.

Theorem 16-7: If $\frac{a}{b}, \frac{c}{d}$, and $\frac{e}{f}$ are rational numbers with $\frac{a}{b} < \frac{c}{d}$ and $\frac{e}{f} < \frac{0}{1}$, then $\frac{a}{b} \cdot \frac{e}{f} > \frac{c}{d} \cdot \frac{e}{f}$.

Proof: Since $\frac{a}{b}<\frac{c}{d}$, suppose that $\frac{c}{d}-\frac{a}{b}=\frac{m}{n}$ where $\frac{m}{n}$ is positive. Further, since

$\frac{e}{f}<\frac{0}{1},\frac{^-e}{f}>\frac{0}{1}$. Therefore both right- and left-hand expressions in

$$\left(\frac{c}{d}-\frac{a}{b}\right)\cdot\frac{^-e}{f}=\frac{m}{n}\cdot\frac{^-e}{f}$$

are positive so that

$$\left(\frac{c}{d}+\frac{^-a}{b}\right)\cdot\frac{^-e}{f}=\frac{c}{d}\cdot\frac{^-e}{f}+\frac{^-a}{b}\cdot\frac{^-e}{f}$$

$$=\frac{^-ce}{df}+\frac{ae}{bf}$$

$$=\frac{ae}{bf}-\frac{ce}{df}$$

$$=\frac{a}{b}\cdot\frac{e}{f}+\frac{c}{d}\cdot\frac{e}{f}$$

is positive. Consequently by Definition 16-1, $\frac{c}{d}\cdot\frac{e}{f}<\frac{a}{b}\cdot\frac{e}{f}$. By using Definition

16–2, we have $\frac{a}{b}\cdot\frac{e}{f}>\frac{c}{d}\cdot\frac{e}{f}.$ ∎

Example: Determine the solution set for the inequality $\frac{^-2}{3}\cdot\frac{x}{y}<\frac{5}{6}$.

Solution: According to Theorem 16-7 and commutativity we may multiply both sides of the inequality by $\frac{^-3}{2}$ and reverse the sense of the inequality to obtain

$$\frac{^-3}{2}\cdot\left(\frac{^-2}{3}\cdot\frac{x}{y}\right)>\frac{^-3}{2}\cdot\frac{5}{6}$$

$$\left(\frac{^-3}{2}\cdot\frac{^-2}{3}\right)\cdot\frac{x}{y}>\frac{^-3}{2}\cdot\frac{5}{6}$$

$$\frac{1}{1}\cdot\frac{x}{y}>\frac{^-3}{2}\cdot\frac{5}{6}$$

$$\frac{x}{y}>\frac{^-3}{2}\cdot\frac{5}{6}$$

$$\frac{x}{y}>\frac{^-15}{12}$$

$$\frac{x}{y}>\frac{^-5}{4}$$

Hence the solution set is the set $\left\{ \dfrac{x}{y} \,\Big|\, \dfrac{x}{y} > \dfrac{^{-}5}{4} \right\}$.

EXERCISE SET 16-2

1. Using the Order Tests listed in this section determine which of the following hold.

   (a) $\dfrac{15}{16} < \dfrac{31}{34}$

   (b) $\dfrac{^{-}13}{24} < \dfrac{^{-}14}{23}$

   (c) $\dfrac{5}{17} < \dfrac{^{-}3}{14}$

   (d) $\dfrac{26}{33} = \dfrac{128}{268}$

   (e) $\dfrac{12}{35} > \dfrac{14}{36}$

   (f) $\dfrac{^{-}17}{19} > \dfrac{^{-}19}{17}$

   (g) $\dfrac{^{-}11}{23} > \dfrac{17}{32}$

2. If both $\dfrac{a}{b} < \dfrac{c}{d}$ and $\dfrac{c}{d} < \dfrac{e}{f}$ then $\dfrac{a}{b} < \dfrac{c}{d} < \dfrac{e}{f}$ and we say that $\dfrac{c}{d}$ is between the other two rationals.

   (a) Find a rational number $\dfrac{x}{y}$ between $\dfrac{3}{7}$ and $\dfrac{4}{3}$.

   (b) Find a rational number $\dfrac{x}{y}$ between $\dfrac{11}{13}$ and $\dfrac{9}{11}$.

3. (a) If $\dfrac{a}{b} \leqslant \dfrac{c}{d} \leqslant \dfrac{e}{f}$, is it necessarily true that $\dfrac{a}{b} < \dfrac{c}{d} < \dfrac{e}{f}$? Why or why not? Give a numerical example to support your answer.

   (b) Make the same consideration for $\dfrac{a}{b} \leqslant \dfrac{c}{d} < \dfrac{e}{f}$.

4. If $\dfrac{a}{4} \leqslant \dfrac{b}{4}$, it is always true that $\dfrac{a+1}{4} \leqslant \dfrac{b+1}{4}$? Why or why not? [Try some numerical examples first.]

5. Explain in your own words why there cannot be a smallest positive rational number. [Hint: See Theorem 16-4.]

6. (a) By using Theorem 16-4, show that there are infinitely many distinct rationals between $\dfrac{0}{1}$ and $\dfrac{1}{1}$.

(b) Are there infinitely many distinct rationals between *any two* distinct rationals?

(c) Use a number line and show how you would establish a mapping to demonstrate your answer to part (b).

7. Do your answers to problem six lead you to believe that the set of rationals is "bigger than" the set of integers?

8. Determine the solution set X for each of the following problems.

(a) $x + \dfrac{3}{7} \geqslant \dfrac{4}{3}$

(g) $\dfrac{^-2x}{3} - \dfrac{^-3}{4} \geqslant \dfrac{2}{1}$

(b) $\dfrac{3}{x} + \dfrac{1}{11} < \dfrac{14}{121}$

(h) $\dfrac{3x}{2} + \dfrac{^-2}{3} \leqslant \dfrac{2x}{3} - \dfrac{1}{6}$

(c) $\dfrac{x}{8} - \dfrac{3}{4} \leqslant \dfrac{1}{2}$

(i) $\dfrac{4x}{3} - \dfrac{3}{5} \geqslant \dfrac{^-2x}{3} + \dfrac{^-2}{5}$

(d) $\dfrac{2}{3} + \dfrac{3}{4} > \dfrac{x}{12}$

(j) $x - \dfrac{^-3}{4} \leqslant \dfrac{^-7}{8}$

(e) $\dfrac{3}{5} + x \geqslant \dfrac{5}{7}$

(k) $\dfrac{^-3}{2x} + \dfrac{1}{2} > \dfrac{^-3}{7}$

(f) $\dfrac{2x}{7} - \dfrac{3}{5} < \dfrac{5}{2}$

9. Which of the sets determined in problem *eight* is
(a) a set of integers?
(b) a set of rational numbers?
(c) a finite set?
(d) an infinite set?

10. (a) If $\dfrac{3}{4} < \dfrac{5}{3}$, is it necessarily true that $\dfrac{3}{4} \div \dfrac{1}{2} < \dfrac{5}{3} \div \dfrac{1}{2}$? Why or why not? Are there any restrictions on the choice of divisors?

(b) See if you can formulate a theorem which will justify (in general) the type of question asked in problem part (a) and prove it.

(c) What would have been the result in part (a) if the divisor had been a negative rational number?

11. Prove Theorem 16-5.

12. Prove that if $\dfrac{a}{b} < \dfrac{c}{d}$ and $\dfrac{e}{f} < \dfrac{g}{h}$, then $\dfrac{a}{b} + \dfrac{e}{f} < \dfrac{c}{d} + \dfrac{g}{h}$.

13. It has been determined that the set of rationals is dense. With this in mind, would you say that between any two points on the rational number line there is another point which represents a rational number? Explain.

3. Absolute Value

There are times when we may wish to consider a number from a different point of view than those which we have discussed previously. As you will recall, we have already located points on graphs counting off a certain number of units up (or down) relative to some convenient reference point. On a rational number line we may determine that the points associated with a rational number and its additive inverse are both a certain number of units away from the zero point which was chosen as the point of reference. For example

$$\frac{2}{3} \text{ and } \frac{^-2}{3} \text{ are both } \frac{2}{3} \text{ of a unit away from } \frac{0}{1},$$

$$\frac{7}{8} \text{ and } \frac{^-7}{8} \text{ are both } \frac{7}{8} \text{ of a unit away from } \frac{0}{1},$$

$$\frac{9}{2} \text{ and } \frac{^-9}{2} \text{ are both } \frac{9}{2} \text{ units away from } \frac{0}{1}, \text{ and so forth.}$$

It should be easy to see from these examples that the positive member of a pair associated with itself while the negative member of a pair is associated with its additive inverse. Since in the pair $\left(\frac{0}{1}, \frac{0}{1}\right)$ both members are non-negative it makes no difference whether we associate $\frac{0}{1}$ with itself or with its additive inverse. In either case $\frac{0}{1}$ is associated with $\frac{0}{1}$. Further, since every rational number has an additive inverse, this particular correspondence is a mapping of the set of all rational numbers onto the set of non-negative rational numbers. Figure 16-2 illustrates such a mapping. Each point on the vertical line in the figure represents the number of units from the zero point of the rationals which are paired to it. Arrows are drawn for some pairs to their respective images to show graphically how the mapping is established.

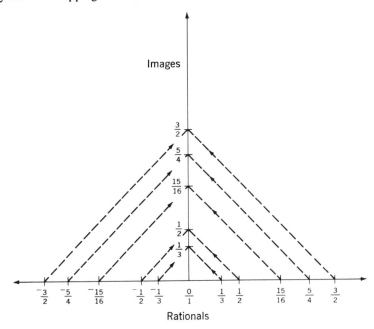

FIGURE 16-2

This mapping of $\{x \mid x$ is a rational number$\}$ onto $\{x \mid x$ is a non-negative rational number$\}$ is usually formalized as the following definition.

Definition 16-6: If $\dfrac{a}{b}$ is a rational number then the **absolute value** of $\dfrac{a}{b}$ is $\dfrac{a}{b}$ if $\dfrac{a}{b} \geqslant \dfrac{0}{1}$ and $\dfrac{^-a}{b}$ if $\dfrac{a}{b} < \dfrac{0}{1}$. The absolute value of a number is also called its **numerical value.**

Generally a more concise shorthand notation is used to denote the absolute value of a number. This notation is given in the following alternative definition.

Definition 16-6a: If $\dfrac{a}{b}$ is a rational number, the **absolute value** of $\dfrac{a}{b}$ is given by

$$(1) \quad \left|\frac{a}{b}\right| = \frac{a}{b} \quad \text{if } \frac{a}{b} \geqslant 0$$

$$(2) \quad \left|\frac{a}{b}\right| = \frac{^-a}{b} \quad \text{if } \frac{a}{b} < 0$$

Examples: (a) $\left|\dfrac{7}{16}\right| = \dfrac{7}{16}$ since $\dfrac{7}{16}$ is greater than or equal to zero.

(b) $\left|\dfrac{^-8}{15}\right| = \left(\dfrac{^-8}{15}\right) = \dfrac{8}{15}$ since $\dfrac{^-8}{15}$ is less than zero.

(c) $\left|\dfrac{0}{1}\right| = \dfrac{0}{1}$ since $\dfrac{0}{1}$ is zero.

Using the concept of absolute value it is sometimes possible to locate the pre-image points on the number line from whence the absolute value arose.

Example: Determine x if $|x| = \dfrac{5}{4}$.

(a) By referring to Figure 16-2 it may be observed that the only two rational numbers whose absolute value is $\dfrac{5}{4}$ are $\dfrac{5}{4}$ and $\dfrac{^-5}{4}$. Thus $\left|\dfrac{5}{4}\right| = \left|\dfrac{^-5}{4}\right| = \dfrac{5}{4}$ so that the solution set is $\left\{\dfrac{5}{4}, \dfrac{^-5}{4}\right\}$. A slightly different, but related, approach to the solution of this problem is illustrated in part (b) below.

(b) By definition, there are just two numbers whose absolute value is $\dfrac{5}{4}$, namely $\dfrac{5}{4}$ or $\dfrac{^-5}{4}$. Since $\left|\dfrac{5}{4}\right| = \left|\dfrac{^-5}{4}\right| = \dfrac{5}{4}$, the set of pre-images is $\left\{\dfrac{5}{4}, \dfrac{^-5}{4}\right\}$. That is $\left\{\dfrac{5}{4}, \dfrac{^-5}{4}\right\}$ is the solution set for $|x| = \dfrac{5}{4}$.

Similarly one may determine pre-image sets (solution sets) for equations of the form $| x - a | = p$ as the following example illustrates.

Example: Determine x if $\left| x - \dfrac{2}{3} \right| = \dfrac{5}{7}$.

Solution: Because of the fact that subtraction of rationals is an operation, the indicated difference, $x - \dfrac{2}{3}$, names some rational number. Therefore the solution really consists of the solutions to two problems:

(1) Determine the number $x - \dfrac{2}{3}$ whose absolute value is $\dfrac{5}{7}$

(2) Solve the two resulting number sentences for x.

Since $\dfrac{5}{7}$ and $\dfrac{^-5}{7}$ are the only rationals whose absolute value is $\dfrac{5}{7}$, the only possibilities for (1) above are

$$x - \frac{2}{3} = \frac{5}{7} \quad \text{or} \quad x - \frac{2}{3} = \frac{^-5}{7}.$$

From the first of the two number sentences we find $x = \dfrac{2}{3} + \dfrac{5}{7} = \dfrac{29}{21}$ and from the second we find $x = \dfrac{^-5}{7} + \dfrac{2}{3} = \dfrac{^-1}{21}$. Thus the solution set for the original equation is $\left\{ \dfrac{29}{21}, \dfrac{^-1}{21} \right\}$.

A slightly different problem is to determine *all* rational numbers within a given number of units of the zero point on the number line. For instance, all rational numbers which are less than $\dfrac{5}{4}$ of a unit from the origin may be represented by the inequality $\dfrac{^-5}{4} < \dfrac{a}{b} < \dfrac{5}{4}$. As can be observed from Figure 16-2, since $\dfrac{a}{b}$ is to be both less than $\dfrac{5}{4}$ and greater than $\dfrac{^-5}{4}$, this means that the pre-image of $\dfrac{a}{b}$ in the original mapping had to have been both to the left of $\dfrac{5}{4}$ and to the right of $\dfrac{^-5}{4}$ on the horizontal line. Another way in which this set of points can be pictured is illustrated in Figure 16-3.

FIGURE 16-3

As you can observe, if any number between $\frac{-5}{4}$ and $\frac{5}{4}$ is selected, the absolute value of that number is less than $\frac{5}{4}$. Thus an equivalent way to describe the original inequality is to write $\left|\frac{a}{b}\right| < \frac{5}{4}$. In general if x is less than p units from the zero point, we write $|x| < p$ with the understanding that it is related to an ordinary inequality as stated in the following theorem, the proof of which is beyond the scope of this exposition.

Theorem 16-8: If x and p are rational numbers then $|x| < p$ if and only if $^-p < x < p$.

Once the result of Theorem 16-8 is known it is possible to solve number sentences of the form $|x - a| < p$. Here again we make use of the fact that since subtraction is an operation on the set of rationals, $x - a$ may be thought of as simply a rational number. Consequently in the initial steps of the solution Theorem 16-8 applies directly.

Example: Determine x if $\left|x - \frac{2}{3}\right| < \frac{3}{4}$.

Solution: By Theorem 16-8, $\left|x - \frac{2}{3}\right| < \frac{3}{4}$ if and only if $\frac{^-3}{4} < x - \frac{2}{3} < \frac{3}{4}$. The latter means that

$$\frac{^-3}{4} < x - \frac{2}{3} \quad \text{and} \quad x - \frac{2}{3} < \frac{3}{4}.$$

Since the same number may be added to both sides of an equality, we add $\frac{2}{3}$ to obtain

$$\frac{^-3}{4} + \frac{2}{3} < \left(x - \frac{2}{3}\right) + \frac{2}{3} \quad \text{and} \quad \left(x - \frac{2}{3}\right) + \frac{2}{3} < \frac{3}{4} + \frac{2}{3}$$

or equivalently

$$\frac{^-9 + 8}{12} < x \quad \text{and} \quad x < \frac{9 + 8}{12}.$$

Thus

$$\frac{^-1}{12} < x \quad \text{and} \quad x < \frac{17}{12}$$

which can be expressed symbolically as $\frac{^-1}{12} < x < \frac{17}{12}$. Hence the set of numbers which satisfy the inequality $\left|x - \frac{2}{3}\right| < \frac{3}{4}$ is $\left\{x \middle| \frac{^-1}{12} < x < \frac{17}{12}\right\}$.

The formal statement of such inequalities which involve absolute value might appear as follows.

Theorem 16-9: If x, a, and p are rational numbers, then $|x - a| < p$ if and only if $a - p < x < a + p$.

Proof: Left as an exercise.

Corresponding to the results of Theorems 16-8 and 16-9 are those with $<$ replaced by the relation $>$. These results may be somewhat unexpected.

Example: Determine the rational numbers $\frac{a}{b}$ such that $\left|\frac{a}{b}\right| > \frac{1}{3}$.

Solution: If we refer again to Figure 16-2 we note that we must consider those rationals whose images under the mapping are above $\frac{1}{3}$ on the vertical line. From this consideration we find that these rational numbers come from two disjoint sets; those to the right of $\frac{1}{3}$ or those to the left of $\frac{^-1}{3}$ on the horizontal line. Thus to say that $\left|\frac{a}{b}\right| > \frac{1}{3}$ means the same as saying that $\frac{a}{b} > \frac{1}{3}$ or $\frac{a}{b} < \frac{^-1}{3}$.

Example: Determine all rationals x such that $|x| > \frac{5}{7}$.

Solution: $|x| > \frac{5}{7}$ means that $x > \frac{5}{7}$ or $x < \frac{^-5}{7}$ (draw a figure similar to Figure 16-3). Thus the solution set appears similar to the regions indicated below.

The general statement of the relationship between absolute value and the relation $>$ is embodied in the following theorem. Theorem 16-10 is a conjecture at this stage which we have based upon the results of two examples. However, even though we shall not prove it, the theorem is valid and we shall feel free to use the results wherever it is convenient to do so.

Theorem 16-10: If x and p are rational numbers then $|x| > p$ if and only if $x > p$ or $x < ^-p$.

As with Theorem 16-8, there is a companion theorem which arises from Theorem 16-10. It is an analogue to Theorem 16-9 and depends on the ability to interpret a difference, $x - a$, as a single rational number. Once this is done and properties of inequalities are used, Theorem 16-11 arises as a natural result.

Theorem 16-11: If x, a, and p are rational numbers, then $|x - a| > p$ if and only if $x > a + p$ or $x < a - p$.

For the sake of completeness, it may be noted that once Theorems 16-8 through Theorem 16-11 have been established, these results may be extended to include the relations $\leqslant$ and $\geqslant$. Then such inequalities may be solved a pair at a time. These latter are called *simultaneous inequalities* and they are used often when trying to draw pictures of complicated curves in several areas of mathematics. A few of these inequalities will be included in the exercise set for your consideration, but they are not of particular value for the development we have undertaken here.

EXERCISE SET 16-3

1. Determine each of the following.

(a) $\left| \dfrac{3}{2} \right|$

(b) $\left| \dfrac{^-5}{7} \right|$

(c) $\left| \dfrac{0}{5} \right|$

(d) $\left| \dfrac{2}{3} + \dfrac{^-1}{4} \right|$

(e) $\left| \dfrac{2}{5} - \dfrac{1}{8} \right|$

(f) $\left| \dfrac{3}{7} - \dfrac{^-1}{2} \right|$

(g) $\left| \dfrac{7}{6} + \dfrac{1}{4} \right|$

(h) $\left| \dfrac{^-1}{4} + \dfrac{2}{3} \right|$

(i) $\left| \dfrac{^-1}{2} - \dfrac{3}{7} \right|$

(j) $\left| \dfrac{3}{2} \right| + \left| \dfrac{^-5}{7} \right|$

(k) $\left| \dfrac{2}{5} \right| - \left| \dfrac{1}{8} \right|$

(l) $\left| \dfrac{3}{7} \right| - \left| \dfrac{^-1}{2} \right|$

(m) Does $\left| \dfrac{2}{3} + \dfrac{^-1}{4} \right| = \left| \dfrac{^-1}{4} + \dfrac{2}{3} \right|$?

(n) Does $\left| \dfrac{3}{2} \right| + \left| \dfrac{^-5}{7} \right| = \left| \dfrac{3}{2} + \dfrac{^-5}{7} \right|$?

(o) Does $\left| \dfrac{3}{7} \right| - \left| \dfrac{^-1}{2} \right| = \left| \dfrac{3}{7} - \dfrac{^-1}{2} \right|$?

(p) Does $\left| \dfrac{3}{7} - \dfrac{^-1}{2} \right| = \left| \dfrac{^-1}{2} - \dfrac{3}{7} \right|$?

2. Determine the solution set X for each of the following

(a) $|x| = \dfrac{3}{5}$

(e) $\left| x - \dfrac{^-3}{7} \right| = \dfrac{5}{7}$

(b) $|x| = \dfrac{^-2}{3}$

(f) $\left| x + \dfrac{4}{3} \right| = \dfrac{^-1}{2}$

(c) $|x| = x + \dfrac{1}{4}$

(g) $\left| x + \dfrac{5}{2} \right| = \dfrac{1}{3}$

(d) $\left| x - \dfrac{2}{5} \right| = \dfrac{4}{3}$

(h) $\left| 2x - \dfrac{3}{8} \right| = x + \dfrac{1}{2}$

3. Determine the solution set X for each of the following inequalities.

(a) $|x| < \dfrac{7}{8}$

(f) $|x| > \dfrac{2}{7}$

(b) $|x| < \dfrac{^-1}{4}$

(g) $|x| > \dfrac{^-1}{4}$

(c) $|3x| < x - \dfrac{1}{4}$

(h) $|2x| > x + \dfrac{1}{3}$

(d) $\left| x - \dfrac{4}{5} \right| < \dfrac{3}{10}$

(i) $\left| x + \dfrac{5}{3} \right| > \dfrac{1}{6}$

(e) $\left| \dfrac{2x}{3} + \dfrac{1}{4} \right| < \dfrac{5}{12}$

(j) $\left| \dfrac{2x}{5} - \dfrac{1}{3} \right| > \dfrac{8}{15}$

4. In Section 16-2 it was determined that any inequalities which hold for $<$ or $>$ hold for $\leqslant$ and $\geqslant$ respectively. Using this fact, determine solution sets for each of the following.

(a) $|3x| \leqslant \dfrac{5}{4}$

(e) $|5x| \geqslant \dfrac{5}{4}$

(b) $\left| x - \dfrac{1}{5} \right| \leqslant \dfrac{1}{2}$

(f) $\left| x - \dfrac{1}{3} \right| \geqslant \dfrac{5}{6}$

(c) $\left| x + \dfrac{2}{3} \right| \leqslant \dfrac{5}{6}$

(g) $\left| x + \dfrac{3}{4} \right| \geqslant \dfrac{5}{8}$

(d) $\left| \dfrac{2x}{5} - \dfrac{3}{15} \right| \leqslant \dfrac{7}{30}$

(h) $\left| \dfrac{5x}{3} + \dfrac{1}{4} \right| \geqslant \dfrac{7}{12}$

5. Rewrite each of the following inequalities as an inequality which involves absolute value.

(a) $\dfrac{^-7}{16} < x < \dfrac{7}{16}$

(e) $x > \dfrac{5}{9}$ or $x < \dfrac{^-5}{9}$

(b) $\dfrac{^-6}{7} \leqslant x \leqslant \dfrac{6}{7}$

(f) $x > \dfrac{13}{4}$ or $x < \dfrac{^-13}{4}$

(c) $\dfrac{1}{10} < x < \dfrac{11}{10}$

(g) $x > \dfrac{3}{2}$ or $x < \dfrac{7}{6}$

(d) $\dfrac{^-5}{6} \leqslant x \leqslant \dfrac{^-1}{2}$

(h) $x \geqslant \dfrac{4}{5}$ or $x \leqslant \dfrac{1}{20}$

6. (a) Calculate $\left|\dfrac{1}{2} - \dfrac{5}{4}\right|$.

   (b) Using the number line, what appears to be the distance between $\dfrac{1}{2}$ and $\dfrac{5}{4}$?

   (c) Calculate $\left|\dfrac{^-7}{8} - \dfrac{^-1}{2}\right|$.

   (d) Using the number line, what appears to be the distance between $\dfrac{^-7}{8}$ and $\dfrac{^-1}{2}$?

   (e) If $\dfrac{a}{b}$ and $\dfrac{c}{d}$ are rational numbers, in what way might the distance between the two be expressed?

   (f) Does your answer to part (e) seem to hold for the rationals $\dfrac{^-5}{3}$ and $\dfrac{4}{3}$?

7. (a) In problem 3 show how the solution sets may be expressed in terms of $\cup$ or $\cap$.

   (b) Do the same for problem 4.

8. For each of the following, determine the set of rational numbers such that both of the given conditions hold and then draw a number line picture to represent this set.

(a) $\left|2x - \dfrac{1}{2}\right| < \dfrac{3}{4}$

       and

    $|x| > \dfrac{1}{4}$

(b) $\left|\dfrac{3}{2}x + \dfrac{5}{8}\right| \geq \dfrac{1}{2}$

       and

    $\left|x - \dfrac{2}{3}\right| \leq \dfrac{1}{1}$

Chapter summary

As indicated earlier, some properties of the order relation were to be relegated to the present chapter. In Chapter 16, we found that order for rationals could be defined in much the same way as was done in the system of integers. Once this was done, we found that each result already established for integers held for rational numbers as well. In addition to this, we were able to establish that between any two different rational numbers there is at least one more rational number which is different from the two originally chosen. This property we refer to as *denseness*. Using the idea, denseness, we can show that

(1) there is no smallest positive rational number, or equivalently

(2) there is no such thing as "a *next* rational number."

Finally, we were able to show as we did in the system of integers that the order relation and the operation subtraction give rise to the Trichotomy Law for rational numbers.

Next we used the idea of a mapping to correspond ordered pairs $\left(\dfrac{^-a}{b}, \dfrac{a}{b} \right)$ to the non negative member of the pair. The non negative member which was the image under the mapping was referred to as the *absolute value* of each member of the ordered pair. By using this idea of mapping in conjunction with a geometric interpretation and the concept of equality, we found a whole new class of number sentences which could be solved, namely equalities involving absolute value. Similarly, if geometry and the concept of order are used in conjunction with the mapping, another class of number sentences, inequalities involving absolute value, arises which is solvable if the numbers involved are rationals. If one pursued the properties of number systems, he would eventually find that the concept of absolute value plays an important role when the idea of measuring distance between points is considered.

CHAPTER 17 Decimal representation of rationals and decimal arithmetic

1. Definition of Decimal Numerals

The development of the rational number system in the preceding chapters utilized numerals for rational numbers of the form $\frac{a}{b}$, where a, $b \neq 0$ represented integers. The question that is now to be considered is one of the existence of other possible numeration systems that might be used for the rational numbers. Since the discussion here is concerned with ways of representing numbers and not with properties of the numbers themselves, questions related to commutativity, associativity, uniqueness, and so forth will not arise. These are properties which the operations in the rational number system have, not properties of the numeration system. By this time you should have acquired a clear understanding of the distinction between a number system and a numeration system and thereby realize that the properties mentioned above have been established for rational numbers in the preceding materials and are therefore not a function of the numeration system selected to represent the numbers.

The reader should recall that for cardinal numbers an expanded form of numerals was discussed in some detail. Consider the base ten cardinal numeral $d_n d_{n-1} \ldots d_1 d_0$ where each $d_i \in \{0,1,2,3,4,5,6,7,8,9\}$. The expanded form of this numeral was expressed in terms of powers of the base ten as

$$d_n \cdot 10^n + d_{n-1} \cdot 10^{n-1} + \ldots + d_1 \cdot 10 + d_0.$$

This form of the numeral was very useful in establishing the validity of several of the algorithms that were discussed in the sections devoted to cardinal number arithmetic. Our interest in this section is to show how a modification of this expanded form can be developed for rational numbers, and then to discuss some of the uses of such numerals in the arithmetic of rational numbers in the remaining sections of this chapter.

No expanded form was developed for numerals used to represent integers in the development of that number system. However, this was by choice and should not have been interpreted to imply that such a form could not be developed. Had this been done the results would have closely paralleled those obtained for the cardinal numbers. Indeed, to have such an expanded form at one's disposal for the system of integers one needs only to appeal to the theorem which states that $^-a = (^-1) \cdot (a)$ for any integer a, and the isomorphism between the cardinal numbers and non-negative integers. This is done in the following definition.

Definition 17-1: (a) If $N = d_n d_{n-1} \ldots d_1 d_0$ is a positive integer, the expanded form of the numeral for N is given by $d_n d_{n-1} \ldots d_1 d_0 = d_n \cdot 10^n + d_{n-1} \cdot 10^{n-1} + \ldots + d_1 \cdot 10 + d_0$.

(b) If $N = {}^-(d_n d_{n-1} \ldots d_1 d_0)$ is a negative integer, the **expanded form** of the numeral for N is given by $^-(d_n d_{n-1} \ldots d_1 d_0) = {}^-1 \cdot (d_n \cdot 10^n + d_{n-1} \cdot 10^{n-1} + \ldots + d_1 \cdot 10 + d_0)$.

Thus for example we may write

(a) $376241 = 3 \cdot 10^5 + 7 \cdot 10^4 + 6 \cdot 10^3 + 2 \cdot 10^2 + 4 \cdot 10^1 + 1$

and

(b) $^-8621349 = {}^-1 \cdot (8 \cdot 10^6 + 6 \cdot 10^5 + 2 \cdot 10^4 + 1 \cdot 10^3 + 3 \cdot 10^2 + 4 \cdot 10 + 9)$

$\quad = {}^-8 \cdot 10^6 + {}^-6 \cdot 10^5 + {}^-2 \cdot 10^4 + {}^-1 \cdot 10^3 + {}^-3 \cdot 10^2 + {}^-4 \cdot 10 + {}^-9$

The problem of deriving an expanded numeral for certain special rational numbers is easily solved if we again appeal to the fact that the set of integers is isomorphic to the subset of rationals having denominator one. Since the rational $\frac{a}{1}$ corresponds to the integer a in this isomorphism, one might suspect that the two numbers might have related expanded numerals. In fact the forms are so similar in appearance that it is impossible to tell from the form alone whether it represents a rational or its corresponding integer. For example the expanded form $4 \cdot 10^2 + 3 \cdot 10 + 2$ could represent the integer 432, the rational $\frac{432}{1}$, or the cardinal 432. One cannot determine which on the basis of the given expanded form of the numeral. This problem should not cause the reader concern since, because of the isomorphisms involved, this problem is theoretical and arises only in abstract studies of number systems. Hence we shall use the same expanded form for rationals with denominator one as for integers. The justification for this is the isomorphism discussed earlier. We state this fact for future reference with regard to the following definition.

Definition 17-2: If $N = \dfrac{d_n d_{n-1} \ldots d_1 d_0}{1}$ is a positive rational number, the expanded form of the numeral for N is given by $\dfrac{d_n d_{n-1} \ldots d_1 d_0}{1} = d_n \cdot 10^n +$

$d_{n-1} \cdot 10^{n-1} + \ldots + d_1 \cdot 10 + d_0.$

(b) If $N = \dfrac{^-(d_n d_{n-1} \ldots d_1 d_0)}{1}$ is a negative rational number, the **expanded**

form of the numeral for N is given by $\dfrac{^-(d_n d_{n-1} \ldots d_1 d_0)}{1} = ^-1 \cdot (d_n \cdot 10^n +$

$d_{n-1} \cdot 10^{n-1} + \ldots + d_1 \cdot 10 + d_0).$

Thus we may write, for example that

$$\frac{537840}{1} = 5 \cdot 10^5 + 3 \cdot 10^4 + 7 \cdot 10^3 + 8 \cdot 10^2 + 4 \cdot 10 + 0$$

and

$$\frac{^-4327963}{1} = ^-1 \cdot (4 \cdot 10^6 + 3 \cdot 10^5 + 2 \cdot 10^4 + 7 \cdot 10^3 + 9 \cdot 10^2 + 6 \cdot 10 + 3)$$

$$= ^-4 \cdot 10^6 + ^-3 \cdot 10^5 + ^-2 \cdot 10^4 + ^-7 \cdot 10^3 + ^-9 \cdot 10^2 + ^-6 \cdot 10 + ^-3$$

Note: When working now with the expanded forms of numerals for rationals, *remember* that these refer to *rational* numbers so that properties of rational numbers must be used to justify steps in problem solving.

Obviously a problem arises immediately in the development of an expanded form for a rational numeral if the rational in question can not be expressed with the denominator of *one*. Before a general solution to this problem can be given we must temporarily digress to an intuitive discussion of rational exponents.

For the purpose of the ensuing discussion the phrase "integral rational" will be used to refer to a rational number that can be expressed in the form $\dfrac{a}{1}$ where a is an integer. The integral rationals will also be expressed as the rational a instead of $\dfrac{a}{1}$. This is permissible because of the existing isomorphism between the integers and the corresponding subset of rationals.

In Section 5-3, the concept of an exponent was introduced for the cardinal number system. The numeral a^n for cardinal numbers a, $n \neq 0$, was defined to represent n factors a. If n were zero and $a \neq 0$ then $a^n = 1$. An analogous definition will be given at this time for the corresponding non-negative integral rationals.

Definition 17-3: If n is a non-negative integral rational and a is a rational number then

$$a^0 = 1, \quad \text{for} \quad a \neq 0$$

and

$$a^n = \underbrace{a \cdot a \cdots a}_{n \text{ factors}} \text{ for } \quad n \neq 0$$

Examples: (a) $^+5^3 = {}^+5 \cdot {}^+5 \cdot {}^+5 = {}^+125$

(b) $\left(\dfrac{^-1}{2}\right)^2 = \dfrac{^-1}{2} \cdot \dfrac{^-1}{2} = \dfrac{1}{4}$

(c) $\left(\dfrac{3}{4}\right)^0 = 1$

(d) $0^3 = 0 \cdot 0 \cdot 0 = 0$

From the above definition one should observe that an analogue to Theorem 5-11 could be established for rational integral exponents, that is, if a is a rational number and $m \neq 0$ and $n \neq 0$ are integral rational exponents then

$$a^m \cdot a^n = a^{m+n}$$

With this property at our disposal consider the problem of determining the quotient of $a^5 \div a^3, a \neq 0$. From Section 15-5, one could write $a^5 \div a^3$ as

$$\frac{a^5}{a^3} = \frac{a \cdot a \cdot a \cdot a \cdot a}{a \cdot a \cdot a}$$

Using the definition of multiplication and the multiplicative identity we write

$$\frac{a^5}{a^3} = \frac{a}{a} \cdot \frac{a}{a} \cdot \frac{a}{a} \cdot \frac{a \cdot a}{1} = a^2$$

From this we have proven that

$$a^5 \div a^3 = a^2 = a^{5-3}$$

Intuitively we might generalize this idea to that of $a^m \div a^n = a^{m-n}$. In fact as long as $m \geqslant n$ no problems would be encountered. However, what is one to do in the case that $m < n$? For example, $a^3 \div a^5, a \neq 0$. If we again write

$$a^3 \div a^5 = \frac{a^3}{a^5} = \frac{a \cdot a \cdot a}{a \cdot a \cdot a \cdot a \cdot a}$$

then from properties of rational numbers it follows that

$$a^3 \div a^5 = \frac{1}{a \cdot a} = \frac{1}{a^2}$$

Now from previous work in division $a^3 \div a^5 = \dfrac{1}{a \cdot a}$ if and only if $\dfrac{1}{a \cdot a} \cdot a^5 = a^3$. Furthermore, if we wish to preserve the property that $a^m \cdot a^n = a^{m+n}$ it seems to follow naturally that a^{-2} might be used as another name for $\dfrac{1}{a \cdot a}$, thereby giving

$$a^3 \div a^5 = \frac{1}{a \cdot a} = \frac{1}{a^2} = a^{-2}.$$

If one accepts the numeral a^{-2} as a representation of $\dfrac{1}{a^2}$ then $a^3 \div a^5 = a^{-2}$ which

satisfies the desired properties of division and exponentiation since $a^{-2} \cdot a^5 =$
$a^{-2+5} = a^3$.

Using this fact as a motivating device we are now ready to formalize the notion of a negative integral rational exponent.

Definition 17-4: If a is a rational number and ^-n is a negative integral rational, then the numeral a^{-n} is defined by

$$a^{-n} = \frac{1}{a^n}$$

Note that a^{-n} could be interpreted to mean $1 \div a^n$ because of the isomorphism established in Section 15-5.

Examples: (a) $10^{-3} = \dfrac{1}{10^3} = \dfrac{1}{1000}$

(b) $\left(\dfrac{3}{4}\right)^{-1} = 1 \div \dfrac{3}{4} = \dfrac{4}{3}$

Let us now return to the problem of developing an expanded form of numerals for rational numbers. First we consider two very special types of rational numbers, namely those rationals which can be expressed with denominators of two or five or powers of two or five. Examples of this type of rational numbers are illustrated below. The form of these related numerals and how they were obtained should be studied carefully in each case.

Examples:

(a) $\dfrac{1}{2} = \dfrac{5}{5} \cdot \dfrac{1}{2} = \dfrac{5}{10} = 5\left(\dfrac{1}{10}\right)$

(b) $\dfrac{5}{2} = \dfrac{5}{5} \cdot \dfrac{5}{2} = \dfrac{25}{10} = \dfrac{20+5}{10} = \dfrac{20}{10} + \dfrac{5}{10} = \dfrac{2}{1} + \dfrac{5}{10} = 2 + 5\left(\dfrac{1}{10}\right)$

(c) $\dfrac{3}{4} = \dfrac{3}{2 \cdot 2} = \dfrac{5}{5} \cdot \dfrac{5}{5} \cdot \dfrac{3}{2 \cdot 2} = \dfrac{75}{100} = \dfrac{70+5}{100} = \dfrac{70}{100} + \dfrac{5}{100} = \dfrac{7}{10} + \dfrac{5}{100}$

$= 7\left(\dfrac{1}{10}\right) + 5\left(\dfrac{1}{100}\right).$

(d) $\dfrac{7}{40} = \dfrac{7}{2 \cdot 2 \cdot 5} = \dfrac{5}{5} \cdot \dfrac{7}{2 \cdot 2 \cdot 5} = \dfrac{35}{100} = \dfrac{30+5}{100} = \dfrac{30}{100} + \dfrac{5}{100} = \dfrac{3}{10} + \dfrac{5}{100}$

$= 3\left(\dfrac{1}{10}\right) + 5\left(\dfrac{1}{100}\right)$

(e) $\dfrac{66}{625} = \dfrac{66}{5 \cdot 5 \cdot 5 \cdot 5} = \dfrac{2}{2} \cdot \dfrac{2}{2} \cdot \dfrac{2}{2} \cdot \dfrac{2}{2} \cdot \dfrac{66}{5 \cdot 5 \cdot 5 \cdot 5} = \dfrac{1056}{10000} = \dfrac{1000 + 50 + 6}{10000}$

$= \dfrac{1000}{10000} + \dfrac{50}{10000} + \dfrac{6}{10000} = \dfrac{1}{10} + \dfrac{5}{1000} + \dfrac{6}{10000}$

$= 1\left(\dfrac{1}{10}\right) + 0\left(\dfrac{1}{100}\right) + 5\left(\dfrac{1}{1000}\right) + 6\left(\dfrac{1}{10000}\right)$

From the examples given, one can observe that a form similar to the expanded form of numerals used in the cardinal number system is present in each case with the exception that reciprocals of powers of ten appear. The method utilized in these examples should also make evident the fact that any rational number that can be expressed with only factors of 1, 2 or 5 in the denominator can be identified with a numeral involving sums as well as powers of ten or their reciprocals. Since we have previously considered the situation where the denominator is one, we need not concern ourselves here with those rationals. Using the examples given as a guideline we state the following theorem without proof.

Theorem 17-1: Any rational number expressible in the form $\dfrac{a}{2^m \cdot 5^n}$, a, m, n integers, can be alternately expressed with a denominator which is a power of ten.

The proof of the theorem could be established by considering the cases where (1) $m = n$, (2) $m < n$, and (3) $m > n$. It may also be observed that for cases (2) and (3) the use of the K-Theorem provides an effective tool by means of which the theorem is readily established.

Example:
$$\frac{7}{2^3 \cdot 5^5} = \frac{7 \cdot 2^2}{2^3 \cdot 5^5 \cdot 2^2}$$
$$= \frac{7 \cdot 2^2}{2^5 \cdot 5^5}$$
$$= \frac{7 \cdot 4}{(2 \cdot 5)^5}$$
$$= \frac{28}{10^5}$$

Indeed, since 2 and 5 are the only positive factors of ten, other than one and ten, one observes that a rational number such as $\dfrac{1}{3}$ can not be expressed using a power of ten as the denominator. This problem arises since there is no integer which gives a product of 10 when multiplied by the denominator 3. Similar situations exist whenever the denominator is not of the form $2^m \cdot 5^n$ as stated in Theorem 17-1. This observation might lead one to conjecture the validity of the following theorem.

Theorem 17-2: Rational numbers that can be expressed in the form $\dfrac{a}{2^m \cdot 5^n}$ a, m, n integers, are the only rationals that can be expressed with denominator which is a power of ten.

Now consider the numeral $\frac{66}{625}$ and related forms given in the above examples. One of the forms given for $\frac{66}{625}$ was $1\left(\frac{1}{10}\right) + 0\left(\frac{1}{100}\right) + 5\left(\frac{1}{1000}\right) + 6\left(\frac{1}{1000}\right)$. It is possible to write $\frac{66}{625}$ this way because of the properties of the rational numbers developed in the preceding chapters and Theorem 17-1. As mentioned above, this numeral appears similar to the expanded form of the numeral discussed in the chapter on cardinal numbers. If Definition 17-4 is used at this point, the rational $\frac{66}{625}$ can be expressed in terms of negative integral powers of ten as

$$1(10^{-1}) + 0(10^{-2}) + 5(10^{-3}) + 6(10^{-4})$$

In comparison with the expanded form of numerals employed in the cardinal number system one might suggest that the numeral 1056 could be written as another name for $\frac{66}{625}$. In fact, there would be nothing wrong with this provided some way were devised to indicate that the digit 1 in 1056 was to be multiplied by 10^{-1} instead of 10^3, the digit 5 was to be multiplied by 10^{-3} instead of 10, and so on, as we have already agreed to do in the systems of cardinal numbers and integers. Such a device to indicate the proper multiples of ten is commonly used and is called a decimal point or a decimal.

Definition 17-5: A **decimal point** is a symbol (usually a dot, period, or comma) used to separate those digits in a place-value numeral which represent multiples of non-negative powers of the base from those used to represent multiples of negative powers of the base.

Examples:

(a) $745.123 = 7(10^2) + 4(10^1) + 5(10^0) + 1(10^{-1}) + 2(10^{-2}) + 3(10^{-3})$

(b) $.2196 = 2(10^{-1}) + 1(10^{-2}) + 9(10^{-3}) + 6(10^{-4})$.

We are now ready to formally introduce a new type of numeral frequently used in the rational number system. These numerals are called decimal numerals, or frequently, decimals.

Definition 17-6: If the rational number $\frac{a}{b}$ has the expanded form

$$\frac{a}{b} = d_n(10^n) + d_{n-1}(10^{n-1}) + \ldots + d_1(10) + d_0 +$$

$$c_1(10^{-1}) + c_2(10^{-2}) + \ldots + c_k(10^{-k})$$

then the associated **decimal numeral** is given by $\frac{a}{b} = d_n d_{n-1} \ldots d_1 d_0 . c_1 c_2 \ldots c_k$, where the letters with subscripts represent digits.

From examples given previously we can now write that

$$\frac{1}{2} = \frac{5}{10} = 5(10^{-1}) = .5$$

$$\frac{5}{2} = \frac{25}{10} = 2(10^0) + 5(10^{-1}) = 2.5$$

$$\frac{3}{4} = \frac{75}{100} = 7(10^{-1}) + 5(10^{-2}) = .75$$

$$\frac{66}{625} = \frac{1056}{10000} = 1(10^{-1}) + 0(10^{-2}) + 5(10^{-3}) + 6(10^{-4}) = .1056$$

One should remember that to this point all of our discussion has centered upon those rationals of the form $\frac{a}{2^m \cdot 5^n}$. The decimal numerals for such rationals are called *terminating decimals* or *finite decimals*. One should readily see why they are given this name, for if we first write the expanded form of the numeral for such a rational this numeral has a *finite* number of non-zero terms. Hence by Definition 17-6 the decimal numeral has a finite number of non-zero digits. That is, it terminates; hence the name termininating decimal.

Note that because of Theorem 17-2, the *only* rationals which have terminating decimal numerals are those of the form $\frac{a}{2^m \cdot 5^n}$. However, the reader is again cautioned to remember that there *are* rationals which have non-terminating decimal numerals. Examples of such rationals are $\frac{1}{3}, \frac{1}{7}, \frac{1}{9}, \frac{1}{13}$, and so on. Consideration of this problem will be taken up in a subsequent section.

A combination of the use of the decimal numeration system and integral rational exponents has been found extremely useful in science. The system is referred to as *scientific notation* and is most useful in expressing very large or very small numbers such as those frequently encountered in the sciences. For the purposes of illustrating the use of scientific notation, consider the number one hundred twenty five billion. The first numeral students usually learn to use to express this number is 125,000,000,000. As one can see, the physical task of writing such a numeral could become somewhat laborious if the necessity arose where one would have to write this numeral several times. To alleviate this problem we could appeal to the properties of the decimal numeration system, the properties of the rational number system, and integral rational exponents and write

$$125,000,000,000 = 1.25 \cdot 10^{11}$$

Similarly one can write

$$.0000000000125 = 1.25 \cdot 10^{-11}$$

To see why one can write such numerals, let us consider the following examples.

Examples:

(a) $125 = 1(10^2) + 2(10) + 5$ Expanded form

$= [1 + 2(10^{-1}) + 5(10^{-2})] \cdot 10^2$ Distributive property
and rules of exponents

$= 1.25 \cdot 10^2$ Decimal notation

(b) $3214.56 = 3(10^3) + 2(10^2) + 1(10) + 4 + 5(10^{-1}) + 6(10^{-2})$

$= [3 + 2(10^{-1}) + 1(10^{-2}) + 4(10^{-3}) + 5(10^{-4}) + 6(10^{-5})] \cdot 10^{\,3}$

$= 3.21456 \cdot 10^3$

(c) $.00032 = 3(10^{-4}) + 2(10^{-5})$

$= [3 + 2(10^{-1})] \cdot 10^{-4}$

$= 3.2 \cdot 10^{-4}$

In general, a numeral is written in scientific notation if it is an expression of the product of a number greater than or equal to one but less than ten times some integral power of ten.

At this point a modified scientific notation will be introduced. This numeral is not being introduced to the reader because of any extensive use that one can find for it, but because of its utility is discussing the arithmetic of decimal numerals. For the lack of any better name this numeral will be referred to in subsequent sections as the standard form of a decimal numeral. Formally such a numeral will be defined as follows.

Definition 17-7: A standard decimal numeral is a numeral of the form

$$d_n d_{n-1} \ldots d_1 d_0 \cdot 10^k$$

where $d_n d_{n-1} \ldots d_1 d_0$ and k represent integral rational numbers.

The following examples illustrate the relationship between the decimal numerals and the standard form of the decimal numeral.

Examples:

(a) $37.59 = 3759 \cdot 10^{-2}$

(b) $.413 = 413 \cdot 10^{-3}$

(c) $1.0037 = 10037 \cdot 10^{-4}$

EXERCISE SET 17-1

1. Write a decimal numeral for each of the following.

(a) $5(10^3) + 2(10^2) + 3(10) + 1$

(b) $4(10^2) + 3(10) + 9 + 5(10^{-1}) + 3(10^{-2})$

(c) $5(10^{-2}) + 3(10^{-3}) + 7(10^{-4})$

(d) $8(10^2) + 3 + 4(10^{-5})$

2. Write the expanded form for each of the following decimal numerals.

(a) 521.27

(b) .00123

(c) 25612.791

(d) 1000.0001

(e) $1.27 \cdot 10^{-3}$

(f) $2.57 \cdot 10^2$

3. Write numerals equivalent to those given without using negative exponents.

(a) $10^5 \cdot 10^{-4}$

(b) $3^{-4} \cdot 5^3$

(c) $2^5 \cdot 3^{-2} \cdot 2^{-4}$

(d) $5^{-6} \cdot 6^{-5}$

(e) $10^{10} \cdot 7^{-3} \cdot 5^{-4} \cdot 13$

(f) $a^{-4} \cdot b^{-1} \cdot c \cdot d^{-5}$

4. Express the following in exponential form.

(a) $\dfrac{5^3}{4^2 \cdot 7^4}$

(b) $\dfrac{10^4}{10^{12}}$

(c) $\dfrac{a^4 b^6}{a^5 b^2 c^3}$

(d) $\dfrac{5^{-2} x^5}{3^3 x^{-2} y^3}$

5. Express the following numerals in scientific notation.

(a) 2,570,000,000

(b) .00012

(c) .152

(d) 27.500

(e) $178.2 \cdot 10^{18}$

(f) $.0057 \cdot 10^5$

(g) .00000000127

(h) $128 \cdot 10^{-17}$

(i) $312000 \cdot 10^{-10}$

6. Write a decimal numeral for each of the following using Theorem 17-1.

(a) $\dfrac{1}{32}$

(b) $\dfrac{7}{50}$

(c) $\dfrac{217}{8}$

(d) $\dfrac{3}{80}$

7. Show that any rational of the form $\dfrac{a}{2^m}$ can be expressed with the denominator a power of ten.

8. Explain why the rational $\dfrac{1}{7}$ cannot be expressed with only a power of ten for a denominator.

9. Write the standard decimal numeral for each of the following.

(a) 1.23

(b) .000175

(c) $6.71 \cdot 10^{-5}$

(d) $89.32 \cdot 10^4$

(e) $.000008 \cdot 10^5$

2. Terminating Decimals

In Section 17-1 the plausibility of extending the expanded form of numerals for integers to include rational numbers with denominator one was discussed. It was found during the course of that discussion that the concept of isomorphism again played a rather important role. Once this was done, the expanded form of numerals was again extended by introducing negative exponents and then decimal numerals for rational numbers were defined. Also discussed was the fact that the only rationals which have decimal numerals of the form listed in Definition 17-6 are those which can be expressed in the form $\dfrac{a}{2^n 5^m}$. Because of the fact that the expanded form of $\dfrac{a}{2^n 5^m}$ has a finite number of non-zero terms, the corresponding decimal numeral is often referred to as a terminating or finite decimal. Thus .2678, 4.2593, and 273.58821 are terminating decimals because their expanded forms have just a finite number of terms.

The fact that decimals play a very important role in everyday life should be evident. This can be observed very easily in almost any business transaction, the keeping of bank accounts, the calculation of average gasoline consumption of automobiles and in many areas of research. In particular, computers perform many calculations which give rise to decimal numerals. Another very important use of decimals is to denote approximations which arise in measurements. For example, measurements of objects vary according to the individual performing the measurement and the instrument used for the measurement. Since such measurements are not exact, terminating decimals are often used to give "close" approximations to the actual measurement.

Because many computations are performed in which not only terminating decimals, but their sums, differences, products, and quotients arise, some consideration should be given to the arithmetic of decimals. This we shall do and in the course of the discussion frequent use will be made of decimal numerals in standard form as defined in Section 17-1.

a. Addition and subtraction

It is common knowledge that in order to add rational numbers by use of terminating decimals and column-wise addition, tenths are placed under tenths, hundredths under hundredths, and so forth when the numerals are written. Then the digits in successive columns are added as in cardinal numbers or positive integers and by some appropriate means the location of the decimal point for the sum is determined. We shall illustrate two methods by which such problems can be done in the case where all of the rationals under consideration are positive.

$$
\begin{array}{r}
6.32 \\
+ \ \ .789 \\
\hline
7.109
\end{array}
$$

Method One (Expanded Notation): Since $6.32 = 6 + 3\left(\dfrac{1}{10}\right) + 2\left(\dfrac{1}{10^2}\right)$ and $.789 = 7\left(\dfrac{1}{10}\right) + 8\left(\dfrac{1}{10^2}\right) + 9\left(\dfrac{1}{10^3}\right)$ we may write

$$6.32 + .789 = 6 + 3\left(\frac{1}{10}\right) + 2\left(\frac{1}{10^2}\right) + 7\left(\frac{1}{10}\right) + 8\left(\frac{1}{10^2}\right) + 9\left(\frac{1}{10^3}\right)$$

Subst., Uniq. (+)

$$= \left(6 + \left[3\left(\frac{1}{10}\right) + 2\left(\frac{1}{10^2}\right)\right]\right) + \left(\left[7\left(\frac{1}{10}\right) + 8\left(\frac{1}{10^2}\right)\right] + 9\left(\frac{1}{10^3}\right)\right)$$

Thm. 14-4

$$= \left[6 + \left(3\left(\frac{1}{10}\right) + \left[2\left(\frac{1}{10^2}\right) + 7\left(\frac{1}{10}\right) \right] \right) \right] + \left[8\left(\frac{1}{10^2}\right) + 9\left(\frac{1}{10^3}\right) \right]$$

Thm. 14-4

$$= \left[6 + \left(3\left(\frac{1}{10}\right) + \left[7\left(\frac{1}{10}\right) + 2\left(\frac{1}{10^2}\right) \right] \right) \right] + \left[8\left(\frac{1}{10^2}\right) + 9\left(\frac{1}{10^3}\right) \right]$$

Thm. 14-3

$$= \left(6 + \left[3\left(\frac{1}{10}\right) + 7\left(\frac{1}{10}\right) \right] \right) + \left(\left[2\left(\frac{1}{10^2}\right) + 8\left(\frac{1}{10^2}\right) \right] + 9\left(\frac{1}{10^3}\right) \right)$$

Thm. 14-4

$$= \left[6 + (3 + 7)\left(\frac{1}{10}\right) \right] + \left[(2 + 8)\left(\frac{1}{10^2}\right) + 9\left(\frac{1}{10^3}\right) \right]$$ Thm. 15-9

$$= \left[6 + 10\left(\frac{1}{10}\right) \right] + \left[10\left(\frac{1}{10^2}\right) + 9\left(\frac{1}{10^3}\right) \right]$$ Why?

$$= \left[6 + \frac{10}{1}\left(\frac{1}{10}\right) \right] + \left[\frac{10}{1}\left(\frac{1}{10^2}\right) + 9\left(\frac{1}{10^3}\right) \right]$$ Why?

$$= \left[6 + \frac{1}{1} \right] + \left[\frac{1}{10} + 9\left(\frac{1}{10^3}\right) \right]$$ Why?

$$= [6 + 1] + \left(\left[\frac{1}{10} + 0\left(\frac{1}{10^2}\right) + 9\left(\frac{1}{10^3}\right) \right] \right)$$ Thm. 14-5

$$= \left[7 + 1\left(\frac{1}{10}\right) \right] + \left[0\left(\frac{1}{10^2}\right) + 9\left(\frac{1}{10^3}\right) \right]$$ Why?

$$= 7 + 1\left(\frac{1}{10}\right) + 0\left(\frac{1}{10^2}\right) + 9\left(\frac{1}{10^3}\right)$$ Thm. 14-4

$$= 7.109$$ Def. 17-7

Two things may be readily observed from this method of adding terminating decimals, namely
    (1) the sum obtained is the same as if the digits (added column-wise) are added as in cardinals or positive integers, and
    (2) the location of the decimal point in the sum is determined by the addend having the most decimal places.

It may also be noticed that the use of expanded notation makes the problem extremely complicated. Because of this, the determination of a solution may become a very tedious task. In order to rectify this, let us use the standard numerals for decimals. If this is done, perhaps some of the time consuming labor can be avoided.

Method Two (Standard Numerals): According to the agreement made in Section 17-1, we have $6.32 = 632 \cdot 10^{-2}$ and $.789 = 789 \cdot 10^{-3}$. Therefore

$$6.32 + .789 = 632 \cdot 10^{-2} + 789 \cdot 10^{-3} \qquad \text{Subst., Uniq. (+)}$$

$$= 6320 \cdot 10^{-3} + 789 \cdot 10^{-3} \qquad \text{Thm. 14-5, Def. 17-7}$$

$$= (6320 + 789) \cdot 10^{-3} \qquad \text{Thm. 15-9}$$

$$= 7109 \cdot 10^{-3} \qquad \text{Def. 14-1}$$

$$= 7.109 \qquad \text{Def. 17-7}$$

One may observe immediately that the problem is now much less complicated than by Method One and at the same time the desired results are obtained. In addition to this, the exponent of 10 allows one to locate the decimal point rather easily by starting at the right-most digit of the sum and

(1) counting to the left if the exponent is negative,

(2) counting to right if the exponent is positive, and

(3) annexing zeros as needed in (1) or (2).

Subtraction problems can be handled by use of Method Two in a fashion similar to that of addition.

Example: Determine $6.32 - .789$.

Solution: Since $6.32 = 6320 \cdot 10^{-3}$ and $.789 = 789 \cdot 10^{-3}$,

$$6.32 - .789 = 6320 \cdot 10^{-3} - 789 \cdot 10^{-3} \qquad \text{Subst. Uniq. (+)}$$

$$= (6320 - 789) \cdot 10^{-3} \qquad \text{Thm. 15-12}$$

$$= 5531 \cdot 10^{-3} \qquad \text{Def. 14-2}$$

$$= 5.531 \qquad \text{Def. 17-7}$$

If other examples of addition and subtraction are worked, it is found that the sum or difference is again a terminating decimal. Such examples would lead one to suspect that in general the sum or difference of two terminating decimals is a terminating decimal and indeed, this is the case. The proof of this fact is straight forward, but since it is quite involved we shall not prove it here.

Theorem 17-3: The sum or difference of two terminating decimals is a terminating decimal.

Once the validity of Theorem 17-3 is established, one may conclude that + and − are operations on the set of terminating decimals and consequently this set is closed with respect to these operations. If this observation is made, the next logical step is to consider whether similar results hold for multiplication and division. These will now be considered in some detail.

b. Multiplication and division

Products of terminating decimals can be handled either by the use of expanded notation or standard decimal numerals. The fact is that expanded notation becomes even more "messy" for multiplication than it is for addition or subtraction. If the student will try a numerical example, this will become painfully clear. For this reason we shall use only the standard decimal numerals for our discussion. In order to illustrate products of decimal numerals we consider the following example problem.

Example: Determine the product of 6.834 and .34.

Solution: Changing the numerals to standard form we have $6.834 = 6834 \cdot 10^{-3}$ and $.34 = 34 \cdot 10^{-2}$. Consequently

$$
\begin{array}{ll}
(6.834) \cdot (.34) = (6834 \cdot 10^{-3}) \cdot (34 \cdot 10^{-2}) & \text{Subst., Uniq. } (\cdot) \\
\quad = 6834[10^{-3} \cdot (34 \cdot 10^{-2})] & \text{Thm. 15-3} \\
\quad = 6834[(10^{-3} \cdot 34) \cdot 10^{-2}] & \text{Thm. 15-3} \\
\quad = 6834[(34 \cdot 10^{-3}) \cdot 10^{-2}] & \text{Thm. 15-2} \\
\quad = (6834 \cdot 34) \cdot (10^{-3} \cdot 10^{-2}) & \text{Thm. 15-3} \\
\quad = (6834 \cdot 34) \cdot 10^{-3+^-2} & a^m \cdot a^n = a^{m+n} \\
\quad = (6834 \cdot 34) \cdot 10^{-5} & \text{Def. 14-1} \\
\quad = 232356 \cdot 10^{-5} & \text{Def. 15-1} \\
\quad = 2.32356 & \text{Def. 17-7}
\end{array}
$$

It can be observed from the above example that the product is again a terminating decimal and it is apparently the case that the number of decimal places in the product is the *sum of those in the original factors.* If other examples are worked in which the factors are terminating decimals, one may conjecture that products of terminating decimals are themselves terminating decimals. This is true and the proof of the general result is much like that outlined in the steps of the preceding example. However, the proof does become somewhat tedious because of the fact that general place-value numerals must be used and for this reason we shall not include the proof here.

Theorem 17-4: The product of two terminating decimals is a terminating decimal.

Of particular interest in decimal arithmetic are the results of multiplying a decimal rational by powers of ten. In this connection you may recall rules similar to the following:

(1) If a decimal rational is multiplied by 10^k, k a positive integral rational,

the decimal point in the product is k places to the right of its original position.

(2) If a decimal rational is multiplied by 10^{-k}, k a positive integral rational, the decimal point in the product is k places to the left of its original position.

Some may use the language "move the decimal point." If so, you may eventually be asked how one "moves a point," so that perhaps the terminology used above will lead to less disagreement. While we shall not belabor the terminology to be used, we do want to consider these results in more detail.

Examples: (a) Calculate $6.7324 \cdot 10^3$.

(b) Calculate $63485.41 \cdot 10^{-4}$.

Solutions: (a) Using the standard decimal numerals we have

$$6.7324 \cdot 10^3 = (67324 \cdot 10^{-4}) \cdot 10^3$$
$$= 67324(10^{-4} \cdot 10^3)$$
$$= 67324 \cdot 10^{-4+3}$$
$$= 67324 \cdot 10^{-1}$$
$$= 6732.4$$

Note that the decimal point in the product is *three* places to the right of its original position. However, we did not "move" the decimal point to its new position.

(b) By again using the standard decimal numerals we obtain

$$63485.41 \cdot 10^{-4} = (6348541 \cdot 10^{-2}) \cdot 10^{-4}$$
$$= 6348541(10^{-2} \cdot 10^{-4})$$
$$= 6348541 \cdot 10^{-2+ -4}$$
$$= 6348541 \cdot 10^{-6}$$
$$= 6.348541$$

Here the exponent on the original multiplier was $^-4$ and the decimal point in the product is *four* places to the left of its original position.

In either of the two examples just worked, the end result is that which we would have obtained had we been able to "move" the decimal point and indeed this may be the way in which the language alluded to earlier came into use.

As you may have suspected, the results illustrated above hold in general for any product of a decimal rational and an integral rational power of ten. The steps of the proofs of these results follow the same general pattern as set forth in the examples above. We list these results in the theorem below.

Theorem 17-5: If $N = d_n d_{n-1} \ldots d_1 d_0 . c_1 c_2 \ldots c_m$ a terminating decimal and if $0 < k \leqslant m$ and $0 < k \leqslant n$, then

(1) $10^k N = d_n d_{n-1} \ldots d_1 d_0 c_1 c_2 \ldots c_k . c_{k+1} \ldots c_m$ and

(2) $10^{-k} N = d_n d_{n-1} \ldots d_k . d_{k-1} \ldots d_1 d_0 c_1 c_2 \ldots c_m$.

Based on the information now at hand, one might suspect that the set of terminating decimals behaves exactly as do rationals in general. Even though this set is closed under addition, subtraction, and multiplication, it can be shown that it is not closed under division by non-zero divisors. This can be demonstrated rather easily by considering the fact that both $\frac{1}{1}$ and $\frac{3}{1}$ have terminating decimal expansions, but $\frac{1}{1} \div \frac{3}{1} = \frac{1}{3}$ does not. This is due to the fact that 3 is not an integral rational power of 10. Consequently the set of terminating decimals is not closed under division. This *apparent defect* in division sets the stage for Section 17-3 where further discussion will be given to the problem.

Even though the set of terminating decimals is not closed under division, many problems which result in routine calculations in decimal arithmetic require division of terminating decimals. Interestingly enough, many of these divisions often yield terminating decimals for answers. In such division problems the division algorithm used for cardinal numbers applies equally well here with appropriate extensions. This process of repeated subtraction can be applied as follows:

$$
\begin{array}{r}
16\,)\,\overline{3} \quad \text{yields} \quad 16\,)\,\overline{3.0000} \\
\underline{1.6} \qquad\qquad -\!- \!- \!- .1 \\
1.40 \\
\underline{1.28} \qquad\qquad -\!- \!- \!- .08 \\
.120 \\
\underline{.112} \qquad\qquad -\!- \!- \!- .007 \\
.0080 \\
\underline{.0080} \qquad\qquad -\!- \!- \!- .0005 \\
\overline{.1875}
\end{array}
$$

The fact that we generally omit the decimal points in the body of the problem is explained and justified by Theorem 15-18. As you will recall, we mentioned before that this theorem would be very important in division of decimal rationals. To illustrate the value of the theorem we shall consider just step one of the problem.

$$\frac{3}{1} \div \frac{16}{1} = \left(\frac{3}{1} \cdot \frac{10}{1} \right) \div \left(\frac{16}{1} \cdot \frac{10}{1} \right)$$

$$= \left(\frac{3}{1} \cdot \frac{10}{1} \right) \cdot \left(\frac{1}{16} \cdot \frac{1}{10} \right)$$

$$= \left[\left(\frac{3}{1} \cdot \frac{10}{1} \right) \cdot \frac{1}{16} \right] \cdot \frac{1}{10}$$

$$= \left[\left(\frac{3}{1} \cdot \frac{10}{1} \right) \div \frac{16}{1} \right] \cdot \frac{1}{10}$$

$$= \left[\left(\frac{16}{1} + \frac{14}{1} \right) \div \frac{16}{1} \right] \cdot \frac{1}{10}$$

$$= \left[\left(\frac{16}{1} \div \frac{16}{1} \right) + \left(\frac{14}{1} \div \frac{16}{1} \right) \right] \cdot \frac{1}{10}$$

$$= \left[\frac{1}{1} + \left(\frac{14}{1} \cdot \frac{1}{16} \right) \right] \cdot \frac{1}{10}$$

$$= \left(\frac{1}{1} \cdot \frac{1}{10} \right) + \left[\left(\frac{14}{1} \cdot \frac{1}{16} \right) \cdot \frac{1}{10} \right]$$

$$= \frac{1}{10} + \left[\left(\frac{14}{1} \cdot \frac{1}{10} \right) \cdot \frac{1}{16} \right]$$

$$= \frac{1}{10} + \left[\left(\frac{14}{1} \cdot \frac{1}{10} \right) \div \frac{16}{1} \right]$$

This gives the partial quotient .1 and leads to the second step of the problem, namely $1.4 \div 16$. This type of process is repeated until the partial quotients .1, .08, .007, and .0005 are obtained respectively and the remainder is zero. As in cardinal numbers, the quotient is the sum of the partial quotients. Since this process gives the same result as "reading in" the decimal point in the body of the problem, they are generally omitted simply for convenience.

Further, if the divisor is a non-integral terminating decimal, the problem may be restated so that the divisor is a rational of the form $\frac{a}{1}$ by means of Theorem 15-18. Consequently all such problems are reducible to the type illustrated above.

Example: Restate $6.789 \overline{) 4.28691}$ so that the divisor is a rational of the form $\frac{a}{1}$.

Solution: By Theorem 15-18, $4.28691 \div 6.789$ is equivalent to $4286.91 \div 6789$. Generally we simply denote this change as follows:

$$6.798 \overline{) 4.28691} \longleftrightarrow 6.798_\wedge \overline{) 4.286_\wedge 91}$$

where the caret indicates that both divisor and dividend are multiplied by the same power of ten. It also turns out that the decimal point in the quotient is determined by the caret in the dividend as may be observed by working a few examples.

EXERCISE SET 17-2

1. Write a terminating decimal numeral for each of the following.

(a) $\frac{3}{75}$

(b) $\dfrac{5}{32}$

(c) $\dfrac{7}{140}$

(d) $\dfrac{9}{200}$

2. By use of expanded notation and appropriate properties of the rational number system determine each of the following sums or differences.
   (a) $1.983 + 34.75$
   (b) $62.009 + .987$
   (c) $3.476 + {}^-2.43$
   (d) ${}^-4.89 + {}^-2.071$
   (e) $2.794 - 4.37$
   (f) $32.453 - {}^-8.667$
   (g) ${}^-4.83 - 2.92$
   (h) ${}^-78.043 - {}^-13.784$

3. By use of standard decimal numerals determine the answer to each of the following.
   (a) $13.468 + 12.357$
   (b) $21.4629 + 3.0705$
   (c) $42.07 - 13.95$
   (d) $6.7954 - 8.5896$

4. Determine the products indicated below by first transforming to standard decimal numerals.
   (a) $(2.89) \cdot (13.41)$
   (b) $(.00071) \cdot (.0695)$
   (c) $(.07019) \cdot (8234.96)$

5. Work each of the following in *two* ways.
   (a) $(.0468) \cdot 10^7$
   (b) $(3.04679) \cdot 10^{-4}$

6. By use of long division show that the quotient is a terminating decimal.
   (a) $13 \div 32$
   (b) $.0840 \div .35$
   (c) $.1517 \div .41$
   (d) $1.3632 \div 9.6$
   (e) $2.73856 \div .064$
   (f) $28.65567 \div .079$

7. In parts (a), (c), and (e) of problem six show how Theorem 15-18 applies in the first step of the division process.

8. Discuss the following statement: "The decimal point in the quotient can be located immediately above the caret in the dividend."

3. Infinite Repeating Decimals

In the preceding section we discussed at some length the arithmetic of terminating decimals and in so doing found that the quotient of two terminating decimals may not be a terminating decimal. For example, 1 and 7 have terminating decimal expansions however $\dfrac{1}{7}$ does not have a terminating decimal expansion.

Since we can annex any finite number of zeros to the right of the decimal when dividing by 7, let us consider a few steps of the division problem $7 \overline{)1}$.

$$
\begin{array}{r}
.142857 \\
7\,\overline{)\,1.000000} \\
7 \\
\hline
30 \\
28 \\
\hline
20 \\
14 \\
\hline
60 \\
56 \\
\hline
40 \\
35 \\
\hline
50 \\
49 \\
\hline
1
\end{array}
$$

In the last step we have obtained the remainder 1, and therefore the same sequence of steps will be repeated in the same order if the division process is continued. Consequently the same set of digits would be repeated in the same order in the quotient, and then the process would continue in the same manner ad infinitum. If we look at this problem more closely we can observe that the digits not only do repeat, but they must repeat. The reason for this becomes clear if we consider the divisor 7. Since the divisor is 7, the only acceptable remainders are 0, 1, 2, 3, 4, 5, and 6. Consequently, since the decimal is non-terminating (we know this because 7 is no factor of 10) some one of the remainders must eventually appear a second time. When this happens, the digits in the quotient must begin to repeat in cycles. Thus, before starting the above example, we know that the sequence of repeating digits can be no more than six digits since zero cannot be a remainder. (Why?) Thus a rational number which has denominator n can have at most a sequence of $(n-1)$ digits which repeat. This sequence of repeating digits is called a *cycle* and the number of digits in the cycle is often referred to as the *length* of the cycle. Thus the decimal expansion for $\frac{1}{7}$ has a cycle of length six and the cycle is 142857. Because of the fact that these cycles repeat continuously and the division process theoretically never ends, the decimal expansions are called *infinite repeating* decimals. The term infinite repeating decimal does not mean that the number represented is infinite, but rather means that the set or cycle of digits repeats infinitely many times. A problem now presents itself in the writing of the decimal numerals and because of this, we shall adopt a standard numeral for infinite repeating decimals. For example we shall write

$.\overline{142857}$	for	$.142857142857142857142857\ldots$
$.\overline{1}$	for	$.1111111111\ldots$
$.\overline{265}$	for	$.265265265265\ldots$
$3.4\overline{16}$	for	$3.4161616161616\ldots$

$$53.78\overline{92} \quad \text{for} \quad 53.78929292929292 \ldots, \text{and so forth}$$

The bar above a set of digits is used to indicate that this is the cycle of digits which continue to repeat in the decimal expansion obtained by the division process.

From the discussion thus far, we have indicated that decimal rationals fall into no more than two categories:

(1) terminating decimals, or

(2) infinite repeating decimals.

Further, every rational number has a decimal expansion which is either terminating or infinite repeating. If a numeral for a rational number can be written with denominator which is a power of 10 the decimal numeral terminates; if not, then the decimal numeral has continuously repeating cycles of digits.

It should be noted with regard to the two classifications listed above that *all* decimal expansions for rational numbers may be regarded as infinite repeating decimals. This is done by annexing $\overline{0}$ to the right end of a terminating decimal numeral so that 0 repeats continuously from that point. Thus one may write $1.6 = 1.6\overline{0}$, $.032 = .032\overline{0}$, and so forth so that only one classification is necessary, namely infinite repeating decimals. If one chooses to do this then the following theorem can be stated to summarize the results achieved in converting from standard rational numerals to decimal numerals.

Theorem 17-6: Every rational number has associated with it an infinite repeating decimal numeral.

If the above choice is not made, then as mentioned before, two types of decimal numerals result, terminating or infinite repeating.

Since it is known that decimal expansions can be determined for each rational number, it is natural to try to reverse the process. As you can observe from Section 17-2, the task for terminating decimals is relatively easy. For terminating decimals one can simply change from decimal form to expanded form, add, and if necessary reduce to lowest terms. However, we have yet to try this for infinite repeating decimals.

Let us begin by considering the decimal rational $R = .\overline{3}$. Using Theorem 17-5, we shall multiply R by 10. Thus

$$
\begin{array}{r}
10R = 3.\overline{3} \\
(-)\ \underline{R = \ .\overline{3}} \\
9R = 3 \\
R = \dfrac{3}{9}
\end{array}
$$

Consequently we obtain the result $\dfrac{1}{3} = .\overline{3}$. As you can readily observe, if 1 is divided by 3 the decimal expansion is found to be $.3333 \cdots$ or $.\overline{3}$, so that the technique illustrated appears to work.

As other examples, consider the following.

Examples: (a) Determine the standard numeral for $R = .\overline{9}$.
(b) Determine the standard numeral for $R = .\overline{265}$.

Solutions:

(a) $10R = 9.\overline{9}$
$(-) \quad R = \;\; .\overline{9}$
$\overline{9R = 9}$

$R = \dfrac{9}{9}$ or $\dfrac{1}{1}$

(b) $1000R = 265.\overline{265}$
$(-) \qquad R = \qquad .\overline{265}$
$\overline{999R = 265}$

$R = \dfrac{265}{999}$

If further examples similar to those just completed are worked, the end result is the following conjecture.

Theorem 17-7: If R has the decimal expansion $.\overline{d_1 d_2 \ldots d_k}$, then

$$R = \frac{d_1 d_2 \ldots d_k}{10^k - 1}$$

As you can observe, the result of this theorem does work in the examples above. For $.\overline{3}$, k, the length of cycle, is 1 and the cycle has 3 as the only digit. Thus according to the theorem we should obtain

$$R = \frac{3}{10^1 - 1} = \frac{3}{10 - 1} = \frac{3}{9}$$

For $R = .\overline{265}$, k is 3, and the cycle has digits 265 so that we should obtain

$$R = \frac{265}{10^3 - 1} = \frac{265}{1000 - 1} = \frac{265}{999}$$

Again we see that the same results are obtained with much less effort than previously.

Of course, there are other possibilities for infinite repeating decimals, for either all digits to the right of the decimal point repeat or else they do not. If they do they are of the general type discussed above. An example of the second type is $26.7\overline{81}$. However, as indicated above the object is to obtain new decimal numerals in such a way that only the same digits (in the same order) appear to the right of the decimal point. For numerals similar to $26.7\overline{81}$ then, perhaps it would be possible to form two different multiples in such a way that exactly the same sequence of digits results to the right of the decimal point in each. If $R = 26.7\overline{81}$ then, consider the following:

$1000R = 26781.\overline{81}$
$(-) \quad 10R = \;\;\; 267.\overline{81}$
$\overline{990R = 26514}$

$$R = \frac{26514}{990}$$

$$R = \frac{1473}{55}$$

If you try other similar examples, you will find that this technique will work. As in the first case considered, the technique may not yield numerals in reduced form, but it will give rise to a pair of integers $\frac{a}{b}$. Once this is done, it is (theoretically) a relatively easy matter to determine the reduced form of the numeral by changing numerator and denominator to products of prime factors and then using the K-Theorem or the property of the multiplicative identity.

To summarize then, infinite repeating decimals may be put into two categories; either all digits to the right of the decimal point repeat or they do not. In either case we have been able to determine a numeral of the form $\frac{a}{b}$ which has the given decimal expansion. If in conjunction with this we take into account that every terminating decimal may also be considered as a special kind of infinite repeating decimal, we find that we can formulate a very interesting statement concerning rational numbers and decimal numerals.

Theorem 17-8: Every rational number corresponds to an infinite repeating decimal and every infinite repeating decimal corresponds to a rational number.

If we now make use of the properties of the rational number system we may draw the following conclusions regarding operations using infinite repeating decimal numerals:

(1) the sum or difference of infinite repeating decimals is an infinite repeating decimal,

(2) the product of infinite repeating decimals is an infinite repeating decimal, and

(3) for non-zero divisors, the quotient of infinite repeating decimals is an infinite repeating decimal.

It should be stressed that the establishing of these results required no further theoretical work, but rather made use of the structure and properties of rational numbers already known.

EXERCISE SET 17-3

1. Show by example that if the denominator of a rational number is not a power of 2 or 5 or a combination of the two, then the decimal expansion is *not* terminating.

2. Determine the decimal expansion for each of the following:

(a) $\frac{1}{3}$ (f) $\frac{1}{11}$

(b) $\frac{1}{4}$ (g) $\frac{3}{13}$

(c) $\frac{1}{5}$ (h) $\frac{1}{9}$

(d) $\dfrac{2}{7}$ (i) $\dfrac{3}{8}$

(e) $\dfrac{8}{9}$ (j) $\dfrac{1}{6}$

3. Write each of the decimal numerals determined in problem two using the "bar" notation to indicate the cycles of repeating digits and for each determine the length of the cycle.

4. Determine the preferred rational numeral for each of the following infinite repeating decimals. (Show your work.)

(a) $.\overline{234}$ (g) $1.\overline{234}$

(b) $.3\overline{7}$ (h) $1.2\overline{34}$

(c) $.3\overline{897}$ (i) $1.23\overline{4}$

(d) $.98\overline{2}$ (j) 37.98

(e) $.6\overline{7894}$ (k) $3.798\overline{23}$

(f) $.\overline{6}$ (l) $6.79\overline{46}$

5. Indicate which of the following represents a rational number and support your answer in each case.

(a) 2.10265438 (e) $.\overline{3} + .\overline{7}$

(b) $1 \cdot 10 + 3 + 2 \left(\dfrac{1}{10}\right) + 5 \left(\dfrac{1}{10^3}\right)$ (f) $.\overline{4} + .\overline{5}$

(c) $\dfrac{9}{212}$ (g) $.\overline{5} + .4\overline{9}$

(d) $\dfrac{2}{.\overline{2}}$ (h) $.\overline{1} + (.\overline{2} + .\overline{3})$

6. Write in preferred form the numeral for the rational number whose decimal expansion is

(a) $.\overline{1}$ (b) $.\overline{10}$ (c) $.0\overline{9}$ (d) $.\overline{101}$

(e) $3.1\overline{4}$ (f) $1.4\overline{14}$ (g) $3.7\overline{37}$ (h) $.076\overline{923}$

7. Determine the answer to each of the following problems. Where possible, write your answer in the same notation as the original problem.

(a) $(.\overline{3} + .\overline{4}) + .\overline{1} =$ (f) $(.\overline{8})(.\overline{7}) + (.\overline{7})(.\overline{6}) =$

(b) $(.\overline{6} + .\overline{5}) + .\overline{7} =$ (g) $(.\overline{8} + .\overline{5})(.\overline{8} - .\overline{5}) =$

(c) $(.\overline{6} + .\overline{8}) - .\overline{9} =$ (h) $(.\overline{9} + .\overline{1})(.\overline{9} - .\overline{1}) =$

(d) $(.\overline{5} + .\overline{34}) - .\overline{62} =$ (i) $(.\overline{8}) \div (.\overline{4}) =$

(e) $(.\overline{8})(.\overline{9}) =$ (j) $(.\overline{6})(.\overline{3}) \div .\overline{7} =$

8. Work each of the following problems.

(a) $\begin{array}{r} .\overline{4} \\ + .\overline{5} \\ \hline \end{array}$ (b) $\begin{array}{r} .\overline{6} \\ + .\overline{3} \\ \hline \end{array}$ (c) $\begin{array}{r} .\overline{7} \\ + .\overline{2} \\ \hline \end{array}$ (d) $\begin{array}{r} .\overline{8} \\ + .\overline{1} \\ \hline \end{array}$

9. Work each of the following problems.

(a) $\begin{array}{r} 1.\overline{4} \\ + .\overline{5} \\ \hline \end{array}$ (b) $\begin{array}{r} 1.\overline{6} \\ + .\overline{3} \\ \hline \end{array}$ (c) $\begin{array}{r} 1.\overline{7} \\ + .\overline{2} \\ \hline \end{array}$

10. Work each of the following problems.

(a) $\begin{array}{r} .\overline{3} \\ + .\overline{4} \\ \hline \end{array}$ (b) $\begin{array}{r} .\overline{5} \\ + .\overline{5} \\ \hline \end{array}$ (c) $\begin{array}{r} .\overline{6} \\ + .\overline{8} \\ \hline \end{array}$ (d) $\begin{array}{r} 1.\overline{2} \\ + 3.\overline{4} \\ \hline \end{array}$

11. After working problems 7 through 10, would you say that the "bar" arithmetic of infinite repeating decimals works as you had expected? Why or why not?

4. An Intuitive Limiting Process

In the preceding section a discussion of infinite repeating decimals was given which cleared up the mystery surrounding the division of terminating decimals. During the course of that development it was found that the quotient of two infinite repeating decimals yielded another infinite repeating decimal. It was also found that every rational number has either a terminating or an infinite repeating decimal expansion. In particular we were able to determine a rational numeral of the form $\frac{a}{b}$ for any infinite repeating decimal. However, if we consider more closely the algorithm which effected this change in numerals, we find that a certain problem arises concerning the mathematical procedures used. For instance, in order to change the decimal numeral $N = .\overline{31}$ to the form $\frac{a}{b}$ we proceeded as follows:

$$100 \cdot N = 31.\overline{31}$$

$$(-) \quad N = \quad .\overline{31}$$

$$99 \cdot N = 31$$

$$N = \frac{31}{99}$$

The questionable mathematical procedure is that of saying that multiplication of $.\overline{31}$ by 100 "moves" the decimal point two places to the right. One should question this because of the facts that the expanded form of $.\overline{31}$ has infinitely many terms and the algorithm used was applicable only to a finite number of terms (see Theorem 17-5). Another way of looking at the problem is to consider the usual multiplication algorithm which we denote

$$xxxxx$$

$$(\cdot) \quad yyy$$

Here the usual procedure is to begin with the right-hand y and x and work from right to left. If there are infinitely many x digits as in $.\overline{31}$, where exactly is the right-hand digit? Again it is apparent that something has been ignored in Section 17-3.

In order to try to explain what actually takes place in these problems involving infinite repeating decimals we shall consider a problem for which the answer is known, namely $\frac{1}{3} = .\overline{3}$. It should be clear that the expanded form could be written as

$$.\overline{3} = \frac{3}{10} + \frac{3}{10^2} + \frac{3}{10^3} + \ldots + \frac{3}{10^n} + \ldots \;.$$

Let us consider, for the moment, the first n terms of $.\overline{3}$ which we shall denote by S_n. S is used to remind us of a *sum* and the subscript n is used to denote the number of terms *being* summed. Thus

$$S_n = \frac{3}{10} + \frac{3}{10^2} + \frac{3}{10^3} + \ldots + \frac{3}{10^{n-1}} + \frac{3}{10^n}$$

and if you count the terms as indexed by the exponents on 10, you can see that we have used exactly n terms of $.\overline{3}$. Since S_n has a finite number of terms we may write that

$$\frac{1}{10} S_n = \frac{1}{10} \cdot \left(\frac{3}{10} + \frac{3}{10^2} + \frac{3}{10^3} + \ldots + \frac{3}{10^{n-1}} + \frac{3}{10^n} \right) \qquad \text{Thm. 15-6}$$

$$= \frac{3}{10^2} + \frac{3}{10^3} + \frac{3}{10^4} + \ldots + \frac{3}{10^n} + \frac{3}{10^{n+1}} \qquad \left\{ \begin{array}{l} \text{Gen. distr. prop.} \\ \text{Def. 15-1} \end{array} \right.$$

$$= \frac{0}{10} + \frac{3}{10^2} + \frac{3}{10^3} + \frac{3}{10^4} + \ldots + \frac{3}{10^n} + \frac{3}{10^{n+1}} \qquad \text{Thm. 14-5}$$

$$= \frac{0}{10} + \frac{3}{10^2} + \frac{3}{10^3} + \frac{3}{10^4} + \ldots + \frac{3}{10^{n-1}} + \frac{3}{10^n} + \frac{3}{10^{n+1}}$$

Next, let us form the difference $S_n - \frac{1}{10} S_n$ as follows:

$$S_n = \frac{3}{10} + \frac{3}{10^2} + \frac{3}{10^3} + \frac{3}{10^4} + \ldots + \frac{3}{10^{n-1}} + \frac{3}{10^n}$$

$$(-) \; \frac{1}{10} S_n = \frac{0}{10} + \frac{3}{10^2} + \frac{3}{10^3} + \frac{3}{10^4} + \ldots + \frac{3}{10^{n-1}} + \frac{3}{10^n} + \frac{3}{10^{n+1}}$$

$$\rule{10cm}{0.4pt}$$

$$S_n - \frac{1}{10} S_n = \frac{3}{10} - \frac{3}{10^{n+1}}$$

Here of course we have really made use of uniqueness of differences, extensions of associative and commutative properties of addition, and a few other concepts. Continuing, we obtain

$$\left(1 - \frac{1}{10}\right) S_n = \frac{3}{10} \left(1 - \frac{1}{10^{n+1}}\right)$$

$$\frac{9}{10} S_n = \frac{3}{10} \left(1 - \frac{1}{10^{n+1}}\right)$$

$$S_n = \frac{10}{9} \cdot \frac{3}{10} \left(1 - \frac{1}{10^{n+1}} \right)$$

$$S_n = \frac{1}{3} \left(1 - \frac{1}{10^{n+1}} \right)$$

$$S_n = \frac{1}{3} \left(1 - \frac{1}{10} \cdot \frac{1}{10^n} \right)$$

In this last expression just derived for S_n let us consider in detail what happens to the quotient $\frac{1}{10^n}$ for several selected positive values of n. Since n is a positive integral rational we want to know what happens to $\frac{1}{10^n}$ for larger and larger integral n. Refer to Table 17-1.

TABLE 17-1

n	$\frac{1}{10^n}$	decimal equivalent of $\frac{1}{10^n}$
1	$\frac{1}{10}$	.1
2	$\frac{1}{10^2}$	.01
3	$\frac{1}{10^3}$	.001
4	$\frac{1}{10^4}$	.0001
10	$\frac{1}{10^{10}}$	.0000000001
20	$\frac{1}{10^{20}}$	.00000000000000000001

It is easy to observe from Table 17-1 that the larger the exponent n selected, the smaller the quotient becomes. However since both 1 and 10^n are positive, the quotient can never be negative. Thus the larger the exponent n selected, the closer the quotient $\frac{1}{10^n}$ is to zero. When this occurs we say that as n becomes large without bound, the quotient approaches zero. This phenomenon is sometimes expressed symbolically as $\underset{n \to \infty}{\text{limit}} \dfrac{1}{10^n} = 0$. The symbol, $n \to \infty$, is read "as n increases without bound" or "as n becomes large without bound." In the example chosen above the quotient $\dfrac{1}{10^n}$ approaches the number on the right hand side of the equals sign, namely 0. The entire symbol, then, would be read "the limit as n increases without bound of $\dfrac{1}{10^n}$ equals zero." Pictorially this limiting process might appear similar to that in Figure 17-1 below where we consider $R \times R$, and where R is the set of rationals.

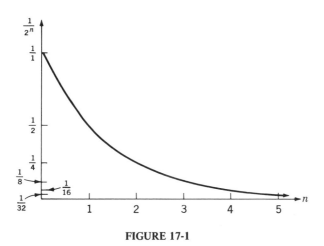

FIGURE 17-1

As can be observed from Figure 17-1, the quotient $\dfrac{1}{2^n}$ approaches more and more closely to the horizontal line; that is, closer to zero. The only difference between $\dfrac{1}{2^n}$ and $\dfrac{1}{10^n}$ is that the latter approaches zero much faster than the former for successively larger choices of n.

Thus the expression

$$\underset{n \to \infty}{\text{limit}} \left(2 + \frac{1}{10^n}\right) = 2$$

means that for any number selected, regardless of how small, there is a number N such that for all $n \geqslant N$ the difference between $2 + \dfrac{1}{10^n}$ and 2 is less than the number selected.

Suppose .1 is selected. Then $N = 2$ is sufficient since $\left(2 + \dfrac{1}{10^2}\right) - 2 = .01$

and $.01 < .1$. Thus for the choice $.1$, $n \geqslant N = 2$ guarantees that $\left(2 + \dfrac{1}{10^N}\right) - 2 < .1$.

If $.01$ had been selected, then a sufficiently large N is 3. For $N = 3$ we have $\left(2 + \dfrac{1}{10^3}\right) - 2 = .001$ and $.001 < .01$. Hence for the choice $.01$, $n \geqslant N = 3$ guarantees that $\left(2 + \dfrac{1}{10^N}\right) - 2 < .01$.

Now let us return to our example and determine the value of S_n as $n \to \infty$. That is, let us determine the limit of S_n as n increases without bound. We have

$$\underset{n \to \infty}{\text{limit }} S_n = \underset{n \to \infty}{\text{limit }} \left[\frac{1}{3}\left(1 - \frac{1}{10^n}\right)\right]$$

$$= \frac{1}{3}(1 - 0)$$

$$= \frac{1}{3}$$

The reason for this is that the numbers $\dfrac{1}{3}$ and 1 depend in no way on n and so the term $\dfrac{1}{10^n}$ is the only one which is affected by increasing n. Since $\dfrac{1}{3} = \underset{n \to \infty}{\text{limit }} S_n$ and $\underset{n \to \infty}{\text{limit }} S_n = \dfrac{3}{10} + \dfrac{3}{10^2} + \ldots + \dfrac{3}{10^n} + \ldots$, our final conclusion must be that $\dfrac{1}{3} = .\overline{3}$.

By the same type of limit process, one can show that $.\overline{9} = 1$. We begin by considering the expanded form of $.\overline{9}$ and forming the sum S_n of the first n terms.

$$S_n = \frac{9}{10} + \frac{9}{10^2} + \frac{9}{10^3} + \ldots + \frac{9}{10^{n-1}} + \frac{9}{10^n}.$$

Then

$$\frac{1}{10} S_n = \frac{9}{10^2} + \frac{9}{10^3} + \frac{9}{10^4} + \ldots + \frac{9}{10^n} + \frac{9}{10^{n+1}}$$

$$= \frac{0}{10} + \frac{9}{10^2} + \frac{9}{10^3} + \ldots + \frac{9}{10^{n-1}} + \frac{9}{10^n} + \frac{9}{10^{n+1}}.$$

Thus

$$S_n - \frac{1}{10} S_n = \left(\frac{9}{10} + \frac{9}{10^2} + \frac{9}{10^3} + \ldots + \frac{9}{10^{n-1}} + \frac{9}{10^n}\right) -$$

$$\left(\frac{0}{10} + \frac{9}{10^2} + \frac{9}{10^3} + \ldots + \frac{9}{10^{n-1}} + \frac{9}{10^n} + \frac{9}{10^{n+1}}\right)$$

$$= \frac{9}{10} - \frac{9}{10^{n+1}}$$

$$= \frac{9}{10}\left(1 - \frac{1}{10^n}\right)$$

Therefore

$$\frac{9}{10} S_n = \frac{9}{10}\left(1 - \frac{1}{10^n}\right)$$

or

$$S_n = 1 - \frac{1}{10^n}$$

Now

$$\lim_{n \to \infty} S_n = \lim_{n \to \infty} \left(1 - \frac{1}{10^n}\right)$$

$$= 1 - 0$$

$$= 1$$

Therefore

$$.\overline{9} = 1$$

As another example, consider $N = .00\overline{3}$. We write

$$S_n = \frac{3}{10^3} + \frac{3}{10^4} + \frac{3}{10^5} + \ldots + \frac{3}{10^n}$$

or

$$S_n = \frac{3}{10^2}\left(\frac{1}{10} + \frac{1}{10^2} + \ldots + \frac{1}{10^{n-2}}\right)$$

$$\frac{1}{10} S_n = \frac{3}{10^2}\left(\frac{1}{10^2} + \frac{1}{10^3} + \ldots + \frac{1}{10^{n-2}} + \frac{1}{10^{n-1}}\right)$$

Then

$$S_n - \frac{1}{10} S_n = \frac{3}{10^2}\left(\frac{1}{10} + \frac{1}{10^2} + \ldots + \frac{1}{10^{n-2}}\right) -$$

$$\frac{3}{10^2}\left(\frac{1}{10^2} + \frac{1}{10^3} + \ldots + \frac{1}{10^{n-2}} + \frac{1}{10^{n-1}}\right)$$

$$\frac{9}{10} S_n = \frac{3}{10^2}\left[\left(\frac{1}{10} + \frac{1}{10^2} + \frac{1}{10^3} + \ldots + \frac{1}{10^{n-2}}\right) -$$

$$\left(\frac{1}{10^2} + \frac{1}{10^3} + \ldots + \frac{1}{10^{n-2}} + \frac{1}{10^{n-1}}\right)\right]$$

$$\frac{9}{10} S_n = \frac{3}{10^2}\left(\frac{1}{10} - \frac{1}{10^{n-1}}\right)$$

$$S_n = \frac{10}{9} \cdot \frac{3}{10^2} \cdot \frac{1}{10}\left(1 - \frac{1}{10^{n-2}}\right)$$

$$= \frac{1}{3} \cdot \frac{1}{10^2}\left(1 - \frac{1}{10^{n-2}}\right)$$

Now

$$\lim_{n \to \infty} S_n = \lim_{n \to \infty}\left[\frac{1}{3} \cdot \frac{1}{10^2}\left(1 - \frac{1}{10^{n-2}}\right)\right]$$

$$= \frac{1}{3} \cdot \frac{1}{10^2}(1 - 0)$$

$$= \frac{1}{3} \cdot \frac{1}{10^2}$$

$$= \frac{1}{300}$$

By using the method of limits just described, we find that even though the mathematical procedures used in Section 17-3 were without a proper mathematical basis, the results obtained are valid. This is the reason the algorithm is used — it gives the correct results quickly. It is important to note however that there is some mathematical justification for it. We shall see shortly that the results just obtained do have further application.

EXERCISE SET 17-4

1. Draw pictures similar to Figure 17-1 of each of the following for $n = 0, 1, 2, 3, 4$.

    (a) $\dfrac{1}{2^n}$

    (b) $\dfrac{1}{3^n}$

    (c) $\dfrac{1}{4^n}$

    (d) $\dfrac{1}{10^n}$

    (e) Which of the graphs gets closer to zero faster?

2. Determine limit S_n in each of the following.
$$n \to \infty$$

(a) $S_n = \left(3 + \dfrac{1}{10^n}\right)$

(b) $S_n = \left(27 - \dfrac{2}{10^n}\right)$

(c) $S_n = \left(4 - \dfrac{3/2}{10^n}\right)$

(d) $S_n = \dfrac{9}{10} + \dfrac{9}{10^2} + \dfrac{9}{10^3} + \ldots + \dfrac{9}{10^n}$

(e) $S_n = \dfrac{9}{10^0} + \dfrac{9}{10^1} + \dfrac{9}{10^2} + \ldots + \dfrac{9}{10^{n-1}}$

(f) $S_n = \dfrac{7}{10} + \dfrac{7}{10^2} + \ldots + \dfrac{7}{10^n}$

(g) $S_n = \dfrac{6}{10} + \dfrac{6}{10^2} + \ldots + \dfrac{6}{10^n}$

3. Show by use of the limit process that

(a) $.\overline{12} = \dfrac{4}{33}$

(b) $.\overline{46} = \dfrac{46}{99}$

(c) $.\overline{621} = \dfrac{69}{11}$

(d) $.\overline{1} = \dfrac{1}{9}$

(e) $.\overline{101} = \dfrac{101}{999}$

5. Percents and Rational Numbers

It was suggested intuitively when the concept of rational number was discussed that one sometimes considers a part of something. In many such situations this can be done by using pairs of positive integers. When this is the case, the part under consideration is often referred to as a "fractional" part. Of these fractional parts, a type which is often considered is "one part out of one hundred." As indicated by the title of this section, we will now consider this latter type, namely percents. The Latin root words for percent, per centum, mean "by the hundred." Thus one percent means one of the hundred. Considering the interpretation given to the word *of* in relation to multiplication, we may make the following formal definition.

Definition 17-8: One **percent** is one hundredth. Symbolically, $1\% = \dfrac{1}{100}$. Knowing what 1% means, multiples of it are easily obtained.

Examples:

(a) $10\% = 10 \cdot 1\% = 10 \cdot \dfrac{1}{100} = \dfrac{1}{10} = .1$

(b) $20\% = 20 \cdot 1\% = 20 \cdot \dfrac{1}{100} = \dfrac{2}{10} = .2$

(c) $25\% = 25 \cdot 1\% = 25 \cdot \dfrac{1}{100} = \dfrac{25}{100} = .25$

(d) $79\% = 79 \cdot 1\% = 79 \cdot \dfrac{1}{100} = \dfrac{79}{100} = .79$

(e) $100\% = 100 \cdot 1\% = 100 \cdot \dfrac{1}{100} = \dfrac{1}{1} = 1$

(f) $300\% = 300 \cdot 1\% = 300 \cdot \dfrac{1}{100} = \dfrac{3}{1} = 3$

(g) $336\% = 336 \cdot 1\% = 336 \cdot \dfrac{1}{100} = \dfrac{336}{100} = \dfrac{300}{100} + \dfrac{36}{100} = \dfrac{3}{1} + \dfrac{36}{100} = 3.36$

Thus if we want to change from percent to decimal notation we may use Definition 17-8 and multiplication facts, change to expanded notation, and finally use Definition 17-6 to change to decimal notation. For example,

$$\dfrac{3}{100}\% = \dfrac{3}{100} \cdot 1\%$$

$$= \dfrac{3}{100} \cdot \dfrac{1}{100}$$

$$= \dfrac{3}{10000}$$

$$= 0\left(\dfrac{1}{10}\right) + 0\left(\dfrac{1}{10^2}\right) + 0\left(\dfrac{1}{10^3}\right) + 3\left(\dfrac{1}{10^4}\right)$$

$$= .0003$$

It is by the above process that one forms the rule "to change from percent to decimal notation, move the decimal two places to the left and drop the percent sign."

In general, if we want to change $\dfrac{a}{b}\%$ to a decimal numeral and b is a power of 10, the process can be simplified as follows.

Example: $\dfrac{6}{1000}\% = .006\% = (.006)\left(\dfrac{1}{100}\right) = .006 \cdot 10^{-2} = .00006.$

As you can observe, powers of 10 can be employed to advantage in this process. For something like $\dfrac{3}{8}\%$ where the denominator is not a power of 10, we first determine the decimal expansion of $\dfrac{3}{8}$. But this can be done by methods discussed in Section 17-1 since the denominator is an integral power of two. Using this information, we obtain

$$\frac{3}{8}\% = \frac{375}{1000}\%$$

$$= .375\%$$

$$= (.375)(.01)$$

$$= .00375$$

The reverse process can also often be accomplished without too much trouble. That is, we can change from decimal numerals to percents.

Example:

$$.0365 = \frac{365}{10000}$$

$$= \frac{365 \cdot 1}{100 \cdot 100}$$

$$= \frac{365}{100} \cdot \frac{1}{100}$$

$$= \frac{365}{100}\%$$

$$= 3.65\%$$

or

$$= 3\frac{13}{20}\% \quad \text{since} \quad \frac{65}{100} = \frac{13}{20}$$

The requirement for changing from decimal to percent is be able to obtain as a factor the rational number $\frac{1}{100}$. Once this is done, the stage is set for the use of Definition 17-8 to change to percent notation.

Now let us reconsider our discussion at the beginning of this section to see where the concept of limits has application. Suppose we wish to change the decimal numeral $.00\overline{3}$ to a percent. From our earlier example involving limits in Section 17-4, we showed that

$$.00\overline{3} = .\overline{3}(.01)$$

$$= .\overline{3}\%$$

But from the previous discussion, $\frac{1}{3} = .\overline{3}$, so that $.00\overline{3} = .\overline{3}\% = \frac{1}{3}\%$. Therefore the algorithm previously used to change decimal numerals to percents does hold, and is now placed on a more solid mathematical basis for use with infinite repeating decimals.

In general, problems involving a change from repeating decimal numerals to percents can be worked in a similar manner. Let us suppose that for a given rational number R the decimal expansion has p zeros between the decimal point and the first cycle of non-zero digits. That is suppose that

$$R = .0_1\, 0_2 \ldots 0_p\, \overline{a_1\, a_2 \ldots a_k}$$

If we consider the sum S_n of the first n cycles of R, we have

$$S_n = \frac{a_1\, a_2 \ldots a_k}{10^{p+k}} + \frac{a_1\, a_2 \ldots a_k}{10^{p+2k}} + \ldots + \frac{a_1\, a_2 \ldots a_k}{10^{p+nk}}$$

Then using an extension of the distributive property

$$S_n = \frac{a_1\, a_2 \ldots a_k}{10^{p+k}} \left[1 + \frac{1}{10^k} + \frac{1}{10^{2k}} + \ldots + \frac{1}{10^{(n-2)k}} + \frac{1}{10^{(n-1)k}} \right]$$

and multiplication of S_n by 10^{-k} gives

$$\frac{1}{10^k} S_n = \frac{a_1\, a_2 \ldots a_k}{10^{p+k}} \cdot \left[\frac{1}{10^k} + \frac{1}{10^{2k}} + \ldots + \frac{1}{10^{(n-1)k}} + \frac{1}{10^{nk}} \right]$$

If we now subtract $\dfrac{1}{10^k} S_n$ from S_n we obtain

$$S_n - \frac{1}{10^k} S_n = \frac{a_1\, a_2 \ldots a_k}{10^{p+k}} \left[1 - \frac{1}{10^{nk}} \right]$$

or

$$S_n \left(1 - \frac{1}{10^k} \right) = \frac{a_1\, a_2 \ldots a_k}{10^{p+k}} \left[1 - \frac{1}{10^{nk}} \right]$$

Continuing, we have

$$S_n \left(\frac{10^k - 1}{10^k} \right) = \frac{a_1\, a_2 \ldots a_k}{10^{p+k}} \left[1 - \frac{1}{10^{nk}} \right]$$

If both sides of the latter equation are multiplied by $\left(\dfrac{10^k}{10^k - 1} \right)$ we find that

$$S_n = \frac{a_1\, a_2 \ldots a_k}{10^{p+k}} \cdot \frac{10^k}{10^k - 1} \left[1 - \frac{1}{10^{nk}} \right]$$

$$= \frac{a_1 \, a_2 \ldots a_k}{10^p \cdot 10^k} \cdot \frac{10^k}{10^k - 1} \left[1 - \frac{1}{10^{nk}} \right]$$

$$= \frac{a_1 \, a_2 \ldots a_k}{10^p(10^k - 1)} \left[1 - \frac{1}{10^{nk}} \right]$$

Then as n increases without bound, we find that

$$\underset{n \to \infty}{\text{limit}} \ S_n = \underset{n \to \infty}{\text{limit}} \ \frac{a_1 \, a_2 \ldots a_k}{10^p(10^k - 1)} \cdot \left[1 - \frac{1}{10^{nk}} \right]$$

$$= \frac{a_1 \, a_2 \ldots a_k}{10^p(10^k - 1)} \cdot 1$$

$$= \frac{a_1 \, a_2 \ldots a_k}{(10^k - 1)10^{p-2}} \cdot \frac{1}{10^2}$$

$$= \frac{a_1 \, a_2 \ldots a_k}{(10^k - 1)10^{p-2}} \%$$

Since $\underset{n \to \infty}{\text{limit}} \ S_n = R$, we finally obtain the equality

$$.0_1 \, 0_2 \, 0_3 \ldots 0_p \, \overline{a_1 \, a_2 \ldots a_k} = \frac{a_1 \, a_2 \ldots a_k}{(10^k - 1)10^{p-2}} \%$$

Now of course if the conversion formula just derived is for the general (pure decimal) case, we should obtain predicted values for $.00\overline{3}$, $.01\overline{6}$, and so forth if we use the expression. Let us try a few examples to show that expected results are obtained.

Examples:

(a) $R = .00\overline{3}$.

Solution: Here $p = 2, k = 1$. So

$$.00\overline{3} = \frac{3}{(10^1 - 1)10^{2-2}} \% = \frac{3}{9 \cdot 1} \% = \frac{1}{3} \%$$

(b) $R = .01\overline{6} = .01 + .00\overline{6}$.

Solution: In $.00\overline{6} \ p = 2, k = 1$ so that

$$.00\overline{6} = \frac{6}{(10^1 - 1)10^{2-2}} \% = \frac{6}{9} \% = \frac{2}{3} \%$$

and

$$.01 = 1\%$$

so that

$$R = 1\frac{2}{3}\%$$

(c) $R = .1\overline{6}$.

Solution: Here write $R = .16 + .00\overline{6}$. For $.00\overline{6}, p = 2, k = 1$ so that

$$.00\overline{6} = \frac{6}{(10^1 - 1)10^{2-2}}\% = \frac{6}{9}\% = \frac{2}{3}\%$$

Since $.16 = 16\%$, we have

$$R = 16\frac{2}{3}\%$$

As the above examples illustrate, general results can be of considerable value. Here, all we had to do was to select p and k and use the general conversion formula. A great deal of work with limits has thus been avoided. This again illustrates the usefulness of generalization in mathematics.

EXERCISE SET 17-5

1. Change each of the following from percent to decimal notation.
   (a) 239%   (b) 34.2%   (c) 4.73%   (d) 33%   (e) 66.66%
   (f) .166%   (g) .04%   (h) .062%   (i) .0125%   (j) 4.033%
2. Change each of the following decimals to a percent.
   (a) 12.1   (b) 2.36   (c) .427   (d) .348   (e) .027
   (f) .0495   (g) .0033   (h) .0666   (i) .00825   (j) 4
3. Change from decimal form to percents by use of the derived conversion formula.
   (a) $.000\overline{3}$ (d) $.00\overline{142857}$ (g) $.01\overline{20}$
   (b) $.01\overline{6}$ (e) $.0\overline{1}$ (h) $.027\overline{50}$
   (c) $.0\overline{6}$ (f) $.000\overline{9}$ (i) $.065\overline{0}$
4. Would you say that the conversion formula derived at the end of this section works for terminating decimals? Explain and give numerical examples to support your contention.
5. Why can one say that $\frac{2}{3}\% = .00\overline{6}$? [Hint: Your argument should make use of the conversion formula.]

Chapter summary

In this chapter we considered one of the more commonly used forms of numeration for rational numbers, the decimal numerals. Decimal numerals were defined by first extending the idea of expanded notation and then associating with the expanded notation a place-value numeral in which the units and tenths places are separated by a *decimal point*. Having done this, we found that the class of rationals of the form $\dfrac{a}{2^n \, 5^m}$ correspond to *terminating* or *finite*   decimals and all other rationals correspond to *infinite repeating* decimals. Further, all infinite repeating and terminating decimals correspond to rational numbers. As with the base numeration systems discussed in Chapter 8, it is true for rationals as well that the properties of the system are independent of the numerals used.

In connection with infinite repeating decimals, an algorithm was discussed which describes a process by which an ordered pair numeral can be determined for any infinite repeating decimal numeral. It was also determined that the algorithm, as given, is not completely justified because of the fact that some number properties are used in its development which do not really apply. To indicate what is really involved in the process is beyond the scope of this book; however the discussion of the concept of *limit* from an intuitive point of view does give some indication of the mathematics required for its complete justification.

CHAPTER 18 Functions graphs and real numbers

1. Mappings and Functions

If one pursues the development of number systems and their properties, he must eventually concern himself with a development of the system of *real* numbers. A rigorous development of the reals becomes quite involved because of other abstract ideas which are required if the development is to be mathematically precise. For this reason, we shall confine ourselves to an intuitive discussion of the concept of real numbers. Our approach will be to use the concept of *function* to show the plausibility of the existence of numbers other than rationals.

In Section 1-2 correspondences between the elements of two sets were discussed and the concept of mappings was introduced. We defined a mapping of a set *A* into a set *B* to consist of many-to-one or one-to-one correspondences. Using the concept of mapping as one of our basic tools, we were able to construct the system of cardinal numbers and from this we later constructed integers and finally rational numbers. Since a mapping of a set *A* into a set *B* determines a set of ordered pairs, it should be easy to see that a mapping of *A* into *B* is a subset of *A* × *B*. It can be observed from Figure 1-1 that the mappings from the first to the second set actually set up a relationship between the two sets involved. Similarly, if we consider a mapping of weights of letters mailed to the amount of postage required, we are saying that the set of letters is related to the amount of postage required to mail the letters. Thus it should be apparent that relations also exist between *different* sets and if just two sets are involved the set of ordered pairs which have the relation is a subset of the Cartesian product of the two. This may be formalized as follows.

Definition 18-1: A **relation** from a set *A* to a set *B* is a subset of *A* × *B*.

Because of the fact that a mapping from a set *A* into a set *B* is a relation, it can be observed that if in a set of ordered pairs we find the pairs (*a,b*) and (*a,c*) where $b \neq c$ then the set does *not* describe a mapping of A into B even though it does describe a relation from A to B.

In mathematics there is a synonym for the term mapping which is often used, namely the term *function*. Thus, a function from a set A to (into) a set B may be defined as follows.

Definition 18-2: A function from a set A to a set B (A into B) is a mapping of A into B. The set A is called the **domain** of the function and the set of images under the mapping is called the **range** of the function.

Since we are saying that functions and mappings are synonyms, this means that every function from a set A to a set B is a relation from A to B because of the fact that mappings are relations. However, not every relation from A to B is a function from A to B.

Example: Is the set $S = \{(a,p), (b,q), (c,q), (d,r), (a,r)\}$ a function from A to B if $A = \{a, b, c, d\}$ and $B = \{p, q, r\}$?

Solution: Since the element a has both p and r as images, the set S is not a mapping of A to B and therefore not a function from A to B. However, S is a relation from A to B since $S \subseteq A \times B$.

In general this relationship between functions and relations may be thought of as pictured below where the region inside the closed curve R represents a relation and the region inside F represents a function.

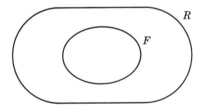

This illustrates that $F \subseteq R$, but it is not necessarily the case that $R \subseteq F$.

Early in our work with sets in Chapter 1, we noted that some sets could be denoted rather easily because of what is often referred to as set-builder notation. That is, $X = \{x \mid \ldots\}$. In this notation the small x inside the set braces is sometimes called a *generic* element of the set X. That is, x is the *kind* of element to be found in the set X. In a similar way, generic elements may be used to denote how the correspondence for a given function is to be formed. If we use the letter f to represent a function from a set A to a set B, we often write $f: a \longrightarrow b$ (read "f maps a to b") where it is understood that $a \in A$ and $b \in B$. Here the lower case letters a and b are taken in a generic sense. As an alternative we sometimes denote the function f which maps A to B by $f: A \longrightarrow B$ (read "f maps set A to set B"). With this notation it is to be understood that since a function is a mapping, f associates with each element of A a unique image in B. There is yet another method for symbolically denoting the mapping of set A to a set B by a function f. Perhaps this method would be more suitable for our purposes. What we shall do is to denote f: $a \longrightarrow b$ or f: $A \longrightarrow B$ by $f(a) = b$ where it is understood that a is a member of the domain of f and b is a member of the range of f. In general if we have

$$X = \{x \mid \ldots\}$$

$$Y = \{y \mid \ldots\}, \text{ and}$$

$$f: X \longrightarrow Y$$

we may write as the relation which defines the function f the statement

$$f(x) = y$$

Here it is understood that x is a member of the domain of f and y is a member of the range of f. The elements x and y are, again, used in a generic sense. To help clarify what has just been said consider the following examples.

Example: Determine the defining relation for a function f: $X \longrightarrow Y$ with the correspondence

$$X = \{0, \ 1, \ 2, \ 3, \ 4, \ldots\}$$
$$\downarrow \ \downarrow \ \downarrow \ \downarrow \ \downarrow$$
$$Y = \{0, \ 2, \ 4, \ 6, \ 8, \ldots\}$$

Solution: Since each element $x \in X$ is mapped to $2x \in Y$, we have f: $x \longrightarrow 2x$ or $f(x) = 2x$ for the defining relation.

Example: If f: $A \longrightarrow B$ where f is a function and the mapping is defined by $f(a) = \dfrac{1}{a}$, determine B if $A = \{a \mid a \text{ is a non-zero rational}\}$.

Solution: If a is a non-zero rational, then say $a = \dfrac{x}{y}$. Thus

$$\frac{1}{a} = \frac{1}{1} \div a$$

$$= \frac{1}{1} \div \frac{x}{y}$$

$$= \frac{1}{1} \cdot \frac{y}{x}$$

$$= \frac{y}{x}$$

Therefore the images $\dfrac{1}{a}$ are the multiplicative inverses of the members a of the domain. Consequently $B = \{b \mid b = \dfrac{1}{a}$ is the multiplicative inverse of a non-zero rational$\}$.

As you may have observed by now, a function consists of three things:
(1) a set called the **domain** of the function,
(2) a set called the **range** of the function, and
(3) a **rule of correspondence** or defining relation which associates with each element of the domain a unique element of the range.

You may also have noted that not all rules of correspondence are written in the form $f(x) = y$. Indeed, many useful functions are defined by tables which express the rule of correspondence. However, the functions which will be of particular interest to us in the next section will have defining relations of the form $f(x) = y$. One such function will be used to suggest the existence of another kind of number.

EXERCISE SET 18-1

1. Determine whether each of the following sets represents a function (F) or merely a relation (R).
    (a) $\{(2,2), (4,2), (3,1), (5,1)\}$
    (b) $\{(1,1), (2,2), (3,3), (4,4), (5,5)\}$
    (c) $\{(1,1), (1,3), (2,1), (3,2), (4,1)\}$
    (d) $\{(1,2), (2,3), (3,4)\}$
    (e) $\{(1,2), (2,4), (^-1,3), (0, 1), (1, 3)\}$
    (f) $\{(x,y) \mid y = 2x + 4$ and x is an integer$\}$
    (g) $\{(a,b) \mid a \leqslant b$ and a and b are cardinals$\}$
    (h) $\{(x,y) \mid y = \dfrac{1}{x}$ and x is a non-zero rational$\}$
    (i) $\{(x,y) \mid x$ and y are cardinals and $y = 1\}$
2. Determine a defining relation of the form $f\colon\ a \longrightarrow b$ for each of the following functions.
    (a) $\{(1,1), (2,3), (3,5), (4,7), (5,9), \ldots\}$
    (b) $\{(0,10), (1,9), (2,8), (3,7), (4,6), (5,5)\}$
    (c) $\{(1,1), (2,4), (3,9), (4,16), (5,25), \ldots\}$
    (d) $\{(1,2), (2,5), (3,10), (4,17), (5,26), \ldots\}$
    (e) $\{(0,0), (1,0), (2,^-2), (3,^-6), (4,^-12), (5,^-20), (6,^-30), \ldots\}$
    (f) $\left\{ \left(\dfrac{1}{0}, \dfrac{0}{1}\right), \left(\dfrac{1}{2}, \dfrac{1}{2}\right), \left(\dfrac{1}{3}, \dfrac{2}{3}\right), \left(\dfrac{1}{4}, \dfrac{3}{4}\right), \left(\dfrac{1}{5}, \dfrac{4}{5}\right), \left(\dfrac{1}{6}, \dfrac{5}{6}\right), \ldots \right\}$
3. For each part of problem 2:
    (a) list the domain of f
    (b) list the range of f
    (c) write the defining relation of f in the form of an equation $f(x) =$ (SOMETHING)
4. Let f be a function whose domain is the set of cardinal numbers and let its defining relation be

$$f(x) = \begin{cases} 2x \text{ if } x \text{ is even} \\ x^2 \text{ if } x \text{ is odd} \end{cases}$$

(a) Write out several of the ordered pairs which belong to f.

(b) Is the range of f the set of even cardinals? Explain.

5. Let a function g with domain the set of integers have the defining relation

$$g(x) = \begin{cases} 2x \text{ if } x \text{ is even} \\ \\ 2x + 1 \text{ if } x \text{ is odd.} \end{cases}$$

(a) List several of the ordered pairs which belong to g.

(b) Is the range of g the entire set of integers?

6. Let us define a function f with domain the set of rationals by

$$f(x) = [\![x]\!],$$

where $[\![x]\!]$ is the largest integral rational which is less than or equal to the rational number x. For example

$$\left[\!\left[\frac{1}{2} \right]\!\right] = 0, \left[\!\left[\frac{5}{4} \right]\!\right] = 1, \left[\!\left[\frac{-3}{4} \right]\!\right] = {}^-1, \left[\!\left[\frac{-7}{3} \right]\!\right] = {}^-3, \text{ and so forth.}$$

Determine each of the following.

(a) $\left[\!\left[\dfrac{9}{8} \right]\!\right]$

(b) $\left[\!\left[\dfrac{21}{9} \right]\!\right]$

(c) $\left[\!\left[\dfrac{{}^-13}{5} \right]\!\right]$

(d) $\left[\!\left[\dfrac{0}{1} \right]\!\right]$

(e) $\left[\!\left[{}^-1\dfrac{7}{8} \right]\!\right]$

(f) $\left[\!\left[\dfrac{5}{3} \right]\!\right] + \left[\!\left[\dfrac{{}^-5}{3} \right]\!\right]$

(g) $\left[\!\left[\dfrac{5}{3} \right]\!\right] \cdot \left[\!\left[\dfrac{3}{5} \right]\!\right]$

7. Consider the function f whose domain is the set of rationals and whose defining relation is $f(x) = |x|$. List the ordered pairs having the following first members: ${}^-2, {}^-1\dfrac{3}{4}, \dfrac{{}^-3}{2}, \dfrac{{}^-5}{4}, \dfrac{{}^-7}{8}, \dfrac{{}^-2}{3}, \dfrac{{}^-1}{16}, \dfrac{0}{1}, \dfrac{1}{4}, \dfrac{1}{3}, \dfrac{13}{16}, \dfrac{5}{6}, 1\dfrac{1}{3}, \dfrac{5}{4}, 1\dfrac{5}{7},$ and 2.

2. Graphs of Functions

In this section we shall study some functions defined on the sets of numbers which have been developed earlier in the book and try to devise a scheme for drawing pictures to represent the functions. We begin by recalling that a function is a relation and because of this it must consist of ordered pairs. Let us first consider a function f from C to C where C is the set of cardinal numbers. Since $f: C \rightarrow C$, f must consist of ordered pairs of cardinal numbers and because of this it appears reasonable to consider a picture of $C \times C$ and select from this picture those points whose ordered-pair-names correspond to the ordered pairs of $C \times C$.

Example: Draw a picture of the function f if $f: C \rightarrow C$ and f is defined by the equation $f(x) = x$.

Solution: Since $f(x) = x$, it should be clear that we want to consider all points which have names (x,x). This is, $(0,0)$, $(1,1)$, $(2,2)$, and so forth. The picture looks similar to Figure 18-1.

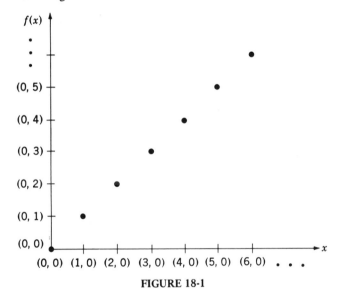

FIGURE 18-1

Such a picture, consisting of the points whose ordered-pair-names belong to a function, is called the *graph* of that given function.

Let us now consider the function f as above except that we shall use the mapping $f: I \rightarrow I$ where I is the set of integers.

Example: Draw the graph of the function f if $f: I \rightarrow I$ and f is defined by the equation $f(x) = x$.

Solution: $f: I \rightarrow I$ means that the domain of f is the set of integers and so we want to consider all points of $I \times I$ which have ordered-pair-names whose first and second members are the same: i.e., $(^-3,^-3)$, $(^-7,^-7)$, $(0, 0)$, $(4, 4)$, $(11, 11)$, and so forth. The picture would be similar to that in Figure 18-2.

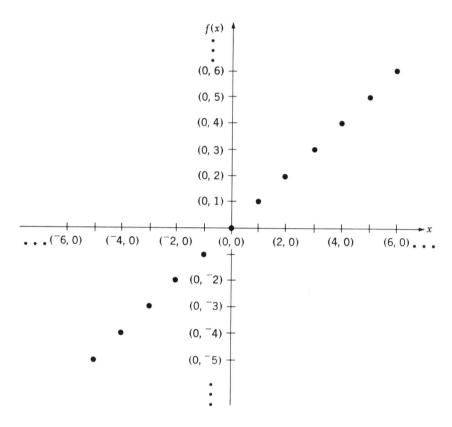

FIGURE 18-2

As you can see, it appears that in *some* sense the picture is becoming "more complete" the more we work in a more complete system of numbers. In Figure 18-2 we have, in a matter of speaking, gained a large set of points to the lower left, the upper right set being congruent to those determined in Figure 18-1. Let us now see what the graph of the function *f* looks like if we use the mapping *f*: $R \rightarrow R$ where R is the set of rational numbers.

Example: Draw the graph of the function *f* if *f*: $R \rightarrow R$ and *f* is defined by the equation $f(x) = x$.

Solution: As before we want all ordered-pair-names (*x,y*) where $y = f(x)$ such that *x* and *y* are rationals and $x = y$. The picture of this function appears in Figure 18-3.

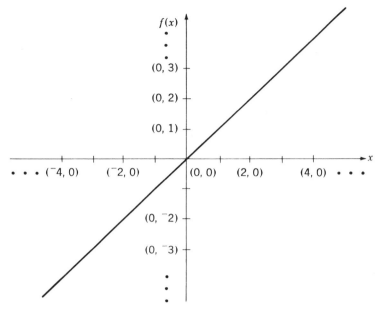

FIGURE 18-3

From the above three examples, it *appears* that if the domain of the function is the set of rational numbers then the "holes" in the previous two graphs are all filled in. If we graph other functions we find that the same type of thing occurs.

Examples: Let the function f be defined by the equation $f(x) = 2x - 1$ with respective domains C, I, and R.

Solutions: The graphs for the three domains chosen appear as in Figure 18-4.

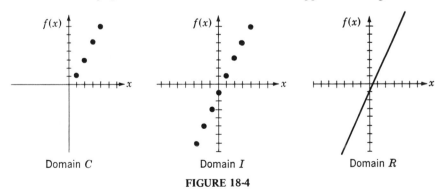

FIGURE 18-4

EXERCISE SET 18-2

1. Draw three graphs of each of the following functions, selecting for the domain of f the sets of cardinals, integers, and rationals.
   (a) $f\colon x \longrightarrow 2x$

(b) $f: x \longrightarrow 3x + 2$

(c) $f: x \longrightarrow x^2 + 1$

(d) $f: x \longrightarrow x^2 + 2$

2. Draw a graph of the relation $x^2 + y^2 = 4$ using first just cardinals, then integers, then rationals. Does this relation represent a function? Explain.

3. Let f be defined by $f(x) = \begin{cases} 2x \text{ if } x \text{ is even} \\ 2x + 1 \text{ if } x \text{ is odd} \end{cases}$ and let the domain of f be the set of integers. Draw a graph to represent f.

4. If f is defined by $f(x) = \begin{cases} 2x \text{ if } x \text{ is an integral rational} \\ 2x - 1 \text{ if } x \text{ is not an integral rational} \end{cases}$ draw a graph of f assuming the domain of f to be the set of rational numbers.

5. Draw graphs of f with respective domains of integers and rationals if f is defined by $f(x) = |x|$.

6. Draw the graph of the function f whose defining relation is $f(x) = [\![x]\!]$ and whose domain is the set of rationals.

7. If one wants to graph functions f and g defined by $f(x) = \dfrac{1}{2}x + 1$ and $g(x) = 3x - 5$, what domain must be selected for each so that the operations involved give images in the same set? Graph five or six points for each function using the domains you select.

8. A function f is called *odd* if $f(-x) = -f(x)$ and is called *even* if $f(-x) = f(x)$.
   (a) Try to find an odd function whose domain is the set of rationals.
   (b) Do the same as in (a) for an even function.
   (c) See if you can find a function which is neither odd nor even.

3. Functions and a New Kind of Number

We shall now use the concepts of function and graph to show that there is a need for numbers which are different from any which we have discussed so far. To do this we shall graph the function f defined by $f(x) = x^2$ and take as domains of f successively the cardinal numbers, integers, and finally the rational numbers. The three graphs of f with these domains are similar to those in Figure 18-5 below.

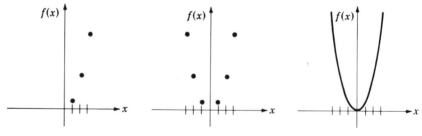

FIGURE 18-5

As indicated previously, it appears that all of the "holes" left by the cardinals and integers have been filled by choosing as the domain of f the set of rational numbers. It might also be noted that if the set of rationals is chosen as the domain of f, the range is the set of non-negative rationals. Let us now restrict our attention to just the right half of the graph of f with domain $\{x \mid x$ is a non-negative rational$\}$. The graph of this portion of the function would appear as that in Figure 18-6.

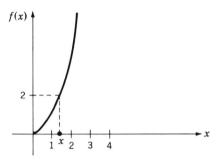

FIGURE 18-6

Now let us consider the range of f. If there are no "holes" in the graph of f, then let us consider $f(x) = 2$ and try to determine what number x in the domain has the image $f(x) = 2$. That is, we shall try to determine a rational number x such that $x^2 = 2$. In contradiction, we shall state and prove a theorem which implies that no such rational number x exists which has the property that $x^2 = 2$. The arguments involved in this proof are complicated, so read slowly and be sure you understand each step.

Theorem 18-1: There is no rational number x such that $x^2 = 2$.

Proof: What we shall attempt to do is to assume that there is such a rational number and show that such an assumption leads to a contradiction. Further, since each rational has a preferred numeral we shall also assume that $x = \dfrac{a}{b}$ where a and b are relatively prime integers. If $x^2 = 2$, then by substitution we have

$$\left(\frac{a}{b}\right)^2 = 2$$

or

$$\frac{a^2}{b^2} = 2$$

so that

$$a^2 = 2b^2$$

Thus a^2 is even since it contains a factor 2. Since a^2 is even and since $a^2 = a \cdot a$, this means that a must be even, otherwise $a \cdot a$ would be an odd number. Therefore for some integer k, $a = 2k$. Substituting in above we obtain

$$(2k)^2 = 2b^2$$

or

$$4k^2 = 2b^2$$

so that

$$2k^2 = b^2$$

and consequently b^2 is even. Since $b \cdot b = b^2$, this means that b itself must be even and therefore contains a factor 2. But if a and b are both even, then this means that they are not relatively prime and so we have a contradiction. Thus there cannot be a rational number $\frac{a}{b}$ such that $\left(\frac{a}{b}\right)^2 = 2$. That is, if a number x exists such that $x^2 = 2$ then it cannot be a rational number. ∎

Theorem 18-1 not only implies that there are numbers other than those already developed, but it also gives us the information that the graph pictured in Figure 18-6 does indeed have "holes" in it in spite of what we were led to believe when we relied on our intuition. Thus we see once again that even though intuition is important in mathematics, we cannot place our complete trust in it. If the number x of Theorem 18-1 does exist and is not a rational number then perhaps we should try to find out more about it. This seems particularly worthwhile since the ordered pair generated by it apparently fills one of the holes in the graph of f in Figure 18-6 and this has at least some esthetic value. What we shall do is to try to determine a decimal numeral which can be associated with this mysterious number x. To begin with we note that x is between 1 and 2 since $1^2 = 1$, $2^2 = 4$, $x^2 = 2$. Since $1 < 2 < 4$, we have $1 < x^2 < 4$; that is, $1 < x < 2$. The technique we shall use is the following:

(1) Choose two estimates, r_1 and r_2, for x between 1 and 2.
(2) Square the estimates chosen.
(3) Repeat steps (1) and (2) until estimates r_1 and r_2 are found such that x is between them; that is, such that $r_1 < x < r_2$.
(4) Determine whether x^2 is closer to r_1^2 or r_2^2 and then use the best estimate as a basis for determination of a better estimate.

We shall illustrate what is meant by the above. Suppose we try first $r_1 = 1.4$ and $r_2 = 1.5$. Then $r_2^3 = 1.96$ and $r_2^2 = 2.25$. Since $1.96 < 2 < 2.25$ and since 2 is closer to 1.96 we select as new estimates numbers which are closer to 1.4 as a basis for the next estimate. Six such successive estimates are listed below in Table 18-1 where we have taken the liberty of already performing the calculations involved.

TABLE 18-1

Choices for r_1, r_2	r_1^2, r_2^2	$r_1 < x < r_2$
$r_1 = 1.4$ $r_2 = 1.5$	1.96 2.25	$1.4 < x < 1.5$
$r_1 = 1.41$ $r_2 = 1.42$	1.9881 2.0164	$1.41 < x < 1.42$
$r_1 = 1.414$ $r_2 = 1.415$	1.999396 2.002225	$1.414 < x < 1.415$
$r_1 = 1.4142$ $r_2 = 1.4143$	1.99996164 2.00024449	$1.4142 < x < 1.4143$
$r_1 = 1.41421$ $r_2 = 1.41422$	1.9999899241 2.0000182084	$1.41421 < x < 1.41422$
$r_1 = 1.414213$ $r_2 = 1.414214$	1.999998409369 2.000001237796	$1.414213 < x < 1.414214$

Thus on number lines (with different unit lengths) we may successively picture the results just obtained as in Figure 18-7. These illustrate graphically the betweenness relation of x with respect to the estimates r_1 and r_2.

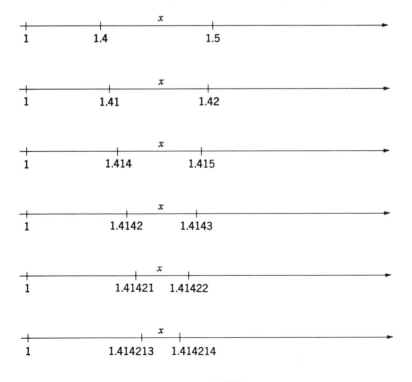

FIGURE 18-7

In each case numbers r_1 and r_2 have been found such that $r_1 < x < r_2$. If the process were to be continued, we would find that the inequality still holds and furthermore the decimal expansions of r_1 and r_2 never begin to repeat. Thus apparently if the process were to be continued ad infinitum, we would be able to determine that this number x could be represented by an infinite non-repeating decimal numeral. This then is a new type of number since we are already aware of the fact that only rationals have infinite repeating decimal numerals.

Definition 18-3: A number whose decimal numeral has an infinite number of digits is called a **real number.**

The number x determined above is a real number called the square root of two and is denoted by $\sqrt{2}$ as you would probably expect. In the preceding discussion however, we only determined a finite number of digits in the decimal expansion of $\sqrt{2}$.

It might be noted that in Definition 18-3 there is a definite reason for calling the set of all infinite decimals the set of real numbers. For if one can show that the resulting arithmetic satisfies the same properties as the system of rational numbers, then he may set up an isomorphism between the rationals and a subset of the reals, namely those reals which have infinite repeating decimals. To actually show that this can be done is beyond the scope of this exposition. Thus we shall simply assume that the usual properties do hold. That is, we shall assume the following.

Some Postulates for Real Numbers (which also hold for rationals): The system F of real numbers consists of the set F of real numbers, two binary operations +, ·, and the relation < defined on F which satisfy the following:

   I. ADDITION
      1. Uniqueness: If $a, a', b, b' \in F$ with $a = a'$ and $b = b'$, then $a + b = a' + b'$.
      2. Commutative: For all $a, b \in F$, $a + b = b + a$.
      3. Associative: For all $a, b, c \in F$, $a + (b + c) = (a + b) + c$.
      4. Identity: There is a number $0 \in F$ such that for each $a \in F$, $0 + a = a$.
      5. Inverse: For each $a \in F$ there is a number $\bar{a} \in F$ such that $a + \bar{a} = 0$.
  II. MULTIPLICATION
      1. Uniqueness: If $a, a', b, b' \in F$ with $a = a'$ and $b = b'$, then $a \cdot b = a' \cdot b'$.
      2. Commutative: For all $a, b \in F$, $a \cdot b = b \cdot a$.
      3. Associative: For all $a, b, c \in F$, $a \cdot (b \cdot c) = (a \cdot b) \cdot c$.
      4. Identity: There is a number $1 \in F$ such that for each $a \in F$, $1 \cdot a = a$.
      5. Inverse: For each $a \in F$ such that $a \neq 0$, there is a number $a^{-1} \in F$ (read "a inverse") such that $a \cdot a^{-1} = 1$.
 III. DISTRIBUTIVE
      For all $a, b, c \in F$, $a \cdot (b + c) = a \cdot b + a \cdot c$.
 IV. ORDER
      1. If $a < b$ and $b < c$, then $a < c$.

2. For $a, b, c, d \in F$, the following hold.

   a. If $a < b$, then $a + c < b + c$.

   b. If $a < b$ and $c > 0$, then $ac < bc$.

   c. If $a < b$ and $c < 0$, then $ac > bc$.

   d. If $a > 0$, then $a^{-1} > 0$.

   e. If $a < 0$, then $a^{-1} < 0$.

As you can observe, not all the number properties we have studied are listed but they can be obtained by use of the postulates listed above. You will recall that once these properties had been established for the rational numbers we were able to prove many which were not listed. The same can be done for the real numbers. Indeed, it is possible to prove all those properties previously considered but not listed. Further, since subtraction is the inverse of addition and division is the inverse of multiplication (for non-zero divisors), the results concerning these properties follow as well. Thus the set of real numbers is closed under subtraction and under division by non-zero divisors. It may also be noted that in I and II of the list of postulates it is redundant to list uniqueness, for this follows directly from the fact that addition and multiplication are functions from $F \times F$ into F.

The postulates listed above really provide nothing new however, for all of the properties listed also hold for rationals. Before discussing the property of real numbers which sets them apart from rationals, let us return for a moment to consider the successive estimates for $\sqrt{2}$ which we listed in Table 18-1. We shall consider more closely the particular set of *lower* estimates (ordered)

$$\{1.4, 1.41, 1.414, 1.4142, 1.41421, 1.414213, \ldots\}.$$

Each of these numbers is less than $\sqrt{2}$ since the square of each is less than 2. Consequently each is less than or equal to $\sqrt{2}$. Whenever for each element $a \in A$ there is an element n such that $a \leq n$, the element n is called an *upper bound* of A. Therefore $\sqrt{2}$ is an upper bound of the set listed above. If we think about it, we may observe that 2 is an upper bound and so are 3, 4, 5, 100, and so forth. Consequently a set of numbers may have a large set of upper bounds and in *that* set there *may* be a smallest member. If there is a smallest number amongst all of these upper bounds, we call it the *least upper bound*.

If we now consider the set of upper bounds for the set

$$\{1.4, 1.41, 1.414, 1.4142, 1.41421, 1.414213, \ldots\},$$

it appears that $\sqrt{2}$ is the least upper bound. The crux of the matter is whether or not the least upper bound belongs to the set from which the subset under consideration was formed. If we consider the above set of decimals as representing rationals then the least upper bound, $\sqrt{2}$, does not belong to the set of rationals since we have already proved that $\sqrt{2}$ is not rational. However, if we consider the decimals listed as representing real numbers, then $\sqrt{2}$ does belong to the set of reals and so we have a non-empty subset of real numbers whose least upper bound is also a real number. This characteristic of the real numbers is referred to as the *completeness property* and we formalize this below.

Completeness Postulate: Every non-empty subset of real numbers which has an upper bound also has a least upper bound which is itself a real number.

What this means geometrically is that if we now select the function f defined by $f(x) = x^2$ with the domain of f being the set of real numbers, then the graph of f contains no holes. The real number system is the first we have discussed which has this property and this completeness is what sets the system of real numbers apart from the rational numbers.

a. A second approach to real numbers

Another approach to the idea of a real number exists which depends upon the base of the numeration system being used and the association between points on a line and numbers. Previously the idea of a number line has been discussed for the cardinal numbers, the integers, and the rational numbers. As each number system was extended, more and more points along a number line became associated with some number. The question that is now asked is whether it is possible to determine the decimal numeral for a number which is to be associated with an arbitrary point on a number line, if such a number exists.

In Chapter 17 the fact was established that any repeating decimal numeral represents a rational number and that any rational number can be represented by an infinite repeating decimal numeral. Still, there are decimal numerals that do not repeat such as 0.101001000100001 . . . , and so, do not represent rational numbers. This fact then suggests that perhaps not all points on a number line are associated with rational numbers.

Let us now return to the problem of constructing the decimal numeral for an arbitrary point on a number line. Let ℓ be the line and x represent the point in question as illustrated in Figure 18-8. For purposes of discussion, suppose x is a point of ℓ between the points associated with 0 and 1.

FIGURE 18-8

In order to determine the corresponding decimal numeral for the point x, one must realize that the numeral depends on the base of the numeration system being employed. Since the decimal system is a base ten system, the line segment between the points 0 and 1 is subdivided into ten equal subintervals. Each subinterval is then associated with one of the ten digits taken in order from 0 to 9. This association from left to right is as shown in Figure 18-9.

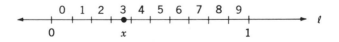

FIGURE 18-9

It can be observed that the point x is in the subinterval associated with the digit 3, and so 3 becomes the first digit of the decimal numeral associated with the point x. In other words, 0.3 is our first approximation to the required number. Now suppose the subinterval containing the point x is itself subdivided into ten equal subintervals as was the line segment between 0 and 1 as illustrated in Figure 18-10.

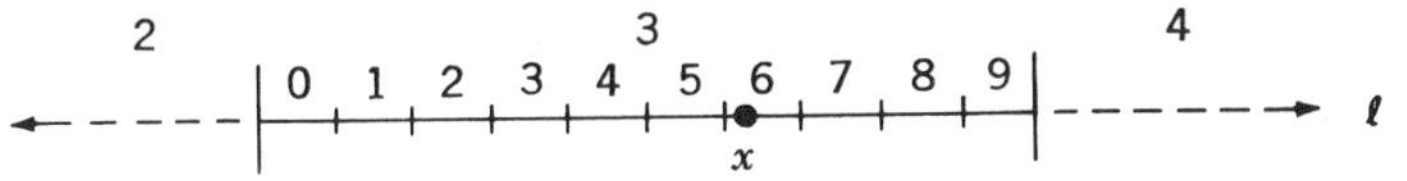

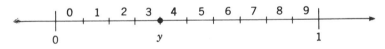

FIGURE 18-10

If the point x now falls in the subinterval associated with the digit 6 as indicated in Figure 18-10, a better approximation for the number in question is 0.36. One could theoretically continue this process to construct the decimal numeral for the number associated with the point x.

At this point a special situation should be discussed. This situation arises if the point x should turn out to be one of the separation points of the sub-intervals at some stage of the process. If the point x is a separation point, then it belongs to neither one of the adjacent subintervals. If this happens, the question arises as to what digit will be associated with such a point at that particular step in the process. Resolving this problem requires only an agreement. This agreement is that we will consistently assign such a point to either the left-hand subinterval or to the right-hand subinterval of the two adjacent ones which it separates.

Figure 18-11 illustrates a situation in which the point y, whose associated decimal numeral is to be determined, is a separation point. Since y falls between the subintervals associated with the digits 3 and 4, a decision has to be made to assign the digit 3 or else the digit 4 to the numeral.

FIGURE 18-11

If the agreement is made to associate such points with the left-hand subinterval, then the first decimal approximation for the number represented by the point y must be 0.3. Any subsequent step would result in the point y being associated with the subinterval 9. Hence the decimal numeral for the number represented by y is $0.3\overline{9}$. On the other hand, if the decision is made to associate separation points with right-hand subintervals, the first approximation for the number in question is 0.4. Any subsequent step would result in determining the digit 0 in the required decimal expansion. Hence the decimal numeral for the number represented by y is $0.4\overline{0}$.

The above discussion appears to indicate that we have arrived at the dilemma of having two different decimal numerals associated with the same number, that is, $0.3\overline{0} = 0.4\overline{0}$. This should not disturb one too much however, since the fact has been encountered many times prior to this discussion that any number has many names. In fact if the methods of Section 17-3 are used, one can show that $0.3\bar{9}$ and $0.4\bar{0}$ are both decimal numerals for the rational number $\frac{2}{5}$. It should be emphasized that this dilemma arises only from the problem of association of separation points with a subinterval in the construction process. If the point in question is not a separation point at any step of the process then the possibility of attaining two different decimal numerals does not arise.

The construction method outlined above is an intuitive approach to the idea that any point on a number line can be associated with a decimal numeral. This decimal numeral is unique if the decision concerning division points is established prior to commencing the construction. If we agree to call that set of numbers by infinite decimal numerals (repeating and non-repeating) the set of real numbers, then we have succeeded in establishing a one-to-one mapping from the points on a line into the real numbers.

With a little thought one should be able to see how the above procedure could be reversed to determine that point on a number line which would be associated with a given infinite decimal. This procedure would result in a unique point since distinct decimal numerals would differ by at least one digit in some decimal position. The first time such a difference occurred would result in determining points in different subintervals and hence a separation of the points representing the decimal numerals. This implies that the set of infinite decimal numerals can be mapped into the set of points on a number line by a one-to-one into mapping.

The fact that there exists a one-to-one into mapping of the set of points of a number line to the set of infinite decimal numerals may seem of relatively little importance. A similar statement may be made about the fact that there exists a one-to-one mapping of the set of infinite decimal numerals into the set of points on the number line. However, the combination of these two facts yields one of the most important and useful concepts in mathematics and is stated in the following theorem.

Theorem 18-2: The set of points of a number line and the set of real numbers can be associated by a one-to-one correspondence.

Theorem 18-2 states that the set of points on a line and the set of real numbers are equivalent. This fact is the fundamental principle on which the graphing of curves in the plane or in space is based since these mathematical ideas can be described in terms of Cartesian products of the real numbers.

EXERCISE SET 18-3

1. Use the graph of $f(x) = x^2$ and the corresponding technique of the text to determine estimates for
   (a) $\sqrt{3}$ (d) $\sqrt{7}$
   (b) $\sqrt{5}$ (e) $\sqrt{8}$
   (c) $\sqrt{6}$
2. (a) Referring to problem one, does it appear that $\sqrt{6}$ could be estimated by using estimates of $\sqrt{2}$ and $\sqrt{3}$?

(b) Does it appear that one could determine $\sqrt{8}$ by using $2\sqrt{2}$?

3. Graph $f(x) = x^3$ with the domain of f the set of rationals and use techniques similar to those of the text to determine the cube root of 2 (denoted $\sqrt[3]{2}$) to the nearest tenth.

4. Determine two upper bounds for each of the following sets of numbers. [C means cardinals, I means integers, R means rationals].

  (a) $\{x \mid x \in C \text{ and } 0 \leqslant x < 10\}$

  (b) $\{x \mid x \in C \text{ and } 5 < x \leqslant 17\}$

  (c) $\{x \mid x \in C \text{ and } x \leqslant 45\}$

  (d) $\{x \mid x \in C\}$

  (e) $\{x \mid x \in I \text{ and } {}^-8 \leqslant x \leqslant {}^-4\}$

  (f) $\{x \mid x \in I \text{ and } {}^-5 < x < 13\}$

  (g) $\{x \mid x \in I \text{ and } x < 0\}$

  (h) $\{.3, .33, .333, .3333, .33333, \ldots\}$

  (i) $\{.49, .499, .4999, .49999, .499999, \ldots\}$

  (j) $\left\{\dfrac{5}{3}\right\}$

5. Which of the sets in problem 4 contains one of its upper bounds as a member of the set itself?

6. Do you think it is possible for a member of a set to be larger than one of its upper bounds? Explain.

7. Try to determine an upper bound for each of the following sets.

  (a) $\left\{\dfrac{0}{1}, \dfrac{1}{2}, \dfrac{2}{3}, \dfrac{3}{4}, \dfrac{4}{5}, \dfrac{5}{6}, \dfrac{6}{7}, \dfrac{7}{8}, \cdots\right\}$

  (b) $\left\{2\dfrac{2}{3}, 2\dfrac{8}{9}, 2\dfrac{26}{27}, 2\dfrac{80}{81}, 2\dfrac{242}{243}, \cdots\right\}$

8. Use a number line and the technique described in Section 18-3a to determine a decimal numeral for each of the following.

  (a) $3\dfrac{7}{8}$

  (b) $\dfrac{15}{16}$

  (c) $\dfrac{5}{32}$

  (d) $5\dfrac{3}{4}$

9. A *basimal numeral* is a "decimal type" numeral written in a numeration system with base $b \neq 10$. Note that if $b = 10$ the numeral is also a basimal numeral but we make this distinction solely for purposes of clarifying the term's use in the following problems. Use a technique similar to that of problem eight to determine a *basimal numeral* for each of the following.

  (a) $1\dfrac{3}{4}$;   base two   (e) $\dfrac{5}{9}$;   base three

  (b) $3\dfrac{7}{8}$;   base two   (f) $\dfrac{13}{27}$;   base three

  (c) $1\dfrac{3}{4} + 3\dfrac{7}{8}$;   base two   (g) $\dfrac{5}{9} + \dfrac{13}{27}$;   base three

    Do it in two ways.   Do it in two ways.

(d) $\dfrac{17}{64} + \dfrac{5}{8}$;   base two

Do it in two ways.

(h) $2\,\dfrac{2}{3} + \dfrac{7}{81}$;   base three

Do it in two ways.

10. It is an interesting fact that whether or not a basimal numeral is infinite or terminating depends on the base system of numeration used. Give an example of a number whose basimal numeral is an infinite numeral in one base but terminating in another base.

11. Discuss the following statement: A rational number has associated with it a terminating or infinite repeating basimal numeral regardless of the base $n \geqslant 2$ used for the numeration system.

4. Approximating Real Numbers

In the preceding section we discussed the existence of a set of numbers which possess all properties exhibited by the rationals and in addition has the completeness property, namely the set of real numbers. We indicated that $\sqrt{2}$ is a real number. Some other real numbers are $\sqrt{3},\ \sqrt{5},\ \sqrt{6},\ 1 + \sqrt{2},\ \dfrac{2}{\sqrt{2}},\ \pi,\ e$ and infinitely many others. As you may recall, π is the ratio of the circumference of a circle to its diameter. The number e arises when one studies logarithms and exponents in relation to functions. Decimal expansions for both π and e have been computed to many decimal places. To fifteen decimal places we have

$$\pi = 3.14159\ 26535\ 89789\ldots$$

and

$$e = 2.71828\ 18284\ 59045\ldots\ .$$

Hence these too are really infinite decimals just as are the others listed above.

Many problems require the use of real numbers, but if computations arise in which decimals are used it is in practice a hopeless task to even try to use the infinite decimal expansions. For this reason one must usually make some kind of adjustment so that the computations can be completed. Even if electronic calculators or computers are used some adjustment must be made for such machines have built-in limitations. The adjustment usually made is to select appropriate terminating decimal rationals which will give usable results sufficiently close to the desired ones and to provide for workable computations whether done manually or by machine. When such decimal rationals are selected, these selections are called *rational approximations.* For instance, 3.14 or 3.1416 are often chosen to represent the real number π even though neither decimal rational really equals π.

Because the set of rationals is isomorphic to a subset of real numbers the rational approximations may also be intuitively thought of as approximations within the system or real numbers itself. In this way computations may be done in the system of reals without transforming back and forth to the rationals via the isomorphism. If we agree to do this we may refer to these "convenient" numbers simply as *approximations*. Thus if we wish to determine the product $\sqrt{2} \cdot \sqrt{3}$, we may use approximations to write

$$\sqrt{2} \cdot \sqrt{3} \approx (1.414)(1.732)$$

$$\approx 2.449048$$

where the symbol $\approx$ is real "is approximately equal to." It may be noted that if the answer obtained is not as close as desired then better approximations may be chosen for $\sqrt{2}$ and $\sqrt{3}$ in order to obtain a closer approximation to $\sqrt{2} \cdot \sqrt{3}$.

The concept of decimal approximation by rationals relies not only on the isomorphism between rational and real numbers, but on the concept of denseness of rationals as well. Since by the isomorphism a subset of real numbers is isomorphic to the rationals, this implies that this subset of real numbers is necessarily a dense set. Because of this the entire set of real numbers also is a dense set. Further, since the development of real numbers resulted in the filling of the "holes" in graphs, this means that given any real number there are infinitely many rationals very near it. Geometrically, given any point which corresponds to a real number there are infinitely many "nearby" points which correspond to rational numbers. Although it was not emphasized then, we have already observed an example of this (see Figure 18-7), namely that

$$1.4 < 1.41 < 1.414 < 1.4142 < \ldots < \sqrt{2}$$

and

$$\sqrt{2} < \ldots < 1.4143 < 1.415 < 1.42 < 1.5.$$

Thus in order to facilitate ease of computation, all that needs to be done is to select a rational approximation (and hence by the isomorphism a real approximation) which is close to the number under consideration and use it to perform the computation. The only limiting factor is the accuracy desired and this in turn may depend on other factors. Perhaps the one most important of such factors is that many problems involving approximations arise when one uses measurements. For this reason we shall consider computations involving approximations from this point of view. Suppose for example that one measures the length and width of a flat rectangular plate and then computes the area of the plate. When the individual measures, there must of necessity arise errors of measurement. These may be due to the individual himself or to the measuring instrument. Let us concentrate on the instrument being used and suppose that the smallest subdivision marked on the instrument is of length 0.01 unit. Then regardless of what point is selected within the subdivision, it is never more than one-half unit from one of the separation points. This is illustrated in Figure 18-12.

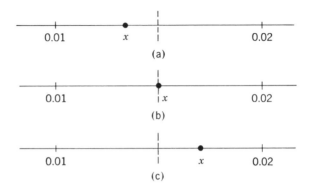

FIGURE 18-12

This means that the *maximum error* introduced in measuring is one-half of the smallest unit marked on the instrument used. Therefore if the width of the plate is listed as 4.82 and the length as 7.36 the actual measurements may have varied as follows:

(1) the width, w is $4.815 \leqslant w \leqslant 4.824$

(2) the length, l, is $7.355 \leqslant l \leqslant 7.364$

assuming that the usual convention has been adopted for *rounding off.* Thus when it is asserted that the area of the plate is 35.4752 the actual area may be any number A such that $35.414325 \leqslant A \leqslant 35.523936$. Since the numbers 4.82 and 7.36 are approximations, they are sometimes referred to as *approximate numbers.* Another way of considering maximum error with reference to decimals is to say that it is one-half of the last decimal place value used in denoting the measurement. Thus if the last decimal place used is tenths, the maximum error is .05, while for hundredths it is .005, for thousandths it is .0005, and so forth. This means that for a given measurement if instruments are used which have smaller and smaller subdivisions (or units), the maximum error becomes successively smaller. Hence if one instrument has smaller units of measure than another the resulting measurements are more *precise* because the maximum error in the measurement is smaller. Consequently the size of the unit used on an instrument determines the precision of the instrument and therefore the precision of the measurement.

There is another meaningful way in which the maximum error may be used to gain information regarding measurement. It should be noted that

(1) the actual measurement of whatever is being measured is unobtainable because of the fact that instruments are used and their precision varies according to the size of the subdivisions marked on the instrument, and

(2) the actual error in a measurement cannot be obtained — all that can be done is to put upper and lower bounds on the error.

Thus if we measure a segment one foot long and say the error is one inch we mean that the measured value is one foot and the maximum error is one inch. A similar statement holds if we claim an error of one inch for a measurement of ten feet. Since the actual error and actual measurement are unobtainable we use the maximum error and the measurement taken to describe what is called the *relative error*. The relative error is the maximum error divided by the measurement taken when these are expressed using the same unit of measure. Thus the relative errors above are $\frac{1}{12}$ and $\frac{1}{120}$ respectively. Because of the fact that $\frac{1}{120} < \frac{1}{12}$, we say that the second of the two measurements is the more *accurate*. That is, the accuracy of a measurement depends on the relative error.

As you may observe, precision and accuracy of measurement are related, but they are by no means the same. A measurement may be precise because a fine instrument is being used, but it may not be very accurate if the relative error is large.

EXERCISE SET 18-4

1. The volume of a box is given by $V = lwh$ where l = length, w = width, and h = height. If l, w, and h are measured as 4.21, 6.37, and 3.4 inches respectively, between what values
   (a) are the lengths of the sides of the box?
   (b) are the areas of the faces of the box?
   (c) is the volume of the box?
2. If the lower estimate of the area of a rectangle is 36.114375 and the measurement given for the width is 5.67, what is the measurement to the nearest hundredth for the length of the rectangle? What is an upper bound which can be placed on the area? What is the least upper bound for the area?
3. Determine the maximum error for each of the following measurements.
   (a) 6
   (b) 5.8
   (c) 7.02
   (d) 18.364
   (e) $4\frac{1}{4}$
   (f) $8\frac{2}{3}$
   (g) $9\frac{7}{16}$
   (h) $10\frac{2}{5}$
4. Which measurement for each of the following pairs is the more precise?
   (a) 3.1 and $4\frac{1}{5}$
   (b) 7.23 and 5.40
   (c) 6.95 and 7.005
   (d) $4\frac{2}{3}$ and $2\frac{3}{4}$
5. For each of the following pairs of measurements, tell which of the two is more accurate.
   (a) 7.261 and 3.47
   (b) $5\frac{4}{5}$ and $4\frac{7}{8}$
   (c) 3.214 and 8.401
   (d) 6.147 and $6\frac{9}{32}$
6. The percentage error of a measurement is determined by changing the relative

error to a percent.   Find the percentage error for each of the following.
(a) 17.81
(b) 11.01
(c) 7.862
(d) 9.3645
7. Can percentage error be used to determine accuracy of a measurement? Explain why or why not.

Chapter summary

The purpose of this chapter has been twofold:
(1) to establish a need for and the plausibility of the existence of real numbers, and
(2) to establish the fact that there does exist a one-to-one mapping between real numbers and points on a number line.

In our discussion we have done both of the above by appealing to the intuition of the reader. The first was done by introducing the concept of *function* and then considering what number had to be chosen in order to obtain a given image. The culmination of this discussion was that there is no rational number x such that $x^2 = 2$. This established a need for numbers other than those previously studied and we called these new numbers real numbers.

The second method discussed made use of the fact that there are infinite decimal numerals which are non repeating. Then all infinite decimals are simply defined to represent real numbers, and we then attempted to discover how to establish a one-to-one mapping between these and points on a number line. In our development we here resorted to the use of the base of the numeration system, in this case base ten. Using this approach, we found it to be the case that such a mapping exists.

Regardless of the approach used, the distinguishing characteristic of the system of real numbers is the *completeness property*. None of the foregoing systems which we discussed have this property. The importance of the above aspects cannot be over-emphasized, for the correspondence between real numbers and points on a number line lays the foundation for drawing graphs and also provides a basis for the association of numbers with sets of points in the study of geometry, namely length, area, and volume.

Answers to selected exercises

CHAPTER 1

Exercise Set 1-1. Pages 8-10

1. $\notin$ $\notin$ $\notin$ $\notin$ 3. (a) {1,2,3,4}   5. {2,4,6,8,...,32,34}
   $\in$ $\in$ $\notin$ $\notin$ (b) {Grover Cleveland}
   $\notin$ $\in$ $\notin$ $\notin$ (c) {February}
   (d) $\emptyset$

7. (a) $\{x \mid x$ is an automobile not manufactured in the U.S.$\}$
   (b) $\{x \mid x$ is a type of tree$\}$
   (c) $\{x \mid x$ is a type of grass$\}$

9. (b) and (f)   11. (a) No   (b) Yes   (c) True   False
                                                   False   True

13. (a) $\emptyset$, $\{a\}$, $\{b\}$, $\{c\}$, $\{a,b\}$, $\{a,c\}$, $\{b,c\}$, $\{a,b,c\}$; $8 = 2^3$
    (b) $\emptyset$, $\{a\}$, $\{b\}$, $\{c\}$, $\{d\}$, $\{a,b\}$, $\{a,c\}$, $\{a,d\}$, $\{b,c\}$, $\{b,d\}$, $\{c,d\}$, $\{a,b,c\}$,
        $\{a,b,d\}$, $\{a,c,d\}$, $\{b,c,d\}$, $\{a,b,c,d\}$; $16 = 2^4$
    (c) If a set contains n elements, 2^n subsets can be formed.

15. (a) $\emptyset$ (b) $\emptyset$, $\{a\}$ (c) $\emptyset$, $\{\{a\}\}$ (d) $\emptyset$, $\{\{a\}\}$, $\{\{b\}\}$, $\{\{a\}, \{b\}\}$
    (e) all except the set itself.

Exercise Set 1-2. Pages 14-15

1. No, because not all elements of A are used.   3. (a) Yes (b) Yes (c) No

5. (a) A to B, A to D, A to F, A to G, A to H, and A to I are mappings.
   (b) A to G, A to H, and A to I are many-to-one.
   (c) A to B, A to D, A to F are one-to-one.

Exercise Set 1-3. Pages 17-18

1. (a) Yes   (b) Yes   (c) Yes   (d) Yes
   (e) No   (f) Yes   (g) Yes

3. $A \sim D, C \sim F, B \sim G$ 5. (a), (c), (e), and (g) are finite.

Exercise Set 1-4. Pages 24-28

1. (a) $\{3,4\}$ (b) $\{1,2,3,4,5,6\}$ (c) $\{5,6,7,8,9\}$
   (d) $\{3,9\}$ (e) $\{1,2,3,4,5,6\}$ (f) $\emptyset$
   (g) $\{2,4,6,8\}$ (h) $\{1,2,3,4\}$ (i) $\{4,5\}$
   (j) $\{4,8,9\}$ (k) $\emptyset$

3. (a) $\mathscr{U}$ (b) $\{1,2,3,5,8,9\}$ (c) $\{0,2,3,4,6,8,9\}$
   (d) $\emptyset$ (e) $\{0,3,6,9\}$ (f) $\mathscr{U}$
   (g) $\{0,2,4,5,6,8\}$
   (h) $\mathscr{U}$ (i) $\{1,4,7\}$ (j) $\emptyset$

5. (a) $\left\{\begin{array}{l}(a,4),(a,5),\\(b,4),(b,5),\\(c,4),(c,5)\end{array}\right\}$ (b) $\left\{\begin{array}{l}(4,a),(4,b),(4,c),\\(5,a),(5,b),(5,c)\end{array}\right\}$

   (c) $\left\{\begin{array}{l}(a,a),(a,b),(a,c),\\(b,a),(b,b),(b,c),\\(c,a),(c,b),(c,c)\end{array}\right\}$ (d) $\left\{\begin{array}{l}(4,4),(4,5),\\(5,4),(5,5)\end{array}\right\}$

   (e) None   (f) No   (g) Yes
   (h) No   (i) Yes   (j) No
   (k) Yes   (l) No   (m) No

7. (a) $\emptyset$ (b) $\emptyset$ (c) $\emptyset$ (d) $\emptyset$
   (e) $\left\{\begin{array}{l}(0,1),(0,2),(0,3),\\(1,1),(1,2),(1,3),\\(2,1),(2,2),(2,3)\end{array}\right\}$ (f) $\left\{\begin{array}{l}(1,0),(1,1),(1,2),\\(2,0),(2,1),(2,2),\\(3,0),(3,1),(3,2)\end{array}\right\}$

   (g) Yes   (h) No   (i) Yes
   (j) Yes   (k) No

9. (a)   (b)

(c)   (d)

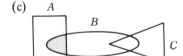

11.

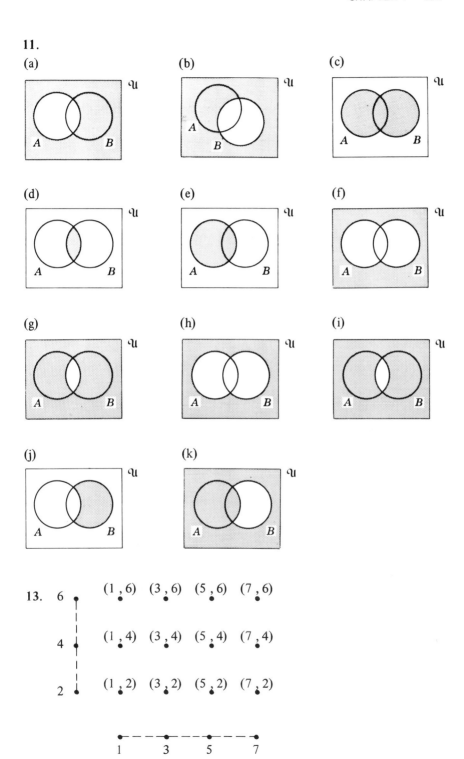

Exercise Set 1-5. Pages 34-35

3. (a) $\{a, b, k, l, m, n, o, p, q, r, s, t, u, v, w, x, y, z\}$

(b) $\{a, b, c, d, e, f, g, q, r, s, t, u, v, w, x, y, z\}$

(c) $\{a, b, q, r, s, t, u, v, w, x, y, z\}$

(d) $\{a, b, c, d, e, f, g, k, l, m, n, o, p, q, r, s, t, u, v, w, x, y, z\}$

(e) same as part (c)   (f) same as part (d)

(g) Yes   (h) Yes   (i) DeMorgan's Laws

(j) $\{a, b, c, d, e, h, i, j\}$ (k) $\{a, b, c, d, e, f, g, h, i, j\}$

(l) $\{a, b, c, d, e, h, i, j, k, l, m, n, o, p\}$ (m) $\{a, b, c, d, e, h, i, j\}$

(n) Yes   (o) $\emptyset$ (p) $\emptyset$

(q) Yes

4. (f)

A	B	C	$A \cup (B \cup C)$		$(A \cup B) \cup C$	
$\in$	$\in$	$\in$	$\in$	$\in$	$\in$	$\in$
$\in$	$\in$	$\notin$	$\in$	$\notin$	$\in$	$\in$
$\in$	$\notin$	$\in$	$\in$	$\notin$	$\in$	$\in$
$\in$	$\notin$	$\notin$	$\in$	$\notin$	$\in$	$\in$
$\notin$	$\in$	$\in$	$\in$	$\in$	$\in$	$\in$
$\notin$	$\in$	$\notin$	$\in$	$\in$	$\in$	$\in$
$\notin$	$\notin$	$\in$	$\in$	$\in$	$\notin$	$\in$
$\notin$	$\notin$	$\notin$	$\notin$	$\notin$	$\notin$	$\notin$

(g)

A	B	C	$[A \cap (B \cup C)]$		$[(A \cap B) \cup (A \cap C)]$		
$\in$	$\in$	$\in$	$\in$	$\in$	$\in$	$\in$	$\in$
$\in$	$\in$	$\notin$	$\in$	$\in$	$\in$	$\in$	$\notin$
$\in$	$\notin$	$\in$	$\in$	$\in$	$\notin$	$\in$	$\in$
$\in$	$\notin$	$\notin$	$\notin$	$\notin$	$\notin$	$\notin$	$\notin$
$\notin$	$\in$	$\in$	$\notin$	$\in$	$\notin$	$\notin$	$\notin$
$\notin$	$\in$	$\notin$	$\notin$	$\in$	$\notin$	$\notin$	$\notin$
$\notin$	$\notin$	$\in$	$\notin$	$\in$	$\notin$	$\notin$	$\notin$
$\notin$	$\notin$	$\notin$	$\notin$	$\notin$	$\notin$	$\notin$	$\notin$

6. (d)

Sets	Regions	Sets	Regions
A	2,3,5,6	A	2,3,5,6
B	3,4,6,7	B	3,4,6,7
C	5,6,7,8	C	5,6,7,8
$B \cap C$	6,7	$A \cap B$	3,6
$A \cap (B \cap C)$	6	$(A \cap B) \cap C$	6

(f)

Sets	Regions	Sets	Regions
A	2,3,5,6	A	2,3,5,6
B	3,4,6,7	B	3,4,6,7
C	5,6,7,8	C	5,6,7,8
$(B \cap C)$	6,7	$A \cup B$	2,3,4,5,6,7
$A \cup (B \cap C)$	2,3,5,6,7	$A \cup C$	2,3,5,6,7,8
		$(A \cup B) \cap (A \cup C)$	2,3,5,6,7

Exercise Set 1-6. Pages 40-41

1.

Relation	(a) R	(b) S	(c) T	(d) Equiv.
R_1	No	No	Yes	No.
R_2	Yes	No	Yes	No
R_3	Yes	Yes	No	No
R_4	Yes	Yes	No	No
R_5	No	No	Yes	No

3.

Relation	R	S	T	Equiv.
a	No	No	Yes	No
b	Yes	No	No	No
c	No	Yes	No	No
d	Yes	Yes	Yes	Yes

Exercise Set 1-7. Pages 43-44

1. (a) Yes   (b) The residents of a given block.

3. (a) Yes   (b) The dogs of a given breed.   5. Yes

6. (a) $A = \{a,b,c\}$; $\{(a,a),(b,b),(c,c),(b,c),(c,b)\}$

   (c) $A = \{a,b,c,d\}$; $\{(a,a),(b,b),(c,c),(d,d),(b,c),(c,b),(b,d),(d,b),(c,d),(d,c)\}$

   (e) $A = \{a,b,c,d\}$; $\{(a,a),(b,b),(c,c),(b,c),(c,b),(d,d)\}$

Exercise Set 1-8. Pages 47-48

1. (a) No, this is not even a set.
  (b) No, it is not a class of sets.
  (c) No, not every member of the class is a set.
  (d) No, the members of the class are not equivalent sets.
  (e) Same as (d).
  (f) Yes, it is an infinite class of equivalent finite sets.
  (g) No, not all of the members are sets.
  (h) No, the members are not sets.
  (i) Yes.
  (j) No, the class if not infinite.
  (k) Yes.
  (l) No, the class is not infinite.

3. (a) No, $\{a,b,c\} \neq \{0,1,2\}$, but $n(\{a,b,c\}) = n(\{0,1,2\})$.
  (b) No. See example in (a).
  (c) No. See example in (a).
  (d) Yes, because this means that A and B must belong to the same equivalence class.

5. Two cannot be equal, for if they were, this would mean that the equivalence class were non-disjoint. This in turn would mean for example that $\{a\} \sim \{a,b\}$ which cannot be.

CHAPTER 2

Exercise Set 2-1. Page 53

1. (a) ◁ ◁ ◁ ▽ ▽

  (b) ▽ ▷ ◁ ◁ ◁ ◁   ▽ ▽ ▽ / ▽ ▽ / ▽

  (c) ▽ ▷ ▽ ▷   ◁ ◁ ◁ / ◁ ◁ ◁   ▽ ▽ ▽ ▽ / ▽ ▽ / ▽ ▽ ;   ▽ ▷ ▽ ▷   ◁ ◁ ◁ / ◁ ◁ ◁   ◁ ▽ ▷ ▽

  (d) ◁ ◁ ◁ ◁ / ◁ ◁ ◁ ◁   ▽ ▽ ▽ / ▽

  (e) ▽ ▷ ▽

3. (a) ⌐△△△Γ‖   (b) 𝖥HHHH△△△Γ‖‖‖

(c) 𝖥𝖥H△△△△‖   or   XXXXX HHHHHH△△△△‖

(d) △△△△Γ‖‖‖   (e) 𝖥𝖥𝖥𝖥MMMM𝖥ˣX𝖥△△△△Γ‖‖‖

5. (a) ∇ , ∇∇ , ∇∇∇ , ∇∇∇∇ , ∇∇∇/∇∇ , ∇∇∇/∇∇∇ , ∇∇∇∇/∇∇∇ , ∇∇∇∇/∇∇∇∇ ,

◁∇▷∇ , ◁ , ◁∇ , ◁∇∇ , ◁∇∇∇ , ◁∇∇∇∇ , ◁∇∇∇/∇∇ ,

◁∇∇∇/∇∇∇ , ◁∇∇∇∇/∇∇∇ , ◁∇∇∇∇/∇∇∇∇ , ◁◁∇▷∇ , ◁◁ ;

(b) ▯ , ▯▯ , ▯▯▯ , ▯▯▯▯ , ▯▯▯/▯▯ , ▯▯▯/▯▯▯ , ▯▯▯▯/▯▯▯ , ▯▯▯▯/▯▯▯▯ , ▯▯▯▯/▯▯▯▯▯ ,

∩ , ∩▯ , ∩▯▯ , ∩▯▯▯ , ∩▯▯▯▯ , ∩▯▯▯/▯▯ , ∩▯▯▯/▯▯▯ , ∩▯▯▯▯/▯▯▯ ,

∩▯▯▯▯/▯▯▯▯ , ∩▯▯▯▯/▯▯▯▯▯ , ∩∩ ;

(c) I , II , III , IIII , Γ , ΓI , ΓII , ΓIII , ΓIIII , △ , △I , △II , △III ,

△IIII , △Γ , △ΓI , △ΓII , △ΓIII , △ΓIIII , △△ ;

(d) I, II, III, IV, V, VI, VII, VIII, IX, X, XI, XII, XIII, XIV, XV, XVI, XVII, XVIII, XIX, XX

Exercise Set 2-2. Pages 58-59

1. (a) $n(A) = 1110_{two}$, $n(B) = 1011_{two}$.   (b) $n(A) = 24_{five}$, $n(B) = 21_{five}$.

(c) $n(A) = 15_{nine}$, $n(B) = 12_{nine}$.   (d) $n(A) = 12_{twelve}$, $n(B) = e_{twelve}$

3. $n(A) = \Delta\gamma$, $n(B) = \gamma\Delta$; $n(A) = \beta\gamma\beta$

5. (a) eight   (b) forty-nine
   (c) six hundred twenty-five   (d) two thousand four hundred one
   (e) twelve   (f) one hundred twenty-one

7. (a) The empty set contains nothing and its cardinality is zero.
   (b) A numeral is a symbol used to represent a number.

Exercise Set 2-3. Page 62

1. (a) 1, 10, 11, 100, 101, 110, 111, 1000, 1001, 1010, 1011, 1100, 1101, 1110, 1111, 10000, 10001, 10010, 10011, 10100, 10101, 10110, 10111, 11000, 11001, 11010

2. (c) 1, 2, 3, 4, 10, 11, 12, 13, 14, 20, 21, 22, 23, 24, 30, 31, 32, 33, 34, 40, 41, 42, 43, 44, 100, 101

   (e) 1, 2, 3, 4, 5, 6, 10, 11, 12, 13, 14, 15, 16, 20, 21, 22, 23, 24, 25, 26, 30, 31, 32, 33, 34, 35

   (g) 1, 2, 3, 4, 5, 6, 7, 8, 9, t, 10, 11, 12, 13, 14, 15, 16, 17, 18, 19, lt, 20, 21, 22, 23, 24

3. (a) base seven   (b) ∠∠   (c) —

   (d) □ , ⧄ , ⧅ , |- , || , |∠ , |△ , |□ , |⧄ , |⧅ , ∠- , ∠| , ∠∠ , ∠△ , ∠□ , ∠⧄ , ∠⧅ , △- , △| , △∠ , △△ , △□ , △⧄ , △⧅ , □- , □| , □∠ , □△   5. (a) ∠⧅   (b) TT

Exercise Set 2-4. Page 65

1. 132_{seven}

3. (a) 72_{twelve} (b) 38_{eleven} (c) 10011_{two}

   (d) 32_{eight} (e) 10030_{four} (f) 140_{six}

   (g) 120_{five} (h) 32_{six}

   (i) 112_{three} (j) 23_{nine}

5. Change both to base ten. Then
   (a) 23_{four} = 11 and 21_{five} = 11,

   (c) 43_{five} = 23 and 35_{six} = 23.

6. Change both to base ten. Then
   (a) 43_{five} = 23 but 33_{seven} = 24,

   (c) 34_{five} = 19 but 35_{six} = 23.

Exercise Set 2-5. Pages 67-68

1.

ℓ	a	b	c	d	e
a	a	a	a	a	a
b	b	b	b	b	b
c	c	c	c	c	c
d	d	d	d	d	d
e	e	e	e	e	e

3. No; Yes in problem one, but No in problem two.

5. Yes, ∘ is an operation on *S*.

CHAPTER 3

Exercise Set 3-1. Page 72

1. (a) $n(A) = 2, n(B) = 5, n(A') = 2, n(B') = 5$

(b) $n(A \cup B) = 7, n(A' \cup B') = 7$

(c) Yes   (d) Yes   (e) Yes   (f) Uniqueness of sums.

3. Try the sets $\{a, b, c, d, e\}$ and $\{d, e, f, g, h, i\}$.

Exercise Set 3-2. Pages 79-81

5. (a) $(a + b + c) + (d + e + f) = (a + d) + (b + e) + (c + f)$

(b) Apply Theorem 3-10 twice.   (c) Follow the pattern of part (b).

6. (a) Yes   (b) No   **7.** Definition of addition and associativity; Yes.

10. (a) $n = 6$ (b) $n = 2$ (c) $n = 1$ (d) $n = 2$

13a. (a) Def. (+)

(b) Assoc. (+)

(c) Comm. (+)

(d) Assoc. (+)

(e) Def. (+)

(f) Add. Ident.

(g) Def. (+)

(h) Thm: $(a+b)+(c+d) = (a+c)+(b+d)$

(i) Def. (+)

(j) Add. Ident.

(k) Def. (+)

13c. (a) Assoc. (+)

(b) Comm. (+)

(c) Assoc. (+)

(d) Add. Ident.

(e) Def. (+)

(f) Thm: $(a+b) + (c+d) = (a+c) + (b+d)$

(g) Def. (+)

(h) Def. (+)

(i) Def. (+)

(j) Comm. (+)

(k) Canc. (+)

CHAPTER 4

Exercise Set 4-1. Pages 83-84

2. Yes, because whenever definition of $<$ holds, so does definition of $\leqslant$.

6. Since $\{a \mid a \leqslant 6\} = \{0,1,2,3,4,5,6\}$ and $\{a \mid a \geqslant 6\} = \{6,7,8,9,10,\ldots\}$, $\{a \mid a \leqslant 6\} \cap \{a \mid a \geqslant 6\} = \{6\}$ so that $a = 6$.

Exercise Set 4-2. Page 85

2. (c) Yes   (d) Uniqueness of differences.

3. A binary operation would map (2,5) into a cardinal number, but subtraction does not do this. Since there are ordered pairs of cardinals which have no image in the set of cardinals under subtraction, it cannot be an operation.

4. No

Exercise Set 4-3. Pages 90-93

1. $4 - 3 \neq 3 - 4$ since $3 - 4$ does not exist; whenever $a = b$.

2. $6 - (5 - 2) = 3$ but $(6 - 5) - 2 = 1 - 2$ does not exist.

5. (a) $n = 20$ (b) $n = 3$ (c) $n = 6$
      (d) $n = 16$ (e) $n = 5$ (f) $n = 9$

7. (a) Yes, write $32 - 24 = (32 - 24) + (6 - 6)$ and then apply Theorem 4-7.

9. (a) Def. (+)   **11.** (a) Def. (+)   **13.** (b) Def. (−)
      (b) Comm. (+)   (b) Comm. (+)   (c) Thm. 4-8
      (c) Thm. 4-8   (c) Thm. 4-8   (d) Prob. 6(b)
      (d) Prob. 6(b)   (d) Prob. 6(b)   (e) Add. Ident.
      (e) Def. (−)   (e) Add. Ident.   (f) Def. (+)
      (f) Assoc. (+)   (f) Prob. 6(b)   (g) Comm. (+)
      (g) Comm. (+)   (h) Thm. 4-8
      (h) Assoc. (+)   (i) Prob. 6(b)
      (i) Def. (+)   (j) Add. Ident.
      (j) Add. Ident.

17. (a) 2   (b) 3   (c) No answer exists.   (d) No.   (e) If $a = b$.

CHAPTER 5

Exercise Set 5-1. Pages 96-97

2. (c) They are the same.   (d) Uniqueness of products.

3. If two cardinal numbers are multiplied, any set representative may be selected which belongs to the cardinal involved.

5. No.

Exercise Set 5-2. Pages 104-107

1. (a) a is arbitrary, $b = 0$.   (c) $a = 0$.   **3.**   Change 2 to $1 + 1$.

7. (a) 8 and 7 respectively.   (b) 2 and 5 respectively.
   (c) 3 and 18 respectively.

9. (a) 4   (b) $\begin{bmatrix} (x,u),(x,v),(x,y),(x,z), \\ (y,u),(y,v),(y,y),(y,z), \\ (z,u),(z,v),(z,y),(z,z) \end{bmatrix}$ (c) 12   (d) 6

(e) 9   (f) No.   (g) Choose B and C disjoint.

11. (a) $2 + (3 \cdot 4) = 2 + 12 = 14$ but $(2 + 3) \cdot (2 + 4) = 5 \cdot 6 = 30$.
    (b) Any choice in which $a = 0$.
    (c) Distributivity of addition with respect to multiplication.

13. (a) 42   45   104   (b) Yes; Yes.   (c) No
        70   77   0   (d) No   (e) No
        48   77   93   (f) No   (g) Yes
       105

15. (a) Def. $(-)$ (i) Def. $(+)$ (q) Assoc. $(+)$
    (b) Def. $(+)$ (j) Thm. 4-8   (r) Def. $(+)$
    (c) Def. $(\cdot)$ (k) Prob. 6(b) [E.S. 4-3]   (s) Def. $(+)$
    (d) Def. $(+)$ (l) Add. Ident.   (t) Def. $(\cdot)$
    (e) Def. $(+)$ (m) Def. $(+)$ (u) Dist. $(\cdot/+)$
    (f) Dist. $(\cdot/+)$ (n) Assoc. $(+)$ (v) Def. $(+)$
    (g) Def. $(\cdot)$ (o) Def. $(+)$ (w) Def. $(\cdot)$
    (h) Thm. 4-8   (p) Comm. $(+)$

Exercise Set 5-3. Pages 110-111

1. No, it's contrary to definition of exponent.   3. (a) 3^6 (b) 7^7

   (c) 2^8 (d) 2^{11} (e) 10^3 5. $a^m \cdot b^m = (a \cdot b)^m$

7. Yes; If $b = m^2$ and $c = n^2$, then $b \cdot c = m^2 \cdot n^2 = (m \cdot n)^2$.

Exercise Set 5-4. Pages 117-118

1. (a) $2, 3, 5, 7, 11, 13, 17, 19, 23$
   (b) $2, 3, 5, 7, 11, 13, 17, 19, 23, 29, 31, 37, 41, 43, 47$
   (c) $2, 3, 5, 7, 11, 13, 17, 19, 23, 29, 31, 37, 41, 43, 47, 53, 59, 61, 67, 71, 73$.
   (d) $2, 3, 5, 7, 11, 13, 17, 19, 23, 29, 31, 37, 41, 43, 47, 53, 59, 61, 67, 71, 73,$
       $79, 83, 89, 97$.

3. (a) $2 \cdot 13$ (b) $2^4 \cdot 3$ (c) 5^4 (d) $3 \cdot 5^3$

   (e) $2^2 \cdot 3^2 \cdot 7$ (f) $3^2 \cdot 5^2$ (g) $2^2 \cdot 3^3 \cdot 5$ (h) $2^6 \cdot 3^2$

5. (a) $24 = 2^3 \cdot 3$ and $48 = 2^4 \cdot 3$ so L.C.M. $(24,48) = 2^4 \cdot 3$ and G.C.F. $(24,48)$ $= 2^3 \cdot 3$

(b) $36 = 2^2 \cdot 3^2$ and $48 = 2^4 \cdot 3$ so L.C.M. $(36,48) = 2^4 \cdot 3^2$ and G.C.F. $(36, 48) = 2^2 \cdot 3$.

(c) $44 = 2^2 \cdot 11$ and $66 = 2 \cdot 3 \cdot 11$ so L.C.M. $(44,66) = 2^2 \cdot 3 \cdot 11$ and G.C.F. $(44,66) = 2 \cdot 11$.

(d) $38 = 2 \cdot 19$ and $52 = 2^2 \cdot 13$ so L.C.M. $(38,52) = 2^2 \cdot 13 \cdot 19$ and G.C.F. $(38,52) = 2$.

(e) $42 = 2 \cdot 3 \cdot 7$ and $98 = 2 \cdot 7^2$ so L.C.M. $(42,98) = 2 \cdot 3 \cdot 7^2$ and G.C.F. $(42,98) = 2 \cdot 7$.

Exercise Set 5-5. Pages 122-126

1. (a) $5 \cdot 10^2 + 7 \cdot 10^1 + 6$ (b) $3 \cdot 10^4 + 5 \cdot 10^3 + 8 \cdot 10^2 + 9 \cdot 10^1 + 2$

(c) $6 \cdot 10^6 + 7 \cdot 10^5 + 7 \cdot 10^4 + 0 \cdot 10^3 + 1 \cdot 10^2 + 5 \cdot 10^1 + 8$

(d) $9 \cdot 10^9 + 2 \cdot 10^8 + 8 \cdot 10^7 + 3 \cdot 10^6 + 0 \cdot 10^5 + 3 \cdot 10^4 + 4 \cdot 10^3 + 8 \cdot 10^2 + 3 \cdot 10^1 + 2$

3.
(a) Expanded form	(h) Assoc. (+)	(o) Assoc. (+)
(b) Assoc. (+)	(i) Mult. Ident.	(p) Comm. (+)
(c) Comm. (+)	(j) Dist. ($\cdot$/+)	(q) Def. ($\cdot$)
(d) Assoc. (+)	(k) Def. (+)	(r) Assoc. (+)
(e) Dist. ($\cdot$/+)	(l) Def. exponent	(s) Expanded form
(f) Def. (+)	(m) Mult. Ident.	
(g) Def. (+)	(n) Add. Ident.	

5.
(a) Expanded form	(c) Dist. ($\cdot$/−)	(e) Expanded form
(b) Thm. 4-7	(d) Def. (−)	

7.
(a) Expanded form	(f) Expanded form	(k) Def. exponent
(b) Dist. ($\cdot$/+)	(g) Dist. ($\cdot$/+)	(l) Dist. ($\cdot$/+)
(c) Comm. ($\cdot$)	(h) Assoc. ($\cdot$)	(m) Def. (+)
(d) Assoc. ($\cdot$)	(i) Def. ($\cdot$)	(n) Assoc. (+)
(e) Def. ($\cdot$)	(j) Assoc. (+)	(o) Expanded form

9.
(a) Expanded form	(d) Def. ($\cdot$)	(g) Add. Ident.
(b) Dist. ($\cdot$/+)	(e) Def. exponent	(h) Def. ($\cdot$)
(c) Assoc. ($\cdot$)	(f) Add. Ident.	(i) Expanded form

14. Distributive Property. Yes, because it is one of the properties of cardinal arithmetic which can be *proved*.

CHAPTER 6

Exercise Set 6-1. Page 130

1. (a) (5,2)   (b) (2,4)   (c) (4,3)   (d) (3,1)

3. Quotient and remainder would no longer be unique because the one-to-one onto mappings could be terminated while such a mapping was still possible. e.g. $20 \div 5$ could yield (4,0) or (3,1).

5. In a physical sense this means that one might distribute more objects than he has.

Exercise Set 6-2. Pages 134-135

1. (a) 8   (b) 9   (c) 3   (d) 5   (e) 13   (f) 93   (g) 6   (h) 15

3. Ferdy uses the method correctly, but his multiplication facts are in error.

5. (a) No; $13 \div 2$ yields (6,1) and $15 \div 2$ yields (7,1), but $28 \div 2$ yields (14,0), not (13,2).
   (b) Yes; $13 \div 6$ yields (2,1), $15 \div 6$ yields (2,3), and $28 \div 6$ yields (4,4) = (2 + 2, 1 + 3).

7. (a) (29,11)   (b) (9,8)   (c) (23,28)   (d) (23,8)

Exercise Set 6-3. Pages 138-139

2. (a) Not always true; $2 \mid 4 \neq 4 \mid 2$.   (b) True when $a \neq 0$, $b \neq 0$, and $a = b$.

3. (a) Yes   (b) Yes   (c) Yes   (d) If $a \mid b$ and $b \mid c$, then $a \mid c$.

5. (a) Yes   (b) Yes   (c) Yes
   (d) If a and b are relatively prime and if $a \mid c$ and $b \mid c$, then $ab \mid c$.

Exercise Set 6-4. Pages 141-142

1. (a) divisible by two, not by five.   (b) not divisible by two or five.
   (c) divisible by two, not by five.   (d) divisible by five, not by two.
   (e) divisible by two, not by five.   (f) not divisible by two or five.

3. (a), (d), (e), and (f) are divisible by four.

5. (a), (c), (d), (e) and (f) are divisible by six.

7. (a) False; $2 \mid 4$ and $4 \mid 4$, but $8 \nmid 4$.
   (b) True because G.C.F. $(3,4) = 1$.
   (c) True because if 8 is a factor so is 4.
   (d) Since G.C.F. $(9,8) = 1$, all combinations of factors of 9 and 8 also divide N, thus $6 \mid N$.

CHAPTER 7

Exercise Set 7-1. Page 146

1. (a), (c), and (e) are order relations.

3. Yes; e.g. "is taller than," "can run faster than," etc.

Exercise Set 7-2. Page 150

1. (a) {3,4,5,6,7,8,9} (b) {0,1,2,3,4,5,6,7}
   (c) {0,1,2,3,4,5,6,7,8,9} (d) {0,1,2,3,4,5,6,7,8,9,10,11,12,13}
   (e) {2,3,4,5} (f) {0,1,2}
   (g) {3,4,5,6} (h) {0,1,2}

3. (a) $\{x \mid x > 7\}$ (b) {3,4,5,6} (c) {0,1,2}
   (d) {9,10,11} (e) {0,1,2,3,4,5,6,7,8,9,10,11} (f) {0,1,2,3,4,5}

5. (a) $\emptyset$ (b) $\emptyset$ (c) $\{y \mid y \geqslant 8\}$ (d) $\emptyset$

CHAPTER 8

Exercise Set 8-1. Pages 158-160

1. (a) 1010000_{two} (b) 11100_{three} (c) 10311_{four}
   (d) 13302_{five} (e) 4233_{seven} (f) 1523_{eight}
   (g) 18462_{eleven} (h) $124e5_{twelve}$

3. (a) 4566_{nine} (b) 3262_{twelve} (c) 1101011_{three} (d) 85955_{eleven}

5. (c), (e), (f), and (h) are true.

7. (a) Expanded form (f) Def. (+) (k) Mult. Ident.
   (b) Assoc. (+) (g) Def. (+) (l) Dist. (·/+)
   (c) Comm. (+) (h) Dist. (·/+) (m) Def. (+)
   (d) Assoc. (+) (i) Assoc. (+) (n) Assoc. (+)
   (e) Dist. (·/+) (j) Def. Exponent (o) Expanded form

9. Three because base six addition was used.

Exercise Set 8-2. Page 164

1.

$+$	$\bar{0}$	$\bar{1}$	$\bar{2}$	$\bar{3}$	$\bar{4}$
$\bar{0}$	$\bar{0}$	$\bar{1}$	$\bar{2}$	$\bar{3}$	$\bar{4}$
$\bar{1}$	$\bar{1}$	$\bar{2}$	$\bar{3}$	$\bar{4}$	$\bar{0}$
$\bar{2}$	$\bar{2}$	$\bar{3}$	$\bar{4}$	$\bar{0}$	$\bar{1}$
$\bar{3}$	$\bar{3}$	$\bar{4}$	$\bar{0}$	$\bar{1}$	$\bar{2}$
$\bar{4}$	$\bar{4}$	$\bar{0}$	$\bar{1}$	$\bar{2}$	$\bar{3}$

$\cdot$	$\bar{0}$	$\bar{1}$	$\bar{2}$	$\bar{3}$	$\bar{4}$
$\bar{0}$	$\bar{0}$	$\bar{0}$	$\bar{0}$	$\bar{0}$	$\bar{0}$
$\bar{1}$	$\bar{0}$	$\bar{1}$	$\bar{2}$	$\bar{3}$	$\bar{4}$
$\bar{2}$	$\bar{0}$	$\bar{2}$	$\bar{4}$	$\bar{1}$	$\bar{3}$
$\bar{3}$	$\bar{0}$	$\bar{3}$	$\bar{1}$	$\bar{4}$	$\bar{2}$
$\bar{4}$	$\bar{0}$	$\bar{4}$	$\bar{3}$	$\bar{2}$	$\bar{1}$

3.

$\ominus$	$\bar{0}$	$\bar{1}$	$\bar{2}$	$\bar{3}$	$\bar{4}$	$\bar{5}$	$\bar{6}$
$\bar{0}$	$\bar{0}$	$\bar{6}$	$\bar{5}$	$\bar{4}$	$\bar{3}$	$\bar{2}$	$\bar{1}$
$\bar{1}$	$\bar{1}$	$\bar{0}$	$\bar{6}$	$\bar{5}$	$\bar{4}$	$\bar{3}$	$\bar{2}$
$\bar{2}$	$\bar{2}$	$\bar{1}$	$\bar{0}$	$\bar{6}$	$\bar{5}$	$\bar{4}$	$\bar{3}$
$\bar{3}$	$\bar{3}$	$\bar{2}$	$\bar{1}$	$\bar{0}$	$\bar{6}$	$\bar{5}$	$\bar{4}$
$\bar{4}$	$\bar{4}$	$\bar{3}$	$\bar{2}$	$\bar{1}$	$\bar{0}$	$\bar{6}$	$\bar{5}$
$\bar{5}$	$\bar{5}$	$\bar{4}$	$\bar{3}$	$\bar{2}$	$\bar{1}$	$\bar{0}$	$\bar{6}$
$\bar{6}$	$\bar{6}$	$\bar{5}$	$\bar{4}$	$\bar{3}$	$\bar{2}$	$\bar{1}$	$\bar{0}$

5. Yes, however now uniqueness is lost just as in trying to define divisibility by zero for cardinals.

CHAPTER 9

Exercise Set 9-1. Pages 184-185

2. (a) $\mathscr{I}$ holds only for (b) and (d).

3. Yes. One can set up the one-to-one onto map between pairs of a class and the cardinals by using either the first or second members of the pairs.

5. Yes, from the choice made in conjunction with the graph of the Cartesian product set.

6. Equality holds in parts (b) and (d) only.

CHAPTER 10

Exercise Set 10-1. Pages 188-189

1. (a) [7,7] (b) [11,6] (c) [9,10]
   (d) [12,13] (e) [17,10] (f) [8,5]

3. Because $\oplus$ maps each pair of integers back into the set of integers; i.e., closure.

5. Yes, because in each case the same integers are added even though different numerals are used.

Exercise Set 10-2. Pages 194-195

1. (a) [10,9] (b) [16,15]

(c) Yes, because both sums name the same integer. Of course symmetric and transitive properties of equality are also required.

3. (a) [5,12] (b) [9,18] (c) [11,14]
   (d) The sum of two negative integers is a negative integer (Thm. 10-11).

5. (a) $^+12$ (b) $^+7$ (c) $^-8$ (d) $^-14$
   (e) $^+3$ (f) $^+2$ (g) $^-3$ (h) $^-1$

7. (a) $^-2$ (b) $^+11$ (c) $^-7$ (d) $^+8$
   (e) 0 (f) [3,2] (g) [0,4] (h) [1,4]
   (i) [8,5] (j) [4,4]

9. (a) $x =^+1$ (b) $y = 0$ (c) $n =^-4$ (d) $t =^-5$
   (e) $k =^-2$ (f) $t =^-9$

10. (a) [5,13] (b) [10,15] (c) No such x
    (d) $y = x + 2$ where $x \in \{0,1,2,\cdots\}$ (e) $y = 15$

Exercise Set 10-3. Page 198

1. (a) [11,9] (b) [9,6] (c) [13,25] (d) [3,5]
   (e) [22,14] (f) [20,16]

3. (a) Yes, $\ominus$ is an operation whereas subtraction of cardinals is not an operation.
   (b) Since $\ominus$ is an operation, closure is automatic because the images under $\ominus$ are integers.

4. No; for then [5,0] $\ominus$ [2,0] = [10,0], not [3,0].

Exercise Set 10-4. Pages 201-203

1. (a) [7,14] (b) {5,10] (c) [16,10] (d) [14,16] (e) [18,7]

4. (a) [3,5] (b) [5,7] (c) [8,10] (d) [6,8] (e) [0,0]

5. (a) Use [2,4] and [5,3], then [2,4] $\ominus$ [5,3] = [5,9] and [5,3] $\ominus$ [2,4] = [9,5]. $\ominus$ is not commutative because [5,9] $\neq$ [9,5].

9. (a) [8,5] ; [3,0] (b) [10,6] ; [4,0] (c) [13,17] ; [0,4]
   (d) [16,11] ; [5,0] (e) [18,11] ; [7,0] (f) [14,14] ; [0,0]
   (g) [4,5] ; [0,1] (h) [18,11] ; [7,0]
   (i) [9,17] ; [0,8] (j) [20,14] ;[6,0]

11. (a) [18,35] (b) [0,6] (c) [21,27] (d) [35,18]
    (e) [112,24] (f) [28,96] (g) [33,42] (h) [57,26]
    (i) No (j) No (k) No (l) No

CHAPTER 11

Exercise Set 11-1. Page 207

1. (a) [49,39] (b) [25,45] (c) [24,39] (d) [43,22]

(e) [108,108]   (f) [40,40]   (g) [86,101]   (h) [190,330]

3. Because each time a product of integers is formed, the result is another integer. That is, $\odot$ is an operation.

Exercise Set 11-2. Pages 218-220

1. [47,52] ; Yes because multiplication is commutative.

3. Yes, distributivity of multiplication over addition.

5. (a) [1,0]   (b) [4,0]   (c) [0,1]   (d) [0,3]   (e) [3,0]
   (f) $^-2$ (g) $^+9$ (h) $^+3$ (i) $^-2$

7. [2,0] $\odot$ [1,2] = [2,4] and [2,4] $\neq$ [2,0] ; hence negative one is not a multiplicative identity.

11. $^-(2 \oplus {}^+4) = {}^-(2) \oplus {}^-({}^+4) = {}^+2 \oplus {}^-4 = {}^-2$ and $^-(2 \oplus {}^+4) = {}^-({}^+2) = {}^-2$.

13. (a) [14,11]   (b) [14,11]   (c) [14,11]   (d) Yes   (e) Theorem 11-15

16. 7 and 8   18. (a) 28   (b) 30   (c) 32   (d) 40
                       (e) $^-30$ (f) $^-33$ (g) 8   (h) $^-4$

19. (a) No by parts (a) and (b).
    (b) No by parts (c) and (d).   (c) No by parts (e) and (f).
    (d) Consider the cases $a > b$, $a < b$. These imply that $a = b$ is the only workable possibility.

Exercise Set 11-3. Page 221

1. Only with the restriction originally insisted upon for subtracting cardinals, for then we developed the inverse definition.

3. No because there is no cardinal corresponding to $^-24$.

5.

$\oplus$	A	B	C	D
A	C	D	B	A
B	D	C	A	B
C	B	A	D	C
D	A	B	C	D

$\odot$	A	B	C	D
A	B	A	C	D
B	A	B	C	D
C	C	C	D	D
D	D	D	D	D

7. (b) Clockwise and counterclockwise rotation of the switch respectively.

CHAPTER 12

Exercise Set 12-1. Page 224

1. It is to be noted that the pairs (q,r) will not be unique for division if the only requirement is that $r < b$.

2. (a) 96   (b) $^-51$ (c) $^-1002$ (d) $^-29$

Exercise Set 12-2. Pages 228-229

3. (a) Yes for non-zero integers. (b) Not in general. Divisibility does
   not have the symmetric property. (c) No   (d) Yes

5. (a) $^{+}1 \cdot 2^2 \cdot 3^2 \cdot 5$ (b) $^{-}1 \cdot 2^3 \cdot 3 \cdot 7$ (c) $^{-}1 \cdot 2^2 \cdot 3 \cdot 7 \cdot 11$ (d) $^{+}1 \cdot 5^3 \cdot 7$

7. (a) 14   (b) 6   (c) 8   (d) 9

9. Because every integer is a factor of the integer zero.

11. (a) $4 \cdot 10^5 + 3 \cdot 10^4 + 7 \cdot 10^3 + 6 \cdot 10^2 + 8 \cdot 10^1 + 5$

   (b) $^{-}1 \cdot (3 \cdot 10^5 + 7 \cdot 10^4 + 4 \cdot 10^3 + 2 \cdot 10^2 + 5 \cdot 10^1 + 1)$

13. The pairs in (a), (b), (c), (d), and (f) are relatively prime.

Exercise Set 12-3. Pages 232-233

1. The valid statements are (a), (c), and (g).

3. The valid statements are (a), (b), and (c).

4. The valid statements are (a), (c), (d), (e), (f), (g), and (h).

5. (a) $\{\cdots, ^{-}5, ^{-}4, ^{-}3\}$ (b) $\{2,3,4, \cdots\}$ (c) $\{\cdots, ^{-}2, ^{-}1, 0\}$
   (d) $\{^{-}4, ^{-}3, ^{-}2, ^{-}1, 0, 1, \cdots\}$ (e) $\{1,2,3, \cdots\}$
   (f) $\{9,10,11, \cdots\}$ (g) $\{7,8,9, \cdots\}$

CHAPTER 13

Exercise Set 13-1. Pages 244-246

2. (a), (b), (e), and (h) satisfy the relation $\mathscr{R}$.   3. (a) $x = ^{-}3$
   (b) There is no such y since the second number is zero.
   (c) $y = ^{-}21$ (d) $x = ^{-}10$

5. (a) $\{..., (8, ^{-}28), (6, ^{-}21), (4, ^{-}14), (2, ^{-}7), (^{-}2, 7), (^{-}4, 14), (^{-}6, 21), ...\}$
   (b) $\{..., (^{-}12, ^{-}16), (^{-}9, ^{-}12), (^{-}6, ^{-}8), (^{-}3, ^{-}4), (3, 4), (6, 8), (9, 12), ...\}$

6. (a) $k = 4$ or $^{-}4$ (c) $k = 8$ or $^{-}8$ (d) $k = 5$ or $^{-}5$

7. (a) $\frac{^{-}2}{3}$ (c) $\frac{1}{3}$ (d) $\frac{^{-}1}{2}$ (f) $\frac{^{-}1}{3}$

9. (a) $x = 3$ (b) $x = ^{-}4$ (d) $x = ^{-}14$ (f) $y = 16$

10. (a) Since $0 \cdot 7 = 2 \cdot 0$, the given statement of equality holds by definition of
    equality.

CHAPTER 14

Exercise Set 14-1. Page 251

1. (a) $\frac{^{-}2}{2}$ or $\frac{^{-}1}{1}$ (c) $\frac{^{-}2}{3}$ 2. (a) $\frac{2}{7}$ (b) $\frac{4}{14}$ (c) Uniqueness of sums.

3. (a) Choose $k = 4$ and $k = 3$ respectively.
   (b) Choose $k = 1$ and $k = 2$ respectively.

(c) Choose $k = 6$ and $k = 5$ respectively.

(d) Choose $k = 3$ and $k = 8$ respectively.   (e) Theorem 14-2

Exercise Set 14-2. Pages 261-264

1. (a) and (b) $\frac{17}{12}$; Commutative Property.

4. (a) $\frac{x}{y} = \frac{5}{5} = \frac{1}{1}$ (b) $\frac{x}{y} = \frac{5}{6}$ (c) $\frac{x}{y} = \frac{7}{12}$ (d) $\frac{x}{y} = \frac{3}{5}$ (e) $x = 1$

(f) $x = 3$ (g) $\frac{x}{y} = \frac{2}{3}$ (h) $\frac{x}{y} = \frac{3}{10}$ (i) $\frac{x}{y} = \frac{19}{28}$ (j) $\frac{x}{y} = \frac{6}{35}$

5. (a) $\frac{2}{3}$ (b) $\frac{^-3}{7}$ (c) $\frac{3}{13}$ (d) $\frac{^-4}{5}$

6. (a) $\frac{x}{y} = \frac{^-1}{12}$ (b) $\frac{x}{y} = \frac{17}{30}$ (c) $\frac{x}{y} = \frac{^-11}{12}$ (d) $\frac{x}{y} = \frac{2}{7}$

8. True for all rationals because $\frac{1}{2} = \frac{2}{6}$.

9. (a) K-Theorem   (b) Comm. $\odot$ (c) Def. $\odot$ (d) Def. (+)   (e) Def. $\oplus$

11. (a) Def. $\odot$ (g) Def. $\oplus$ (m) Def. $\oplus$

(b) K-Theorem   (h) Def. (=)   (n) K-Theorem

(c) Assoc. (+)   (i) Assoc. (+)   (o) Def. $\odot$

(d) Comm. (+)   (j) Comm. (+)

(e) Assoc. (+)   (k) Assoc. (+)   (p) Def. (+)

(f) Def. (+)   (l) Def. (+)   (q) Def. $\oplus$

13. (a) No, since c could be zero.   (b) Yes

(c) No. Try $\frac{2}{3} \triangle \frac{4}{5}$ and $\frac{4}{5} \triangle \frac{2}{3}$.   (d) No. Try $\frac{1}{2}, \frac{2}{3}$, and $\frac{3}{4}$.

(e) No, for then b or d would have to be zero.   (f) Yes, if $\frac{c}{d} \neq \frac{0}{1}$.

Exercise Set 14-3. Pages 268-272

3. (a) $\frac{2}{3} + \frac{^-3}{4}$ (b) $\frac{^-7}{8} - \frac{^-3}{5}$ (c) $\frac{7}{6} + \frac{2}{3}$ (d) $\frac{^-3}{5} - \frac{2}{3}$

7. Try $\frac{4}{5}$ and $\frac{2}{3}$. Then $\frac{2}{15} \neq \frac{^-2}{15}$.   9. (a) $21k$ where k is a positive integer.

(c) $507k$ where k is a positive integer.

(e) $455k$ where k is a positive integer.

13. (a) $\frac{x}{y} = \frac{17}{12}$ (b) $\frac{x}{y} = \frac{^-1}{12}$ (c) No such x.   (d) $x = 0, y = 2$

(e) $x = 0, y = ^-20$ (f) $x = ^-4$ (g) $\frac{x}{y} = \frac{^-37}{20}$ (h) No such x

(i) No such x.   (j) $x = 0, y = ^-2$ (k) $x = 0, y = 20$

(l) $x = 4$ (m) $\frac{x}{y} = \frac{^-67}{20}$ (n) $\frac{x}{y} = \frac{37}{20}$.

Note: Parts (d),(e),(j) and (k) have many pairs x and y which will work.

15. The theorem is true; for a hint refer to the proof of Theorem 4-7.

17. (b) (a) Ex. 15

    (b) Def. (+)

    (c) Def. $\oplus$

    (d) *K*-Theorem

    (e) Def. $\odot$

    (f) Def. (+)

    (g) Def. $\oplus$

    (h) *K*-Theorem

    (i) Def. $\odot$

    (j) Def. (−)

    (k) Def. $\oplus$

    (l) Cor. Ex. 15

    (m) Def. $\ominus$

    (n) Ident. $\oplus$

CHAPTER 15

Exercise Set 15-1. Page 276

2. (a) Left side yields $\dfrac{^{-}12}{45}$; right side yields $\dfrac{^{-}180}{675}$. These two are equal since $^{-}8100 = {}^{-}8100$.

   (b) Uniqueness of products.   (c) Yes, because $\dfrac{6}{10} = \dfrac{3}{5}$ and $\dfrac{^{-}28}{63} = \dfrac{^{-}4}{9}$.

Exercise Set 15-2. Pages 286-290

1. Commutativity of products.
4. Definition of addition and multiplicative inverse.
5. (a) $\dfrac{2}{3}$; multiplicative inverse.

   (b) $\dfrac{1}{1}$; multiplicative identity and multiplicative inverse.

   (c) $\dfrac{5}{6}$; multiplicative inverse and multiplicative identity.

6. (a) $\dfrac{x}{y} = \dfrac{^{-}5}{4}$ (b) $\dfrac{x}{y} = \dfrac{^{-}7}{5}$ (c) $\dfrac{x}{y} = \dfrac{2}{1}$ (d) $\dfrac{x}{y} = \dfrac{^{-}9}{10}$

   (e) $x = 10$ (f) $\dfrac{x}{y} = \dfrac{3}{5}$ (g) $\dfrac{x}{y} = \dfrac{9}{1}$ (h) $y \neq 0, x = 3y$

   (i) $\dfrac{x}{y} = \dfrac{2}{3}$ (j) $x = 28$ (k) $x = 3$

7. Add first and then multiply or use the distributive property twice.

9. (a) Identity $\odot$, Def. $\odot$ (b) Assoc. $(\cdot)$
   (c) Def. $(\cdot)$ (d) Identity $\odot$ (e) Def. (=)   (f) Identity $\odot$
   (g) Def. $(\cdot)$ (h) Identity $\odot$ (i) Def. $\odot$ (j) Def. $\odot$

11. (a) Theorem 14-15   (b) Def. $\odot$ (c) Def. $\ominus$
   (d) Def. $(\cdot)$ (e) Def. $\odot$

13. (a) *K*-Theorem   (b) Def. $\odot$ (c) Def. (−)
   (d) Def. $\ominus$ (e) Def. $(\cdot)$ (f) Def. $\odot$

16. Yes

19. (a) Hint: Work down both sides of the equality, then use the symmetric and transitive properties of equality.

22. Use associativity then apply the distributive property twice.

25. (a) $\frac{x}{y} = \frac{3}{2}$ or $\frac{3}{5}$ (b) $\frac{u}{v} = \frac{^-2}{3}$ or $\frac{0}{1}$ (c) $\frac{x}{y} = \frac{1}{2}$ or $\frac{^-1}{2}$ (d) $\frac{x}{y} = \frac{^-1}{1}$ or $\frac{2}{5}$

Exercise Set 15-3. Page 293

2. (a) $\frac{2}{7} \div \frac{6}{4}$ (b) $\frac{3}{4} \div \frac{3}{4}$ (c) $\frac{3}{5} \cdot \frac{3}{5}$

(d) $\left(\frac{3}{7} \cdot \frac{3}{4}\right) \cdot \frac{4}{7}$ (e) $\left(\frac{3}{8} \cdot \frac{6}{4}\right) \cdot \frac{16}{9}$

3. (b) $\frac{1}{1}$ (c) $\frac{9}{25}$ (d) $\frac{16}{49}$

4. (a) $\frac{9}{35}$ (b) $\frac{^-35}{9}$ (c) $\frac{^-32}{15}$ (d) $\frac{15}{32}$

5. Because if it were then every pair of rationals is mapped to another rational. However, if the divisor is $\frac{0}{1}$ then there is no image possible.

Exercise Set 15-4. Pages 298-301

1. Yes, one can show this by using $\frac{2}{3}$ and $\frac{4}{5}$ for example.

3. (a) No, $\frac{1}{5} \neq \frac{5}{1}$.   (b) Yes

4. (a) $\frac{5}{1}$ (b) $\frac{5}{1}$ (c) Yes   (d) Theorem 15-16

7. (a) $\frac{x}{y} = \frac{3}{14}$ (b) $\frac{x}{y} = \frac{3}{14}$ (c) $\frac{x}{y} = \frac{9}{10}$

(d) $\frac{x}{y} = \frac{1}{1}$ (e) $3x = 2y, x \neq 0$ (f) $\frac{x}{y} = \frac{^-2}{5}$

(g) $\frac{x}{y} = \frac{^-10}{9}$ (h) $\frac{x}{y} = \frac{15}{4}$ (i) $\frac{x}{y} = \frac{^-86}{105}$ (j) $x = {}^-2y, x \neq 0$

13. (a) $\frac{7}{9} ; \frac{7}{9}$ (b) $\frac{8}{5} ; \frac{8}{5}$ (c) $\frac{^-5}{8} ; \frac{^-5}{8}$

(d) $\frac{5}{^-11} ; \frac{^-5}{11}$ (e) $\frac{^-4}{^-19} ; \frac{4}{19}$ (f) $\frac{^-10}{^-13} ; \frac{10}{13}$

(g) Yes, addition and subtraction.

(i) Use uniqueness and choose different numerals whose denominators are the same (perhaps by use of the K-Theorem).

17. (a) Theorem 15-16   (b) Def. (·)   (c) Comm. ⊙   (d) K-Theorem
(e) Def. (÷), Inverse (·)   (f) Def. (÷)   (g) Def. (·)   (h) Def. ⊙

(i) *K*-Theorem   (j) Identity ⊙   (k) Def. (+)   (l) Def. ⊕

Exercise Set 15-5. Page 303

1. They are isomorphic to the set of rationals which have denominator one.
3. (a) The system of cardinals is embedded in the system of integers and the system of integers is embedded in the system of rationals.
   (b)

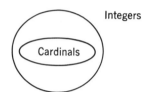

CHAPTER 16

Exercise Set 16-1. Pages 307-309

1. Parts (a), (b), (f), and (g) are true.
3. Parts (a), (b), (e), (f), (g), (h), (i), (k), and (l) are true.   4. $\dfrac{0}{1}$

6. (a) True   (b) True   (c) False, $\dfrac{3}{4} \leqslant \dfrac{3}{4}$, but $\dfrac{3}{4} \not< \dfrac{3}{4}$.

   (d) False, $\dfrac{3}{4} \geqslant \dfrac{3}{4}$, but $\dfrac{3}{4} \not> \dfrac{3}{4}$.   (e) True   (f) True

Exercise Set 16-2. Pages 318-319

2. (a) $\dfrac{7}{10}$ or $\dfrac{37}{42}$ (There are others.)   (b) $\dfrac{20}{24}$ or $\dfrac{119}{143}$ (There are others.)

6. (b) Yes

(c)

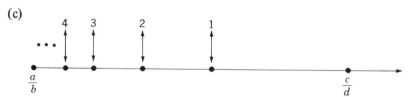

8. (a) $X = \left\{ x \mid x \geqslant \dfrac{19}{21} \right\}$ (c) $X = \{x \mid x \leqslant 10, x \text{ an integer}\}$

   (e) $X = \left\{ x \mid x \geqslant \dfrac{4}{35} \right\}$ (g) $X = \{x \mid x \geqslant {}^{-}1, x \text{ an integer}\}$

   (i) $X = \{x \mid x \geqslant 1, x \text{ an integer}\}$ (k) $X = \{x \mid x \geqslant 2, x \text{ an integer}\}$

9. (a) Those of parts (b), (c), (d), (f), (g), (h), (i), and (k).
   (b) Those of parts (a), (e), and (j).

Exercise Set 16-3. Pages 325-327

1. (a) $\frac{3}{2}$ (b) $\frac{5}{7}$ (c) $\frac{0}{1}$ (d) $\frac{5}{12}$

   (e) $\frac{11}{40}$ (f) $\frac{13}{14}$ (g) $\frac{17}{12}$ (h) $\frac{5}{12}$

   (i) $\frac{13}{14}$ (j) $\frac{31}{14}$ (k) $\frac{11}{40}$ (l) $\frac{^-1}{14}$

   (m) Yes   (n) No   (o) No   (p) Yes

2. (a) $X = \left\{ \frac{3}{5}, \frac{^-3}{5} \right\}$ (c) $X = \left\{ \frac{^-1}{8} \right\}$ (e) $X = \left\{ \frac{2}{7}, \frac{^-8}{7} \right\}$

   (g) $X = \left\{ \frac{^-13}{6}, \frac{^-17}{6} \right\}$

3. (b) $X = \emptyset$ (d) $X = \left\{ x \mid \frac{1}{2} < x < \frac{11}{10} \right\}$

   (f) $X = \left\{ x \mid x > \frac{2}{7} \right\} \cup \left\{ x \mid x < \frac{^-2}{7} \right\}$

   (h) $X = \left\{ x \mid x > \frac{1}{3} \right\} \cup \left\{ x \mid x < \frac{^-1}{9} \right\}$

   (j) $X = \{ x \mid x > 2, x \text{ an integer} \} \cup \{ x \mid x \leqslant {}^-1, x \text{ an integer} \}$

4. (a) $X = \left\{ x \mid \frac{^-5}{12} \leqslant x \leqslant \frac{5}{12} \right\}$

   (c) $X = \left\{ x \mid \frac{^-3}{2} \leqslant x \leqslant \frac{1}{6} \right\}$

   (f) $X = \left\{ x \mid x \leqslant \frac{^-1}{2} \right\} \cup \left\{ x \mid x \geqslant \frac{7}{6} \right\}$

   (g) $X = \left\{ x \leqslant \frac{^-11}{8} \right\} \cup \left\{ x \mid x \geqslant \frac{^-1}{8} \right\}$

5. (a) $|x| < \frac{7}{16}$ (b) $|x| \leqslant \frac{6}{7}$ (c) $\left| x - \frac{3}{5} \right| < \frac{1}{2}$

   (d) $\left| x + \frac{2}{3} \right| \leqslant \frac{1}{6}$ (e) $|x| > \frac{5}{9}$ (f) $\left| x \right| > \frac{13}{4}$

   (g) $\left| x - \frac{4}{3} \right| > \frac{1}{6}$ (h) $\left| x - \frac{17}{40} \right| \geqslant \frac{3}{8}$

8. (a) $\left\{ x \mid \frac{^-1}{8} < x < \frac{5}{8} \right\} \cap \left(\left\{ x \mid x < \frac{^-1}{4} \right\} \cup \left\{ x \mid x > \frac{1}{4} \right\} \right) = \left\{ x \mid \frac{1}{4} < x < \frac{5}{8} \right\}$

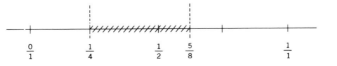

$\frac{0}{1}$ $\frac{1}{4}$ $\frac{1}{2}$ $\frac{5}{8}$ $\frac{1}{1}$

CHAPTER 17

Exercise Set 17-1. Pages 337-338

1. (a) 5231.   (b) 439.53   (c) .0537   (d) 803.00004

2. (a) $5(10^2) + 2(10^1) + 1 + 2(10^{-1}) + 7(10^{-2})$

   (b) $0(10^{-1}) + 0(10^{-2}) + 1(10^{-3}) + 2(10^{-4}) + 3(10^{-5})$

   (e) $0(10^{-1}) + 0(10^{-2}) + 1(10^{-3}) + 2(10^{-4}) + 7(10^{-5})$

3. (a) 10^1 (b) $\dfrac{5^3}{3^4}$ (c) $\dfrac{2}{9}$ (e) $\dfrac{10^{10} \cdot 13}{7^3 \cdot 5^4}$

4. (a) $5^3 \cdot 4^{-2} \cdot 7^4$ (b) $a^{-1} b^4 c^{-3}$ 5. (a) $2.57 \cdot 10^9$ (c) $1.52 \cdot 10^{-1}$

   (e) $1.782 \cdot 10^{20}$ (g) $1.27 \cdot 10^{-9}$ (i) $3.12 \cdot 10^{-5}$ 6. (a) .03125

   (d) .0375   9. (a) $123 \cdot 10^{-2}$ (b) $175 \cdot 10^{-6}$ (c) $671 \cdot 10^{-7}$

   (d) $8932 \cdot 10^2$ (e) $8 \cdot 10^{-1}$

Exercise Set 17-2. Pages 345-346

1. (a) .04   (b) .15625   (c) .05   (d) .045
2. (a) 36.733   (b) 62.996   (c) 1.046   (d) ⁻6.961
   (e) ⁻1.576   (f) 41.120   (g) ⁻7.75   (h) ⁻64.259
3. (a) $25825 \cdot 10^{-3}$ (b) $245334 \cdot 10^{-4}$ (c) $2812 \cdot 10^{-2}$ (d) $^{-}17942 \cdot 10^{-4}$

4. (a) 38.7549   (b) .000049345   (c) 578.0118424
6. (a) .40625   (b) .24   (c) .37
   (d) .142   (e) 42.79   (f) 362.73

Exercise Set 17-3. Pages 350-352

2. (a) .33333···   (c) .2   (e) .8888···   (g) .230769230769···   (i) .375
3. (a) $.\overline{3}$ (e) $.\overline{8}$ (g) $.\overline{230769}$
4. (a) $\dfrac{26}{111}$ (c) $\dfrac{433}{1111}$ (e) $\dfrac{67894}{99999}$ (g) $\dfrac{137}{111}$ (i) $\dfrac{1111}{900}$ (k) $\dfrac{15041}{3960}$

6. (a) $\dfrac{1}{9}$ (c) $\dfrac{1}{11}$ (e) $\dfrac{311}{99}$ (g) $\dfrac{370}{99}$

8. (a) $.\overline{9}$ (b) $.\overline{9}$ (c) $.\overline{9}$ (d) $.\overline{9}$
10. (a) $.\overline{7}$ (b) $1.\overline{1}$ (c) $1.\overline{5}$ (d) $4.\overline{6}$
11. No, if the sum is larger than $.\overline{9}$ the sums do not behave as expected.

Exercise Set 17-4. Pages 358-359

2. (a) $\displaystyle\lim_{n \to \infty} S_n = 3$ (b) $\displaystyle\lim_{n \to \infty} S_n = 27$ (c) $\displaystyle\lim_{n \to \infty} S_n = 4$ (d) $\displaystyle\lim_{n \to \infty} S_n = 1$

(e) $\displaystyle\lim_{n \to \infty} S_n = 10$ (f) $\displaystyle\lim_{n \to \infty} S_n = \frac{7}{9}$ (g) $\displaystyle\lim_{n \to \infty} S_n = \frac{2}{3}$

Exercise Set 17-5. Page 364

1. (a) 2.39   (c) .0473   (e) .6666   (g) .0004   (i) .000125
2. (b) 236%   (d) 34.8%   (f) 4.95%   (h) 6.66%   (j) 400%

3. (a) $\frac{1}{30}\%$ (b) $1\frac{2}{3}\%$ (c) $6\frac{2}{3}\%$ (d) $\frac{1}{7}\%$

CHAPTER 18

Exercise Set 18-1. Pages 369-370

1. Parts (c), (e), and (g) represent relations, the remaining parts being functions.
2. (a) $f: a \to 2a - 1$ (c) $f: a \to a^2$ (d) $f: a \to a(1 - a)$
6. (a) 1   (b) 2   (c) ⁻3   (d) 0   (e) ⁻2   (f) ⁻1   (g) 0

7. (⁻2,2), $\left(-1\frac{3}{4}, 1\frac{3}{4}\right)$, $\left(\frac{-3}{2}, \frac{3}{2}\right)$, $\left(\frac{-5}{4}, \frac{5}{4}\right)$, $\left(\frac{-7}{8}, \frac{7}{8}\right)$, $\left(\frac{-2}{3}, \frac{2}{3}\right)$, $\left(\frac{-1}{16}, \frac{1}{16}\right)$,

$\left(\frac{0}{1}, \frac{0}{1}\right)$, $\left(\frac{1}{4}, \frac{1}{4}\right)$, $\left(\frac{1}{3}, \frac{1}{3}\right)$, $\left(\frac{13}{16}, \frac{13}{16}\right)$, $\left(\frac{5}{6}, \frac{5}{6}\right)$, $\left(1\frac{1}{3}, 1\frac{1}{3}\right)$, $\left(\frac{5}{4}, \frac{5}{4}\right)$,

$\left(1\frac{5}{7}, 1\frac{5}{7}\right)$, (2,2)

Exercise Set 18-2. Pages 373-374

1. (b)

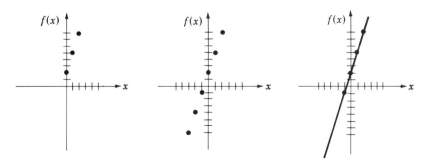

(d)

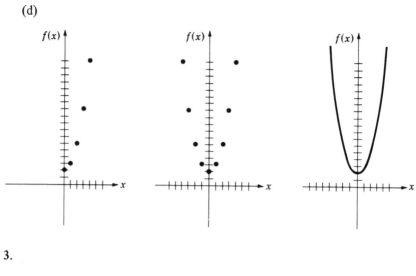

3.

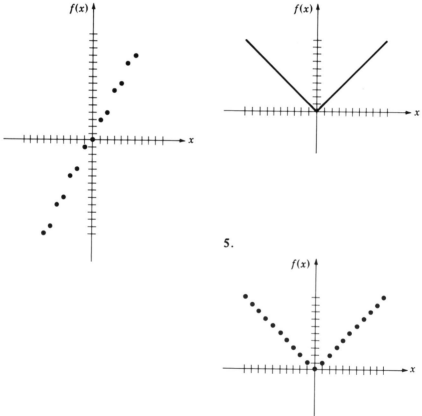

5.

7. Rational numbers must be used for f and integers for g.

Exercise Set 18-3. Pages 382-384

1. (a) 1.732051   (b) 2.236068   (c) 2.449490   (d) 2.645751
(e) 2.828427   **3.** 1.3

4. (a) 10, 11   (b) 17, 18   (c) 45, 46   (d) none   (e) $^-4, ^-3$

(f) 13, 14   (g) 0, 1   (h) $\frac{1}{3}, .34$ (i) .5, .6   (j) $\frac{5}{3}, 2$

5. (b), (c), (e), and (j).   **7.** (a) 1   (b) 3

8. (a) 3.875   (b) .9375   (c) .15625   (d) 5.75

9. (a) 1.11   (b) 11.111   (c) 101.101   (d) .111001

10. $\frac{1}{3} = .\overline{3}$ in base ten but $\frac{1}{3} = .1$ in base three notation.

Exercise Set 18-4. Pages 387-388

1. (a) $4.205 \leqslant 1 \leqslant 4.214 , 6.365 \leqslant w \leqslant 6.374 , 3.35 \leqslant h \leqslant 3.44$
(b) 26.764825 and 26.860036 ; 14.08675 and 14.49616 ;
21.32275 and 21.92656.   (c) $89.66216375 \leqslant v \leqslant 92.39852384$

2. length = 6.37; An upper bound for area is 37; l.u.b. = 36.166076.

3. (a) .5   (b) .05   (c) .005   (d) .0005

(e) $\frac{1}{8}$ (f) $\frac{1}{6}$ (g) $\frac{1}{32}$ (h) $\frac{1}{10}$

4. (a) 3.1   (b) neither   (c) 7.005   (d) $2\frac{3}{4}$

5. (a) 7.261   (b) $4\frac{7}{8}$ (c) 8.401   (d) $6\frac{9}{32}$

Index

*(Numerals in **boldface** refer to the pages on which terms are defined or explained.)*